THE WORLD OF
LAW

A treasury of great writing about and in the law—
short stories, plays, essays, accounts, letters, opinions,
pleas, transcripts of testimony—from Biblical times to
the present

Edited by Ephraim London

I
The Law *in* Literature

SIMON AND SCHUSTER : NEW YORK

To Pearl and Peter

Contents

I

The Law IN *Literature*

CASES AND TRIALS IN FICTION

LAWYERS, JUDGES, JURORS AND
A WITNESS

ACKNOWLEDGMENTS

I am most indebted and grateful to all at Simon and Schuster who helped with this book, particularly Max Schuster for his encouragement, guidance and the choice of title; to Peter Schwed, who commissioned the work; to Robert Gottlieb for his editorial advice and direction; to Phyllis Levy, who helped with the initial organization; to Vicki Goldberg, who arranged for the many, many permissions; and to Helen Barrow for her fine taste and fastidiousness in superintending the production of the books.

E. L.

Introduction

Disraeli said that he was depressed by the law but exalted by literature. If he meant that law and literature are disparates, the statement
is without meaning, for the term "literature" is merely a judgment of
the quality of writing. Court proceedings, testimony, arguments, pleas
and judgments, and the discussion of legal theories—all, as I hope the
second volume of this anthology will prove, may be read as literature
if the expression and thought are of a high order. Even statutory law
can attain the level of literature. It was Stendhal's position that there
was only one example of perfect style, and that was the Code Napoléon.

There is no Plimsoll line, to borrow a metaphor from the law, for the
judgment of literature. Great literature should ignite or inspire; but
whether it does depends in part on the reader. I believe each work included here met that test when I read it, though in some instances the
flame gave more light than heat. No other test or system was used in
the selection of the material, except that I avoided technical writings
that would not be understood by a reasonably intelligent person un-
trained in the law.

There are of necessity many omissions in this book. Perhaps something should be said of the inclusion of two opinions of Mr. Justice
Holmes (in addition to his essay and letter), two of Judge Learned
Hand, and none of Mansfield, Jessel, Marshall, Bowen and Bok, or of a
number of the other great writer-judges. The first draft of this anthology included three sections that were later deleted; one was devoted to
writing by judges, a second to history and anthropology of the law, and
a third to biographical material. The publisher had contracted for a

book of about 500 pages, then graciously consented to the publication of two oversized volumes, but balked at printing five. The works of a number of my heroes and some of my friends had to be sacrificed. The opinions finally selected were chosen because of the dilemmas they present and because they deal with problems of more immediate interest than those omitted, some of which were grander in style and of greater importance historically and in the development of the law.

In selecting the Daniel Webster summation, the one of greatest historical importance—made in the Dartmouth College case—was again rejected in favor of one less significant; but I find the plea included—made to the jury in the White Murder Case—better reasoned and more artfully and interestingly developed.

Parenthetically, I believe Webster has been much libeled in the general reports of his argument to the Supreme Court in the Dartmouth College Case. According to legend, the climax of his speech was the completely inane statement, "It is, as I have said, a small college, yet there are those who love it." The Encyclopaedia Britannica describes all present as so affected by that remark that even Chief Justice John Marshall's "cheek expanded with emotion and his eyes suffused with tears." Beveridge in his The Life of John Marshall reports the incident in virtually the same language, having taken it from the same inaccurate source. I have heard it repeated countless times. If ever the line was uttered by Webster—and I doubt that it was—he had the good sense to delete it from his own copy of the speech.

Excepting The Ring and the Book, which would require a separate volume, the inclusion of the single poem "Law Like Love" in this collection is not due to want of space but to ignorance of any other worthy of inclusion. I have read a very great deal of poetry about law and lawyers, and almost all of it is terrible.

No generalization can be made about the law in fiction or the works of fiction included here. The law deals with every aspect of life, and the literature about the law deals with every subject, condition and circumstance and in almost every conceivable manner. The word "anthology" is derived from the Greek anthos (flower) and legein (to gather). These books are intended as an anthology in the sense that the origin of the word suggests. It was my intent to present a gathering or collection of writing centered in the law, each of such excellence that it may be described as literature.

EPHRAIM LONDON

Quotations

Lawyers, I suppose, were children once.

CHARLES LAMB

The law, in its majestic equality, forbids the rich as well as the poor to sleep under bridges.

ANATOLE FRANCE

Between ourselves, we are an illiterate profession.

SIR FREDERICK POLLOCK

Why is it that, though lawyers are trained in the use of words as doctors are not, so few of them can handle the English language with terseness and with charm, while so many doctors, from Osler through Zinsser and Heiser to Binger, write with cultivation and distinction?

LEWIS GANNETT

Injustice is relatively easy to bear; what stings is justice.

H. L. MENCKEN

Apollodorus being present, one who loved Socrates extremely, said to him: But it grieveth me, my Socrates, to have you die so unjustly!
Socrates, with much tenderness laying his hand upon his head, answered smiling: And what, my much-loved Apollodorus! wouldst thou rather they had condemned me justly?

XENOPHON

I think sometimes one can tell more about the morals of our society from the inmates of its jails than from the inmates of its universities.

JOHN DEWEY

. . . litigants and their lawyers are supposed to want justice, but in reality there is no such thing as justice either in or out of court. In fact, the word cannot be defined.

CLARENCE DARROW

. . . in almost every case except the very plainest, it would be possible to decide the issue either way with reasonable legal justification . . .

LORD MACMILLAN

I must say that, as a litigant, I should dread a law suit beyond almost anything else short of sickness and death.

JUDGE LEARNED HAND

Government like dress is the badge of lost innocence.

THOMAS PAINE, *Common Sense*

A precedent embalms a principle.

WILLIAM SCOTT

It is a maxim among these lawyers that whatever has been done before may legally be done again; and therefore they take special care to record all the decisions formerly made against common justice and the general reason of mankind. These, under the name of precedents, they produce as authorities. . . .

JONATHAN SWIFT

Poverty or wealth will make all the differences in securing the substance or only the shadow of constitutional protections.

JUSTICE RUTLEDGE

When I hear a man talk of unalterable law, the effect it produces upon me is to convince me that he is an unalterable fool.

SIDNEY SMITH

Be of good comfort, Master Ridley, and play the man. We shall this day light such a candle by God's grace in England as I trust shall never be put out.

HUGH LATIMLER, *Bishop of Worcester, the day he and Bishop Ridley were burned at the stake for heresy*

I told him it was law logic—an artificial system of reasoning, exclusively used in courts of justice, but good for nothing anywhere else.

JOHN QUINCY ADAMS

Lawyers have been known to wrest from reluctant juries triumphant verdicts of acquittal for their clients even when those clients, as often happens, were clearly and unmistakably innocent.

OSCAR WILDE

It is revolting to have no better reason for a rule of law than that it was laid down in the time of Henry IV. It is still more revolting if the grounds upon which it was laid down have vanished long since and the rule simply persists from blind imitation of the past.

MR. JUSTICE HOLMES

Mr. Glacier met Mr. Roger and Mr. Plumb in the law courts and thanked them for their help. "But what a lot of time and money," he said, "it has cost to arrive at the truth." "The truth?" said Roger. "No one in Court said anything about arriving at the truth."

HENRY CECIL

Judges spend their lives in consigning their fellow creatures to prison; and when some whisper reaches them that prisons are horribly cruel and destructive places, and that no creature fit to live should be sent there, they only remark calmly that prisons are not meant to be comfortable, which is no doubt the consideration that reconciled Pontius Pilate to the practice of crucifixion.

GEORGE BERNARD SHAW, *The Crime of Imprisonment*

Manners are of more importance than laws. Upon them, in a great measure, the laws depend. The law touches us but here and there, and now and then. Manners are what vex or soothe, corrupt or purify, exalt or debase, barbarize or refine us, by a constant, steady, uniform, insensible operation, like that of the air we breathe in.

EDMUND BURKE

As for the philosophers, they make imaginary laws for imaginary commonwealths; and their discourses are as the stars, which give little light because they are so high. For the lawyers, they write according to the states where they live, what is received law and not what ought to be law.

FRANCIS BACON

. . . the battle for one's legal rights is the poetry of character. . . . If I were called upon to pass judgment upon the practical importance of the two principles: "Do not injustice," and: "Suffer no injustice," I would say that the first rule was "Suffer no injustice," and the second: "Do none! . . . Every man is a born battler for the law in the interest of society. . . . Every despotism has begun with attacks on private law, with the violation of the legal rights of the individual.

RUDOLF VON JHERING

The profession of the law does not imply large ownership; but since no taint of usefulness, for other than competitive purposes, attaches to the lawyer's trade, it grades high in the conventional scheme. The lawyer is exclusively occupied with the details of predatory fraud, either in achieving or checkmating chicane, and success in the profession is therefore accepted as marking a large endowment of that barbarian astuteness which has always commanded man's respect and fear.

THORSTEIN VEBLEN

But the extensional facts are that "federal power" or "states' rights" may *both* be used *either for or against* the liberties of the individual. Federal power can tyrannize, but it can also protect individuals against the tyrannies of states, or states against the tyrannies of great national corporations or combines. States can also tyrannize or protect against tyranny. Most of the uproar about "federal power" and "states' rights" has *no meaning* apart from specific proposals as to *what powers* (state or federal) are to be exercised in *what ways* for what purposes.

S. I. HAYAKAWA

It is true that at the present time the lawyer does not hold that position with the people that he held fifty years ago, but the reason is not, in my opinion, lack of opportunity. It is because, instead of holding a position of independence between the wealthy and the people, prepared to curb the excesses of either, the able lawyers have to a great extent allowed themselves to become an adjunct of the great corporations and have neglected their obligations to use their powers for the protection of the people.

LOUIS D. BRANDEIS

The one thing that is wrong about this case is that your Honor cannot find against both parties to this suit. From the standpoint of personal merit neither of them ought to win. Neither of them came into court with clean hands, and I have doubts about their feet. But Anthony has paid the taxes for many years on the property, and in so doing has contributed to the revenue of the State and County. This is playing the part of the good citizen, a part that is new to him and set awkwardly upon him, and one that startles the community with its novelty. But since he is playing this part he ought to be encouraged in it by being permitted to win this suit. When you find one doing right for the first time in his life, the thought of discouraging him revolts the judicial conscience.

JOHN H. ATWOOD

"I understand it."

"No you don't. Every man's supposed to have certain rights."

"Certain inalienable rights," Starke said, "to liberty, equality and the pursuit of happiness. I learnt it in school, as a kid."

"Not that," Prew said. "That's the Constitution. Nobody believes that any more."

"Sure they do," Starke said. "They all believe it. They just don't do it. But they believe it."

"Sure," Prew said. "That's what I mean."

"But at least in this country they believe it," Starke said, "even if they don't do it. . . ."

JAMES JONES

I cannot tell, good Sir, for which of his virtues it was, but he was certainly whipped out of the Court.

SHAKESPEARE

The life of the law has not been logic; it has been experience. The felt necessities of the time, the prevalent moral and political theories, intuitions of public policy, avowed or unconscious, even the prejudices which judges share with their fellow men, have had a good deal more to do than the syllogism in determining the rules by which men should be governed. The law embodies the story of a nation's development through many centuries, and it cannot be dealt with as if it contained only the axioms and corollaries of a book of mathematics. In order to know what it is we must know what it has been and what it tends to become.

MR. JUSTICE HOLMES

In civil jurisprudence it too often happens that there is so much law that there is no room for justice; and that the claimant expires of wrong in the midst of right, as mariners die of thirst in the midst of water.

COLTON

Judge: Thou runagate, heretic and traitor, hast thou heard what these honest gentlemen have witnessed against thee?
Faithful: May I speak a few words in my own defense?
Judge: Sirrah, sirrah, thou deservest to live no longer, but to be slain immediately upon the place; yet that all men may see our gentleness to thee let us hear what thou, vile runagate, hast to say.

JOHN BUNYAN

Can anything be more preposterous than this preference of taste to justice, and of solemnity to truth? What an eulogium of a trial to say, "I am by no means satisfied that the jury were right in finding the prisoner guilty; but everything was carried on with the utmost decorum! The verdict was wrong; but there was the most perfect propriety and order in the proceedings. The man will be unfairly hanged; but all was genteel!"

SYDNEY SMITH

I knew almost nothing about the law and less about court procedure, but I had a loud mouth and an easy flow of words and soon found these an effective substitute. An arrest for policy is not a very serious matter, but for the prisoner it is a big event and he likes to have it handled with proper style and flourish. When I cross-examined a cop, or flung big words around extolling the virtues of my defendant, it was something to make his friends and relatives on the back benches sit up and enjoy themselves. Even if my client went to jail, he felt he was doing so in a fitting atmosphere of drama and excitement.

J. RICHARD (DIXIE) DAVIS

You know as well as we do that right, as the world goes, is only in question for equals in power; the strong do what they can, and the weak suffer what they must.

THUCYDIDES

The condition of the world requires morality to be defined and degraded into compulsory law.

ULRICI

Our civilization has decided, and very justly decided, that determining the guilt or innocence of men is a thing too important to be trusted to trained men. If it wishes for light upon that awful matter, it asks men who know no more law than I know, but who can feel the things that I felt in the jury box. When it wants a library catalogued, or the solar system discovered, or any trifle of that kind, it uses up its specialists. But when it wishes anything done that is really serious, it collects twelve of the ordinary men standing about. The same thing was done, if I remember right, by the Founder of Christianity.

GILBERT K. CHESTERTON

CASES AND TRIALS
IN FICTION

The Apocrypha

:

SUSANNA AND THE ELDERS

There dwelt a man in Babylon, called Joacim: and he took a wife, whose name was Susanna, the daughter of Chelcias, a very fair woman, and one that feared the Lord. Her parents also were righteous, and taught their daughter according to the law of Moses.

Now Joacim was a great rich man, and had a fair garden joining unto his house: and to him resorted the Jews; because he was more honorable than all others.

The same year were appointed two of the ancients of the people to be judges, such as the Lord spoke of, that wickedness came from Babylon from ancient judges, who seemed to govern the people. These kept much at Joacim's house: and all that had any suits in law came unto them.

Now when the people departed away at noon, Susanna went into her husband's garden to walk. And the two elders saw her going in every day, and walking; so that their lust was inflamed toward her. And they perverted their own mind, and turned away their eyes, that they might not look unto heaven, nor remember just judgments.

And albeit they both were wounded with her love, yet durst not one show another his grief. For they were ashamed to declare their lust, that they desired to have to do with her. Yet they watched diligently from day to day to see her. And the one said to the other, "Let us now go home: for it is dinner time."

So when they were gone out, they parted the one from the other, and

5

turning back again they came to the same place; and after that they had asked one another the cause, they acknowledged their lust: then appointed they a time both together, when they might find her alone.

And it fell out, as they watched a fit time, she went in as before with two maids only, and she was desirous to wash herself in the garden: for it was hot. And there was nobody there save the two elders, that had hid themselves, and watched her.

Then she said to her maids, "Bring me oil and washing balls, and shut the garden doors, that I may wash me."

And they did as she bade them, and shut the garden doors, and went out themselves at privy doors to fetch the things that she had commanded them: but they saw not the elders, because they were hid.

Now when the maids were gone forth, the two elders rose up, and ran unto her, saying, "Behold, the garden doors are shut, that no man can see us, and we are in love with thee; therefore consent unto us, and lie with us. If thou wilt not, we will bear witness against thee, that a young man was with thee: and therefore thou didst send away thy maids from thee."

Then Susanna sighed, and said, "I am straitened on every side: for if I do this thing, it is death unto me: and if I do it not, I cannot escape your hands. It is better for me to fall into your hands, and not do it, than to sin in the sight of the Lord."

With that Susanna cried with a loud voice: and the two elders cried out against her. Then ran the one, and opened the garden door.

So when the servants of the house heard the cry in the garden, they rushed in at a privy door, to see what was done unto her. But when the elders had declared their matter, the servants were greatly ashamed: for there was never such a report made of Susanna.

And it came to pass the next day, when the people were assembled to her husband Joacim, the two elders came also full of mischievous imagination against Susanna to put her to death; and said before the people, "Send for Susanna, the daughter of Chelcias, Joacim's wife."

And so they sent. So she came with her father and mother, her children, and all her kindred. Now Susanna was a very delicate woman, and beauteous to behold. And these wicked men commanded to uncover her face (for she was covered), that they might be filled with her beauty. Therefore her friends and all that saw her wept.

Then the two elders stood up in the midst of the people, and laid their hands upon her head. And she weeping looked up toward heaven: for her heart trusted in the Lord. And the elders said, "As we walked in the garden alone, this woman came in with two maids, and shut the garden doors, and sent the maids away. Then a young man, who there was hid, came unto her, and lay with her. Then we that stood in a corner of the garden, seeing this wickedness, ran unto them. And when we saw them together, the man we could not hold: for he was stronger than we, and opened the door, and leaped out. But having taken this woman, we asked who the young man was, but she would not tell us: these things do we testify."

Then the assembly believed them, as those that were the elders and judges of the people: so they condemned her to death.

Then Susanna cried out with a loud voice, and said, "O everlasting God, that knowest the secrets, and knowest all things before they be: thou knowest that they have borne false witness against me, and, behold, I must die; whereas I never did such things as these men have maliciously invented against me."

And the Lord heard her voice.

Therefore when she was led to be put to death, the Lord raised up the holy spirit of a young youth, whose name was Daniel: who cried with a loud voice, "I am clear from the blood of this woman."

Then all the people turned them toward him, and said, "What mean these words that thou hast spoken?"

So he standing in the midst of them said, "Are ye such fools, ye sons of Israel, that without examination or knowledge of the truth ye have condemned a daughter of Israel? Return again to the place of judgment: for they have borne false witness against her."

Wherefore all the people turned again in haste, and the elders said unto him, "Come, sit down among us, and show it us, seeing God hath given thee the honor of an elder."

Then said Daniel unto them, "Put these two aside one far from another, and I will examine them."

So when they were put asunder one from another, he called one of them, and said unto him, "O thou that art waxed old in wickedness, now thy sins which thou hast committed aforetime are come to light: for thou hast pronounced false judgment, and has condemned the innocent, and hast let the guilty go free; albeit the Lord saith, 'The innocent and righteous shalt thou not slay.' Now then, if thou hast seen her, tell me under what tree sawest thou them companying together?"

Who answered, "Under the mastic tree."

And Daniel said, "Very well; thou hast lied against thine own head; for even now the angel of God hath received the sentence of God to cut thee in two."

So he put him aside, and commanded to bring the other, and said unto him, "O thou seed of Chanaan, and not of Juda, beauty hath deceived thee, and lust hath perverted thine heart. Thus have ye dealt with the daughters of Israel, and they for fear companied with you: but the daughter of Juda would not abide your wickedness. Now therefore tell me under what tree didst thou take them companying together?"

Who answered, "Under a holm tree."

Then said Daniel unto him, "Well; thou hast also lied against thine own head: for the angel of God waiteth with the sword to cut thee in two, that he may destroy you."

With that all the assembly cried out with a loud voice, and praised God, who saveth them that trust in him. And they arose against the two elders, for Daniel had convicted them of false witness by their own mouth: and according to the law of Moses they did unto them in such sort as they maliciously intended to do to their neighbor: and they put them to death. Thus the innocent blood was saved the same day.

Therefore Chelcias and his wife praised God for their daughter Susanna, with Joacim her husband, and all the kindred, because there was no dishonesty found in her.

Cervantes

:

THE CASES JUDGED BY SANCHO PANZA

from *Don Quixote*

Sancho with all his train arrived at a village of around a thousand in-
habitants, one of the best in the duke's domains. They informed him
that it was called Barataria Island, either because the real name of the
village was Baratario, or by reason of the *barato* which had led to the
government being bestowed upon him. As they reached the town, which
had a wall around it, the officers of the municipality came out to meet
them, the bells rang, and all the townspeople evidenced their satisfaction. With much pomp they conducted him to the cathedral to give
thanks to God, and then, with a few mock ceremonies, they handed over
to him the keys of the city, acknowledging him to be the island's per-
petual governor.

The new governor's apparel, his beard, and his little fat figure astonished all those who were not in on the joke, and even those who were,
and they were many. Finally, upon leaving the church, they took him to
the judge's chair and seated him in it, and the duke's major-domo then
addressed him.

"Sir Governor," he said, "it is an ancient and obligatory custom in
this famous island for the one who comes to take possession of it to answer a question that is put to him, one that shall be somewhat difficult

9

and intricate, so that from his answer the people may be able to form an idea of their ruler's intelligence and judge for themselves as to whether they should hail his coming with joy or look upon it with sorrow."

All the time the major-domo was saying this, Sancho was gazing steadily at some large letters inscribed upon the wall facing him, and inasmuch as he did not know how to read, he asked what they were.

"Sir," was the reply, "that inscription is a notation of the day upon which your Lordship took possession of this island. It reads: 'On this day—such and such a day of such and such a year—Don Sancho Panza took over the government of this island and many years may he enjoy it.' "

"And who is it that they call 'Don Sancho Panza'?" asked Sancho.

"Your Lordship," the major-domo answered, "for no other Panza has set foot here except the one who is seated in that chair."

"Well, then, brother," said Sancho, "I will let you know that there has never been any 'Don' in my family. Plain Sancho Panza they call me, and Sancho was my father's name before me, and my grandfather's before him; they all were Panzas, without any 'Dons' or 'Doñas' tacked on. In this island, I imagine, there must be more 'Dons' than there are stones. But enough of that; God knows what I mean. It may be, if my government lasts four days, I'll weed them all out; for there are so many of them they must be as troublesome as gnats. Go ahead with your question, Señor Major-domo, and I'll reply the best way I can, whether the people are sorry or not."

At this moment there came into the court two men, one dressed like a peasant, the other like a tailor, for this latter held in his hands a pair of shears.

"Sir Governor," said the tailor, "I and this peasant have come before your Grace to have you settle a difference between us. Yesterday this good man entered my shop—for, begging the pardon of those present, I am a licensed tailor, God be praised—and, putting a piece of cloth in my hands, he asked me, 'Señor, is there enough here to make me a cap?' Feeling the cloth, I told him there was. He must have supposed— as I supposed, and I supposed right—that I undoubtedly meant to make away with a part of the material, being led to think so by his own maliciousness and the bad opinion that people have of tailors. He then asked me to look and see if there would be enough for two. Guessing what was in his mind, I said yes; whereupon he, persisting in his damnable first intention, went on adding cap after cap, with me saying, yes, yes, until we were up to five caps in all. Just a while ago he came to call for them and I gave them to him, but he doesn't want to pay me for my labor but insists I should pay *him* or give him back his cloth."

"Is all this true, brother?" inquired Sancho.

"Yes, sir," replied the man, "but will your Grace please have him show the five caps that he made for me?"

"I'll be glad to," said the tailor. And, with this, he at once brought his hand out from under his cloak, displaying the five caps upon his four fingers and thumb. "There they are, and I swear by God and my conscience there's not a scrap of cloth left; I am willing to submit my work to the inspectors of the trade."

All those present had a laugh over the number of caps and the novel character of this lawsuit. As for Sancho, he considered the matter for a while and then said, "It appears to me that in this case there is no need of lengthy arguments; all that is called for is the judgment of an honest man. And so my decision is that the tailor shall lose his work and the peasant his cloth, and the caps shall go to the prisoners in the jail, and let us hear no more about it."

If the decision in the case of the cattle-driver's purse had aroused the admiration of the bystanders, this one provoked them to laughter; but the governor's orders were nonetheless carried out. Two old men were the next to present themselves before him, one of whom carried a reed by way of staff. It was the one without a staff who was the first to speak.

"My lord," he began, "some days ago I lent this good man ten gold crowns by way of service duly rendered, on condition that he should repay me upon demand. A long time went by without my demanding payment, for the reason that I did not wish to cause him an even greater hardship than that which he was suffering when he sought the loan. However, when I saw that he was making no effort to pay me, I asked him for the money, not once but many times, and he not only failed to reimburse me, he even refused to do so, saying I had never let him take the ten crowns in question. I have no witnesses of the loan, and naturally there are none of the payment since no payment was made. Accordingly, I would have your Grace put him under oath, and if he swears that he did pay me, then I will cancel the debt, here and before God."

"What do you say to that, old man with the staff?" Sancho asked.

"My lord," replied the old man, "I admit that he lent them to me; but your Grace may lower that rod, for, seeing that he has had me put under oath, I will also swear that I paid him back, really and truly."

The governor lowered the rod that he held, and in the meanwhile the old man who had spoken handed his staff over to the other one while he took the oath, as if he found it in his way. Then, placing his hand upon the cross of the rod, he once more affirmed that it was true that he had borrowed the ten crowns that were being demanded of him but that he had paid them back into the other's hand, the only thing being that the other old man did not appear to realize it but was all the time asking for his money. In view of this, the great governor then asked the creditor what he had to say in reply to his adversary's statement; whereupon the old fellow who now held the staff replied that his debtor must undoubtedly be speaking the truth, as he knew him to be a worthy man and a good Christian. The one who had lent the crowns added that he must surely have forgotten how and when they had been repaid and from that time forth he would never ask his adversary for anything.

The debtor thereupon took back his staff and, with bowed head, left the court. When he saw the defendant leaving in this manner, without saying another word, and when he perceived how resigned the plaintiff was, Sancho dropped his chin to his bosom and, placing the forefinger of his right hand in turn upon his eyebrows and his nose, remained lost in thought for a short while. Then he raised his head and ordered them to call back the old man with the staff who had already left.

They did so, and as soon as Sancho saw him, he said, "Good man, give me that staff. I have need of it."

"Gladly," replied the old man. "Here it is, my lord." And he placed it in the governor's hand.

Sancho took it and handed it to the other old man, remarking, "Go in peace, for you are now repaid."

"Repaid, my lord? And is this reed worth ten gold crowns?"

"Yes," said the governor, "it is; or if it is not, then I am the biggest blockhead in the world. We will see right now whether or not I have it in me to govern an entire kingdom."

With this, he ordered that the reed be broken and laid open there in the sight of all, and in the heart of it they found the ten gold crowns. They were all greatly astonished at this, looking upon their governor as another Solomon. When they inquired of him how he knew that the crowns were there, he replied that it had come to him when he saw the old man hand the staff to his adversary while he was taking an oath to the effect that he had really and truly paid his creditor, and then, when he was through, had heard him ask for it back again. From which it was to be deduced that, even when those who governed were simpletons, God sometimes guided them in their judgments. Moreover, he had heard the curate of his village tell of another case like this one, and if it was a question of not forgetting what he had need to remember, there was not another memory like his own in all the island.

The short of the matter is, one old man went off crestfallen, the other with his money in hand, while those present continued to marvel at the thing. As for him whose duty it was to record Sancho's words, deeds, and movements, he could not make up his mind as to whether he should take the new governor for a fool or set him down as a wise man.

When this case had been concluded, there came into the court a woman holding on tightly to a man who was dressed like a rich drover.

"Justice, Señor Governor! Justice!" she cried, "and if I don't find it on earth, I'll go look for it in Heaven! Beloved Governor, this evil man caught me in the middle of a field and made use of my body as if it had been some filthy rag. Ah, poor me! he has taken from me that which I had guarded more than twenty-three years, defending it alike against Moors and Christians, foreigners and native-born. I was always hard as corkwood, keeping myself as pure as a salamander in the flames or wool among the brambles, and now this fine fellow comes along and handles me with clean hands!"

"It remains to be seen," said Sancho, "whether this gallant has clean hands or not." And, turning to the man, he ordered him to reply to the complaint which the woman had made against him.

The defendant was in a state of confusion. "Good sirs," he answered, "I am but a poor dealer in hogs. This morning I left the village to sell—begging your pardon—four pigs, and what with taxes and cheating they took away from me practically all that they came to. As I was returning home, I fell in with this good dame, and the devil, who likes to jumble everything, saw to it that we were yoked together. I paid her quite enough, but she, dissatisfied, laid hold of me and would not let me go until she had dragged me here. She says that I forced her, but she lies by the oath that I am taking or am ready to take. And that is the whole truth, every particle of it."

The governor asked the man if he had any silver coins with him, and the drover replied that he had some twenty ducats in a purse that was hidden in his bosom. Sancho then directed him to take the purse out and hand it over to the plaintiff, which the drover did, trembling all the while. The woman took it and, with many curtsies to all present, offered a prayer to God for the life and health of the Señor Governor who thus looked after damsels and orphans in distress. With this, she left the court, grasping the purse with both hands, but not until she first had looked to see if the coins in it were of silver. No sooner was she gone than Sancho turned to the drover, who, with eyes and heart following the purse, was on the verge of tears.

"My good man," he said, "go after that woman, take the purse away from her whether she is willing to give it up or not, and come back here with it."

He was not talking to a fool or a deaf man, for the drover was off at once like a streak of lightning, to carry out the order that had been given him. The bystanders, meanwhile, waited eagerly to see what the outcome of this case would be. Within a short while the pair returned, engaged in more of a struggle than before; she had her petticoat up with the purse in the lap of it while he strove to take it from her. This was not possible, however, so stoutly did she defend herself.

"Justice!" she was crying, "God's justice and the world's justice, too! Behold, Señor Governor, how bold and shameless this ruffian is. In the center of the town and middle of the street he tried to take away from me the purse which your Grace had ordered him to give me!"

"And did he take it?" asked the governor.

"Take it?" replied the woman. "I'd give up my life sooner than I would the purse. A fine young thing I'd be! They'll have to throw other rats in my face! Hammers and pincers, mallets and chisels, would not be enough to get it out of my clutches, nor even a lion's claws. They'd take the soul from out my body before they'd do that!"

"She's right," said the man. "I give up. I admit I haven't the strength to take it away from her." And he let go his hold.

Sancho then addressed the woman. "Let us have a look at that purse, my respectable and valiant one," he said. She gave it to him and he then handed it back to the man, saying, as he did so, to the one who had been forced and who had not been forced, "Sister, if you had shown the same or even half the courage and valor in defending your body that you have in protecting the purse, the might of Hercules would not have been sufficient to overcome you. Be on your way, in God's name, and bad luck to you, and do not show yourself again in this entire island or for six leagues around, under pain of two hundred lashes. Go, then, I say, you shameless, cheating hussy! Be off with you!"

Frightened by this, the woman left with her head down, very much disgruntled.

"My good man," said Sancho to the defendant, "return to your village with your money and may God go with you; and hereafter, if you do not want to lose your purse, see to it that you do not take it into your head to yoke with anyone."

Mumbling his thanks, the man departed, and the spectators once again expressed their astonishment at the wise decisions made by their new governor. All of which the chronicler duly noted down, to be forwarded to the duke who was eagerly awaiting his report.

Charles Dickens

·

THE TRIAL OF BARDELL v. PICKWICK

from *The Pickwick Papers*

"I wonder what the foreman of the jury, whoever he'll be, has got for breakfast," said Mr. Snodgrass, by way of keeping up a conversation on the eventful morning of the fourteenth of February.

"Ah!" said Perker, "I hope he's got a good one."

"Why so?" inquired Mr. Pickwick.

"Highly important; very important, my dear sir," replied Perker. "A good, contented, well-breakfasted juryman is a capital thing to get hold of. Discontented or hungry jurymen, my dear sir, always find for the plaintiff."

"Bless my heart," said Mr. Pickwick, looking very blank; "what do they do that for?"

"Why, I don't know," replied the little man, coolly; "saves time, I suppose. If it's near dinner-time, the foreman takes out his watch when the jury has retired, and says, 'Dear me, gentlemen, ten minutes to five, I declare! I dine at five, gentlemen.' 'So do I,' says everybody else, except two men who ought to have dined at three, and seem more than half disposed to stand out in consequence. The foreman smiles, and puts up his watch—'Well, gentlemen, what do we say, plaintiff or defendant, gentlemen? I rather think, so far as I am concerned, gentle-men—I say, I rather think—but don't let that influence you—I *rather* think the plaintiff's the man.' Upon this, two or three other men are sure to say that they think so too—as of course they do; and then they get on very unanimously and comfortably. Ten minutes past nine!" said

16

the little man, looking at his watch. "Time we were off, my dear sir; breach of promise trial—court is generally full in such cases. You had better ring for a coach, my dear sir, or we shall be rather late."

Mr. Pickwick immediately rang the bell; and a coach having been procured, the four Pickwickians and Mr. Perker ensconced themselves therein, and drove to Guildhall; Sam Weller, Mr. Lowten, and the blue bag, following in a cab.

"Lowten," said Perker, when they reached the outer hall of the court, "put Mr. Pickwick's friends in the students' box; Mr. Pickwick himself had better sit by me. This way, my dear, sir, this way." Taking Mr. Pickwick by the coat-sleeve, the little man led him to the low seat just beneath the desks of the King's Counsel, which is constructed for the convenience of attorneys, who from that spot can whisper into the ear of the leading counsel in the case, any instructions that may be necessary during the progress of the trial. The occupants of this seat are invisible to the great body of spectators, inasmuch as they sit on a much lower level than either the barristers or the audience, whose seats are raised above the floor. Of course they have their backs to both, and their faces towards the judge.

"That's the witness-box, I suppose?" said Mr. Pickwick, pointing to a kind of pulpit, with a brass rail, on his left hand.

"That's the witness-box, my dear sir," replied Perker, disinterring a quantity of papers from the blue bag, which Lowten had just deposited at his feet.

"And that," said Mr. Pickwick, pointing to a couple of enclosed seats on his right, "that's where the jurymen sit, is it not?"

"The identical place, my dear sir," replied Perker, tapping the lid of his snuff-box.

Mr. Pickwick stood up in a state of great agitation, and took a glance at the court. There were already a pretty large sprinkling of spectators in the gallery, and a numerous muster of gentlemen in wigs, in the barristers' seats: who presented, as a body, all that pleasing and extensive variety of nose and whisker for which the bar of England is so justly celebrated. Such of the gentlemen as had a brief to carry, carried it in as conspicuous a manner as possible, and occasionally scratched their noses therewith, to impress the fact more strongly on the observation of the spectators. Other gentlemen, who had no briefs to show, carried under their arms goodly octavos, with a red label behind, and that under-done-piecrust-colored cover, which is technically known as "law calf."

Others, who had neither briefs nor books, thrust their hands into their pockets, and looked as wise as they conveniently could; others, again, moved here and there with great restlessness and earnestness of manner, content to awaken thereby the admiration and astonishment of the uninitiated strangers. The whole, to the great wonderment of Mr. Pickwick, were divided into little groups, who were chatting and discussing the news of the day in the most unfeeling manner possible—just as if no trial at all were coming on.

A bow from Mr. Phunky, as he entered, and took his seat behind the row appropriated to the King's Counsel, attracted Mr. Pickwick's attention; and he had scarcely returned it, when Mr. Sergeant Snubbin appeared, followed by Mr. Mallard, who half hid the Sergeant behind a large crimson bag, which he placed on his table, and, after shaking hands with Perker, withdrew. Then there entered two or three more Sergeants; and among them, one with a fat body and a red face, who nodded in a friendly manner to Mr. Sergeant Snubbin, and said it was a fine morning.

"Who's that red-faced man, who said it was a fine morning, and nodded to our counsel?" whispered Mr. Pickwick.

"Mr. Sergeant Buzfuz," replied Perker. "He's opposed to us; he leads on the other side. That gentleman behind him is Mr. Skimpin, his junior."

Mr. Pickwick was on the point of inquiring, with great abhorrence of the man's cold-blooded villainy, how Mr. Sergeant Buzfuz, who was counsel for the opposite party, dared to presume to tell Mr. Sergeant Snubbin, who was counsel for him, that it was a fine morning, when he was interrupted by a general rising of the barristers, and a loud cry of "Silence!" from the officers of the court. Looking round, he found that this was caused by the entrance of the judge.

Mr. Justice Stareleigh (who sat in the absence of the Chief Justice, occasioned by indisposition) was a most particularly short man, and so fat, that he seemed all face and waistcoat. He rolled in, upon two little turned legs, and having bobbed gravely to the bar, who bobbed gravely to him, put his little legs underneath his table, and his little three-cornered hat upon it; and when Mr. Justice Stareleigh had done this, all you could see of him was two queer little eyes, one broad pink face, and somewhere about half of a big and very comical-looking wig.

The judge had no sooner taken his seat, than the officer on the floor of the court called out "Silence!" in a commanding tone, upon which another officer in the gallery cried "Silence!" in an angry manner, whereupon three or four more ushers shouted "Silence!" in a voice of indignant remonstrance. This being done, a gentleman in black, who sat below the judge, proceeded to call over the names of the jury; and after a great deal of bawling, it was discovered that only ten special jurymen were present. Upon this, Mr. Sergeant Buzfuz prayed a *tales;* the gentleman in black then proceeded to press into the special jury, two of the common jurymen; and a greengrocer and a chemist were caught directly.

"Answer to your names, gentlemen, that you may be sworn," said the gentleman in black. "Richard Upwitch."

"Here," said the greengrocer.

"Thomas Groffin."

"Here," said the chemist.

"Take the book, gentlemen. You shall well and truly try—"

"I beg this court's pardon," said the chemist, who was a tall, thin, yellow-visaged man, "but I hope this court will excuse my attendance."

"On what grounds, sir?" said Mr. Justice Stareleigh.

"I have no assistant, my Lord," said the chemist.

"I can't help that, sir," replied Mr. Justice Stareleigh. "You should hire one."

"I can't afford it, my Lord," rejoined the chemist.

"Then you ought to be able to afford it, sir," said the judge, reddening; for Mr. Justice Stareleigh's temper bordered on the irritable, and brooked not contradiction.

"I know I *ought* to do, if I got on as well as I deserved, but I don't, my Lord," answered the chemist.

"Swear the gentleman," said the judge, peremptorily.

The officer had got no further than the "You shall well and truly try," when he was again interrupted by the chemist.

"I am to be sworn, my Lord, am I?" said the chemist.

"Certainly, sir," replied the testy little judge.

"Very well, my Lord," replied the chemist, in a resigned manner. "Then there'll be murder before this trial's over; that's all. Swear me, if you please, sir"; and sworn the chemist was, before the judge could find words to utter.

"I merely wanted to observe, my Lord," said the chemist, taking his seat with great deliberation, "that I've left nobody but an errand-boy in my shop. He is a very nice boy, my Lord, but he is not acquainted with drugs; and I know that the prevailing impression on his mind is, that Epsom salts means oxalic acid; and syrup of senna, laudanum. That's all, my Lord." With this, the tall chemist composed himself into a comfortable attitude, and, assuming a pleasant expression of countenance, appeared to have prepared himself for the worst.

Mr. Pickwick was regarding the chemist with feelings of the deepest horror, when a slight sensation was perceptible in the body of the court; and immediately afterwards Mrs. Bardell, supported by Mrs. Cluppins, was led in, and placed, in a drooping state, at the other end of the seat on which Mr. Pickwick sat. An extra-sized umbrella was then handed in by Mr. Dodson, and a pair of pattens by Mr. Fogg, each of whom had prepared a most sympathizing and melancholy face for the occasion. Mrs. Sanders then appeared, leading in Master Bardell. At sight of her child, Mrs. Bardell started; suddenly recollecting herself, she kissed him in a frantic manner; then relapsing into a state of hysterical imbecility, the good lady requested to be informed where she was. In reply to this, Mrs. Cluppins and Mrs. Sanders turned their heads away and wept, while Messrs. Dodson and Fogg entreated the plaintiff to compose herself. Sergeant Buzfuz rubbed his eyes very hard with a large white handkerchief, and gave an appealing look towards the jury, while the judge was visibly affected, and several of the beholders tried to cough down their emotions.

"Very good notion that, indeed," whispered Perker to Mr. Pickwick. "Capital fellows those Dodson and Fogg; excellent ideas of effect, my dear sir, excellent."

As Perker spoke, Mrs. Bardell began to recover by slow degrees, while Mrs. Cluppins, after a careful survey of Master Bardell's buttons and the button-holes to which they severally belonged, placed him on the floor of the court in front of his mother—a commanding position in which he could not fail to awaken the full commiseration and sympathy of both judge and jury. This was not done without considerable opposition, and many tears, on the part of the young gentleman himself, who had certain inward misgivings that the placing him within the full glare of the judge's eye was only a formal prelude to his being immediately ordered away for instant execution, or for transportation beyond the seas, during the whole term of his natural life, at the very least.

"Bardell and Pickwick," cried the gentleman in black, calling on the case, which stood first on the list.

"I am for the plaintiff, my Lord," said Mr. Sergeant Buzfuz.

"Who is with you, brother Buzfuz?" said the judge. Mr. Skimpin bowed, to intimate that he was.

"I appear for the defendant, my Lord," said Mr. Sergeant Snubbin.

"Anybody with you, brother Snubbin?" inquired the court.

"Mr. Phunky, my Lord," replied Sergeant Snubbin.

"Sergeant Buzfuz and Mr. Skimpin for the plaintiff," said the judge, writing down the names in his notebook, and reading as he wrote; "for the defendant, Sergeant Snubbin and Mr. Monkey."

"Beg your Lordship's pardon, Phunky."

"Oh, very good," said the judge; "I never had the pleasure of hearing the gentleman's name before." Here Mr. Phunky bowed and smiled, and the judge bowed and smiled too, and then Mr. Phunky, blushing into the very whites of his eyes, tried to look as if he didn't know that everybody was gazing at him: a thing which no man ever succeeded in doing yet, or in all reasonable probability, ever will.

"Go on," said the judge.

The ushers again called silence, and Mr. Skimpin proceeded to "open the case"; and the case appeared to have very little inside it when he had opened it, for he kept such particulars as he knew, completely to himself, and sat down, after a lapse of three minutes, leaving the jury in precisely the same advanced stage of wisdom as they were in before.

Sergeant Buzfuz then rose with all the majesty and dignity which the grave nature of the proceedings demanded, and having whispered to Dodson, and conferred briefly with Fogg, pulled his gown over his shoulders, settled his wig, and addressed the jury.

Sergeant Buzfuz began by saying, that never, in the whole course of his professional experience—never, from the very first moment of his applying himself to the study and practice of law—had he approached a case with feelings of such deep emotion, or with such a heavy sense of the responsibility imposed upon him—a responsibility, he would say, which he could never have supported, were he not buoyed up and sustained by a conviction so strong that it amounted to positive certainty that the cause of truth and justice, or, in other words, the cause of his much-injured and most oppressed client, must prevail with the high-minded and intelligent dozen of men whom he now saw in that box before him.

Counsel usually begin in this way, because it puts the jury on the very best terms with themselves, and makes them think what sharp fellows they must be. A visible effect was produced immediately; several jurymen beginning to take voluminous notes with the utmost eagerness.

"You have heard from my learned friend, gentlemen," continued Sergeant Buzfuz, well knowing that, from the learned friend alluded to, the gentlemen of the jury had heard just nothing at all—"you have heard from my learned friend, gentlemen, that this is an action for a breach of promise of marriage, in which the damages are laid at £1500. But you have not heard from my learned friend, inasmuch as it did not come within my learned friend's province to tell you, what are the facts and circumstances of the case. Those facts and circumstances, gentlemen, you shall hear detailed by me, and proved by the unimpeachable female whom I will place in that box before you."

Here Mr. Sergeant Buzfuz, with a tremendous emphasis on the word "box," smote his table with a mighty sound, and glanced at Dodson and Fogg, who nodded admiration of the Sergeant, and indignant defiance of the defendant.

"The plaintiff, gentlemen," continued Sergeant Buzfuz, in a soft and melancholy voice, "the plaintiff is a widow; yes, gentlemen, a widow. The late Mr. Bardell, after enjoying, for many years, the esteem and confidence of his sovereign, as one of the guardians of his royal revenues, glided almost imperceptibly from the world, to seek elsewhere for that repose and peace which a custom-house can never afford."

At this pathetic description of the decease of Mr. Bardell, who had been knocked on the head with a quart-pot in a public-house cellar, the learned Sergeant's voice faltered, and he proceeded with emotion—

"Some time before his death, he had stamped his likeness upon a little boy. With this little boy, the only pledge of her departed exciseman, Mrs. Bardell shrunk from the world, and courted the retirement and tranquillity of Goswell Street; and here she placed in her front-parlor window a written placard, bearing this inscription—'Apartments furnished for a single gentleman. Inquire within.'" Here Sergeant Buzfuz paused, while several gentlemen of the jury took a note of the document.

"There is no date to that, is there, sir?" inquired a juror.

"There is no date, gentlemen," replied Sergeant Buzfuz; "but I am instructed to say that it was put in the plaintiff's parlor-window just this time three years. I entreat the attention of the jury to the wording of this document. 'Apartments furnished for a single gentleman'! Mrs. Bardell's opinions of the opposite sex, gentlemen, were derived from a long contemplation of the inestimable qualities of her lost husband. She had no fear, she had no distrust, she had no suspicion, all was confidence and reliance. 'Mr. Bardell,' said the widow; 'Mr. Bardell was a man of honor, Mr. Bardell was a man of his word, Mr. Bardell was no deceiver, Mr. Bardell was once a single gentleman himself; *to* single gentlemen I look for protection, for assistance, for comfort, and for consolation; *in* single gentlemen I shall perpetually see something to remind me of what Mr. Bardell was, when he first won my young and untried affections; to a single gentleman, then, shall my lodgings be let.' Actuated by this beautiful and touching impulse (among the best impulses of our imperfect nature, gentlemen) the lonely and desolate widow dried her tears, furnished her first floor, caught the innocent boy to her maternal bosom, and put the bill up in her parlor-window. Did it remain there long? No. The serpent was on the watch, the train was laid, the mine was preparing, the sapper and miner was at work. Before the bill had been in the parlor-window three days—three days—gentlemen—a Being, erect upon two legs, and bearing all the outward semblance of a man, and not of a monster, knocked at the door of Mrs. Bardell's house. He inquired within; he took the lodgings; and on the very next day he entered into possession of them. This man was Pickwick—Pickwick, the defendant."

Sergeant Buzfuz, who had proceeded with such volubility that his face was perfectly crimson, here paused for breath. The silence awoke Mr. Justice Stareleigh, who immediately wrote down something with a pen without any ink in it, and looked unusually profound, to impress the jury with the belief that he always thought most deeply with his eyes shut. Sergeant Buzfuz proceeded.

"Of this man Pickwick I will say little; the subject presents but few attractions; and I, gentlemen, am not the man, nor are you, gentlemen, the men, to delight in the contemplation of revolting heartlessness, and of systematic villainy."

Here Mr. Pickwick, who had been writhing in silence for some time, gave a violent start, as if some vague idea of assaulting Sergeant Buzfuz, in the august presence of justice and law, suggested itself to his mind. An admonitory gesture from Perker restrained him, and he listened to the learned gentleman's continuation with a look of indignation, which contrasted forcibly with the admiring faces of Mrs. Cluppins and Mrs. Sanders.

"I say systematic villainy, gentlemen." said Sergeant Buzfuz, looking through Mr. Pickwick, and talking *at* him; "and when I say systematic villainy, let me tell the defendant Pickwick, if he be in court, as I am informed he is, that it would have been more decent in him, more becoming, in better judgment, and in better taste, if he had stopped away. Let me tell him, gentlemen, that any gestures of dissent or disapprobation in which he may indulge in this court will not go down with you; that you will know how to value and how to appreciate them; and let me tell him further, as my Lord will tell you, gentlemen, that a counsel, in the discharge of his duty to his client, is neither to be intimidated nor bullied, nor put down; and that any attempt to do either the one or the other, or the first, or the last, will recoil on the head of the attempter, be he plaintiff or be he defendant, be his name Pickwick, or Noakes, or Stoakes, or Stiles, or Brown, or Thompson."

This little divergence from the subject in hand, had of course the intended effect of turning all eyes to Mr. Pickwick. Sergeant Buzfuz, having partially recovered from the state of moral elevation into which he had lashed himself, resumed—

"I shall show you, gentlemen, that for two years Pickwick continued to reside constantly, and without interruption or intermission, at Mrs. Bardell's house. I shall show you that Mrs. Bardell, during the whole of that time, waited on him, attended to his comforts, cooked his meals, looked out his linen for the washerwoman when it went abroad, darned, aired, and prepared it for wear, when it came home, and, in short, enjoyed his fullest trust and confidence. I shall show you that, on many occasions, he gave halfpence, and on some occasions even sixpences, to her little boy; and I shall prove to you, by a witness whose testimony it will be impossible for my learned friend to weaken or controvert, that on one occasion he patted the boy on the head, and, after inquiring whether he had won any *alley tors* or *commoneys* lately (both of which I understand to be a particular species of marbles much prized by the youth of this town), made use of this remarkable expression: 'How should you like to have another father?' I shall prove to you, gentlemen, that about a year ago, Pickwick suddenly began to absent himself from home, during long intervals, as if with the intention of gradually breaking off from my client; but I shall show you also, that his resolution was not at that time sufficiently strong, or that his better feelings conquered, if better feelings he has, or that the charms and accomplishments of my client prevailed against his unmanly intention; by proving to you, that on one occasion, when he returned from the country, he distinctly and in terms, offered her marriage: previously, however, taking special care that there should be no witness to their solemn contract; and I am in a situation to prove to you, on the testimony of three of his own friends—most unwilling witnesses, gentlemen—most unwilling witnesses—that on that morning he was discovered by them holding the plaintiff in his arms, and soothing her agitation by his caresses and endearments."

A visible impression was produced upon the auditors by this part of the learned Sergeant's address. Drawing forth two very small scraps of paper, he proceeded—

"And now, gentlemen, but one word more. Two letters have passed between these parties, letters which are admitted to be in the handwriting of the defendant, and which speak volumes indeed. These letters, too, bespeak the character of the man. They are not open, fervent, eloquent epistles, breathing nothing but the language of affectionate attachment. They are covert, sly, underhanded communications, but, fortunately, far more conclusive than if couched in the most glowing language and the most poetic imagery—letters that must be viewed with a cautious and suspicious eye—letters that were evidently intended at the time, by Pickwick, to mislead and delude any third parties into whose hands they might fall. Let me read the first—'Garraway's twelve o'clock. Dear Mrs. B.—Chops and Tomata sauce. Yours, PICKWICK.' Gentlemen, what does this mean? Chops and Tomata sauce. Yours, Pickwick! Chops! Gracious heavens! and Tomata sauce! Gentlemen, is the happiness of a sensitive and confiding female to be trifled away by such shallow artifices as these? The next has no date whatever which is in itself suspicious. 'Dear Mrs. B., I shall not be at home till to-morrow. Slow coach.' And then follows this very remarkable expression. 'Don't trouble yourself about the warming-pan.' The warming-pan! Why, gentlemen, who *does* trouble himself about a warming-pan? When was the peace of mind of man or woman broken or disturbed by a warming-pan, which is in itself a harmless, a useful, and I will add, gentlemen, a comforting article of domestic furniture? Why is Mrs. Bardell so earnestly entreated not to agitate herself about this warming-pan, unless (as is no doubt the case) it is a mere cover for hidden fire—a mere substitute for some endearing word of promise, agreeably to a preconcerted system of correspondence, artfully contrived by Pickwick with a view to his contemplated desertion, and which I am not in a condition to explain? And what does this allusion to the slow coach mean? For aught I know, it may be a reference to Pickwick himself, who has most unquestionably been a criminally slow coach during the whole of this transaction, but whose speed will now be very unexpectedly accelerated, and whose wheels, gentlemen, as he will find to his cost, will very soon be greased by you!"

Mr. Sergeant Buzfuz paused in this place, to see whether the jury smiled at his joke; but as nobody took it but the greengrocer, whose sensitiveness on the subject was very probably occasioned by his having subjected a chaise-cart to the process in question on that identical morning, the learned Sergeant considered it advisable to undergo a slight relapse into the dismals before he concluded.

"But enough of this, gentlemen," said Mr. Sergeant Buzfuz, "it is difficult to smile with an aching heart; it is ill jesting when our deepest sympathies are awakened. My client's hopes and prospects are ruined, and it is no figure of speech to say that her occupation is gone indeed. The bill is down—but there is no tenant. Eligible single gentlemen pass and repass—but there is no invitation for them to inquire within or without. All is gloom and silence in the house; even the voice of the child is hushed; his infant sports are disregarded when his mother weeps; his 'alley tor' and his 'commoneys' are alike neglected; he forgets the long familiar cry of 'knuckle down,' and at tip-cheese, or odd and even, his hand is out. But Pickwick, gentlemen, Pickwick, the ruthless destroyer of this domestic oasis in the desert of Goswell Street—Pickwick, who has choked up the well, and thrown ashes on the sward—Pickwick, who comes before you to-day with his heartless Tomata sauce and warming-pans—Pickwick still rears his head with unblushing effrontery, and gazes without a sigh on the ruin he has made. Damages, gentlemen—heavy damages—is the only punishment with which you can visit him; the only recompense you can award to my client. And for those damages she now appeals to an enlightened, a high-minded, a right-feeling, a conscientious, a dispassionate, a sympathizing, a contemplative jury of her civilized countrymen." With this beautiful peroration, Mr. Sergeant Buzfuz sat down, and Mr. Justice Stareleigh woke up.

"Call Elizabeth Cluppins," said Sergeant Buzfuz, rising a minute afterwards, with renewed vigor.

The nearest usher called for Elizabeth Tuppins; another one, at a little distance off, demanded Elizabeth Jupkins; and a third rushed in a breathless state into King Street, and screamed for Elizabeth Muffins till he was hoarse.

Meanwhile Mrs. Cluppins, with the combined assistance of Mrs. Bardell, Mrs. Sanders, Mr. Dodson, and Mr. Fogg, was hoisted into the witness-box; and when she was safely perched on the top step, Mrs. Bardell stood on the bottom one, with the pocket handkerchief and pattens in one hand, and a glass bottle that might hold about a quarter of a pint of smelling salts in the other, ready for any emergency. Mrs. Sanders, whose eyes were intently fixed on the judge's face, planted herself close by, with the large umbrella: keeping her right thumb pressed on the spring with an earnest countenance, as if she were fully prepared to put it up at a moment's notice.

"Mrs. Cluppins," said Sergeant Buzfuz, "pray compose yourself, ma'am." Of course, directly Mrs. Cluppins was desired to compose herself she sobbed with increased vehemence, and gave divers alarming manifestations of an approaching fainting fit, or, as she afterwards said, of her feelings being too many for her.

"Do you recollect, Mrs. Cluppins?" said Sergeant Buzfuz, after a few unimportant questions, "do you recollect being in Mrs. Bardell's back one pair of stairs, on one particular morning in July last, when she was dusting Pickwick's apartment?"

"Yes, my Lord and Jury, I do," replied Mrs. Cluppins.

"Mr. Pickwick's sitting-room was the first-floor front, I believe?"

"Yes, it were, sir," replied Mrs. Cluppins.

"What were you doing in the back room, ma'am?" inquired the little judge.

"My Lord and Jury," said Mrs. Cluppins, with interesting agitation, "I will not deceive you."

"You had better not, ma'am," said the little judge.

"I was there," resumed Mrs. Cluppins, "unbeknown to Mrs. Bardell; I had been out with a little basket, gentlemen, to buy three pound of red kidney purtaties which was three pound tuppence ha'penny, when I see Mrs. Bardell's street door on the jar."

"On the what?" exclaimed the little judge.

"Partly open, my Lord," said Sergeant Snubbin.

"She *said* on the jar," said the little judge, with a cunning look.

"It's all the same, my Lord," said Sergeant Snubbin. The little judge looked doubtful, and said he'd make a note of it. Mrs. Cluppins then resumed—

"I walked in, gentlemen, just to say good mornin', and went, in a permiscuous manner, upstairs, and into the back room. Gentlemen, there was the sound of voices in the front room, and—"

"And you listened, I believe, Mrs. Cluppins?" said Sergeant Buzfuz.

"Beggin' your pardon, sir," replied Mrs. Cluppins, in a majestic manner, "I would scorn the haction. The voices was very loud, sir, and forced themselves upon my ear."

"Well, Mrs. Cluppins, you were not listening, but you heard the voices. Was one of those voices, Pickwick's?"

"Yes, it were, sir."

And Mrs. Cluppins, after distinctly stating that Mr. Pickwick addressed himself to Mrs. Bardell, repeated by slow degrees, and by dint of many questions, the conversation with which our readers are already acquainted.

The jury looked suspicious, and Mr. Sergeant Buzfuz smiled and sat down. They looked positively awful when Sergeant Snubbin intimated that he should not cross-examine the witness, for Mr. Pickwick wished it to be distinctly stated that it was due to her to say that her account was in substance correct.

Mrs. Cluppins having once broken the ice, thought it a favorable opportunity for entering into a short dissertation on her own domestic affairs; so, she straightway proceeded to inform the court that she was the mother of eight children at that present speaking, and that she entertained confident expectations of presenting Mr. Cluppins with a ninth, somewhere about that day six month. At this interesting point, the little judge interposed most irascibly; and the effect of the interposition was, that both the worthy lady and Mrs. Sanders were politely taken out of court, under the escort of Mr. Jackson, without further parley.

"Nathaniel Winkle!" said Mr. Skimpin.

"Here!" replied a feeble voice. Mr. Winkle entered the witness-box, and having been duly sworn, bowed to the judge with considerable deference.

"Don't look at me, sir," said the judge, sharply, in acknowledgment of the salute; "look at the jury."

Mr. Winkle obeyed the mandate, and looked at the place where he thought it most probable the jury might be; for seeing anything in his then state of intellectual complication was wholly out of the question.

Mr. Winkle was then examined by Mr. Skimpin, who, being a promising young man of two or three and forty, was of course anxious to confuse a witness who was notoriously predisposed in favor of the other side, as much as he could.

"Now, sir," said Mr. Skimpin, "have the goodness to let his Lordship and the jury know what your name is, will you?" and Mr. Skimpin inclined his head on one side to listen with great sharpness to the answer and glanced at the jury meanwhile, as if to imply that he rather expected Mr. Winkle's natural taste for perjury would induce him to give some name which did not belong to him.

"Winkle," replied the witness.

"What's your Christian name, sir?" angrily inquired the little judge.

"Nathaniel, sir."

"Daniel—any other name?"

"Nathaniel, sir—my Lord, I mean."

"Nathaniel Daniel, or Daniel Nathaniel?"

"No, my Lord, only Nathaniel; not Daniel at all."

"What did you tell me it was Daniel for, then, sir?" inquired the judge.

"I didn't, my Lord," replied Mr. Winkle.

"You did, sir," replied the judge, with a severe frown. "How could I get Daniel on my notes, unless you told me so, sir?"

This argument, was, of course, unanswerable.

"Mr. Winkle has rather a short memory, my Lord," interposed Mr. Skimpin, with another glance at the jury. "We shall find means to refresh it before we have quite done with him, I dare say."

"You had better be careful, sir," said the little judge, with a sinister look at the witness.

Poor Mr. Winkle bowed, and endeavored to feign an easiness of manner, which, in his then state of confusion, gave him rather the air of a disconcerted pickpocket.

"Now, Mr. Winkle," said Mr. Skimpin, "attend to me, if you please, sir; and let me recommend you, for your own sake, to bear in mind his Lordship's injunction to be careful. I believe you are a particular friend of Pickwick, the defendant, are you not?"

"I have known Mr. Pickwick now, as well as I recollect at this moment, nearly—"

"Pray, Mr. Winkle, do not evade the question. Are you, or are you not, a particular friend of the defendant's?"

"I was just about to say, that—"

"Will you, or will you not, answer my question, sir?"

"If you don't answer the question you'll be committed, sir," interposed the little judge, looking over his notebook.

"Come, sir," said Mr. Skimpin, "yes or no, if you please."

"Yes, I am," replied Mr. Winkle.

"Yes, you are. And why couldn't you say that at once, sir? Perhaps you know the plaintiff, too? Eh, Mr. Winkle?"

"I don't know her; I've seen her."

"Oh, you don't know her, but you've seen her? Now, have the goodness to tell the gentlemen of the jury what you mean by *that,* Mr. Winkle."

"I mean that I am not intimate with her, but I have seen her when I went to call on Mr. Pickwick in Goswell Street."

"How often have you seen her, sir?"

"How often?"

"Yes, Mr. Winkle, how often? I'll repeat the question for you a dozen times, if you require it, sir." And the learned gentleman, with a firm and steady frown placed his hands on his hips, and smiled suspiciously at the jury.

On this question there arose the edifying brow-beating, customary on such points. First of all, Mr. Winkle said it was quite impossible for him to say how many times he had seen Mrs. Bardell. Then he was asked if he had seen her twenty times, to which he replied, "Certainly —more than that." Then he was asked whether he hadn't seen her a hundred times—whether he couldn't swear that he had seen her more than fifty times—whether he didn't know that he had seen her at least seventy-five times—and so forth; the satisfactory conclusion which was arrived at, at last, being, that he had better take care of himself, and mind what he was about. The witness having been by these means reduced to the requisite ebb of nervous perplexity, the examination was continued as follows—

"Pray, Mr. Winkle, do you remember calling on the defendant Pickwick at these apartments in the plaintiff's house in Goswell Street, on one particular morning in the month of July last?"

"Yes, I do."

"Were you accompanied on that occasion by a friend of the name of Tupman, and another of the name of Snodgrass?"

"Yes, I was."

"Are they here?"

"Yes, they are," replied Mr. Winkle, looking very earnestly towards the spot where his friends were stationed.

"Pray attend to me, Mr. Winkle, and never mind your friends," said Mr. Skimpin, with another expressive look at the jury. "They must tell their stories without any previous consultation with you, if none has yet taken place (another look at the jury). Now, sir, tell the gentlemen of the jury what you saw on entering the defendant's room, on this particular morning. Come; out with it, sir; we must have it, sooner or later."

"The defendant, Mr. Pickwick, was holding the plaintiff in his arms, with his hands clasping her waist," replied Mr. Winkle with natural hesitation, "and the plaintiff appeared to have fainted away."

"Did you hear the defendant say anything?"

"I heard him call Mrs. Bardell a good creature, and I heard him ask her to compose herself, for what a situation it was, if anybody should come, or words to that effect."

"Now, Mr. Winkle, I have only one more question to ask you, and I beg you to bear in mind his Lordship's caution. Will you undertake to swear that Pickwick the defendant, did not say on the occasion in question, "My dear Mrs. Bardell, you're a good creature; compose yourself to this situation, for to this situation you must come," or words to *that* effect?"

"I—I didn't understand him so, certainly," said Mr. Winkle, astounded at this ingenious dovetailing of the few words he had heard. "I was on the staircase, and couldn't hear distinctly; the impression on my mind is—"

"The gentlemen of the jury want none of the impressions on your mind, Mr. Winkle, which I fear would be of little service to honest, straightforward men," interposed Mr. Skimpin. "You were on the staircase, and didn't distinctly hear; but you will not swear that Pickwick did not make use of the expressions I have quoted? Do I understand that?"

"No, I will not," replied Mr. Winkle; and down sat Mr. Skimpin with a triumphant countenance.

Mr. Pickwick's case had not gone off in so particularly happy a manner up to this point that it could very well afford to have any additional suspicion cast upon it. But as it could afford to be placed in a rather better light, if possible, Mr. Phunky rose for the purpose of getting something important out of Mr. Winkle in cross-examination. Whether he did get anything important out of him, will immediately appear.

"I believe, Mr. Winkle," said Mr. Phunky, "that Mr. Pickwick is not a young man?"

"Oh no," replied Mr. Winkle; "old enough to be my father."

"You have told my learned friend that you have known Mr. Pickwick a long time. Had you ever any reason to suppose or believe that he was about to be married?"

"Oh no; certainly not," replied Mr. Winkle with so much eagerness, that Mr. Phunky ought to have got him out of the box with all possible dispatch. Lawyers hold that there are two kinds of particularly bad witnesses: a reluctant witness, and a too-willing witness: it was Mr. Winkle's fate to figure in both characters.

"I will even go further than this, Mr. Winkle," continued Mr. Phunky in a most smooth and complacent manner. "Did you ever see anything in Mr. Pickwick's manner and conduct towards the opposite sex, to induce you to believe that he ever contemplated matrimony of late years, in any case?"

"Oh no; certainly not," replied Mr. Winkle.

"Has his behavior, when females have been in the case, always been that of a man, who, having attained a pretty advanced period of life, content with his own occupations and amusements, treats them only as a father might his daughters?"

"Not the least doubt of it," replied Mr. Winkle, in the fullness of his heart. "That is—yes—oh yes—certainly."

"You have never known anything in his behavior towards Mrs. Bardell, or any other female, in the least degree suspicious?" said Mr. Phunky, preparing to sit down; for Sergeant Snubbin was winking at him.

"N—n—no," replied Mr. Winkle, "except on one trifling occasion, which, I have no doubt, might be easily explained."

Now, if the unfortunate Mr. Phunky had sat down when Sergeant Snubbin winked at him, or if Sergeant Buzfuz had stopped this irregular cross-examination at the outset (which he knew better than to do;

observing Mr. Winkle's anxiety, and well knowing it would, in all probability, lead to something serviceable to him), this unfortunate admission would not have been elicited. The moment the words fell from Mr. Winkle's lips, Mr. Phunky sat down, and Sergeant Snubbin rather hastily told him he might leave the box, which Mr. Winkle prepared to do with great readiness, when Serjeant Buzfuz stopped him.

"Stay, Mr. Winkle, stay!" said Sergeant Buzfuz, "will your Lordship have the goodness to ask him, what this one instance of suspicious behavior towards females on the part of this gentleman, who is old enough to be his father, was?"

"You hear what the learned counsel says, sir," observed the judge, turning to the miserable and agonized Mr. Winkle. "Describe the occasion to which you refer."

"My Lord," said Mr. Winkle, trembling with anxiety, "I—I'd rather not."

"Perhaps so," said the little judge; "but you must."

Amid the profound silence of the whole court, Mr. Winkle faltered out, that the trifling circumstance of suspicion was Mr. Pickwick's being found in a lady's sleeping apartment at midnight; which had terminated, he believed, in the breaking off of the projected marriage of the lady in question, and had led, he knew, to the whole party being forcibly carried before George Nupkins, Esq., magistrate and justice of the peace, for the borough of Ipswich!

"You may leave the box, sir," said Sergeant Snubbin. Mr. Winkle *did* leave the box, and rushed with delirious haste to the George and Vulture, where he was discovered some hours after, by the waiter, groaning in a hollow and dismal manner, with his head buried beneath the sofa cushions.

Tracy Tupman, and Augustus Snodgrass, were severally called into the box; both corroborated the testimony of their unhappy friend; and each was driven to the verge of desperation by excessive badgering.

Susannah Sanders was then called, and examined by Sergeant Buzfuz, and cross-examined by Sergeant Snubbin. Had always said and believed that Pickwick would marry Mrs. Bardell; knew that Mrs. Bardell's being engaged to Pickwick was the current topic of conversation in the neighborhood, after the fainting in July; had been told it herself by Mrs. Mudberry which kept a mangle, and Mrs. Bunkin which clear-starched, but did not see either Mrs. Mudberry or Mrs. Bunkin in court. Had heard Pickwick ask the little boy how he should like to have another father. Did not know that Mrs. Bardell was at that time keeping company with the baker, but did know that the baker was then a single man and is now married. Couldn't swear that Mrs. Bardell was not very fond of the baker, but should think that the baker was not very fond of Mrs. Bardell, or he wouldn't have married somebody else. Thought Mrs. Bardell fainted away on the morning in July, because Pickwick asked her to name the day; knew that she (witness) fainted away stone dead when Mr. Sanders asked *her* to name the day, and believed that everybody as called herself a lady would do the same, under similar circumstances. Heard Pickwick ask the boy the question about the marbles, but upon her oath did not know the difference between an alley tor and a commoney.

By the COURT—During the period of her keeping company with Mr. Sanders, had received love letters, like other ladies. In the course of their correspondence, Mr. Sanders had often called her a "duck," but never "chops," nor yet "tomata sauce." He was particularly fond of ducks. Perhaps if he had been as fond of chops and tomata sauce, he might have called her that as a term of affection.

Sergeant Buzfuz now rose with more importance than he had yet exhibited, if that were possible, and vociferated, "Call Samuel Weller."

It was quite unnecessary to call Samuel Weller; for Samuel Weller stepped briskly into the box the instant his name was pronounced; and placing his hat on the floor, and his arms on the rail, took a bird's-eye view of the bar, and a comprehensive survey of the bench, with a remarkably cheerful and lively aspect.

"What's your name, sir?" inquired the judge.

"Sam Weller, my Lord," replied that gentleman.

"Do you spell it with a 'V' or a 'W'?" inquired the judge.

"That depends upon the taste and fancy of the speller, my Lord," replied Sam; "I never had occasion to spell it more than once or twice in my life, but I spells it with a 'V.' "

Here a voice in the gallery exclaimed aloud, "Quite right too, Samivel, quite right. Put it down a we, my Lord, put it down a we."

"Who is that, who dares to address the court?" said the little judge, looking up. "Usher."

"Yes, my Lord."

"Bring that person here instantly."

"Yes, my Lord."

But as the usher didn't find the person, he didn't bring him; and, after a great commotion, all the people who had got up to look for the culprit, sat down again. The little judge turned to the witness as soon as his indignation would allow him to speak, and said—

"Do you know who that was, sir?"

"I rayther suspect it was my father, my Lord," replied Sam.

"Do you see him here now?" said the judge.

"No, I don't, my Lord," replied Sam, staring right up into the lantern in the roof of the court.

"If you could have pointed him out, I would have committed him instantly," said the judge.

Sam bowed his acknowledgments and turned, with unimpaired cheerfulness of countenance, towards Sergeant Buzfuz.

"Now, Mr. Weller," said Sergeant Buzfuz.

"Now, sir," replied Sam.

"I believe you are in the service of Mr. Pickwick, the defendant in this case. Speak up, if you please, Mr. Weller."

"I mean to speak up, sir," replied Sam; "I am in the service o' that 'ere gen'l'm'n, and a wery good service it is."

"Little to do, and plenty to get, I suppose?" said Sergeant Buzfuz, with jocularity.

"Oh, quite enough to get, sir, as the soldier said ven they ordered him three hundred and fifty lashes," replied Sam.

"You must not tell us what the soldier, or any other man, said, sir," interposed the judge; "it's not evidence."

"Wery good, my Lord," replied Sam.

"Do you recollect anything particular happening on the morning when you were first engaged by the defendant; eh, Mr. Weller?" said Sergeant Buzfuz.

"Yes, I do, sir," replied Sam.

"Have the goodness to tell the jury what it was."

"I had a reg'lar new fit out o' clothes that mornin', gen'l'm'n of the jury," said Sam, "and that was a wery partickler and uncommon circumstance vith me in those days."

Hereupon there was a general laugh; and the little judge, looking with an angry countenance over his desk, said, "You had better be careful, sir."

"So Mr. Pickwick said at the time, my Lord," replied Sam; "and I was wery careful o' that 'ere suit o' clothes; wery careful indeed, my Lord."

The judge looked sternly at Sam for full two minutes, but Sam's features were so perfectly calm and serene that the judge said nothing, and motioned Sergeant Buzfuz to proceed.

"Do you mean to tell me, Mr. Weller," said Sergeant Buzfuz, folding his arms emphatically, and turning half-round to the jury, as if in mute assurance that he would bother the witness yet: "Do you mean to tell me, Mr. Weller, that you saw nothing of this fainting on the part of the plaintiff in the arms of the defendant, which you have heard described by the witnesses?"

"Certainly not," replied Sam, "I was in the passage till they called me up, and then the old lady was not there."

"Now, attend, Mr. Weller," said Sergeant Buzfuz, dipping a large pen into the inkstand before him, for the purpose of frightening Sam into a show of taking down his answer. "You were in the passage, and yet saw nothing of what was going forward. Have you a pair of eyes, Mr. Weller?"

"Yes, I have a pair of eyes," replied Sam, "and that's just it. If they wos a pair o' patent double million magnifyin' gas microscopes of hextra power, p'raps I might be able to see through a flight o' stairs and a deal door; but bein' only eyes, you see, my wision's limited."

At this answer, which was delivered without the slightest appearance of irritation, and with the most complete simplicity and equanimity of manner, the spectators tittered, the little judge smiled, and Sergeant Buzfuz looked particularly foolish. After a short consultation with Dodson and Fogg, the learned Sergeant again turned towards Sam, and said with a painful effort to conceal his vexation, "Now, Mr. Weller, I'll ask you a question on another point, if you please."

"If you please, sir," rejoined Sam, with the utmost good-humor.

"Do you remember going up to Mrs. Bardell's house, one night in November last?"

"Oh yes, wery well."

"Oh, you *do* remember that, Mr. Weller," said Sergeant Buzfuz recovering his spirits; "I thought we should get at something at last."

"I rayther thought that, too, sir," replied Sam; and at this the spectators tittered again.

"Well; I suppose you went up to have a little talk about this trial—eh, Mr. Weller?" said Sergeant Buzfuz, looking knowingly at the jury.

"I went up to pay the rent; but we *did* get a talkin' about the trial," replied Sam.

"Oh, you did get a talking about the trial," said Sergeant Buzfuz, brightening up with the anticipation of some important discovery. "Now what passed about the trial; will you have the goodness to tell us, Mr. Weller?"

"Vith all the pleasure in life, sir," replied Sam. "After a few unimportant obserwations from the two wirtuous females as has been examined here to-day, the ladies gets into a very great state o' admiration at the honorable conduct of Mr. Dodson and Fogg—them two gen'l'm'n as is settin' near you now." This, of course, drew general attention to Dodson and Fogg, who looked as virtuous as possible.

"The attorneys for the plaintiff," said Mr. Sergeant Buzfuz. "Well! They spoke in high praise of the honorable conduct of Messrs. Dodson and Fogg, the attorneys for the plaintiff, did they?"

"Yes," said Sam, "they said what a wery gen'rous thing it was o' them to have taken up the case on spec, and to charge nothing at all for costs, unless they got 'em out of Mr. Pickwick."

At this very unexpected reply, the spectators tittered again, and Dodson and Fogg, turning very red, leant over to Sergeant Buzfuz, and in a hurried manner whispered something in his ear.

"You are quite right," said Sergeant Buzfuz aloud, with affected composure. "It's perfectly useless, my Lord, attempting to get at any evidence through the impenetrable stupidity of this witness. I will not trouble the court by asking him any more questions. Stand down, sir."

"Would any other gen'l'm'n like to ask me anythin'?" inquired Sam, taking up his hat, and looking round most deliberately.

"Not I, Mr. Weller, thank you," said Sergeant Snubbin, laughing.

"You may go down, sir," said Sergeant Buzfuz, waving his hand impatiently. Sam went down accordingly, after doing Messrs. Dodson and Fogg's case as much harm as he conveniently could, and saying just as little respecting Mr. Pickwick as might be, which was precisely the object he had in view all along.

"I have no objection to admit, my Lord," said Sergeant Snubbin, "if it will save the examination of another witness, that Mr. Pickwick has retired from business, and is a gentleman of considerable independent property."

"Very well," said Sergeant Buzfuz, putting in the two letters to be read, "then that's my case, my Lord."

Sergeant Snubbin then addressed the jury on behalf of the defendant; and a very long and a very emphatic address he delivered,

in which he bestowed the highest possible eulogiums on the conduct and
character of Mr. Pickwick; but inasmuch as our readers are far better
able to form a correct estimate of that gentleman's merits and deserts,
than Sergeant Snubbin could possibly be, we do not feel called upon
to enter at any length into the learned gentleman's observations. He attempted to show that the letters which had been exhibited, merely related to Mr. Pickwick's dinner, or to the preparations for receiving him
in his apartments on his return from some country excursion. It is sufficient to add in general terms, that he did the best he could for Mr.
Pickwick; and the best, as everybody knows, on the infallible authority
of the old adage, could do no more.

Mr. Justice Stareleigh summed up, in the old-established and most
approved form. He read as much of his notes to the jury as he could
decipher on so short a notice, and made running comments on the evidence as he went along. If Mrs. Bardell were right, it was perfectly
clear that Mr. Pickwick was wrong, and if they thought the evidence of
Mrs. Cluppins worthy of credence they would believe it, and, if they
didn't, why they wouldn't. If they were satisfied that a breach of promise of marriage had been committed, they would find for the plaintiff
with such damages as they thought proper; and if, on the other hand, it
appeared to them that no promise of marriage had ever been given,
they would find for the defendant with no damages at all. The jury then
retired to their private room to talk the matter over, and the judge retired to *his* private room, to refresh himself with a mutton chop and a
glass of sherry.

An anxious quarter of an hour elapsed; the jury came back; the
judge was fetched in. Mr. Pickwick put on his spectacles, and gazed at
the foreman with an agitated countenance and a quickly beating heart.

"Gentlemen," said the individual in black, "are you all agreed upon
your verdict?"

"We are," replied the foreman.

"Do you find for the plaintiff, gentlemen, or for the defendant?"

"For the plaintiff."

"With what damages, gentlemen?"

"Seven hundred and fifty pounds."

Mr. Pickwick took off his spectacles, carefully wiped the glasses,
folded them into their case, and put them in his pocket; then having
drawn on his gloves with great nicety, and stared at the foreman all the

while, he mechanically followed Mr. Perker and the blue bag out of court.

They stopped in a side room while Perker paid the court fees; and here, Mr. Pickwick was joined by his friends. Here, too, he encountered Messrs. Dodson and Fogg, rubbing their hands with every token of outward satisfaction.

"Well, gentlemen," said Mr. Pickwick.

"Well, sir," said Dodson: for self and partner.

"You imagine you'll get your costs, don't you, gentlemen?" said Mr. Pickwick.

Fogg said they thought it rather probable. Dodson smiled, and said they'd try.

"You may try, and try, and try again, Messrs. Dodson and Fogg," said Mr. Pickwick vehemently, "but not one farthing of costs or damages do you ever get from me, if I spend the rest of my existence in a debtors' prison."

"Ha, ha!" laughed Dodson. "You'll think better of that, before next term, Mr. Pickwick."

"He, he, he! We'll soon see about that, Mr. Pickwick," grinned Fogg.

Speechless with indignation, Mr. Pickwick allowed himself to be led by his solicitor and friends to the door, and there assisted into a hackney-coach, which had been fetched for the purpose, by the ever-watchful Sam Weller.

Sam had put up the steps, and was preparing to jump upon the box, when he felt himself gently touched on the shoulder; and looking round, his father stood before him. The old gentleman's countenance wore a mournful expression, as he shook his head gravely, and said, in warning accents—

"I know'd what 'ud come o' this here mode o' doin' bis'ness. Oh Sammy, Sammy, vy worn't there a alleybi!"

[EDITOR'S NOTE: Pickwick and Mrs. Bardell did not take the stand, for under English law then in effect, parties to an action were not permitted to give evidence.]

Charles Dickens

.

IN CHANCERY

from *Bleak House*

London. Michaelmas Term lately over, and the Lord Chancellor sitting in Lincoln's Inn Hall. Implacable November weather. As much mud in the streets, as if the waters had but newly retired from the face of the earth, and it would not be wonderful to meet a Megalosaurus, forty feet long or so, waddling like an elephantine lizard up Holborn Hill. Smoke lowering down from chimney-pots, making a soft black drizzle, with flakes of soot in it as big as full-grown snowflakes—gone into mourning, one might imagine, for the death of the sun. Dogs, undistinguishable in mire. Horses, scarcely better; splashed to their very blinkers. Foot passengers, jostling one another's umbrellas, in a general infection of ill-temper, and losing their foothold at street-corners, where tens of thousands of other foot passengers have been slipping and sliding since the day broke (if this day ever broke), adding new deposits to the crust upon crust of mud, sticking at those points tenaciously to the pavement, and accumulating at compound interest.

Fog everywhere. Fog up the river, where it flows among green aits and meadows; fog down the river, where it rolls defiled among the tiers of shipping, and the waterside pollutions of a great (and dirty) city. Fog on the Essex marshes, fog on the Kentish heights. Fog creeping into the cabooses of collier-brigs; fog lying out on the yards, and hovering in the rigging of great ships; fog drooping on the gunwales of barges and small boats. Fog in the eyes and throats of ancient Greenwich pensioners, wheezing by the firesides of their wards; fog in the stem and bowl of the afternoon pipe of the wrathful skipper, down in his close cabin; fog cruelly pinching the toes and fingers of his shivering little 'prentice boy on deck. Chance people on the bridges peeping over the parapets into a nether sky of fog, with fog all round them, as if they were up in a balloon, and hanging in the misty clouds.

Gas looming through the fog in divers places in the streets, much as the sun may, from the spongy fields, be seen to loom by husbandman and ploughboy. Most of the shops lighted two hours before their time— as the gas seems to know, for it has a haggard and unwilling look.

The raw afternoon is rawest, and the dense fog is densest, and the muddy streets are muddiest, near that leaden-headed old obstruction, appropriate ornament for the threshold of a leaden-headed old corporation: Temple Bar. And hard by Temple Bar, in Lincoln's Inn Hall, at the very heart of the fog, sits the Lord High Chancellor in his High Court of Chancery.

Never can there come fog too thick, never can there come mud and mire too deep, to assort with the groping and floundering condition which this High Court of Chancery, most pestilent of hoary sinners, holds, this day, in the sight of heaven and earth.

On such an afternoon, if ever, the Lord High Chancellor ought to be sitting here—as here he is—with a foggy glory round his head, softly fenced in with crimson cloth and curtains, addressed by a large advocate with great whiskers, a little voice, and an interminable brief, and outwardly directing his contemplation to the lantern in the roof, where he can see nothing but fog. On such an afternoon, some score of members of the High Court of Chancery bar ought to be—as here they are— mistily engaged in one of the ten thousand stages of an endless cause, tripping one another up on slippery precedents, groping knee-deep in technicalities, running their goat-hair and horse-hair warded heads against walls of words, and making a pretense of equity with serious faces, as players might. On such an afternoon, the various solicitors in the cause, some two or three of whom have inherited it from their fathers, who made a fortune by it, ought to be—as are they not?— ranged in a line, in a long matted well (but you might look in vain for Truth at the bottom of it), between the registrar's red table and the silk gowns, with bills, cross-bills, answers, rejoinders, injunctions, affidavits, issues, references to masters, masters' reports, mountains of costly nonsense, piled before them. Well may the court be dim, with wasting candles here and there; well may the fog hang heavy in it, as if it would never get out; well may the stained glass windows lose their color, and admit no light of day into the place; well may the uninitiated from the streets, who peep in through the glass panes in the door, be deterred from entrance by its owlish aspect, and by the drawl languidly echoing to the roof from the padded dais where the Lord High Chancellor looks into the lantern that has no light in it, and where the attendant wigs are all stuck in a fog-bank! This is the Court of Chancery; which has its decaying houses and its blighted lands in every shire; which has its worn-out lunatic in every madhouse, and its dead in every churchyard; which has its ruined suitor, with his slipshod heels and threadbare dress, borrowing and begging through the round of every man's acquaintance; which gives to monied might, the means abundantly of wearying out the right; which so exhausts finances, patience, courage, hope; so overthrows the brain and breaks the heart; that there is not an honorable man among its practitioners who would not give—who does not often give—the warning, "Suffer any wrong that can be done you, rather than come here!"

Who happen to be in the Lord Chancellor's court this murky afternoon besides the Lord Chancellor, the counsel in the cause, two or three counsel who are never in any cause, and the well of solicitors before mentioned? There is the registrar below the Judge, in wig and gown; and there are two or three maces, or petty-bags, or privy purses, or whatever they may be, in legal court suits. These are all yawning; for no crumb of amusement ever falls from JARNDYCE AND JARNDYCE (the cause in hand), which was squeezed dry years upon years ago. The shorthand writers, the reporters of the court, and the reporters of the newspapers, invariably decamp with the rest of the regulars when Jarndyce and Jarndyce comes on. Their places are a blank. Standing on a seat at the side of the hall, the better to peer into the curtained sanctuary, is a little mad old woman in a squeezed bonnet, who is always in court, from its sitting to its rising, and always expecting some incomprehensible judgment to be given in her favor. Some say she really is, or was, a party to a suit; but no one knows for certain, because no one cares. She carries some small litter in a reticule which she calls her documents; principally consisting of paper matches and dry lavender. A sallow prisoner has come up, in custody, for the half-dozenth time, to make a personal application "to purge himself of his contempt"; which, being a solitary surviving executor who has fallen into a state of conglomeration about accounts of which it is not pretended that he had ever any knowledge, he is not at all likely ever to do. In the meantime his prospects in life are ended. Another ruined suitor, who periodically appears from Shropshire, and breaks out into efforts to address the Chancellor at the close of the day's business, and who can by no means be made to understand that the Chancellor is legally ignorant of his existence after making it desolate for a quarter of a century, plants himself in a good place and keeps an eye on the Judge, ready to call out "My Lord!" in a voice of sonorous complaint, on the instant of his rising. A few lawyers' clerks and others who know this suitor by sight, linger, on the chance of his furnishing some fun, and enlivening the dismal weather a little.

Jarndyce and Jarndyce drones on. This scarecrow of a suit has, in course of time, become so complicated, that no man alive knows what it means. The parties to it understand it least; but it has been observed that no two Chancery lawyers can talk about it for five minutes, without coming to a total disagreement as to all the premises. Innumerable children have been born into the cause; innumerable young people have married into it; innumerable old people have died out of it. Scores of persons have deliriously found themselves made parties in Jarndyce and Jarndyce, without knowing how or why; whole families have inherited legendary hatreds with the suit. The little plaintiff or defendant, who was promised a new rocking-horse when Jarndyce and Jarndyce should be settled, has grown up, possessed himself of a real horse, and trotted away into the other world. Fair wards of court have faded into mothers and grandmothers; a long procession of Chancellors has come in and gone out; the legion of bills in the suit have been transformed into mere bills of mortality; there are not three Jarndyces left upon the earth perhaps, since old Tom Jarndyce in despair blew his brains out at a coffee-house in Chancery Lane; but Jarndyce and Jarndyce still drags its dreary length before the Court, perennially hopeless.

Jarndyce and Jarndyce has passed into a joke. That is the only good that has ever come of it. It has been death to many, but it is a joke in the profession. Every master in Chancery has had a reference out of it. Every Chancellor was "in it," for somebody or other, when he was counsel at the bar. Good things have been said about it by blue-nosed, bulbous-shoed old benchers, in select port-wine committee after dinner in hall. Articled clerks have been in the habit of fleshing their legal wit upon it. The last Lord Chancellor handled it neatly, when, correcting Mr. Blowers the eminent silk gown who said that such a thing might happen when the sky rained potatoes, he observed, "or when we get through Jarndyce and Jarndyce, Mr. Blowers"—a pleasantry that particularly tickled the maces, bags, and purses.

How many people out of the suit, Jarndyce and Jarndyce has stretched forth its unwholesome hand to spoil and corrupt, would be a very wide question. From the master, upon whose impaling files reams of dusty warrants in Jarndyce and Jarndyce have grimly writhed into many shapes; down to the copying-clerk in the Six Clerks' Office, who has copied his tens of thousands of Chancery-folio-pages under that eternal heading; no man's nature has been made better by it. In trickery, evasion, procrastination, spoilation, botheration, under false pretenses of all sorts, there are influences that can never come to good. The very solicitors' boys who have kept the wretched suitors at bay, by protesting time out of mind that Mr. Chizzle, Mizzle, or otherwise, was particularly engaged and had appointments until dinner, may have got an extra moral twist and shuffle into themselves out of Jarndyce and Jarndyce. The receiver in the cause has acquired a goodly sum of money by it, but has acquired too a distrust of his own mother, and a contempt for his own kind. Chizzle, Mizzle, and otherwise, have lapsed into a habit of vaguely promising themselves that they will look into that outstanding little matter, and see what can be done for Drizzle—who was not well used—when Jarndyce and Jarndyce shall be got out of the office. Shirking and sharking, in all their many varieties, have been sown broadcast by the ill-fated cause; and even those who have contemplated its history from the outermost circle of such evil, have been insensibly tempted into a loose way of letting bad things alone to take their own bad course, and a loose belief that if the world go wrong, it was, in some offhand manner, never meant to go right.

Thus, in the midst of the mud and at the heart of the fog, sits the Lord High Chancellor in his High Court of Chancery.

"Mr. Tangle," says the Lord High Chancellor, latterly something restless under the eloquence of that learned gentleman.

"Mlud," said Mr. Tangle. Mr. Tangle knows more of Jarndyce and Jarndyce than anybody. He is famous for it—supposed never to have read anything else since he left school.

"Have you nearly concluded your argument?"

"Mlud, no—variety of points—feel it my duty tsubmit—ludship," is the reply that slides out of Mr. Tangle.

"Several members of the bar are still to be heard, I believe?" says the Chancellor, with a slight smile.

Eighteen of Mr. Tangle's learned friends, each armed with a little summary of eighteen hundred sheets, bob up like eighteen hammers in a pianoforte, make eighteen bows, and drop into their eighteen places of obscurity.

"We will proceed with the hearing on Wednesday fortnight," says the Chancellor. For, the question at issue is only a question of costs, a mere bud on the forest tree of the parent suit, and really will come to a settlement one of these days.

The Chancellor rises; the bar rises; the prisoner is brought forward in a hurry; the man from Shropshire cries, "My lord!" Maces, bags, and purses, indignantly proclaim silence, and frown at the man from Shropshire.

"In reference," proceeds the Chancellor, still on Jarndyce and Jarndyce, "to the young girl—"

"Begludship's pardon—boy," says Mr. Tangle, prematurely.

"In reference," proceeds the Chancellor, with extra distinctness, "to the young girl and boy, the two young people . . ."

(Mr. Tangle crushed.)

"Whom I directed to be in attendance today, and who are now in my private room, I will see them and satisfy myself as to the expediency of making the order for their residing with their uncle."

Mr. Tangle on his legs again.

"Begludship's pardon—dead."

"With their," Chancellor looking through his double eye-glass at the papers on his desk, "grandfather."

"Begludship's pardon—victim of rash action—brains."

Suddenly a very little counsel, with a terrific bass voice, arises, fully inflated, in the back settlements of the fog, and says, "Will your lordship allow me? I appear for him. He is a cousin, several times removed. I am not at the moment prepared to inform the Court in what exact remove he is a cousin; but he *is* a cousin."

Leaving this address (delivered like a sepulchral message) ringing in the rafters of the roof, the very little counsel drops, and the fog knows him no more. Everybody looks for him. Nobody can see him.

"I will speak with both the young people," says the Chancellor anew, "and satisfy myself on the subject of their residing with their cousin. I will mention the matter tomorrow morning when I take my seat."

The Chancellor is about to bow to the bar, when the prisoner is presented. Nothing can possibly come of the prisoner's conglomeration, but

his being sent back to prison; which is soon done. The man from Shropshire ventures another remonstrative "My lord!" but the Chancellor,
being aware of him, has dexterously vanished. Everybody else quickly
vanishes too. A battery of blue bags is loaded with heavy charges of papers and carried off by clerks; the little mad old woman marches off with
her documents; the empty court is locked up. If all the injustice it has
committed, and all the misery it has caused, could only be locked up with
it, and the whole burnt away in a great funeral pyre—why so much the
better for other parties than the parties in Jarndyce and Jarndyce!

Terence Rattigan

:

THE WINSLOW BOY

ACT I: *A Sunday Morning in July*
ACT II: *An Evening in April (nine months later)*
ACT III: *An Evening in January (nine months later)*
ACT IV: *An Afternoon in June (five months later)*

The action of the play takes place in Arthur Winslow's house in Kensington, London, and extends over two years of a period preceding the war of 1914-1918.

Dramatis Personnae

RONNIE WINSLOW	CATHERINE WINSLOW
VIOLET	JOHN WATHERSTONE
ARTHUR WINSLOW	DESMOND CURRY
GRACE WINSLOW	MISS BARNES
DICKIE WINSLOW	FRED
SIR ROBERT MORTON	

A C T   I

SCENE: *The drawing-room of a house in Courtfield Gardens, South Kensington, on a morning in July, at some period not long before the war of 1914-1918.*

The furnishings betoken solid but not undecorative upper middle-class comfort.

On the rise of the curtain A BOY *of about fourteen, dressed in the uniform of an Osborne naval cadet, is discovered. There is something rigid and tense in his attitude, and his face is blank and without expression.*

There is the sound of someone in the hall. As the sound comes nearer, he looks despairingly round, as if contemplating flight. An elderly maid (VIOLET) *comes in, and stops in astonishment at sight of him.*

VIOLET: Master Ronnie!

RONNIE (*With ill-managed sang-froid*): Hello, Violet.

VIOLET: Why, good gracious! We weren't expecting you back till Tuesday.

RONNIE: Yes, I know.

VIOLET: Why ever didn't you let us know you were coming, you silly boy? Your mother should have been at the station to meet you. The idea of a child like you wandering all over London by yourself. I never did. However did you get in? By the garden, I suppose.

RONNIE: No. The front door. I rang and cook opened it.

VIOLET: And where's your trunk and your tuck box?

RONNIE: Upstairs. The taximan carried them up——

VIOLET: Taximan? You took a taxi?

RONNIE *nods.*

All by yourself? Well, I don't know what little boys are coming to, I'm sure. What your father and mother will say, I don't know——

RONNIE: Where are they, Violet?

VIOLET: Church, of course.

RONNIE (*Vacantly*): Oh, yes. It's Sunday, isn't it?

VIOLET: What's the matter with you? What have they been doing to you at Osborne?

RONNIE (*Sharply*): What do you mean?

VIOLET: They seem to have made you a bit soft in the head, or something. Well—I suppose I'd better get your unpacking done—Mr. Dickie's been using your chest of drawers for all his dress clothes and things. I'll just clear 'em out and put 'em on his bed—that's what I'll do. He can find room for 'em somewhere else.

RONNIE: Shall I help you?

VIOLET (*Scornfully*): I know *your* help. With *your* help I'll be at it all day. No, you just wait down here for your mother and father. They'll be back in a minute.

> RONNIE *nods and turns hopelessly away.* VIOLET *looks at his retreating back, puzzled.*

Well?

RONNIE (*Turning*): Yes?

VIOLET: Don't I get a kiss or are you too grown up for that now?

RONNIE: Sorry, Violet.

> *He goes up to her and is enveloped in her ample bosom.*

VIOLET: That's better. My, what a big boy you're getting!

> *She holds him at arm's length and inspects him.*

Quite the little naval officer, aren't you?

RONNIE (*Smiling forlornly*): Yes. That's right.

VIOLET: Well, well—I must be getting on——

> *She goes out.* RONNIE, *left alone, resumes his attitude of utter dejection. He takes out of his pocket a letter in a sealed envelope. After a second's hesitation, he opens it, and reads the contents. The perusal appears to increase his misery.*
>
> *He makes for a moment as if to tear it up; then changes his mind again, and puts it back in his pocket. He gets up and takes two or three quick steps towards the hall door. Then he stops, uncertainly.*
>
> *There is the sound of voices in the hall.* RONNIE *jumps to his feet; then, with a strangled sob runs to the garden door, and down the iron steps into the garden.*
>
> *The hall door opens and the rest of the Winslow family file in. They are* ARTHUR *and* GRACE—*Ronnie's father and mother—and* DICKIE *and* CATHERINE—*his brother and sister. All are carrying prayer-books, and wear that faintly unctuous after-church air.*
>
> ARTHUR *leans heavily on a stick. He is a man of about sixty, with a rather deliberately cultured patriarchal air.* GRACE *is about ten years younger, with the faded remnants of prettiness.* DICKIE *is an*

Oxford undergraduate, large, noisy, and cheerful. CATHERINE, *approaching thirty, has an air of masculinity about her which is at odd variance with her mother's intense femininity.*

GRACE (*As she enters*):—But he's so old, dear. From the back of the church you really can't hear a word he says——

ARTHUR: He's a good man, Grace.

GRACE: But what's the use of being good, if you're inaudible?

CATHERINE: A problem in ethics for you, Father.

> ARTHUR *is standing with his back to fireplace. He looks round at the open garden door.*

ARTHUR: There's a draught, Grace.

> GRACE *goes to the door and closes it.*

GRACE: Oh, dear—it's coming on to rain.

DICKIE: I'm on Mother's side. The old boy's so doddery now he can hardly finish the course at all. I timed him today. It took him seventy-five seconds dead from a flying start to reach the pulpit, and then he needed the whip coming round the bend. I call that pretty bad going.

ARTHUR: I don't think that's very funny, Richard.

DICKIE: Oh, don't you, Father?

ARTHUR: Doddery though Mr. Jackson may seem now, I very much doubt if he failed in his pass mods. when he was at Oxford.

DICKIE (*Aggrieved*): Dash it—Father—you promised not to mention that again this vac——

GRACE: You did, you know, Arthur.

ARTHUR: There was a condition to my promise—if you remember—that Dickie should provide me with reasonable evidence of his intentions to work.

DICKIE: Well, haven't I, Father? Didn't I stay in all last night—a Saturday night—and work?

ARTHUR: You stayed in, Dickie. I would be the last to deny that.

GRACE: You *were* making rather a noise, dear, with that old gramophone of yours. I really can't believe you could have been doing much work with that going on all the time——

DICKIE: Funnily enough, Mother, it helps me to concentrate——

ARTHUR: Concentrate on what?

DICKIE: Work, of course.

ARTHUR: That was not what you appeared to be concentrating on when I came down to fetch a book—sleep, may I say, having been rendered out of the question by the hideous sounds emanating from this room.

DICKIE: Edwina and her father had just looked in on their way to the Graham's dance—they only stayed a minute——

GRACE: What an idiotic girl that is! Oh, sorry, Dickie—I was forgetting. You're rather keen on her, aren't you?

ARTHUR: You would have had ample proof of that fact, Grace, if you had seen them in the attitude I caught them in last night.

DICKIE: We were practicing the Bunny Hug.

GRACE: The what, dear?

DICKIE: The Bunny Hug. It's the new dance.

CATHERINE (*Helpfully*): It's like the Turkey Trot—only more dignified.

GRACE: I thought that was the tango.

DICKIE: No. More like a Fox Trot, really. Something between a Boston Glide and a Kangaroo Hop.

ARTHUR: We appear to be straying from the point. Whatever animal was responsible for the posture I found you in does not alter the fact that you have not done one single stroke of work this vacation.

DICKIE: Oh. Well, I do work awfully fast, you know—once I get down to it.

ARTHUR: That assumption can hardly be based on experience, I take it.

DICKIE: Dash it, Father! You are laying in to me this morning.

ARTHUR: It's time you found out, Dickie, that I'm not spending two hundred pounds a year keeping you at Oxford, merely to learn to dance the Bunny Hop.

DICKIE: Hug, Father.

ARTHUR: The exact description of the obscenity is immaterial.

GRACE: Father's quite right, you know, dear. You really have been going the pace a bit, this vac.

DICKIE: Yes, I know, Mother—but the season's nearly over now——

GRACE (*With a sigh*): I wish you were as good about work as Ronnie.

DICKIE (*Hotly*): I like that. That's a bit thick, I must say. All Ronnie ever has to do with his footling little homework is to add two and two.

ARTHUR: Ronnie is at least proving a good deal more successful in adding two and two than you were at his age.

DICKIE (*Now furious*): Oh, yes, I know. I know. He got into Osborne and I failed. That's going to be brought up again——

GRACE: Nobody's bringing it up, dear——

DICKIE: Oh, yes they are. It's going to be brought up against me all my life. Ronnie's the good little boy, I'm the bad little boy. You've just stuck a couple of labels on us that nothing on earth is ever going to change.

GRACE: Don't be so absurd, dear——

DICKIE: It's not absurd. It's quite true. Isn't it, Kate?

CATHERINE *looks up from a book she has been reading in the corner.*

CATHERINE: I'm sorry, Dickie. I haven't been listening. Isn't what quite true?

DICKIE: That in the eyes of Mother and Father nothing that Ronnie does is ever wrong, and nothing I do is ever right?

CATHERINE (*After a pause*): If I were you, Dickie dear, I'd go and have a nice lie down before lunch.

DICKIE (*After a further pause*): Perhaps you're right.

He goes towards the hall door.

ARTHUR: If you're going to your room I suggest you take that object with you.

He points to a gramophone—1912 model, with horn—lying on a table.

It's out of place in a drawing-room.

DICKIE, *with an air of hauteur, picks up the gramophone and carries it to the door.*

It might help you to concentrate on the work you're going to do this afternoon.

DICKIE *stops at the door, and then turns slowly.*

DICKIE (*With dignity*): That is out of the question, I'm afraid.

ARTHUR: Indeed? Why?

DICKIE: I have an engagement with Miss Gunn.

ARTHUR: On a Sunday afternoon? Escorting her to the National Gallery, no doubt?

DICKIE: No. The Victoria and Albert Museum.

He goes out with as much dignity as is consistent with the carrying of a very bulky gramophone.

GRACE: How stupid of him to say that about labels. There's no truth in it at all—is there, Kate?

CATHERINE (*Deep in her book*): No, Mother.

GRACE: Oh, dear, it's simply pelting. What are you reading, Kate?

CATHERINE: Len Rogers's Memoirs.

GRACE: Who's Len Rogers?

CATHERINE: A Trades Union Leader.

GRACE: Does John know you're a Radical?

CATHERINE: Oh, yes.

GRACE: And a Suffragette?

CATHERINE: Certainly.

GRACE (*With a smile*): And he still wants to marry you?

CATHERINE: He seems to.

GRACE: Oh, by the way, I've asked him to come early for lunch—so that he can have a few words with Father first.

CATHERINE: Good idea. I hope you've been primed, have you, Father?

ARTHUR (*Who has been nearly asleep*): What's that?

CATHERINE: You know what you're going to say to John, don't you? You're not going to let me down and forbid the match, or anything, are you? Because I warn you, if you do, I shall elope——

ARTHUR (*Taking her hand*): Never fear, my dear. I'm far too delighted at the prospect of getting you off our hands at last.

CATHERINE (*Smiling*): I'm not sure I like that "at last."

GRACE: Do you love him, dear?

CATHERINE: John? Yes, I do.

GRACE: You're such a funny girl. You never show your feelings much, do you? You don't behave as if you were in love.

CATHERINE: How does one behave as if one is in love?

ARTHUR: One doesn't read Len Rogers. One reads Byron.

CATHERINE: I do both.

ARTHUR: An odd combination.

CATHERINE: A satisfying one.

GRACE: I meant—you don't talk about him much, do you?

CATHERINE: No. I suppose I don't.

GRACE (*Sighing*): I don't think you modern girls have the feelings our generation did. It's this New Woman attitude.

CATHERINE: Very well, Mother. I love John in every way that a woman can love a man, and far, far more than he loves me. Does that satisfy you?

GRACE (*Embarrassed*): Well, really, Kate darling—I didn't ask for anything quite like that—— (*To* ARTHUR) What are you laughing at, Arthur?

ARTHUR (*Chuckling*): One up to the New Woman.

GRACE: Nonsense. She misunderstood me, that's all. (*At the window*) Just look at the rain! (*Turning to* CATHERINE) Kate, darling, does Desmond know about you and John?

The Law IN *Literature*

CATHERINE: I haven't told him. On the other hand, if he hasn't guessed, he must be very dense.

ARTHUR: He *is* very dense.

GRACE: Oh, no. He's quite clever, if you really get under his skin.

ARTHUR: Oddly enough, I've never had that inclination.

GRACE: I think he's a dear. Kate darling, you *will* be kind to him, won't you?

CATHERINE (*Patiently*): Yes, Mother. Of course I will.

GRACE: He's really a very good sort——

She breaks off suddenly and stares out of the window.

Hullo! There's someone in our garden.

CATHERINE (*Coming to look*): Where?

GRACE (*Pointing*): Over there, do you see?

CATHERINE: No.

GRACE: He's just gone behind that bush. It was a boy, I think. Probably Mrs. Williamson's awful little Dennis.

CATHERINE (*Leaving the window*): Well, whoever it is must be getting terribly wet.

GRACE: Why can't he stick to his own garden?

There is a sound of voices outside in the hall.

GRACE: Was that John?

CATHERINE: It sounded like it.

GRACE (*After listening*): Yes. It's John. (*To* CATHERINE) Quick! In the dining-room!

CATHERINE: All right.

She dashes across to the dining-room door.

GRACE: Here! You've forgotten your bag.

She darts to the table and picks it up.

ARTHUR (*Startled*): What on earth is going on?

GRACE (*In a stage whisper*): We're leaving you alone with John. When you've finished cough or something.

ARTHUR (*Testily*): What do you mean, or something?

GRACE: I know. Knock on the floor with your stick—three times. Then we'll come in.

ARTHUR: You don't think that might look a trifle coincidental?

GRACE: Sh!

She disappears from view as the hall door opens and VIOLET *comes in.*

VIOLET (*Announcing*): Mr. Watherstone.

JOHN WATHERSTONE *comes in. He is a man of about thirty, dressed in an extremely well-cut morning coat and striped trousers, an attire which, though excused by church parade, we may well feel has been donned for this occasion.*

ARTHUR: How are you, John? I'm very glad to see you.

JOHN: How do you do, sir?

ARTHUR: Will you forgive me not getting up? My arthritis has been troubling me rather a lot, lately.

JOHN: I'm very sorry to hear that, sir. Catherine told me it was better.

ARTHUR: It was, for a time. Now it's worse again. Do you smoke? (*He indicates a cigarette-box.*)

JOHN: Yes, sir. I do. Thank you. (*He takes a cigarette, adding hastily*) In moderation, of course.

ARTHUR (*With a faint smile*): Of course.

    Pause, while JOHN *lights his cigarette and* ARTHUR *watches him.*
Well, now. I understand you wish to marry my daughter.

JOHN: Yes, sir. That's to say, I've proposed to her and she's done me the honor of accepting me.

ARTHUR: I see. I trust when you corrected yourself, your second statement wasn't a denial of your first? (JOHN *looks puzzled*) I mean, you do *really* wish to marry her?

JOHN: Of course, sir.

ARTHUR: Why, of course? There are plenty of people about who don't wish to marry her.

JOHN: I mean, of course, because I proposed to her.

ARTHUR: That, too, doesn't necessarily follow. However, we don't need to quibble. We'll take the sentimental side of the project for granted. As regards the more practical aspect, perhaps you won't mind if I ask you a few rather personal questions?

JOHN: Naturally not, sir. It's your duty.

ARTHUR: Quite so. Now, your income. Are you able to live on it?

JOHN: No, sir. I'm in the regular army.

ARTHUR: Yes, of course.

JOHN: But my army pay is supplemented by an allowance from my father.

ARTHUR: So I understand. Now, your father's would be, I take it, about twenty-four pounds a month.

JOHN: Yes, sir, that's exactly right.

ARTHUR: So that your total income—with your subaltern's pay and allowances plus the allowance from your father, would be, I take it, about four hundred and twenty pounds a year?

JOHN: Again, exactly the figure.

ARTHUR: Well, well. It all seems perfectly satisfactory. I really don't think I need delay my congratulations any longer.

(*He extends his hand, which* JOHN, *gratefully, takes.*)

JOHN: Thank you, sir, very much.

ARTHUR: I must say, it was very good of you to be so frank and informative.

JOHN: Not at all.

ARTHUR: Your answers to my questions deserve an equal frankness from me about Catherine's own affairs. I'm afraid she's not—just in case you thought otherwise—the daughter of a rich man.

JOHN: I didn't think otherwise, sir.

ARTHUR: Good. Well, now——

He suddenly cocks his head on one side and listens. There is the sound of a gramophone playing "Hitchy-koo" from somewhere upstairs.

Would you be so good as to touch the bell?

JOHN *does so.*

Thank you. Well, now, continuing about my own financial affairs. The Westminster Bank pay me a small pension—three hundred and fifty to be precise—and my wife has about two hundred a year of her own. Apart from that we have nothing, except such savings as I've been able to make during my career at the bank. The interest from which raises my total income to approximately eight hundred pounds per annum.

VIOLET *comes in.*

VIOLET: You rang, sir?

ARTHUR: Yes, Violet. My compliments to Mr. Dickie and if he doesn't stop that cacophonous hullaballoo at once, I'll throw him and his infernal machine into the street.

VIOLET: Yes, sir. What was that word again? Cac—something——

ARTHUR: Never mind. Say anything you like, only stop him.

VIOLET: Well, sir, I'll do my best, but you know what Master Dickie's like with his blessed old ragtime.

ARTHUR: Yes, Violet, I do.

VIOLET: I could say you don't think it's quite right on a Sunday.

ARTHUR (*Roaring*): You can say I don't think it's quite right on any
day. Just stop him making that confounded din, that's all.

VIOLET: Yes, sir.

She goes out.

ARTHUR (*Apologetically*): Our Violet has no doubt already been explained to you?

JOHN: I don't think so, sir. Is any explanation necessary?

ARTHUR: I fear it is. She came to us direct from an orphanage when she
was fourteen, as a sort of under-between-maid on probation, and in
that capacity she was quite satisfactory; but I am afraid, as parlormaid, she has developed certain marked eccentricities in the performance of her duties, due, no doubt, to the fact that she has never fully
known what those duties were. Well, now, where were we? Ah, yes.
I was telling you about my sources of income, was I not?

JOHN: Yes, sir.

ARTHUR: Now, in addition to the ordinary expenses of life, I have to
maintain two sons—one at Osborne, and the other at Oxford—
neither of whom, I'm afraid, will be in a position to support themselves for some time to come—one because of his extreme youth and
the other because of—er—other reasons.

The gramophone stops suddenly.

So, you see, I am not in a position to be very lavish as regards Catherine's dowry.

JOHN: No, sir. I quite see that.

ARTHUR: I propose to settle on her one-sixth of my total capital, which,
worked out to the final fraction, is exactly eight hundred and thirty-
three pounds six shillings and eight pence. But let us deal in round
figures and say eight hundred and fifty pounds.

JOHN: I call that very generous, sir.

ARTHUR: Not as generous as I would have liked, I'm afraid. However—
as my wife would say—beggars can't be choosers.

JOHN: Exactly, sir.

ARTHUR: Well, then, if you're agreeable to that arrangement, I don't
think there's anything more we need discuss.

JOHN: No, sir.

ARTHUR: Splendid.

Pause. ARTHUR *takes his stick, and raps it, with an air of studied
unconcern, three times on the floor. Nothing happens.*

JOHN: Pretty rotten weather, isn't it?

ARTHUR: Yes. Vile.

> *He raps again. Again nothing happens.*

Would you care for another cigarette?

JOHN: No, thank you, sir. I'm still smoking.

> ARTHUR *takes up his stick to rap again, and then thinks better of it. He goes slowly but firmly to the dining-room door, which he throws open.*

ARTHUR (*In apparent surprise*): Well, imagine that! My wife and daughter are in here of all places. Come in, Grace. Come in, Catherine. John's here.

> GRACE *comes in, with* CATHERINE *behind.*

GRACE: Why, John—how nice! (*She shakes hands*) My, you do look a swell! Doesn't he, Kate, darling?

CATHERINE: Quite one of the Knuts.

> *Pause.* GRACE *is unable to repress herself.*

GRACE (*Coyly*): Well?

ARTHUR: Well, what?

GRACE: How did your little talk go?

ARTHUR (*Testily*): I understood you weren't supposed to know we were having a little talk.

GRACE: Oh, you are infuriating! Is everything all right, John?

> JOHN *nods, smiling.*

Oh, I'm so glad. I really am.

JOHN: Thank you, Mrs. Winslow.

GRACE: May I kiss you? After all, I'm practically your mother, now.

JOHN: Yes. Of course.

> *He allows himself to be kissed.*

ARTHUR: While I, by the same token, am practically your father, but if you will forgive me——

JOHN (*Smiling*): Certainly, sir.

ARTHUR: Grace, I think we might allow ourselves a little modest celebration at luncheon. Will you find me the key of the cellars?

> *He goes out through the hall door.*

GRACE: Yes, dear. (*She turns at the door. Coyly*) I don't suppose you two will mind being left alone for a few minutes, will you?

> *She follows her husband out.* JOHN *goes to* CATHERINE *and kisses her.*

CATHERINE: Was it an ordeal.

JOHN: I was scared to death.

CATHERINE: My poor darling——

JOHN: The annoying thing was that I had a whole lot of neatly turned phrases ready for him and he wouldn't let me use them.

CATHERINE: Such as?

JOHN: Oh—how proud and honored I was by your acceptance of me, and how determined I was to make you a loyal and devoted husband —and to maintain you in the state to which you were accustomed—all that sort of thing. All very sincerely meant.

CATHERINE: Anything about loving me a little?

JOHN (*Lightly*): That I thought we could take for granted. So did your father, incidentally.

CATHERINE: I see. (*She gazes at him*) Goodness, you do look smart!

JOHN: Not bad, is it? Poole's.

CATHERINE: What about *your* father? How did he take it?

JOHN: All right.

CATHERINE: I bet he didn't.

JOHN: Oh, yes. He's been wanting me to get married for years. Getting worried about grandchildren, I suppose.

CATHERINE: He disapproves of me, doesn't he?

JOHN: Oh, no. Whatever makes you think that?

CATHERINE: He has a way of looking at me through his monocle that shrivels me up.

JOHN: He's just being a colonel, darling, that's all. All colonels look at you like that. Anyway, what about the way your father looks at me! Tell me, are all your family as scared of him as I am?

CATHERINE: Dickie is, of course; and Ronnie, though he doesn't need to be. Father worships him. I don't know about Mother being scared of him. Sometimes, perhaps. I'm not—ever.

JOHN: You're not scared of anything, are you?

CATHERINE: Oh, yes. Heaps of things.

JOHN: Such as?

CATHERINE (*With a smile*): Oh—they're nearly all concerned with you.

RONNIE *looks cautiously in at the window door. He now presents a very bedraggled and woebegone appearance, with his uniform wringing wet, and his damp hair over his eyes.*

JOHN: You might be a little more explicit——

RONNIE (*In a low voice*): Kate!

CATHERINE *turns and sees him.*

CATHERINE (*Amazed*): Ronnie! What on earth——

RONNIE: Where's Father?

CATHERINE: I'll go and tell him——

RONNIE (*Urgently*): No, don't. Please, Kate, don't!

> CATHERINE, *halfway to the door, stops, puzzled.*

CATHERINE: What's the trouble, Ronnie?

> RONNIE, *trembling on the edge of tears, does not answer her. She approaches him.*

You're wet through. You'd better go and change.

RONNIE: No.

CATHERINE (*Gently*): What's the trouble, darling? You can tell me.

> RONNIE *looks at* JOHN.

You know John Watherstone, Ronnie. You met him last holidays, don't you remember?

> RONNIE *remains silent, obviously reluctant to talk in front of a comparative stranger.*

JOHN (*Tactfully*): I'll disappear.

CATHERINE (*Pointing to dining-room*): In there, do you mind?

> JOHN *goes out quietly.* CATHERINE *gently leads* RONNIE *further into the room.*

Now, darling, tell me. What is it? Have you run away?

> RONNIE *shakes his head, evidently not trusting himself to speak.*

What is it, then?

> RONNIE *pulls out the document from his pocket which we have seen him reading in an earlier scene, and slowly hands it to her.* CATHERINE *reads it quietly.*

Oh, God!

RONNIE: I didn't do it.

> CATHERINE *re-reads the letter in silence.*

RONNIE: Kate, I didn't. Really, I didn't.

CATHERINE (*Abstractedly*): No, darling. (*She seems uncertain what to do*) This letter is addressed to Father. Did you open it?

RONNIE: Yes.

CATHERINE: You shouldn't have done that——

RONNIE: I was going to tear it up. Then I heard you come in from church and ran into the garden—I didn't know what to do——

CATHERINE (*Still distracted*): Did they send you up to London all by yourself?

RONNIE: They sent a petty officer up with me. He was supposed to wait and see Father, but I sent him away. (*Indicating letter*) Kate—shall we tear it up, now?

CATHERINE: No, darling.

RONNIE: We could tell Father term had ended two days sooner——

CATHERINE: No, darling.

RONNIE: I didn't do it—really I didn't——

> DICKIE *comes in from the hall. He does not seem surprised to see* RONNIE.

DICKIE (*Cheerfully*): Hullo, Ronnie, old lad. How's everything?

> RONNIE *turns away from him.*

CATHERINE: You knew he was here?

DICKIE: Oh, yes. His trunks and things are all over our room. Trouble?

CATHERINE: Yes.

DICKIE: I'm sorry.

CATHERINE: You stay here with him. I'll find Mother.

DICKIE: All right.

> CATHERINE *goes out by the hall door. There is a pause.*

DICKIE: What's up, old chap?

RONNIE: Nothing.

DICKIE: Come on—tell me.

RONNIE: It's all right.

DICKIE: Have you been sacked.

> RONNIE *nods.*

Bad luck. What for?

RONNIE: I didn't do it!

DICKIE (*Reassuringly*): No, of course you didn't.

RONNIE: Honestly, I didn't.

DICKIE: That's all right, old chap. No need to go on about it. I believe you.

RONNIE: You don't.

DICKIE: Well, I don't know what it is they've sacked you for, yet——

RONNIE (*In a low voice*): Stealing.

DICKIE (*Evidently relieved*): Oh, is that all? Good Lord! I didn't know they sacked chaps for *that,* these days.

RONNIE: I didn't do it.

DICKIE: Why, good heavens, at school we used to pinch everything we could jolly well lay our hands on. All of us. I remember there was one

chap—Carstairs his name was—captain of cricket, believe it or not—
absolutely nothing was safe with him—nothing at all. Pinched a squash
racket of mine once, I remember——

He has quietly approached RONNIE, *and now puts his arm on his
shoulder.*

Believe me, old chap, pinching's nothing. Nothing at all. I say—you're
a bit damp, aren't you?

RONNIE: I've been out in the rain——

DICKIE: You're shivering a bit, too, aren't you? Oughtn't you to go and
change? I mean, we don't want you catching pneumonia——

RONNIE: I'm all right.

GRACE *comes in, with* CATHERINE *following.* GRACE *comes quickly
to* RONNIE, *who, as he sees her, turns away from* DICKIE *and runs
into her arms.*

GRACE: There, darling! It's all right, now.

RONNIE *begins to cry quietly, his head buried in her dress.*

RONNIE (*His voice muffled*): I didn't do it, Mother.

GRACE: No, darling. Of course you didn't. We'll go upstairs now, shall
we, and get out of these nasty wet clothes.

RONNIE: Don't tell Father.

GRACE: No, darling. Not yet. I promise. Come along now.

She leads him towards the door held open by CATHERINE.

Your new uniform, too. What a shame!

She goes out with him.

DICKIE: I'd better go and keep "cave" for them. Ward off the old man if
he looks like going upstairs.

CATHERINE *nods.*

(*At door*) I say—who's going to break the news to him eventually? I
mean, someone'll have to.

CATHERINE: Don't let's worry about that now.

DICKIE: Well, you can count me out. In fact, I don't want to be within
a thousand miles of that explosion.

He goes out. CATHERINE *comes to the dining-room door, which she
opens, and calls "John!"* JOHN *comes in.*

JOHN: Bad news?

CATHERINE *nods. She is plainly upset, and dabs her eyes with her
handkerchief.*

That's rotten for you. I'm awfully sorry.

CATHERINE (*Violently*): How can people be so cruel!

JOHN (*Uncomfortably*): Expelled, I suppose?

He gets his answer from her silence, while she recovers herself.

CATHERINE: God, how little imagination some people have! Why should they torture a child of that age, John, darling? What's the point of it?

JOHN: What's he supposed to have done?

CATHERINE: Stolen some money.

JOHN: Oh.

CATHERINE: Ten days ago, it said in the letter. Why on earth didn't they let us know? Just think what that poor little creature has been going through these last ten days down there, entirely alone, without anyone to look after him, knowing what he had to face at the end of it! And then, finally, they send him up to London with a petty officer—is it any wonder he's nearly out of his mind?

JOHN: It does seem pretty heartless, I admit.

CATHERINE: Heartless! It's cold, calculated inhumanity. God, how I'd love to have that Commanding Officer here for just two minutes! I'd— I'd——

JOHN (*Gently*): Darling, it's quite natural you should feel angry about it, but you must remember, he's not really at school. He's in the Service.

CATHERINE: What difference does that make?

JOHN: Well, they have ways of doing things in the Service which may seem to an outsider horribly brutal—but at least they're always scrupulously fair. You can take it from me, that there must have been a very full inquiry before they'd take a step of this sort. What's more, if there's been a delay of ten days, it would only have been in order to give the boy a better chance to clear himself——

Pause. CATHERINE *is silent.*

I'm sorry, Catherine, darling. I'd have done better to keep my mouth shut.

CATHERINE: No. What you said was perfectly true——

JOHN: It was tactless of me to say it, though. I'm sorry.

CATHERINE (*Lightly*): That's all right.

JOHN: Forgive me?

He lays his arm on her shoulder.

CATHERINE (*Taking his hand*): Nothing to forgive.

JOHN: Believe me, I'm awfully sorry. (*After a pause*) How will your father take it?

CATHERINE (*Simply*): It might kill him——

There is the sound of voices in the hall.

Oh, heavens! We've got Desmond to lunch. I'd forgotten——

JOHN: Who?

CATHERINE: Desmond Curry—our family solicitor. Oh, Lord! (*In a hasty whisper*) Darling—be polite to him, won't you?

JOHN: Why? Am I usually so rude to your guests?

CATHERINE: No, but he doesn't know about us yet——

JOHN: Who does?

CATHERINE (*Still in a whisper*): Yes, but he's been in love with me for years—it's a family joke——

    VIOLET *comes in.*

VIOLET (*Announcing*): Mr. Curry.

    DESMOND CURRY *comes in. He is a man of about forty-five, with the figure of an athlete gone to seed. He has a mildly furtive manner, rather as if he had just absconded with his firm's petty cash, but hopes no one is going to be too angry about it.* JOHN, *when he sees him, cannot repress a faint smile at the thought of his loving* CATHERINE. VIOLET *has made her exit.*

CATHERINE: Hullo, Desmond. I don't think you know John Watherstone——

DESMOND: No—but, of course, I've heard a lot about him——

JOHN: How do you do?

    He wipes the smile off his face, as he meets CATHERINE'S *glance. There is a pause.*

DESMOND: Well, well, well. I trust I'm not early.

CATHERINE: No. Dead on time, Desmond—as always.

DESMOND: Capital. Capital.

    There is another pause, broken by CATHERINE *and* JOHN *both suddenly speaking at once.*

CATHERINE ⎫
        ⎬ (*Simultaneously*): ⎰ Tell me, Desmond——
JOHN ⎭ ⎱ Pretty ghastly this rain——

JOHN: I'm so sorry——

CATHERINE: It's quite all right. I was only going to ask how you did in your cricket match yesterday, Desmond.

DESMOND: Not too well, I'm afraid. My shoulder's still giving me trouble——

    There is another pause.

(*At length*) Well, well. I hear I'm to congratulate you both——

CATHERINE: Desmond—you know?

DESMOND: Violet told me, just now—in the hall. Yes—I must congratulate you both.

CATHERINE: Thank you so much, Desmond.

JOHN: Thank you.

DESMOND: Of course, it's quite expected, I know. Quite expected. Still it was rather a surprise, hearing it like that from Violet in the hall——

CATHERINE: We were going to tell you, Desmond dear. It was only official this morning, you know. In fact, you're the first person to hear it.

DESMOND: Am I? Am I, indeed? Well, I'm sure you'll both be very happy.

CATHERINE ⎫ (*Murmuring* ⎰ Thank you, Desmond.
JOHN ⎭ *together*): ⎱ Thank you.

DESMOND: Only this morning? Fancy.

GRACE *comes in.*

GRACE: Hullo, Desmond, dear.

DESMOND: Hullo, Mrs. Winslow.

GRACE (*To* CATHERINE): I've got him to bed——

CATHERINE: Good.

DESMOND: Nobody ill, I hope?

GRACE: No, no. Nothing wrong at all——

ARTHUR *comes in, with a bottle under his arm. He rings the bell.*

ARTHUR: Grace, when did we last have the cellars seen to?

GRACE: I can't remember, dear.

ARTHUR: Well, they're in a shocking condition. Hullo, Desmond. How are you? You're not looking well.

DESMOND: Am I not? I've strained my shoulder, you know——

ARTHUR: Well, why do you play these ridiculous games of yours? Resign yourself to the onrush of middle age, and abandon them, my dear Desmond.

DESMOND: Oh, I could never do that. Not give up cricket. Not altogether.

JOHN (*Making conversation*): Are you any relation of D. W. H. Curry who used to play for Middlesex?

DESMOND (*Whose moment has come*): I am D. W. H. Curry.

GRACE: Didn't you know we had a great man in the room?

JOHN: Gosh! Curry of Curry's match?

DESMOND: That's right.

JOHN: Hat trick against the Players in—what year was it?

DESMOND: 1895. At Lord's. Twenty-six overs, nine maidens, thirty-seven runs, eight wickets.

JOHN: Gosh! Do you know you used to be a schoolboy hero of mine?

DESMOND: Did I? Did I, indeed?

JOHN: Yes. I had a signed photograph of you.

DESMOND: Yes. I used to sign a lot once, for schoolboys, I remember.

ARTHUR: Only for schoolboys, Desmond?

DESMOND: I fear so—yes. Girls took no interest in cricket in those days.

JOHN: Gosh! D. W. H. Curry, in person. Well, I'd never have thought it.

DESMOND (*Sadly*): I know. Very few people would nowadays——

CATHERINE (*Quickly*): Oh, John didn't mean that, Desmond——

DESMOND: I fear he did. (*He moves his arm*) This is the main trouble. Too much office work and too little exercise, I fear.

ARTHUR: Nonsense. Too much exercise and too little office work.

> *Violet comes in, in response to a bell rung by* ARTHUR *some moments before.*

VIOLET: You rang, sir?

ARTHUR: Yes, Violet. Bring some glasses, would you?

VIOLET: Very good, sir.

> *She goes out.*

ARTHUR: I thought we'd try a little of the Madeira before luncheon— we're celebrating, you know, Desmond——

> GRACE *jogs his arm furtively, indicating* DESMOND.

(*Adding hastily*) —my wife's fifty-fourth birthday——

GRACE: Arthur! Really!

CATHERINE: It's all right, father. Desmond knows——

DESMOND: Yes, indeed. It's wonderful news, isn't it? I'll most gladly drink a toast to the—er—to the——

ARTHUR (*Politely*): Happy pair, I think, is the phrase that is eluding you——

DESMOND: Well, as a matter of fact, I was looking for something new to say——

ARTHUR (*Murmuring*): A forlorn quest, my dear Desmond.

GRACE (*Protestingly*): Arthur, really! You mustn't be so rude.

ARTHUR: I meant, naturally, that no one—with the possible exception of Voltaire—could find anything new to say about an engaged couple——

> DICKIE *comes in.*

Ah, my dear Dickie—just in time for a glass of Madeira in celebration of Kate's engagement to John——

VIOLET comes in with a tray of glasses. ARTHUR *begins to pour out the wine.*

DICKIE: Oh, is that all finally spliced up now? Kate definitely being entered for the marriage stakes. Good egg!

ARTHUR: Quite so. I should have added just now—with the possible exception of Voltaire and Dickie Winslow. (*To* VIOLET) Take these round, will you, Violet?

    VIOLET *goes first to* GRACE, *then to* CATHERINE, *then to* JOHN, DESMOND, DICKIE, *and finally* ARTHUR.

CATHERINE: Are we allowed to drink our own healths?

ARTHUR: I think it's permissible.

GRACE: No. It's bad luck.

JOHN: We defy augury. Don't we, Kate?

GRACE: You mustn't say that, John dear. I know. You can drink each other's healths. That's all right.

ARTHUR: Are my wife's superstitious terrors finally allayed? Good.

    The drinks have now been handed round.

ARTHUR (*Toasting*): Catherine and John!

    All drink—CATHERINE *and* JOHN *to each other.* VIOLET *lingers, smiling, in the doorway.*

(*Seeing* VIOLET) Ah, Violet. We mustn't leave you out. You must join this toast.

VIOLET: Well—thank you, sir.

    He pours her out a glass.

Not too much, sir, please. Just a sip.

ARTHUR: Quite so. Your reluctance would be more convincing if I hadn't noticed you'd brought an extra glass——

VIOLET (*Taking glass from* ARTHUR): Oh, I didn't bring it for myself, sir. I brought it for Master Ronnie—— (*She extends her glass*) Miss Kate and Mr. John.

    She takes a sip, makes a wry face, and hands the glass back to ARTHUR.

ARTHUR: You brought an extra glass for Master Ronnie, Violet?

VIOLET (*Mistaking his bewilderment*): Well—I thought you might allow him just a sip, sir. Just to drink the toast. He's that grown up these days.

    She turns to go. The others, with the exception of DESMOND, *who is staring gloomily into his glass, are frozen with apprehension.*

ARTHUR: Master Ronnie isn't due back from Osborne until Tuesday, Violet.

VIOLET (*Turning*): Oh, no, sir. He's back already. Came back unexpected this morning, all by himself.

ARTHUR: No, Violet. That isn't true. Someone has been playing a joke——

VIOLET: Well, I saw him with my own two eyes, sir, as large as life, just before you come in from church—and then I heard Mrs. Winslow talking to him in his room——

ARTHUR: Grace—what does this mean?

CATHERINE (*Instinctively taking charge*): All right, Violet. You can go——

VIOLET: Yes, miss.

 She goes out.

ARTHUR (*To* CATHERINE): Did *you* know Ronnie was back?

CATHERINE: Yes——

ARTHUR: And you, Dickie?

DICKIE: Yes, Father.

ARTHUR: Grace?

GRACE (*Helplessly*): We thought it best you shouldn't know—for the time being. Only for the time being, Arthur.

ARTHUR (*Slowly*): Is the boy very ill?

 No one answers. ARTHUR *looks from one face to another in bewilderment.*

Answer me, someone! Is the boy very ill? Why must I be kept in the dark like this? Surely I have the right to know. If he's ill I must be with him——

CATHERINE (*Steadily*): No, Father. He's not ill.

 ARTHUR *suddenly realizes the truth from her tone of voice.*

ARTHUR: Will someone tell me what has happened, please?

 GRACE *looks at* CATHERINE *with helpless inquiry.*

 CATHERINE *nods.* GRACE *takes a letter from her dress.*

GRACE (*Timidly*): He brought this letter for you—Arthur.

ARTHUR: Read it to me, please——

GRACE: Arthur—not in front of——

ARTHUR: Read it to me, please.

 GRACE *again looks at* CATHERINE *for advice, and again receives a nod.* GRACE *begins to read.*

GRACE (*Reading*): "Confidential. I am commanded by My Lords Commissioners of the Admiralty to inform you that they have received a communication from the Commanding Officer of the Royal Naval College at Osborne, reporting the theft of a five-shilling postal order at the College on the 7th instant, which was afterwards cashed at the Post Office. Investigation of the circumstances of the case leaves no other conclusion possible than that the postal order was taken by your son, Cadet Ronald Arthur Winslow. My Lords deeply regret that they must therefore request you to withdraw your son from the College." It's signed by someone—I can't quite read his name——

> *She turns away quickly to hide her tears.* CATHERINE *puts a comforting arm on her shoulder.* ARTHUR *has not changed his attitude. There is a pause, during which we can hear the sound of a gong in the hall outside.*

ARTHUR (*At length*): Desmond—be so good as to call Violet.

> DESMOND *does so. There is another pause, until* VIOLET *comes in.*

VIOLET: Yes, sir.

ARTHUR: Violet, will you ask Master Ronnie to come down and see me, please?

GRACE: Arthur—he's in bed.

ARTHUR: You told me he wasn't ill.

GRACE: He's not at all well.

ARTHUR: Do as I say, please, Violet.

VIOLET: Very good, sir.

> *She goes out.*

ARTHUR: Perhaps the rest of you would go in to luncheon? Grace, would you take them in?

GRACE (*Hovering*): Arthur—don't you think——

ARTHUR (*Ignoring her*): Dickie, will you decant that bottle of claret I brought up from the cellar? I put it on the sideboard in the dining-room.

DICKIE: Yes, Father.

> *He goes out.*

ARTHUR: Will you go in, Desmond? And John?

> *The two men go out into the dining-room, in silence.* GRACE *still hovers.*

GRACE: Arthur?

ARTHUR: Yes, Grace?

GRACE: Please don't—please don't—— (*She stops, uncertainly.*)

ARTHUR: What mustn't I do?

GRACE: Please don't forget he's only a child———

> ARTHUR *does not answer her.*
>
> CATHERINE *takes her mother's arm.*

CATHERINE: Come on, Mother.

> *She leads her mother to the dining-room door. At the door* GRACE *looks back at* ARTHUR. *He has still not altered his position and is ignoring her. She goes into the dining-room, followed by* CATHERINE. ARTHUR *does not move after they are gone. After an appreciable pause there comes a timid knock on the door.*

ARTHUR: Come in.

> RONNIE *appears in the doorway. He is in a dressing-gown. He stands on the threshold.*

Come in and shut the door.

> RONNIE *closes the door behind him.*

Come over here.

> RONNIE *walks slowly up to his father.* ARTHUR *gazes at him steadily for some time, without speaking.*

(*At length*) Why aren't you in your uniform?

RONNIE (*Murmuring*): It got wet.

ARTHUR: How did it get wet?

RONNIE: I was out in the garden in the rain.

ARTHUR: Why?

RONNIE (*Reluctantly*): I was hiding.

ARTHUR: From me?

> RONNIE *nods.*

Do you remember once, you promised me that if ever you were in trouble of any sort you would come to me first?

RONNIE: Yes, Father.

ARTHUR: Why didn't you come to me now? Why did you have to go and hide in the garden?

RONNIE: I don't know, Father.

ARTHUR: Are you so frightened of me?

> RONNIE *does not reply.* ARTHUR *gazes at him for a moment, then picks up the letter.*

In this letter it says you stole a postal order.

> RONNIE *opens his mouth to speak.*
>
> ARTHUR *stops him.*

Now, I don't want you to say a word until you've heard what *I've* got to say. If you did it, you must tell me. I shan't be angry with you, Ronnie—provided you tell me the truth. But if you tell me a lie, I shall know it, because a lie between you and me can't be hidden. I shall know it, Ronnie—so remember that before you speak. (*Pause*) Did you steal this postal order?

RONNIE (*Without hesitation*): No, Father. I didn't.

ARTHUR (*Staring into his eyes*): Did you steal this postal order?

RONNIE: No, Father. I didn't.

ARTHUR *continues to stare into his eyes for a second, then relaxes and pushes him gently away.*

ARTHUR: Go on back to bed.

RONNIE *goes gratefully to the door.*

And in future I trust that a son of mine will at least show enough sense to come in out of the rain.

RONNIE: Yes, Father.

He disappears. ARTHUR *gets up quite briskly and goes to the telephone in the corner of the room.*

ARTHUR (*At telephone*): Hullo. Are you there? (*Speaking very distinctly*) I want to put a trunk call through, please. A trunk call . . . Yes . . . The Royal Naval College, Osborne . . . That's right . . . Replace receiver? Certainly.

He replaces receiver and then, after a moment's meditation, turns and walks briskly into the dining-room.

CURTAIN

ACT II

SCENE: *The same, nine months later. It is about six o'clock, of a spring evening.*

DICKIE *is winding up his gramophone which, somehow or other, appears to have found its way back into the drawing-room. A pile of books and an opened notebook on the table provide evidence of interrupted labors.*

The gramophone, once started, emits a scratchy and muffled rendering of an early ragtime. DICKIE *listens for a few seconds with evident appreciation, then essays a little pas seul.*

CATHERINE *comes in. She is in evening dress.* DICKIE *switches off gramophone.*

DICKIE: Hullo. Do you think the old man can hear this upstairs?

CATHERINE: I shouldn't think so. I couldn't.

DICKIE: Soft needle and an old sweater down the horn. Is the doctor still with him?

CATHERINE *nods.*

What's the verdict, do you know?

CATHERINE: I heard him say Father needed a complete rest.

DICKIE: Don't we all.

CATHERINE (*Indicating book*): It doesn't look as if *you* did. He said he ought to go to the country and forget all his worries——

DICKIE: Fat chance there is of that, I'd say.

CATHERINE: I know.

DICKIE: I say, you look a treat. New dress?

CATHERINE: Is it likely? No, it's an old one I've had done up.

DICKIE: Where are you going to?

CATHERINE: Daly's. Dinner first—at the Cri.

DICKIE: Nice. You wouldn't care to take me along with you, I suppose?

CATHERINE: You suppose quite correctly.

DICKIE: John wouldn't mind.

CATHERINE: I dare say not. I would.

DICKIE: I wish I had someone to take me out. In your new feminist world do you suppose women will be allowed to do some of the paying?

CATHERINE: Certainly.

DICKIE: Really? Then the next time you're looking for someone to chain themselves to Mr. Asquith you can jolly well call on me——

CATHERINE (*Laughing*): Edwina might take you out if you gave her the hint. She's very rich——

DICKIE: If I gave Edwina a hint of that sort I wouldn't see her this side of doomsday.

CATHERINE: You sound a little bitter, Dickie dear.

DICKIE: Oh, no. Not bitter. Just realistic.

VIOLET *comes in with an evening paper on a salver.*

DICKIE: Good egg! The *Star!*

CATHERINE *makes a grab for it and gets it before* DICKIE.

VIOLET: You won't throw it away, will you, miss? If there's anything in it again, cook and I would like to read it, after you.

CATHERINE *is hastily turning over the pages, with* DICKIE *craning his head over her shoulder.*

CATHERINE: No. That's all right, Violet.

    VIOLET *goes out.*

Here it is. (*Reading*) "The Osborne Cadet." There are two more letters. (*Reading*) "Sir. I am entirely in agreement with your correspondent, Democrat, concerning the scandalously high-handed treatment by the Admiralty of the case of the Osborne Cadet. The efforts of Mr. Arthur Winslow to secure a fair trial for his son have evidently been thwarted at every turn by a soulless oligarchy——"

DICKIE: Soulless oligarchy. That's rather good——

CATHERINE: —"it is high time private and peaceful citizens of this country awoke to the increasing encroachment of their ancient freedom by the new despotism of Whitehall. The Englishman's home was once said to be his castle. It seems it is rapidly becoming his prison. Your obedient servant, *Libertatis Amator.*"

DICKIE: Good for old Amator!

CATHERINE: The other's from Perplexed. (*Reading*) "Dear Sir. I cannot understand what all the fuss is about in the case of the Osborne Cadet. Surely we have more important matters to get ourselves worked up about than a fourteen-year-old boy and a five-shilling postal order." Silly old fool!

DICKIE: How do you know he's old?

CATHERINE: Isn't it obvious? (*Reading*) "With the present troubles in the Balkans and a certain major European Power rapidly outbuilding our navy, the Admiralty might be forgiven if it stated that it had rather more urgent affairs to deal with than Master Ronnie Winslow's little troubles. A further inquiry before the Judge Advocate of the Fleet has now fully confirmed the original findings that the boy was guilty. I sincerely trust that this will finally end this ridiculous and sordid little storm in a teacup. I am, sir, etc., Perplexed."

    Pause.

DICKIE (*Reading over her shoulder*): "This correspondence must now cease.—Editor." Damn!

CATHERINE: Oh, dear! How hopeless it seems, sometimes.

DICKIE: Yes, it does, doesn't it? (*Thoughtfully, after a pause*) You know, Kate—don't give me away to the old man, will you—but the awful thing is, if it hadn't been by own brother, I think I might quite likely have seen Perplexed's point.

CATHERINE: Might you?

DICKIE: Well, I mean—looking at it from every angle and all that—it does seem rather a much ado about damn all. I mean to say—a mere matter of pinching. (*Bitterly*) And it's all so beastly expensive. Let's cheer ourselves up with some music. (*He sets machine going.*)

CATHERINE (*Listening to the record*): Is that what it's called?

DICKIE: Come and practice a few steps.

> CATHERINE *joins him and they dance, in the manner of the period, with arms fully outstretched and working up and down, pump-handle style.*

(*Surprised*) I say! Jolly good!

CATHERINE: Thank you, Dickie.

DICKIE: Who taught you? John, I suppose.

CATHERINE: No. I taught John, as it happens——

DICKIE: Feminism—even in love?

> CATHERINE *nods, smiling. Pause, while they continue to dance.*

When's the happy date now?

CATHERINE: Postponed again.

DICKIE: Oh, no. Why?

CATHERINE: His father's gone abroad for six months.

DICKIE: Why pay any attention to that old—(*He substitutes the word*) —gentleman?

CATHERINE: I wouldn't—but John does—so I have to.

> *Something in her tone makes* DICKIE *stop dancing and gaze at her seriously.*

DICKIE: I say—nothing wrong, is there?

> CATHERINE *shakes her head, smiling, but not too emphatically.*

I mean—you're not going to be left on the altar rails or anything, are you?

CATHERINE: Oh, no. I'll get him past the altar rails, if I have to drag him there.

DICKIE (*As they resume their dance*): Do you think you might have to?

CATHERINE: Quite frankly, yes.

DICKIE: Competition?

CATHERINE: Not yet. Only—differences of opinion.

DICKIE: I see. Well, take some advice from an old hand, will you?

CATHERINE: Yes, Dickie.

DICKIE: Suppress your opinions. Men don't like 'em in their lady friends, even if they agree with 'em. And if they don't—it's fatal. Pretend to be half-witted, like Edwina, then he'll adore you.

CATHERINE: I know. I do, sometimes, and then I forget. Still, you needn't worry. If there's ever a clash between what I believe and what I feel, there's not much doubt about which will win.

DICKIE: That's the girl. Of course, I don't know why you didn't fall in love with Ramsay MacDonald——

> ARTHUR *comes in. He is walking with more difficulty than when we last saw him.* DICKIE *and* CATHERINE *hastily stop dancing, and* DICKIE *turns off the gramophone.*

CATHERINE (*Quickly*): It was entirely my fault, Father. I enticed Dickie from his work to show me a few dance steps.

ARTHUR: Oh? I must admit I am surprised you succeeded.

DICKIE (*Getting off the subject*): What did the doctor say, Father?

ARTHUR: He said, if I remember his exact words, that we weren't quite as well as when we last saw each other. That information seems expensive at a guinea. (*Seeing the evening paper*) Oh, is that the *Star*? Let me see it, please.

> CATHERINE *brings it over to him.*

John will be calling for you here, I take it?

CATHERINE: Yes, Father.

ARTHUR: It might be better, perhaps, if you didn't ask him in. This room will shortly be a clutter of journalists, solicitors, barristers, and other impedimenta.

CATHERINE: Is Sir Robert Morton coming to see you here?

ARTHUR (*Deep in the* Star): I could hardly go and see him, could I?

> DICKIE, *in deference to his father's presence, has returned to his books.* ARTHUR *reads the* Star. CATHERINE *glances at herself in the mirror, and then wanders to the door.*

CATHERINE: I must go and do something about my hair.

DICKIE: What's the matter with your hair?

CATHERINE: Nothing, except I don't like it very much.

> *She goes out.* DICKIE *opens two more books with a busy air and chews his pencil.* ARTHUR *finishes reading the* Star *and stares moodily into space.*

ARTHUR (*At length*): I wonder if I could sue "Perplexed."

DICKIE: It might be a way of getting the case into court.

ARTHUR: On the other hand, he has not been libelous. Merely base.

> *He throws the paper away and regards* DICKIE *thoughtfully.*
> DICKIE, *feeling his father's eye on him, is elaborately industrious.*

ARTHUR (*At length, politely*): Do you mind if I disturb you for a moment?

DICKIE (*Pushing books away*): No, Father.

ARTHUR: I want to ask you a question. But before I do I must impress on you the urgent necessity for an absolutely truthful answer.

DICKIE: Naturally.

ARTHUR: Naturally means by nature, and I'm afraid I have not yet noticed that it has invariably been your nature to answer my questions truthfully.

DICKIE: Oh. Well, I will this one, Father, I promise.

ARTHUR: Very well. (*He stares at him for a moment*) What do you suppose one of your bookmaker friends would lay in the way of odds against your getting a degree?

   Pause.

DICKIE: Oh. Well, let's think. Say—about evens.

ARTHUR: Hm. I rather doubt if at that price your friend would find many takers.

DICKIE: Well—perhaps seven to four against.

ARTHUR: I see. And what about the odds against you eventually becoming a Civil Servant?

DICKIE: Well—a bit steeper, I suppose.

ARTHUR: Exactly. Quite a bit steeper.

   Pause.

DICKIE: You don't want to have a bet, do you?

ARTHUR: No, Dickie. I'm not a gambler. And that's exactly the trouble. Unhappily I'm no longer in a position to gamble two hundred pounds a year on what you yourself admit is an outside chance.

DICKIE: Not an outside chance, Father. A good chance.

ARTHUR: Not good enough, Dickie, I'm afraid—with things as they are at the moment. Definitely not good enough. I fear my mind is finally made up.

   There is a long pause.

DICKIE: You want me to leave Oxford—is that it?

ARTHUR: I'm very much afraid so, Dickie.

DICKIE: Oh. Straight away?

ARTHUR: No. You can finish your second year.

DICKIE: And what then?

ARTHUR: I can get you a job in the bank.

DICKIE (*Quietly*): Oh, Lord!

    Pause.

ARTHUR (*Rather apologetically*): It'll be quite a good job, you know. Luckily my influence in the bank still counts for something.

    DICKIE *gets up and wanders about, slightly in a daze.*

DICKIE: Father—if I promise you—I mean, *really* promised you—that from now on I'll work like a black——

    ARTHUR *shakes his head slowly.*

It's the case, I suppose?

ARTHUR: It's costing me a lot of money.

DICKIE: I know. It must be. Still, couldn't you—I mean, isn't there any way——

    ARTHUR *again shakes his head.*

Oh, Lord!

ARTHUR: I'm afraid this is rather a shock for you. I'm sorry.

DICKIE: What? No. No, it isn't really. I've been rather expecting it, as a matter of fact—especially since I've heard you are hoping to brief Sir Robert Morton. Still, I can't say but what it isn't a bit of a slap in the face.

    There is a ring at the front door.

ARTHUR: There is a journalist coming to see me. Do you mind if we talk about this some other time?

DICKIE: No. Of course not, Father.

    DICKIE *begins forlornly to gather his books.*

ARTHUR (*With a half-smile*): I should leave those there, if I were you.

DICKIE: Yes. I will. Good idea.

ARTHUR (*Politely*): Tell me—how is your nice friend, Miss Edwina Gunn, these days?

DICKIE: Very well, thanks awfully.

ARTHUR: You don't suppose she'd mind if you took her to the theater— or gave her a little present perhaps?

DICKIE: Oh, I'm sure she wouldn't.

ARTHUR: I'm afraid I can only make it a couple of sovereigns.

    ARTHUR *has taken out his sovereign case and now extracts two sovereigns.* DICKIE *comes and takes them.*

DICKIE: Thanks awfully, Father.

ARTHUR: With what's left over you can always buy something for yourself.

DICKIE: Oh. Well, as a matter of fact, I don't suppose there will be an awful lot left over. Still, it's jolly decent of you—I say, Father—I think I could do with a little spot of something. Would you mind?

ARTHUR: Of course not. You'll find the decanter in the dining-room.

DICKIE: Thanks awfully.

> *He goes to dining-room door.*

ARTHUR: I must thank you, Dickie, for bearing what must have been a very unpleasant blow with some fortitude.

DICKIE (*Uncomfortably*): Oh. Rot, Father.

> *He goes out.* ARTHUR *sighs deeply.*
>
> VIOLET *comes in at the hall door.*

VIOLET (*Announcing proudly*): The *Daily News!*

> MISS BARNES *comes in. She is a rather untidily dressed woman of about forty with a gushing manner.*

MISS BARNES: Mr. Winslow? So good of you to see me.

ARTHUR: How do you do?

MISS BARNES (*Simpering*): You're surprised to see a lady reporter? I know. Everyone is. And yet why not? What could be more natural?

ARTHUR: What indeed! Pray sit down——

MISS BARNES: My paper usually sends me out on stories which have a special appeal to women—stories with a little heart, you know, like this one—a father's fight for his little boy's honor——

> ARTHUR *visibly winces.*

ARTHUR: I venture to think this case has rather wider implications than that——

MISS BARNES: Oh, yes. The political angle. I know. Very interesting but not *quite* my line of country. Now, what I'd really like to do—is to get a nice picture of you and your little boy together. I've brought my assistant and camera. They're in the hall. Where is your little boy?

ARTHUR: My son is arriving from school in a few minutes. His mother has gone to the station to meet him.

MISS BARNES (*Making a note*): From school? How interesting. So you got a school to take him? I mean, they didn't mind the unpleasantness?

ARTHUR: No.

MISS BARNES: And why is he coming back this time?

ARTHUR: He hasn't been expelled again, if that is what you're implying. He is coming to London to be examined by Sir Robert Morton, whom we are hoping to brief——

MISS BARNES: Sir Robert Morton! (*She whistles appreciatively*) Well!

ARTHUR: Exactly.

MISS BARNES (*Doubtingly*): But do you *really* think he'll take a little case like this?

ARTHUR (*Explosively*): It is *not* a little case, madam——

MISS BARNES: No, no. Of course not, But still—Sir Robert Morton!

ARTHUR: I understand that he is the best advocate in the country. He is certainly the most expensive——

MISS BARNES: Oh, yes. I suppose if one is prepared to pay his fee one can get him for almost *any* case.

ARTHUR: Once more, madam—this is *not* almost any case——

MISS BARNES: No, no. Of course not. Well, now, perhaps you wouldn't mind giving me a few details. When did it all start?

ARTHUR: Nine months ago. The first I knew of the charge was when my son arrived home with a letter from the Admiralty informing me of his expulsion. I telephoned Osborne to protest and was referred by them to the Lords of the Admiralty. My solicitors then took the matter up, and demanded from the Admiralty the fullest possible inquiry. For weeks we were ignored, then met with a blank refusal, and only finally got reluctant permission to view the evidence.

MISS BARNES (*Indifferently*): Really?

ARTHUR: My solicitors decided that the evidence was highly unsatisfactory, and fully justified the re-opening of proceedings. We applied to the Admiralty for a Court Martial. They ignored us. We applied for a civil trial. They ignored us again.

MISS BARNES: They ignored you?

ARTHUR: Yes. But after tremendous pressure had been brought to bear —letters to the papers, questions in the House, and other means open to private citizens of this country—the Admiralty eventually agreed to what they called an independent inquiry.

MISS BARNES (*Vaguely*): Oh, good!

ARTHUR: It was not good, madam. At that independent inquiry, conducted by the Judge Advocate of the Fleet—against whom I am saying nothing, mind you—my son—a child of fourteen, was not represented by counsel, solicitors, or friends. What do you think of that?

MISS BARNES: Fancy!

ARTHUR: You may well say fancy.

MISS BARNES: And what happened at the inquiry?

ARTHUR: What do you think happened? Inevitably he was found guilty again, and thus branded for the second time before the world as a thief and a forger——

MISS BARNES (*Her attention wandering*): What a shame!

ARTHUR: I need hardly tell you, madam, that I am not prepared to let the matter rest there. I shall continue to fight this monstrous injustice with every weapon and every means at my disposal. Now, it happens I have a plan——

MISS BARNES: Oh, what charming curtains! What are they made of? (*She rises and goes to window.*)

   ARTHUR *sits for a moment in paralyzed silence.*

ARTHUR (*At last*): Madam—I fear I have no idea.

   There is the sound of voices in the hall.

MISS BARNES: Ah. Do I hear the poor little chap himself?

   The hall door opens and RONNIE *comes in boisterously, followed by* GRACE. *He is evidently in the highest of spirits.*

RONNIE: Hullo, Father! (*He runs to him.*)

ARTHUR: Hullo, Ronnie.

RONNIE: I say, Father! Mr. Moore says I'm to tell you I needn't come back until Monday if you like. So that gives me three whole days.

ARTHUR: Mind my leg!

RONNIE: Sorry, Father.

ARTHUR: How are you, my boy?

RONNIE: Oh, I'm absolutely tophole, Father. Mother says I've grown an inch——

MISS BARNES: Ah! Now that's exactly the way I'd like to take my picture. Would you hold it, Mr. Winslow? (*She goes to hall door and calls*) Fred! Come in now, will you?

RONNIE (*In a sibilant whisper*): Who's she?

   FRED *appears. He is a listless photographer, complete with apparatus.*

FRED (*Gloomily*): Afternoon, all.

MISS BARNES: That's the pose I suggest.

FRED: Yes. It'll do.

   He begins to set up his apparatus. ARTHUR, *holding* RONNIE *close against him in the pose suggested, turns his head to* GRACE.

ARTHUR: Grace, dear, this lady is from the *Daily News*. She is extremely interested in your curtains.

GRACE (*Delighted*): Oh, really! How nice!

MISS BARNES: Yes, indeed. I was wondering what they were made of.

GRACE: Well, it's an entirely new material, you know. I'm afraid I don't know what it's called, but I got them at Barkers last year. Apparently it's a sort of mixture of wild silk and——

MISS BARNES (*Now genuinely busy with her pencil and pad*): Just a second, Mrs. Winslow. I'm afraid my shorthand isn't very good. I must just get that down——

RONNIE (*To* ARTHUR): Father, are we going to be in the *Daily News?*

ARTHUR: It appears so——

RONNIE: Oh, good! They get the *Daily News* in the school library and everyone's bound to see it——

FRED: Quite still, please——

He takes his photograph.

All right, Miss Barnes. (*He goes out.*)

MISS BARNES (*Engrossed with* GRACE): Thank you, Fred. (*To* ARTHUR) Goodbye, Mr. Winslow, and the very best of good fortune in your inspiring fight. (*Turning to* RONNIE) Goodbye, little chap. Remember, the darkest hour is just before the dawn. Well, it was very good of you to tell me all that, Mrs. Winslow. I'm sure our readers will be most interested.

GRACE *shows her out.*

RONNIE: What's she talking about?

ARTHUR: The case, I imagine.

RONNIE: Oh, the case. Father, do you know the train had fourteen coaches?

ARTHUR: Did it indeed?

RONNIE: Yes. All corridor.

ARTHUR: Remarkable.

RONNIE: Of course, it was one of the biggest expresses. I walked all the way down it from one end to the other.

ARTHUR: I had your half-term report, Ronnie.

RONNIE (*Suddenly silenced by perturbation*): Oh, yes?

ARTHUR: On the whole it was pretty fair.

RONNIE: Oh, good.

ARTHUR: I'm glad you seem to be settling down so well. Very glad indeed.

GRACE *comes in.*

GRACE: What a charming woman, Arthur!

ARTHUR: Charming. I trust you gave her full details about our curtains?

GRACE: Oh, yes. I told her everything.

ARTHUR (*Wearily*): I'm so glad.

GRACE: I do think women reporters are a good idea——

RONNIE (*Excitedly*): I say, Father, will it be all right for me to stay till Monday? I mean, I won't be missing any work—only Divinity ——(*He jogs his father's leg again.*)

ARTHUR: Mind my leg!

RONNIE: Oh, sorry, Father. Is it bad?

ARTHUR :Yes, it is. (*To* GRACE) Grace, take him upstairs and get him washed. Sir Robert will be here in a few minutes.

GRACE (*To* RONNIE): Come on, darling.

RONNIE: All right. (*On his way to the door with his mother*) I say, do you know how long the train took? 123 miles in two hours and fifty-two minutes. That's an average of 46.73 recurring miles an hour—I worked it out. Violet! Violet! I'm back.

   He disappears, still chattering shrilly. GRACE *stops at the door.*

GRACE: Did the doctor say anything, dear?

ARTHUR: A great deal; but very little to the purpose.

GRACE: Violet says he left an ointment for your back. Four massages a day. Is that right?

ARTHUR: Something of the kind.

GRACE: I think you had better have one now, hadn't you, Arthur?

ARTHUR: No.

GRACE: But, dear, you've got plenty of time before Sir Robert comes, and if you don't have one now, you won't be able to have another before you go to bed.

ARTHUR: Precisely.

GRACE: But really, Arthur, it does seem awfully silly to spend all this money on doctors if you're not even going to do what they say.

ARTHUR (*Impatiently*): All right, Grace. All right. All right.

GRACE: Thank you, dear.

   CATHERINE *comes in.*

CATHERINE: Ronnie's back, judging by the noise——

GRACE (*Examining her*): I must say that old frock has come out very well. John'll never know it isn't brand new——

CATHERINE: He's late, curse him.

ARTHUR: Grace, go on up and attend to Ronnie, and prepare the witch's brew for me. I'll come up when you are ready.

GRACE: Very well, dear. (*To* CATHERINE) Yes, that does look good. I must say Mme. Dupont's a treasure.

She goes out.

ARTHUR (*Wearily*): Oh, Kate, Kate! Are we both mad, you and I?

CATHERINE: What's the matter, Father?

ARTHUR: I don't know. I suddenly feel suicidally inclined. (*Bitterly*) A father's fight for his little boy's honor. Special appeal to all women. Photo inset of Mrs. Winslow's curtains! Is there any hope for the world?

CATHERINE (*Smiling*): I think so, Father.

ARTHUR: Shall we drop the whole thing, Kate?

CATHERINE: I don't consider that a serious question, Father.

ARTHUR (*Slowly*): You realize that, if we go on, your marriage settlement must go?

CATHERINE (*Lightly*): Oh, yes. I gave that up for lost weeks ago.

ARTHUR: Things are all right between you and John, aren't they?

CATHERINE: Oh, yes, Father, of course. Everything's perfect.

ARTHUR: I mean—it won't make any difference between you, will it?

CATHERINE: Good heavens, no!

ARTHUR: Very well, then. Let us pin our faith to Sir Robert Morton.

CATHERINE *is silent.* ARTHUR *looks at her as if he had expected an answer, then nods.*

I see I'm speaking only for myself in saying that.

CATHERINE (*Lightly*): You know what I think of Sir Robert Morton, Father. Don't let's go into it again, now. It's too late, anyway.

ARTHUR: It's not too late. He hasn't accepted the brief yet.

CATHERINE (*Shortly*): Then I'm rather afraid I hope he never does. And that has nothing to do with my marriage settlement either.

Pause. ARTHUR *looks angry for a second, then subsides.*

ARTHUR (*Mildly*): I made inquiries about that fellow you suggested— I am told he is not nearly as good an advocate as Morton——

CATHERINE: He's not nearly so fashionable.

ARTHUR (*Doubtfully*): I want the best——

CATHERINE: The best in this case certainly isn't Morton.

ARTHUR: Then why does everyone say he is?

CATHERINE (*Roused*): Because if one happens to be a large monopoly attacking a Trade Union or a Tory paper libeling a Labor Leader, he *is* the best. But it utterly defeats me how you or anyone else could expect a man of his record to have even a tenth of his heart in a case where the boot is entirely on the other foot——

ARTHUR: Well, I imagine, if his heart isn't in it, he won't accept the brief.

CATHERINE: He might still. It depends what there is in it for him. Luckily there isn't much——

ARTHUR (*Bitterly*): There is a fairly substantial check——

CATHERINE: He doesn't want money. He must be a very rich man.

ARTHUR: What does he want, then?

CATHERINE: Anything that advances his interests.

ARTHUR *shrugs his shoulders. Pause.*

ARTHUR: I believe you are prejudiced because he spoke against woman's suffrage.

CATHERINE: I am. I'm prejudiced because he is always speaking against what is right and just. Did you read his speech in the House on the Trades Disputes Bill?

GRACE (*Calling off*): Arthur! Arthur!

ARTHUR (*Smiling*): Oh, well—in the words of the Prime Minister—let us wait and see.

(*He turns at the door*) You're my only ally, Kate. Without you I believe I should have given up long ago.

CATHERINE: Rubbish.

ARTHUR: It's true. Still, you must sometimes allow me to make my own decisions. I have an instinct about Morton.

CATHERINE *does not reply.*

(*Doubtfully*) We'll see which is right—my instinct or your reason, eh? *He goes out.*

CATHERINE (*Half to herself*): I'm afraid we will.

DICKIE *comes out of the dining-room door.*

DICKIE (*Bitterly*): Hullo, Kate.

CATHERINE: Hullo, Dickie.

DICKIE *crosses mournfully to the other door.*

What's the matter? Edwina jilted you or something?

DICKIE: Haven't you heard?

CATHERINE *shakes her head.*

I'm being scratched from the Oxford Stakes at the end of the year——

CATHERINE: Oh, Dickie! I'm awfully sorry——

DICKIE: Did you know it was in the wind?

CATHERINE: I knew there was a risk——

DICKIE: You might have warned a fellow. I fell plumb into the old man's trap. My gosh, I could just about murder that little brother of mine. (*Bitterly*) What's he have to go about pinching postal orders for? And why the hell does he have to get himself nabbed doing it? Silly little blighter!

He goes out gloomily. There is a ring at the front door. CATHERINE, *obviously believing it is* JOHN, *picks up her cloak and goes to the hall door.*

CATHERINE (*Calling*): All right, Violet. It's only Mr. Watherstone. I'll answer it.

She goes out. There is the sound of voices in the hall, and then CATHERINE *reappears, leading in* DESMOND *and* SIR ROBERT MORTON. SIR ROBERT *is a man in the early forties, cadaverous and immensely elegant. He wears a long overcoat, and carries his hat and stick. He looks rather a fop, and his supercilious expression bears out this view.*

(*As she re-enters*) I'm so sorry. I was expecting a friend. Won't you sit down, Sir Robert! My father won't be long.

SIR ROBERT *bows slightly, and sits down on a hard chair, still in his overcoat.*

Won't you sit here? It's far more comfortable.

SIR ROBERT: No, thank you.

DESMOND (*Fussing*): Sir Robert has a most important dinner engagement, so we came a little early.

CATHERINE: I see.

DESMOND: I'm afraid he can only spare us a very few minutes of his most valuable time this evening. Of course, it's a long way for him to come—so far from his chambers—and very good of him to do it, too, if I may say so——

He bows to SIR ROBERT, *who bows slightly back.*

CATHERINE: I know. I can assure you we're very conscious of it.

SIR ROBERT *gives her a quick look, and a faint smile.*

DESMOND: Perhaps I had better advise your father of our presence——

CATHERINE: Yes, do, Desmond. You'll find him in his bedroom—having his back rubbed.

DESMOND: Oh, I see.

He goes out. There is a pause.

CATHERINE: Is there anything I can get you, Sir Robert? A whisky and soda or a brandy?

SIR ROBERT: No, thank you.

CATHERINE: Will you smoke?

SIR ROBERT: No, thank you.

CATHERINE (*Holding her cigarette*): I hope you don't mind me smoking?

SIR ROBERT: Why should I?

CATHERINE: Some people find it shocking.

SIR ROBERT (*Indifferently*): A lady in her own home is surely entitled to behave as she wishes.

> *Pause.*

CATHERINE: Won't you take your coat off, Sir Robert?

SIR ROBERT: No, thank you.

CATHERINE: You find it cold in here? I'm sorry.

SIR ROBERT: It's perfectly all right.

> *Conversation languishes again.* SIR ROBERT *looks at his watch.*

CATHERINE: What time are you dining?

SIR ROBERT: Eight o'clock.

CATHERINE: Far from here?

SIR ROBERT: Devonshire House.

CATHERINE: Oh. Then of course you mustn't on any account be late.

SIR ROBERT: No.

> *There is another pause.*

CATHERINE: I suppose you know the history of this case, do you, Sir Robert?

SIR ROBERT (*Examining his nails*): I believe I have seen most of the relevant documents.

CATHERINE: Do you think we can bring the case into Court by a collusive action?

SIR ROBERT: I really have no idea——

CATHERINE: Curry and Curry seem to think that might hold——

SIR ROBERT: Do they? They are a very reliable firm.

> *Pause.* CATHERINE *is on the verge of losing her temper.*

CATHERINE: I'm rather surprised that a case of this sort should interest you, Sir Robert.

SIR ROBERT: Are you?

CATHERINE: It seems such a very trivial affair, compared to most of your great forensic triumphs.

> SIR ROBERT, *staring languidly at the ceiling, does not reply.*

I was in Court during your cross-examination of Len Rogers, in the Trades Union embezzlement case.

SIR ROBERT: Really?

CATHERINE: It was masterly.

SIR ROBERT: Thank you.

CATHERINE: I suppose you heard that he committed suicide a few months ago?

SIR ROBERT: Yes. I had heard.

CATHERINE: Many people believed him innocent, you know.

SIR ROBERT: So I understand. (*After a faint pause*) As it happens, however, he was guilty.

GRACE *comes in hastily.*

GRACE: Sir Robert? My husband's so sorry to have kept you, but he's just coming.

SIR ROBERT: It's perfectly all right. How do you do?

CATHERINE: Sir Robert is dining at Devonshire House, Mother.

GRACE: Oh, really? Oh, then you have to be punctual, of course, I do see that. It's the politeness of princes, isn't it?

SIR ROBERT: So they say.

GRACE: In this case the other way round, of course. Ah, I think I hear my husband on the stairs. I hope Catherine entertained you all right?

SIR ROBERT (*With a faint bow to* CATHERINE): Very well, thank you.

ARTHUR *comes in, followed by* DESMOND.

ARTHUR: Sir Robert? I am Arthur Winslow.

SIR ROBERT: How do you do?

ARTHUR: I understand you are rather pressed for time.

GRACE: Yes. He's dining at Devonshire House——

ARTHUR: Are you indeed? My son should be down in a minute. I expect you will wish to examine him.

SIR ROBERT (*Indifferently*): Just a few questions. I fear that is all I will have time for this evening——

ARTHUR: I am rather sorry to hear that. He has made the journey especially from school for this interview and I was hoping that by the end of it I should know definitely yes or no if you would accept the brief.

DESMOND (*Pacifically*): Well, perhaps Sir Robert would consent to finish his examination some other time?

SIR ROBERT: It might be arranged.

ARTHUR: Tomorrow?

SIR ROBERT: Tomorrow is impossible. I am in Court all the morning and in the House of Commons for the rest of the day. (*Carelessly*) If a further examination should prove necessary it will have to be some time next week.

ARTHUR: I see. Will you forgive me if I sit down. (*He sits in his usual chair*) Curry has been telling me you think it might be possible to proceed by Petition of Right.

CATHERINE: What's a Petition of Right?

DESMOND: Well—granting the assumption that the Admiralty, as the Crown, can do no wrong——

CATHERINE (*Murmuring*): I thought that was exactly the assumption we refused to grant.

DESMOND: In law, I mean. Now, a subject can sue the Crown, nevertheless, by Petition of Right, redress being granted as a matter of grace —and the custom is for the Attorney-General—on behalf of the King —to endorse the Petition, and allow the case to come to Court.

SIR ROBERT: It is interesting to note that the exact words he uses on such occasions are: Let Right be done.

ARTHUR: Let Right be done? I like that phrase, sir.

SIR ROBERT: It has a certain ring about it—has it not? (*Languidly*) Let Right be done.

> RONNIE *comes in. He is in an Eton suit, looking very spic and span.*

ARTHUR: This is my son Ronald. Ronnie, this is Sir Robert Morton.

RONNIE: How do you do, sir?

ARTHUR: He is going to ask you a few questions. You must answer them all truthfully—as you always have. (*He begins to struggle out of his chair*) I expect you would like us to leave——

SIR ROBERT: No. Provided, of course, that you don't interrupt.

> (*To* CATHERINE) Miss Winslow, will you sit down, please?
>
> CATHERINE *takes a seat abruptly.*

SIR ROBERT (*To* RONNIE): Will you stand at the table, facing me? (RONNIE *does so*) That's right.

> SIR ROBERT *and* RONNIE *now face each other across the table.* SIR ROBERT *begins his examination very quietly.*

Now, Ronald, how old are you?

RONNIE: Fourteen and seven months.

SIR ROBERT: You were, then, thirteen and ten months old when you left Osborne: is that right?

RONNIE: Yes, sir.

SIR ROBERT: Now I would like you to cast your mind back to July 7th of last year. Will you tell me in your own words exactly what happened to you on that day?

RONNIE: All right. Well, it was a half-holiday, so we didn't have any work after dinner——

SIR ROBERT: Dinner? At one o'clock?

RONNIE: Yes. At least, until prep at seven.

SIR ROBERT: Prep at seven?

RONNIE: Just before dinner I went to the Chief Petty Officer and asked him to let me have fifteen and six out of what I had in the school bank——

SIR ROBERT: Why did you do that?

RONNIE: I wanted to buy an air pistol.

SIR ROBERT: Which cost fifteen and six?

RONNIE: Yes, sir.

SIR ROBERT: And how much money did you have in the school bank at the time?

RONNIE: Two pounds three shillings.

ARTHUR: So you see, sir, what incentive could there possibly be for him to steal five shillings?

SIR ROBERT (*Coldly*): I must ask you to be good enough not to interrupt me, sir. (*To* RONNIE) After you had withdrawn the fifteen and six what did you do?

RONNIE: I had dinner.

SIR ROBERT: Then what?

RONNIE: I went to the locker-room and put the fifteen and six in my locker.

SIR ROBERT: Yes. Then?

RONNIE: I went to get permission to go down to the Post Office. Then I went to the locker-room again, got out my money, and went down to the Post Office.

SIR ROBERT: I see. Go on.

RONNIE: I bought my postal order——

SIR ROBERT: For fifteen and six?

RONNIE: Yes. Then I went back to college. Then I met Elliot minor, and he said: "I say, isn't it rot? Someone's broken into my locker and pinched a postal order. I've reported it to the P.O."

SIR ROBERT: Those were Elliot minor's exact words?

RONNIE: He might have used another word for rot——

SIR ROBERT: I see. Continue—

RONNIE: Well, then just before prep I was told to go along and see Commander Flower. The woman from the Post Office was there, and the Commander said: "Is this the boy?" and she said: "It might be. I can't be sure. They all look so much alike."

ARTHUR: You see? She couldn't identify him.

> SIR ROBERT *glares at him.*

SIR ROBERT (*To* RONNIE): Go on.

RONNIE: Then she said: "I only know that the boy who bought a postal order for fifteen and six was the same boy that cashed one for five shillings." So the Commander said: "Did you buy a postal order for fifteen and six?" And I said: "Yes," and then they made me write Elliot minor's name on an envelope, and compared it to the signature on the postal order—then they sent me to the sanatorium and ten days later I was sacked—I mean—expelled.

SIR ROBERT: I see. (*Quietly*) Did you cash a postal order belonging to Elliot minor for five shillings?

RONNIE: No, sir.

SIR ROBERT: Did you break into his locker and steal it?

RONNIE: No, sir.

SIR ROBERT: And that is the truth, the whole truth, and nothing but the truth?

RONNIE: Yes, sir.

> DICKIE *has come in during this, and is standing furtively in the doorway, not knowing whether to come in or go out.* ARTHUR *waves him impatiently to a seat.*

SIR ROBERT: Right. When the Commander asked you to write Elliot's name on an envelope, how did you write it? With Christian name or initials?

RONNIE: I wrote Charles K. Elliot.

SIR ROBERT: Charles K. Elliot. Did you by any chance happen to see the forged postal order in the Commander's office?

RONNIE: Oh, yes. The Commander showed it to me.

SIR ROBERT: Before or after you had written Elliot's name on the envelope?

RONNIE: After.

SIR ROBERT: After. And did you happen to see how Elliot's name was written on the postal order?

RONNIE: Yes, sir. The same.

SIR ROBERT: The same? Charles K. Elliot?

RONNIE: Yes, sir.

SIR ROBERT: When you wrote on the envelope, what made you choose that particular form?

RONNIE: That was the way he usually signed his name——

SIR ROBERT: How did you know?

RONNIE: Well—he was a great friend of mine——

SIR ROBERT: That is no answer. How did you know?

RONNIE: I'd seen him sign things.

SIR ROBERT: What things?

RONNIE: Oh—ordinary things.

SIR ROBERT: I repeat: what things?

RONNIE (*Reluctantly*): Bits of paper.

SIR ROBERT: Bits of paper? And why did he sign his name on bits of paper?

RONNIE: I don't know.

SIR ROBERT: You do know. Why did he sign his name on bits of paper?

RONNIE: He was practicing his signature.

SIR ROBERT: And you saw him?

RONNIE: Yes.

SIR ROBERT: Did he know you saw him?

RONNIE: Well—yes——

SIR ROBERT: In other words he showed you exactly how he wrote his signature?

RONNIE: Yes. I suppose he did.

SIR ROBERT: Did you practice writing it yourself?

RONNIE: I might have done.

SIR ROBERT: What do you mean you might have done? Did you or did you not?

RONNIE: Yes——

ARTHUR (*Sharply*): Ronnie! You never told me that.

RONNIE: It was only for a joke——

SIR ROBERT: Never mind whether it was for a joke or not. The fact is you practiced forging Elliot's signature——

RONNIE: It wasn't forging——

SIR ROBERT: What do you call it then?

RONNIE: Writing.

SIR ROBERT: Very well. Writing. Whoever stole the postal order and cashed it also *wrote* Elliot's signature, didn't he?

RONNIE: Yes.

SIR ROBERT: And, oddly enough, in the exact form in which you had earlier been practicing *writing* his signature——

RONNIE (*Indignantly*): I say. Which side are you on?

SIR ROBERT (*Snarling*): Don't be impertinent! Are you aware that the Admiralty sent up the forged postal order to Mr. Ridgely-Pearce— the greatest handwriting expert in England?

RONNIE: Yes.

SIR ROBERT: And you know that Mr. Ridgely-Pearce affirmed that there was no doubt that the signature on the postal order and the signature you wrote on the envelope were by one and the same hand?

RONNIE: Yes.

SIR ROBERT: And you still say that you didn't forge that signature?

RONNIE: Yes, I do.

SIR ROBERT: In other words, Mr. Ridgely-Pearce doesn't know his job?

RONNIE: Well, he's wrong anyway.

SIR ROBERT: When you went into the locker-room after dinner, were you alone?

RONNIE: I don't remember.

SIR ROBERT: I think you do. Were you alone in the locker-room?

RONNIE: Yes.

SIR ROBERT: And you knew which was Elliot's locker?

RONNIE: Yes. Of course.

SIR ROBERT: Why did you go in there at all?

RONNIE: I've told you. To put my fifteen and six away.

SIR ROBERT: Why?

RONNIE: I thought it would be safer.

SIR ROBERT: Why safer than your pocket?

RONNIE: I don't know.

SIR ROBERT: You had it in your pocket at dinner-time. Why this sudden fear for its safety?

RONNIE (*Plainly rattled*): I tell you, I don't know——

SIR ROBERT: It was rather an odd thing to do, wasn't it? The money was perfectly safe in your pocket. Why did you suddenly feel yourself impelled to put it away in your locker?

RONNIE (*Almost shouting*): I don't know.

SIR ROBERT: Was it because you knew you would be alone in the locker-room at that time?

RONNIE: No.

SIR ROBERT: Where was Elliot's locker in relation to yours?

RONNIE: Next to it, but one.

SIR ROBERT: Next, but one. What time did Elliot put his postal order in his locker?

RONNIE: I don't know. I didn't even know he had a postal order in his locker. I didn't know he had a postal order at all——

SIR ROBERT: Yet you say he was a great friend of yours——

RONNIE: He didn't tell me he had one.

SIR ROBERT: How very secretive of him! What time did you go to the locker-room?

RONNIE: I don't remember.

SIR ROBERT: Was it directly after dinner?

RONNIE: Yes. I think so.

SIR ROBERT: What did you do after leaving the locker-room?

RONNIE: I've told you. I went for permission to go to the Post Office.

SIR ROBERT: What time was that?

RONNIE: About a quarter past two.

SIR ROBERT: Dinner is over at a quarter to two. Which means that you were in the locker-room for half an hour?

RONNIE: I wasn't there all that time——

SIR ROBERT: How long were you there?

RONNIE: About five minutes.

SIR ROBERT: What were you doing for the other twenty-five?

RONNIE: I don't remember.

SIR ROBERT: It's odd that your memory is so good about some things and so bad about others——

RONNIE: Perhaps I waited outside the C.O.'s office.

SIR ROBERT (*With searing sarcasm*): Perhaps you waited outside the C.O.'s office! And perhaps no one saw you there either?

RONNIE: No. I don't think they did.

SIR ROBERT: What were you thinking about outside the C.O.'s office for twenty-five minutes?

RONNIE (*Wildly*): I don't even know if I was there. I can't remember. Perhaps I wasn't there at all.

SIR ROBERT: No. Perhaps you were still in the locker-room rifling Elliot's locker——

ARTHUR (*Indignantly*): Sir Robert, I must ask you——

SIR ROBERT: Quiet!

RONNIE: I remember now. I remember. Someone did see me outside the C.O.'s office. A chap called Casey. I remember I spoke to him.

SIR ROBERT: What did you say?

RONNIE: I said: "Come down to the Post Office with me. I'm going to cash a postal order."

SIR ROBERT (*Triumphantly*): *Cash* a postal order.

RONNIE: I mean get.

SIR ROBERT: You said cash. Why did you say cash if you meant get.

RONNIE: I don't know.

SIR ROBERT: I suggest cash was the truth.

RONNIE: No, no. It wasn't. It wasn't really. You're muddling me.

SIR ROBERT: You seem easily muddled. How many other lies have you told?

RONNIE: None. Really I haven't——

SIR ROBERT (*Bending forward malevolently*): I suggest your whole testimony is a lie——

RONNIE: No! It's the truth——

SIR ROBERT: I suggest there is barely one single word of truth in anything you have said either to me, or to the Judge Advocate, or to the Commander. I suggest that you broke into Elliot's locker, that you stole the postal order for five shillings belonging to Elliot, that you cashed it by means of forging his name——

RONNIE (*Wailing*): I didn't. I didn't.

SIR ROBERT: I suggest that you did it for a joke, meaning to give Elliot the five shillings back, but that when you met him and he said he had reported the matter you got frightened and decided to keep quiet——

RONNIE: No, no, no. It isn't true——

SIR ROBERT: I suggest that by continuing to deny your guilt you are causing great hardship to your own family, and considerable annoyance to high and important persons in this country——

CATHERINE (*On her feet*): That's a disgraceful thing to say!

ARTHUR: I agree.

SIR ROBERT (*Leaning forward and glaring at* RONNIE *with the utmost venom*): I suggest, that the time has at last come for you to undo some of the misery you have caused by confessing to us all now that you are a forger, a liar, and a thief!

RONNIE (*In tears*): I'm not! I'm not! I'm not! I didn't do it——

GRACE *has flown to his side and now envelops him.*

ARTHUR: This is outrageous, sir——

JOHN *appears at the door, dressed in evening clothes.*

JOHN: Kate, dear, I'm late. I'm most terribly sorry——

He stops short as he takes in the scene, with RONNIE *sobbing hysterically on his mother's breast, and* ARTHUR *and* CATHERINE *glaring indignantly at* SIR ROBERT, *who is engaged in putting his papers together.*

SIR ROBERT (*To* DESMOND): Can I drop you anywhere? My car is at the door.

DESMOND: Er—no—I thank you——

SIR ROBERT (*Carelessly*): Well, send all this stuff round to my chambers tomorrow morning, will you?

DESMOND: But—but will you need it now?

SIR ROBERT: Oh, yes. The boy is plainly innocent. I accept the brief.

He bows to ARTHUR *and* CATHERINE *and walks languidly to the door, past the bewildered* JOHN, *to whom he gives a polite nod as he goes out.* RONNIE *continues to sob hysterically.*

CURTAIN

ACT III

SCENE: *The same, nine months later. The time is about ten-thirty P.M.*

ARTHUR *is sitting in his favorite armchair, reading aloud from an evening paper, whose wide headline:* "WINSLOW DEBATE: FIRST LORD REPLIES" *we can read on the front page. Listening to him are* RONNIE *and* GRACE, *though neither of them seems to be doing so with much concentration.* RONNIE *is finding it hard to keep his eyes open, and* GRACE, *darning socks in the other armchair, has evidently other and, to her, more important matters on her mind.*

ARTHUR (*Reading*): —"The Admiralty, during the whole of this long-drawn-out dispute, have at no time acted hastily or ill-advisedly, and it is a matter of mere histrionic hyperbole for the right honorable and learned gentleman opposite to characterize the conduct of my department as that of callousness so inhuman as to amount to deliberate malice towards the boy Winslow. Such unfounded accusations I can well choose to ignore. (An honorable Member: 'You can't.') Honorable Members opposite may interrupt as much as they please, but I repeat—there is nothing whatever that the Admiralty has done, or

failed to do, in the case of this cadet for which I, as First Lord, need
to apologize. (Further Opposition interruptions.)" (*He stops reading
and looks up*) I must say it looks as if the First Lord's having rather a
rough passage—— (*He breaks off, noticing* RONNIE'S *head has fallen
back on the cushions and he is asleep*) I trust my reading isn't keeping you awake. (*There is no answer*) I say I trust my reading isn't
keeping you awake! (*Again there is no answer. Helplessly*) Grace!

GRACE: My poor sleepy little lamb! It's long past his bedtime, Arthur.

ARTHUR: Grace, dear—at this very moment your poor sleepy little lamb
is the subject of a very violent and heated debate in the House of Commons. I should have thought, in the circumstances, it might have been
possible for him to contrive to stay awake for a few minutes past his
bedtime——

GRACE: I expect he's over-excited.

> ARTHUR *and* GRACE *both look at the tranquilly oblivious form on
> the sofa.*

ARTHUR: A picture of over-excitement. (*Sharply*) Ronnie! (*No answer*)
Ronnie!

RONNIE (*Opening his eyes*): Yes, Father?

ARTHUR: I am reading the account of the debate. Would you like to
listen, or would you rather go to bed?

RONNIE: Oh, I'd like to listen, of course, Father. I was listening, too,
only I had my eyes shut——

ARTHUR: Very well. (*Reading*) "The First Lord continued amid further
interruptions: The chief point of criticism against the Admiralty appears to center in the purely legal question of the Petition of Right
brought by Mr. Arthur Winslow and the Admiralty's demurrer there-
to. Sir Robert Morton has made great play with his eloquent reference
to the liberty of the individual menaced, as he puts it, by the new
despotism of bureaucracy—and I was as moved as any honorable
Member opposite by his resonant use of the words: Let Right be done
—the time-honored phrase with which in his opinion the Attorney-
General should without question have endorsed Mr. Winslow's Petition of Right. Nevertheless, the matter is not nearly as simple as he
appears to imagine. Cadet Ronald Winslow is a servant of the Crown,
and has therefore no more right than any other member of his Majesty's forces to sue the Crown in open court. To allow him to do so
would undoubtedly raise the most dangerous precedents. There is no

doubt whatever in my mind that in certain cases private rights may have to be sacrificed for the public good——" (*He looks up*) And what other excuse, pray, did Charles the First make for ship money and——

> RONNIE, *after a manful attempt to keep his eyes open by self-pinchings and other devices, has once more succumbed to oblivion.* (*Sharply*) Ronnie! Ronnie!
>
> RONNIE *stirs, turns over, and slides more comfortably into the cushions.*

Would you believe it!

GRACE: He's dead tired. I'd better take him up to his bed——

ARTHUR: No. If he must sleep, let him sleep there.

GRACE: Oh, but he'd be much more comfy in his little bed——

ARTHUR: I dare say: but the debate continues and until it's ended the cause of it all will certainly not make himself comfy in his little bed.

> VIOLET *comes in.*

VIOLET: There are three more reporters in the hall, sir. Want to see you very urgently. Shall I let them in?

ARTHUR: No. Certainly not. I issued a statement yesterday. Until the debate is over I have nothing more to say.

VIOLET: Yes, sir. That's what I told them, but they wouldn't go.

ARTHUR: Well, make them. Use force, if necessary.

VIOLET: Yes, sir, And shall I cut some sandwiches for Miss Catherine, as she missed her dinner?

GRACE: Yes, Violet. Good idea.

> VIOLET *goes out.*

VIOLET (*Off*): It's no good. No more statements.

> *Voices answer her, fading at length into silence.* GRACE *puts a rug over* RONNIE, *now sleeping very soundly.*

ARTHUR: Grace, dear——

GRACE: Yes?

ARTHUR: I fancy this might be a good opportunity of talking to Violet.

GRACE (*Quite firmly*): No, dear.

ARTHUR: Meaning that it isn't a good opportunity? Or meaning that you have no intention at all of ever talking to Violet?

GRACE: I'll do it one day, Arthur. Tomorrow, perhaps. Not now.

ARTHUR: I believe you'd do better to grasp the nettle. Delay only adds to your worries——

GRACE (*Bitterly*): My worries? What do you know about my worries?

ARTHUR: A good deal, Grace. But I feel they would be a lot lessened if you faced the situation squarely.

GRACE: It's easy for you to talk, Arthur. You don't have to do it.

ARTHUR: I will, if you like.

GRACE: No, dear.

ARTHUR: If you explain the dilemma to her carefully—if you even show her the figures I jotted down for you yesterday—I venture to think you won't find her unreasonable.

GRACE: It won't be easy for her to find another place.

ARTHUR: We'll give her an excellent reference.

GRACE: That won't alter the fact that she's never been properly trained as a parlormaid and—well—you know yourself how we're always having to explain her to people. No, Arthur, I don't mind how many figures she's shown, it's a brutal thing to do.

ARTHUR: Facts are brutal things.

GRACE (*A shade hysterically*): Facts? I don't think I know what facts are any more——

ARTHUR: The facts, at this moment, are that we have a half of the income we had a year ago and we're living at nearly the same ratio. However you look at it that's bad economics——

GRACE: I'm not talking about economics, Arthur. I'm talking about ordinary, common or garden facts—things we took for granted a year ago and which now don't seem to matter any more.

ARTHUR: Such as?

GRACE (*With rising voice*): Such as a happy home and peace and quiet and an ordinary respectable life, and some sort of future for us and our children. In the last year you've thrown all that overboard, Arthur. There's your return for it, I suppose. (*She indicates the headline in the paper*) And it's all very exciting and important, I'm sure, but it doesn't bring back any of the things that we've lost. I can only pray to God that you know what you're doing.

> RONNIE *stirs in his sleep.* GRACE *lowers her voice at the end of her speech. There is a pause.*

ARTHUR: I know exactly what I'm doing, Grace. I'm going to publish my son's innocence before the world, and for that end I am not prepared to weigh the cost.

GRACE: But the cost may be out of all proportion——

ARTHUR: It may be. That doesn't concern me. I hate heroics, Grace, but you force me to say this. An injustice has been done. I am going to set it right, and there is no sacrifice in the world I am not prepared to make in order to do so.

GRACE (*With sudden violence*): Oh, I wish I could see the sense of it all! (*Pointing to* RONNIE) He's perfectly happy, at a good school, doing very well. No one need ever have known about Osborne, if you hadn't gone and shouted it out to the whole world. As it is, whatever happens now, he'll go through the rest of his life as the boy in that Winslow case—the boy who stole that postal order——

ARTHUR (*Grimly*): The boy who didn't steal that postal order.

GRACE (*Wearily*): What's the difference? When millions are talking and gossiping about him, a did or a didn't hardly matters. The Winslow boy is enough. You talk about sacrificing everything for him: but when he's grown up he won't thank you for it, Arthur—even though you've given your life to—publish his innocence as you call it.

ARTHUR *makes an impatient gesture.*

Yes, Arthur—your life. You talk gaily about arthritis and a touch of gout and old age and the rest of it, but you know as well as any of the doctors what really is the matter with you. (*Nearly in tears*) You're destroying yourself, Arthur, and me and your family besides. For what, I'd like to know? I've asked you and Kate to tell me a hundred times but you never will. For what, Arthur?

ARTHUR *has struggled painfully out of his seat and now approaches her.*

ARTHUR (*Quietly*): For Justice, Grace.

GRACE: That sounds very noble. Are you sure it's true? Are you sure it isn't just plain pride and self-importance and sheer brute stubbornness?

ARTHUR (*Putting a hand out*): No, Grace. I don't think it is. I really don't think it is——

GRACE (*Shaking off his hand*): No. This time I'm not going to cry and say I'm sorry, and make it all up again. I can stand anything if there is a reason for it. But for no reason at all, it's unfair to ask so much of me. It's unfair——

She breaks down. As ARTHUR *puts a comforting arm around her she pushes him off and goes out of the door.* RONNIE *has, meanwhile, opened his eyes.*

RONNIE: What's the matter, Father?

ARTHUR (*Turning from the door*): Your mother is a little upset——

RONNIE (*Drowsily*): Why? Aren't things going well?

ARTHUR: Oh, yes. (*Murmuring*) Very well. (*He sits with more than his usual difficulty, as if he were utterly exhausted*) Very well indeed.

RONNIE *contentedly closes his eyes again.*

(*Gently*) You'd better go to bed now, Ronnie. You'll be more comfortable——

He sees RONNIE *is asleep again. He makes as if to wake him, then shrugs his shoulders and turns away.* VIOLET *comes in with sandwiches on a plate and a letter on a salver.*

Thank you, Violet.

VIOLET *puts the sandwiches on the table and hands* ARTHUR *the letter.* ARTHUR *puts it down on the table beside him without opening it.* VIOLET *turns to go out.*

ARTHUR: Oh, Violet——

VIOLET (*Turning placidly*): Yes, sir?

ARTHUR: How long have you been with us?

VIOLET: Twenty-four years come April, sir.

ARTHUR: As long as that?

VIOLET: Yes, sir. Miss Kate was that high when I first came. (*She indicates a small child*) and Mr. Dickie hadn't even been thought of——

ARTHUR: I remember you coming to us now. I remember it well. What do you think of this case, Violet?

VIOLET: A fine old rumpus that is, and no mistake.

ARTHUR: It is, isn't it? A fine old rumpus.

VIOLET: There was a bit in the *Evening News*. Did you read it, sir?

ARTHUR: No. What did it say?

VIOLET: Oh, about how it was a fuss about nothing and a shocking waste of the Government's time, but how it was a good thing all the same because it could only happen in England——

ARTHUR: There seems to be a certain lack of logic in that argument——

VIOLET: Well, perhaps they put it a bit different, sir. Still, that's what it said all right. And when you think it's all because of our Master Ronnie—I have to laugh about it sometimes. I really do. Wasting the Government's time at his age! I never did. Well, wonders will never cease.

ARTHUR: I know. Wonders will never cease.

VIOLET: Well—would that be all, sir?

ARTHUR: Yes, Violet. That'll be all.

CATHERINE *comes in.*

CATHERINE: Good evening, Violet.

VIOLET: Good evening, miss.

She goes out.

CATHERINE: Hullo, Father. (*She kisses him. Indicating* RONNIE) An honorable Member described that this evening as a piteous little figure, crying aloud to humanity for justice and redress. I wish he could see him now.

ARTHUR (*Testily*): It's long past his bedtime. What's happened? Is the debate over?

CATHERINE: As good as. The First Lord gave an assurance that in future there would be no inquiry at Osborne or Dartmouth without informing the parents first. That seemed to satisfy most Members——

ARTHUR: But what about *our* case. Is he going to allow us a fair trial?

CATHERINE: Apparently not.

ARTHUR: But that's iniquitous. I thought he would be forced to——

CATHERINE: I thought so, too. The House evidently thought otherwise.

ARTHUR: Will there be a division?

CATHERINE: There may be. If there is the Government will win.

ARTHUR: What is the motion?

CATHERINE: To reduce the First Lord's salary by a hundred pounds. (*With a faint smile*) Naturally no one really wants to do that. (*Indicating sandwiches*) Are these for me?

ARTHUR: Yes.

CATHERINE *starts to eat the sandwiches.*

So we're back where we started, then?

CATHERINE: It looks like it.

ARTHUR: The debate has done us no good at all?

CATHERINE: It's aired the case a little, perhaps. A few more thousand people will say to each other at breakfast tomorrow: "That boy ought to be allowed a fair trial."

ARTHUR: What's the good of that, if they can't make themselves heard?

CATHERINE: I think they can—given time.

ARTHUR: Given time?

Pause.

But didn't Sir Robert make any protest when the First Lord refused a trial?

CATHERINE: Not a verbal protest. Something far more spectacular and dramatic. He'd had his feet on the Treasury table and his hat over his eyes during most of the First Lord's speech—and he suddenly got up very deliberately, glared at the First Lord, threw a whole bundle of notes on the floor, and stalked out of the House. It made a magnificent effect. If I hadn't known I could have sworn he was genuinely indignant——

ARTHUR: Of course he was genuinely indignant. So would any man of feeling be——

CATHERINE: Sir Robert, Father dear, is not a man of feeling. I don't think any emotion at all can stir that fishy heart——

ARTHUR: Except perhaps a single-minded love of justice.

CATHERINE: Nonsense. A single-minded love of Sir Robert Morton.

ARTHUR: You're very ungrateful to him considering all he's done for us these last months——

CATHERINE: I'm not ungrateful, Father. He's been wonderful—I admit it freely. No one could have fought a harder fight.

ARTHUR: Well, then——

CATHERINE: It's only his motives I question. At least I *don't* question them at all. I know them.

ARTHUR: What are they?

CATHERINE: First—publicity—you know—look at me, the staunch defender of the little man—and then second—a nice popular stick to beat the Government with. Both very useful to an ambitious man. Luckily for him we've provided them.

ARTHUR: Luckily for us too, Kate.

CATHERINE: Oh, I agree. But don't fool yourself about him, Father, for all that. The man is a fish, a hard, cold-blooded, supercilious, sneering fish.

  VIOLET *enters.*

VIOLET (*Announcing*): Sir Robert Morton.

  CATHERINE *chokes over her sandwich.*

  SIR ROBERT *comes in.*

SIR ROBERT: Good evening.

CATHERINE (*Still choking*): Good evening.

SIR ROBERT: Something gone down the wrong way?

CATHERINE: Yes.

SIR ROBERT: May I assist? (*He pats her on the back.*)

CATHERINE: Thank you.

SIR ROBERT (*To* ARTHUR): Good evening sir. I thought I would call and give you an account of the day's proceedings, but I see your daughter has forestalled me.

CATHERINE: Did you know I was in the gallery?

SIR ROBERT (*Gallantly*): With such a charming hat, how could I have missed you?

ARTHUR: It was very good of you to call, sir, nevertheless——

SIR ROBERT (*Seeing* RONNIE): Ah. The *casus belli*—dormant——

ARTHUR *goes to wake him.*

SIR ROBERT: No, no. I beg of you. Please do not disturb his innocent slumbers.

CATHERINE: *Innocent* slumbers?

SIR ROBERT: Exactly. Besides, I fear since our first encounter he is, rather pardonably, a trifle nervous of me.

CATHERINE: Will you betray a technical secret, Sir Robert? What happened in that first examination to make you so sure of his innocence?

SIR ROBERT: Three things. First of all, he made far too many damaging admissions. A guilty person would have been much more careful and on his guard. Secondly, I laid him a trap; and thirdly, left him a loophole. Anyone who was guilty would have fallen into the one and darted through the other. He did neither.

CATHERINE: The trap was to ask him suddenly what time Elliot put the postal order in his locker, wasn't it?

SIR ROBERT: Yes.

ARTHUR: And the loophole?

SIR ROBERT: I then suggested to him that he had stolen the postal order for a joke—which, had he been guilty, he would surely have admitted to as being the lesser of two evils.

CATHERINE: I see. It was very cleverly thought out.

SIR ROBERT (*With a little bow*): Thank you.

ARTHUR: May we offer you some refreshment, Sir Robert? A whisky and soda?

SIR ROBERT: No thank you. Nothing at all.

ARTHUR: My daughter has told me of your demonstration during the First Lord's speech. She described it as—magnificent.

SIR ROBERT (*With a glance at* CATHERINE): Did she? That was good of her. It's a very old trick, you know. I've done it many times in the Courts. It's nearly always surprisingly effective——

CATHERINE *catches her father's eye and nods triumphantly.*

(*To* CATHERINE) Was the First Lord at all put out by it—did you notice?

CATHERINE: How could he have failed to be? (*To* ARTHUR, *approaching his chair*) I wish you could have seen it, Father—it was—— (*She notices the letter on the table beside* ARTHUR *and snatches it up with a sudden gesture. She examines the envelope*) When did this come?

ARTHUR: A few minutes ago. Do you know the writing?

CATHERINE: Yes. (*She puts the letter back on the table.*)

ARTHUR: Whose is it?

CATHERINE: I shouldn't bother to read it, if I were you.

　　ARTHUR *looks at her, puzzled, then takes up the letter.*

ARTHUR (*To* SIR ROBERT): Will you forgive me?

SIR ROBERT: Of course.

　　ARTHUR *opens the letter and begins to read.* CATHERINE *watches him for a moment, and then turns with a certain forced liveliness to* SIR ROBERT.

CATHERINE: Well, what do you think the next step should be?

SIR ROBERT: I have already been considering that, Miss Winslow. I believe that perhaps the best plan would be to renew our efforts to get the Director of Public Prosecutions to act.

CATHERINE (*With one eye on her father*): But do you think there's any chance of that?

SIR ROBERT: Oh, yes. In the main it will chiefly be a question of making ourselves a confounded nuisance——

CATHERINE: We've certainly done that quite successfully so far—thanks to you——

SIR ROBERT (*Suavely*): Ah. That is perhaps the only quality I was born with—the ability to make myself a confounded nuisance.

　　He, too, has his eye on ARTHUR, *sensing something amiss.*

　　ARTHUR *finishes reading the letter.*

CATHERINE (*With false vivacity*): Father—Sir Robert thinks we might get the Director of Public Prosecutions to act——

ARTHUR: What?

SIR ROBERT: We were discussing how to proceed with the case——

ARTHUR: The case? (*He stares, a little blankly, from one to the other*) Yes. We must think of that, mustn't we? (*Pause*) How to proceed with the case? (*To* SIR ROBERT, *abruptly*) I'm afraid I don't think, all things considered, that much purpose would be served by going on——

SIR ROBERT *and* CATHERINE *stare at him blankly.*

CATHERINE *goes quickly to him and snatches the letter from his lap. She begins to read.*

SIR ROBERT (*With a sudden change of tone*): Of course we must go on.

ARTHUR (*In a low voice*): It is not for you to choose, sir. The choice is mine.

SIR ROBERT (*Harshly*): Then you must reconsider it. To give up now would be insane.

ARTHUR: Insane? My sanity has already been called in question tonight —for carrying the case as far as I have.

SIR ROBERT: Whatever the contents of that letter, or whatever has happened to make you lose heart, I insist that we continue the fight——

ARTHUR: Insist? We? It is my fight—my fight alone—and it is for me alone to judge when the time has come to give up.

SIR ROBERT (*Violently*): But why give up? Why? In heaven's name, man, why?

ARTHUR (*Slowly*): I have made many sacrifices for this case. Some of them I had no right to make, but I made them none the less. But there is a limit and I have reached it. I am sorry, Sir Robert. More sorry, perhaps, than you are, but the Winslow case is now closed.

SIR ROBERT: Balderdash!

ARTHUR *looks surprised at this unparliamentary expression.* CATHERINE *has read and re-read the letter, and now breaks the silence in a calm, methodical voice.*

CATHERINE: My father doesn't mean what he says, Sir Robert.

SIR ROBERT: I am glad to hear it.

CATHERINE: Perhaps I should explain this letter——

ARTHUR: No, Kate.

CATHERINE: Sir Robert knows so much about our family affairs, Father, I don't see it will matter much if he learns a little more. (*To Sir* ROBERT) This letter is from a certain Colonel Watherstone who is the father of the man I'm engaged to. We've always known he was opposed to the case, so it really comes as no surprise. In it he says that our efforts to discredit the Admiralty in the House of Commons today have resulted merely in our making the name of Winslow a nation-wide laughing-stock. I think that's his phrase. (*She consults the letter*) Yes. That's right. A nation-wide laughing-stock.

SIR ROBERT: I don't care for his English.

CATHERINE: It's not very good, is it? He goes on to say that unless my father will give him a firm understanding to drop this whining and reckless agitation—I suppose he means the case—he will exert every bit of influence he has over his son to prevent him marrying me.

SIR ROBERT: I see. An ultimatum.

CATHERINE: Yes—but a pointless one.

SIR ROBERT: He has no influence over his son?

CATHERINE: Oh, yes. A little, naturally. But his son is of age, and his own master——

SIR ROBERT: Is he dependent on his father for money?

CATHERINE: He gets an allowance. But he can live perfectly well—we both can live perfectly well without it.

> *Pause.* SIR ROBERT *stares hard at her, then turns abruptly to* ARTHUR.

SIR ROBERT: Well, sir?

ARTHUR: I'm afraid I can't go back on what I have already said. I will give you a decision in a few days——

SIR ROBERT: Your daughter seems prepared to take the risk——

ARTHUR: I am not. Not, at least, until I know how great a risk it is——

SIR ROBERT: How do you estimate the risk, Miss Winslow?

> *Pause.* CATHERINE, *for all her bravado, is plainly scared. She is engaged in lighting a cigarette as* SIR ROBERT *asks his question.*

CATHERINE (*At length*): Negligible.

> SIR ROBERT *stares at her again. Feeling his eyes on her, she returns his glance defiantly. Pause.*

SIR ROBERT (*Returning abruptly to his languid manner*): I see. May I take a cigarette, too?

CATHERINE: Yes, of course. I thought you didn't smoke.

SIR ROBERT: Only occasionally. (*To* ARTHUR) I really must apologize to you, sir, for speaking to you as I did just now. It was unforgivable.

ARTHUR: Not at all, sir. You were upset at giving up the case—and, to be frank, I liked you for it——

SIR ROBERT (*With a deprecating gesture*): It has been rather a tiring day. The House of Commons is a peculiarly exhausting place, you know. Too little ventilation, and far too much hot air—I really am most truly sorry.

ARTHUR: Please.

SIR ROBERT (*Carelessly*): Of course, you must decide about the case as you wish. That really is a most charming hat, Miss Winslow——

CATHERINE: I'm glad you like it.

SIR ROBERT: It seems decidedly wrong to me that a lady of your political persuasion should be allowed to adorn herself with such a very feminine allurement. It really looks so awfully like trying to have the best of both worlds——

CATHERINE: I'm not a militant, you know, Sir Robert. I don't go about breaking shop windows with a hammer or pouring acid down pillar boxes.

SIR ROBERT (*Languidly*): I am truly glad to hear it. Both those activities would be highly unsuitable in that hat——

    CATHERINE *glares at him but suppresses an angry retort.*

I have never yet fully grasped what active steps you take to propagate your cause, Miss Winslow.

CATHERINE (*Shortly*): I'm an organizing secretary at the West London Branch of the Woman's Suffrage Association.

SIR ROBERT: Indeed? Is the work hard?

CATHERINE: Very.

SIR ROBERT: But not, I should imagine, particularly lucrative.

CATHERINE: The work is voluntary and unpaid.

SIR ROBERT (*Murmuring*): Dear me! What sacrifices you young ladies seem prepared to make for your convictions——

    VIOLET *enters.*

VIOLET (*To* CATHERINE) Mr. Watherstone is in the hall, miss. Says he would like to have a word with you in private—most particular——

    Pause.

CATHERINE: Oh. I'll come out to him——

ARTHUR: No. See him in here.

    He begins to struggle out of his chair. SIR ROBERT *assists him.*

You wouldn't mind coming to the dining-room, would you, Sir Robert, for a moment?

SIR ROBERT: Not in the least.

CATHERINE: All right, Violet.

VIOLET: Will you come in, sir.

    JOHN *comes in. He is looking depressed and anxious.* CATHERINE *greets him with a smile, which he returns only half-heartedly. This exchange is lost on* ARTHUR, *who has his back to them, but not on* SIR ROBERT.

CATHERINE: Hullo, John.

JOHN: Hullo (*To* ARTHUR): Good evening, sir.

ARTHUR: Good evening, John. (*He goes on towards dining-room.*)

CATHERINE: I don't think you've met Sir Robert Morton.

JOHN: No, I haven't. How do you do, sir?

SIR ROBERT: I think you promised me a whisky and soda. (*Turning to* JOHN) May I offer my very belated congratulations?

JOHN: Congratulations? Oh, yes. Thank you.

ARTHUR *and* SIR ROBERT *go into dining-room. There is a pause.* CATHERINE *is watching* JOHN *with an anxious expression.*

JOHN (*Indicating* RONNIE): Is he asleep?

CATHERINE: Yes.

JOHN: Sure he's not shamming?

CATHERINE: Yes.

JOHN (*After a pause*): My father's written your father a letter.

CATHERINE: I know. I've read it.

JOHN: Oh.

CATHERINE: Did you?

JOHN: Yes. He showed it to me.

Pause. JOHN *is carefully not looking at her.*

(*At length*) Well, what's his answer?

CATHERINE: My father? I don't suppose he'll send one.

JOHN: You think he'll ignore it?

CATHERINE: Isn't that the best answer to blackmail?

JOHN (*Muttering*): It was damned high-handed of the old man, I admit.

CATHERINE: High-handed?

JOHN: I tried to get him not to send it——

CATHERINE: I'm glad.

JOHN: The trouble is—he's perfectly serious.

CATHERINE: I never thought he wasn't.

JOHN: If your father does decide to go on with the case, I'm very much afraid he'll do everything he threatens.

CATHERINE: Forbid the match?

JOHN: Yes.

CATHERINE (*Almost pleadingly*): Isn't that rather an empty threat, John?

JOHN (*Slowly*): Well, there's always the allowance——

CATHERINE (*Dully*): Yes, I see. There's always the allowance.

JOHN: I tell you, Kate darling, this is going to need damned careful handling; otherwise we'll find ourselves in the soup.

CATHERINE: Without your allowance would we be in the soup?

JOHN: And without your settlement. My dear girl, of course we would. Dash it all, I can't even live on my pay as it is, but with two of us——

CATHERINE: I've heard it said that two can live as cheaply as one.

JOHN: Don't you believe it. Two can live as cheaply as two, and that's all there is to it.

CATHERINE: Yes, I see. I didn't know.

JOHN: Unlike you I have a practical mind, Kate. I'm sorry, but it's no good dashing blindly ahead without thinking of these things first. The problem has got to be faced.

CATHERINE: I'm ready to face it, John. What do you suggest?

JOHN (*Cautiously*): Well—I think you should consider very carefully before you take the next step——

CATHERINE: I can assure you we will, John. The question is—what *is* the next step?

JOHN: Well—this is the way I see it. I'm going to be honest now. I hope you don't mind——

CATHERINE: No. I should welcome it.

JOHN: Your young brother over there pinches or doesn't pinch a five-bob postal order. For over a year you and your father fight a magnificent fight on his behalf, and I'm sure everyone admires you for it——

CATHERINE: Your father hardly seems to——

JOHN: Well, he's a diehard. Like these old Admirals you've been up against. I meant ordinary reasonable people, like myself. But now look —you've had two inquiries, the Petition of Right case which the Admiralty has thrown out of Court, and the Appeal. And now, good heavens, you've had the whole damned House of Commons getting themselves worked up into a frenzy about it. Surely, darling, that's enough for you? My God! Surely the case can end there?

CATHERINE (*Slowly*): Yes. I suppose the case can end there.

JOHN (*Pointing to* RONNIE): *He* won't mind.

CATHERINE: No. I know he won't.

JOHN: Look at him! Perfectly happy and content. Not a care in the world. How do you know what's going on in his mind? How can you be so sure he didn't do it?

CATHERINE (*Also gazing down at* RONNIE): I'm not so sure he didn't do it.

JOHN (*Appalled*): Good Lord! Then why in heaven's name have you and your father spent all this time and money trying to prove his innocence?

CATHERINE (*Quietly*): His innocence or guilt aren't important to me. They are to my father. Not to me. I believe he didn't do it; but I may be wrong. To prove that he didn't do it is of hardly more interest to me than the identity of the college servant, or whoever it was, who did it. All that I care about is that people should know that a Government Department has ignored a fundamental human right and that it should be forced to acknowledge it. That's all that's important to me.

JOHN: But, darling, after all those long noble words, it does really resolve itself to a question of a fourteen-year-old kid and a five-bob postal order, doesn't it?

CATHERINE: Yes, it does.

JOHN (*Reasonably*): Well now, look. There's a European war blowing up, there's a coal strike on, there's a fair chance of civil war in Ireland, and there's a hundred and one other things on the horizon at the moment that I think you genuinely could call *important*. And yet, with all that on its mind, the House of Commons takes a whole day to discuss him (*pointing to* RONNIE) and his bally postal order. Surely you must see that's a little out of proportion——

    Pause. CATHERINE *raises her head slowly.*

CATHERINE (*With some spirit*): All I know is, John, that if ever the time comes that the House of Commons has so much on its mind that it can't find time to discuss a Ronnie Winslow and his bally postal order, this country will be a far poorer place than it is now. (*Wearily*) But you needn't go on, John dear. You've said quite enough. I entirely see your point of view.

JOHN: I don't know whether you realize that all this publicity you're getting is making the name of Winslow a bit of a—well——

CATHERINE (*Steadily*): A nation-wide laughing-stock, your father said.

JOHN: Well, that's putting it a bit steep. But people do find the case a bit ridiculous, you know. I mean, I get chaps coming up to me in the mess all the time and saying: "I say, is it true you're going to marry the Winslow girl? You'd better be coreful. You'll find yourself up in front of the House of Lords for pinching the Adjutant's bath." Things like that. They're not awfully funny——

CATHERINE: That's nothing. They're singing a verse about us at the Alhambra—

> Winslow one day went to heaven
> And found a poor fellow in quod.
> The fellow said I didn't do it,
> So naturally Winslow sued God.

JOHN: Well, darling—you see——

CATHERINE: Yes. I see. (*Quietly*) Do you want to marry me, John?

JOHN: What?

CATHERINE: I said: Do you want to marry me?

JOHN: Well, of course I do. You know I do. We've been engaged for over a year now. Have I ever wavered before?

CATHERINE: No. Never before.

JOHN (*Correcting himself*): I'm not wavering now. Not a bit—I'm only telling you what I think is the best course for us to take.

CATHERINE: But isn't it already too late? Even if we gave up the case, would you still want to marry—the Winslow girl?

JOHN: All that would blow over in no time.

CATHERINE (*Slowly*): And we'd have the allowance——

JOHN: Yes. We would.

CATHERINE: And that's so important——

JOHN (*Quietly*): It is, darling. I'm sorry, but you can't shame me into saying it isn't.

CATHERINE: I didn't mean to shame you——

JOHN: Oh, yes you did. I know that tone of voice.

CATHERINE (*Humbly*): I'm sorry.

JOHN (*Confidently*): Well, now—what's the answer?

CATHERINE (*Slowly*): I love you, John, and I want to be your wife.

JOHN: Well, then, that's all I want to know. Darling! I was sure nothing so stupid and trivial could possibly come between us.

He kisses her. She responds wearily. The telephone rings. After a pause she releases herself and picks up the receiver.

CATHERINE: Hullo . . . Yes . . . Will you wait a minute? (*She goes to the dining-room door and calls*) Sir Robert! Someone wants you on the telephone——

SIR ROBERT *comes out of the dining-room.*

SIR ROBERT: Thank you. I'm so sorry to interrupt.

CATHERINE: You didn't. We'd finished our talk.

SIR ROBERT *looks at her inquiringly. She gives him no sign. He walks to the telephone.*

SIR ROBERT (*Noticing sandwiches*): How delicious. May I help myself?

CATHERINE: Do.

SIR ROBERT (*Into receiver*): Hello . . . Yes, Michael . . . F.E.? I didn't know he was going to speak . . . I see . . . Go on . . .

SIR ROBERT *listens, with closed eyelids, munching a sandwich, meanwhile.*

(*At length*) Thank you, Michael.

He rings off. ARTHUR *has appeared in the dining-room doorway.*

SIR ROBERT (*To* ARTHUR): There has been a most interesting development in the House, sir.

ARTHUR: What?

SIR ROBERT: My secretary tells me that a barrister friend of mine who, quite unknown to me, was interested in the case, got on his feet shortly after nine-thirty and delivered one of the most scathing denunciations of a Government Department ever heard in the House. (*To* CATHERINE) What a shame we missed it—his style is quite superb——

ARTHUR: What happened?

SIR ROBERT: The debate revived, of course, and the First Lord, who must have felt himself fairly safe, suddenly found himself under attack from all parts of the House. It appears that rather than risk a division he has this moment given an undertaking that he will instruct the Attorney-General to endorse our Petition of Right. The case of Winslow versus Rex can now therefore come to Court.

There is a pause. ARTHUR *and* CATHERINE *stare at him unbelievingly.* (*At length*) Well, sir. What are my instructions?

ARTHUR (*Slowly*): The decision is no longer mine, sir. You must ask my daughter.

SIR ROBERT: What are my instructions, Miss Winslow?

CATHERINE *looks down at the sleeping* RONNIE. ARTHUR *is watching her intently.* SIR ROBERT, *munching sandwiches, is also looking at her.*

CATHERINE (*In a flat voice*): Do you need my instructions, Sir Robert? Aren't they already on the Petition? Doesn't it say: Let Right be done?

JOHN *makes a move of protest towards her. She does not look at him. He turns abruptly to the door.*

JOHN (*Furiously*): Kate! Good night.

He goes out. SIR ROBERT, *with languid speculation, watches him go.*

SIR ROBERT (*His mouth full*): Well, then—we must endeavor to see that it is.

CURTAIN

A C T   I V

SCENE: *The same, about five months later. It is a stiflingly hot June day—nearly two years less one month since* RONNIE'S *dismissal from Osborne. The glass door to the garden stands open, and a bath chair, unoccupied, has been placed near by.* ON THE RISE OF THE CURTAIN *the stage is empty and the telephone is ringing insistently.*

DICKIE *comes in from the hall carrying a suitcase, evidently very hot, his straw hat pushed on to the back of his head and panting from his exertions. He is wearing a neat, dark blue suit, a sober tie, and a stiff collar. He puts the suitcase down and mops his face with his handkerchief. Then he goes to the hall door and calls:*

DICKIE: Mother! (*There is no reply*) Violet! (*Again no reply*) Anyone about?

He goes to the telephone—taking off the receiver.

Hullo . . . No, not senior—junior . . . I don't know where he is . . . *Daily Mail?* . . . No, I'm the brother . . . Elder brother— that's right . . . Well—I'm in the banking business . . . That's right. Following in father's footsteps . . . My views on the case? Well—I—er—I don't know I have any, except, I mean, I hope we win and all that . . . No, I haven't been in Court. I've only just arrived from Reading . . . Reading . . . Yes. That's where I work . . . Yes, I've come up for the last two days of the trial. Verdict's expected tomorrow, isn't it? . . . Twenty-two, last March . . . *Seven* years older . . . No. He was thirteen when it happened, but now he's fifteen . . . Well, I suppose, if I'm anything I'm a sort of Liberal-Conservative . . . Single . . . No. No immediate prospects. I say, is this at all interesting to you? . . . Well, a perfectly ordinary kid, just like any other—makes a noise, does fretwork, doesn't wash and all that . . . Doesn't wash . . . (*Alarmed*) I say, don't take that too literally. I mean he does, sometimes . . . Yes. All right. Good-bye . . .

He rings off and exits through center door. Telephone rings again.

He comes back to answer it, when GRACE *dressed for going out,
comes out of the dining-room.*

GRACE: Oh, hullo, darling. When did you get here?

She picks up the telephone receiver.

(*Into receiver*) Everyone out.

She rings off and embraces DICKIE.

You're thinner. I like your new suit.

DICKIE: Straight from Reading's Savile Row. Off the peg at three and
a half guineas. (*Pointing to telephone*) I say—does that go on all the
time?

GRACE: All blessed day. The last four days it simply hasn't stopped.

DICKIE: I had to fight my way in through an army of reporters and
people——

GRACE: Yes, I know. You didn't say anything, I hope, Dickie dear. It's
better not to say a word——

DICKIE: I don't think I said anything much . . . (*Carelessly*) Oh, yes.
I did say that I personally thought he did it——

GRACE (*Horrified*): Dickie! You didn't! (*He is smiling at her*) Oh, I see.
It's a joke. You mustn't say things like that, even in fun, Dickie
dear——

DICKIE: How's it all going?

GRACE: I don't know. I've been there all four days now and I've hardly
understood a word that's going on. Kate says the judge is against us,
but he seems a charming old gentleman to me. (*Faintly shocked*) Sir
Robert's so rude to him——

Telephone rings. GRACE *answers it automatically.*

Nobody in.

She rings off and turns to garden door.

(*Calling*) Arthur! Lunch! I'll come straight down. Dickie's here. (*To*
DICKIE) Kate takes the morning session, then she comes home and
relieves me with Arthur, and I go to the Court in the afternoons, so
you can come with me as soon as she's in.

DICKIE: Will there be room for me?

GRACE: Oh, yes. They reserve places for the family. You never saw such
crowds in all your life. And such excitement! Cheers and applause and
people being turned out. It's thrilling—you'll love it, Dickie.

DICKIE: Well—if I don't understand a word——

GRACE: Oh, that doesn't matter. They all get so terribly worked up you
find yourself getting worked up, too. Sir Robert and the Attorney-

General go at each other hammer and tongs—you wait and hear them
—all about Petitions and demurrers and prerogatives and things.
Nothing to do with Ronnie at all—seems to me——

DICKIE: How did Ronnie get on in the witness box?

GRACE: Two days he was cross-examined. Two whole days. Imagine it,
the poor little pet! I must say he didn't seem to mind much. He said
two days with the Attorney-General wasn't nearly as bad as two
minutes with Sir Robert. Kate says he made a very good impression
with the jury——

DICKIE: How is Kate, Mother?

GRACE: Oh, all right. You heard about John, I suppose——

DICKIE: Yes. That's what I meant. How has she taken it?

GRACE: You can never tell with Kate. She never lets you know what she's
feeling. We all think he's behaved very badly——

ARTHUR *appears at the garden door, walking very groggily.*

Arthur! You shouldn't have come up the stairs by yourself.

ARTHUR: I had little alternative.

GRACE: I'm sorry, dear. I was talking to Dickie.

GRACE *helps* ARTHUR *into the bath chair.*

ARTHUR: How are you, Dickie?

DICKIE (*Shaking hands*) Very well, thank you, Father.

ARTHUR: I've been forced to adopt this ludicrous form of propulsion. I
apologize.

He wheels himself into the room and examines DICKIE.

You look very well. A trifle thinner, perhaps——

DICKIE: Hard work, Father.

ARTHUR: Or late hours?

DICKIE: You can't keep late hours in Reading.

ARTHUR: You could keep late hours anywhere. I've had quite a good
report about you from Mr. Lamb.

DICKIE: Good egg! He's a decent old stick, the old baa-lamb. I took him
racing last Saturday. Had the time of his life and lost his shirt.

ARTHUR: Did he? I have no doubt that, given the chance, you'll succeed
in converting the entire Reading branch of the Westminster Bank into
a bookmaking establishment. Mr. Lamb says you've joined the Ter-
ritorials.

DICKIE: Yes, Father.

ARTHUR: Why have you done that?

DICKIE: Well, from all accounts there's a fair chance of a bit of a scrap quite soon. If there is I don't want it to be all over before I can get in on it——

ARTHUR: If there is what you call a scrap you'll do far better to stay in the bank——

DICKIE: Oh, no, Father. I mean, the bank's all right—but still—a chap can't help looking forward to a bit of a change—I can always go back to the bank afterwards——

The telephone rings. ARTHUR *takes receiver off and puts it down on table.*

GRACE: Oh, no, dear. You can't do that.

ARTHUR: Why not?

GRACE: It annoys the exchange.

ARTHUR: I prefer to annoy the exchange rather than have the exchange annoy me. (*To* GRACE) Catherine's late. She was in at half-past yesterday.

GRACE: Perhaps they're taking the lunch interval later today.

ARTHUR: Lunch interval? This isn't a cricket match. (*Looking at her*) Nor, may I say, is it a matinée at the Gaiety. Why are you wearing that highly unsuitable get-up?

GRACE: Don't you like it, dear? I think it's Mme. Dupont's best.

ARTHUR: Grace—your son is facing a charge of theft and forgery——

GRACE: Oh, dear! It's so difficult! I simply can't be seen in the same old dress, day after day. (*A thought strikes her*) I tell you what, Arthur. I'll wear my black coat and skirt tomorrow—for the verdict.

ARTHUR *glares at her, helplessly, then turns his chair to the dining-room.*

ARTHUR: Did you say my lunch was ready?

GRACE: Yes, dear. It's only cold. I did the salad myself. Violet and cook are at the trial.

DICKIE: Is Violet still with you? She was under sentence last time I saw you——

GRACE: She's been under sentence for the last six months, poor thing—only she doesn't know it. Neither your father nor I have the courage to tell her——

ARTHUR (*Stopping at door*): I have the courage to tell her.

GRACE: It's funny that you don't, then, dear.

ARTHUR: I will.

GRACE (*Hastily*): No, no, you mustn't. When it's to be done, I'll do it.

ARTHUR: You see, Dickie? These taunts of cowardice are daily flung at my head; but should I take them up I'm forbidden to move in the matter. Such is the logic of women.

He goes into the dining-room. DICKIE, *who has been holding the door open, closes it after him.*

DICKIE (*Seriously*): How *is* he?

GRACE *shakes her head quietly.*

Will you take him away after the trial?

GRACE: He's promised to go into a nursing home.

DICKIE: Do you think he will?

GRACE: How do I know? He'll probably find some new excuse——

DICKIE: But surely, if he loses this time, he's lost for good, hasn't he?

GRACE (*Slowly*): So they say, Dickie dear— I can only hope it's true.

DICKIE: How did you keep him away from the trial?

GRACE: Kate and Sir Robert together. He wouldn't listen to me or the doctor.

DICKIE: Poor old Mother! You must have been having a pretty rotten time of it, one way and another——

GRACE: I've said my say, Dickie. He knows what I think. Not that he cares. He never has—all his life. Anyway, I've given up worrying. He's always said he knew what he was doing. It's my job to try and pick up the pieces, I suppose.

CATHERINE *comes in.*

CATHERINE: Lord! The heat! Mother, can't you get rid of those reporters —Hullo, Dickie.

DICKIE (*Embracing her*): Hullo, Kate.

CATHERINE: Come to be in at the death.

DICKIE: Is that what it's going to be?

CATHERINE: Looks like it. I could cheerfully strangle that old brute of a judge, Mother. He's dead against us.

GRACE (*Fixing her hat in the mirror*): Oh, dear!

CATHERINE: Sir Robert's very worried. He said the Attorney-General's speech made a great impression on the jury. I must say it was very clever. To listen to him yesterday you would have thought that a verdict for Ronnie would simultaneously cause a mutiny in the Royal Navy and triumphant jubilation in Berlin.

ARTHUR *appears in his chair, at the dining-room door.*

ARTHUR: You're late, Catherine.

CATHERINE: I know, Father. I'm sorry. There was such a huge crowd outside as well as inside the Court that I couldn't get a cab. And I stayed to talk to Sir Robert.

GRACE (*Pleased*): Is there a bigger crowd even than yesterday, Kate?

CATHERINE: Yes, Mother. Far bigger.

ARTHUR: How did it go this morning?

CATHERINE: Sir Robert finished his cross-examination of the postmistress. I thought he'd demolished her completely. She admitted she couldn't identify Ronnie in the Commander's office. She admitted she couldn't be sure of the time he came in. She admitted that she was called away to the telephone while he was buying his fifteen-and-six postal order, and that all Osborne cadets looked alike to her in their uniforms, so that it might quite easily have been another cadet who cashed the five shillings. It was a brilliant cross-examination. So gentle and quiet. He didn't bully her, or frighten her—he just coaxed her into tying herself into knots. Then, when he'd finished the Attorney-General asked her again whether she was absolutely positive that the same boy that bought the fifteen-and-six postal order also cashed the five-shilling one. She said yes. She was quite, quite sure because Ronnie was such a good-looking little boy that she had specially noticed him. She hadn't said that in her examination-in-chief. I could see those twelve good men and true nodding to each other. I believe it undid the whole of that magnificent cross-examination.

ARTHUR: If she thought him so especially good-looking, why couldn't she identify him the same evening?

CATHERINE: Don't ask me, Father. Ask the Attorney-General. I'm sure he has a beautifully reasonable answer.

DICKIE: Ronnie good-looking! What utter rot! She must be lying, that woman.

GRACE: Nonsense, Dickie! I thought he looked very well in the box yesterday, didn't you, Kate?

CATHERINE: Yes, Mother.

ARTHUR: Who else gave evidence for the other side?

CATHERINE: The Commander, the Chief Petty Officer, and one of the boys at the College.

ARTHUR: Anything very damaging?

CATHERINE: Nothing that we didn't expect. The boy showed obviously he hated Ronnie and was torn to shreds by Sir Robert. The Commander scored, though. He's an honest man and genuinely believes Ronnie did it.

GRACE: Did you see anybody interesting in Court, dear?

CATHERINE: Yes, Mother. John Watherstone.

GRACE: John? I hope you didn't speak to him, Kate.

CATHERINE: Of course I did.

GRACE: Kate, how could you! What did he say?

CATHERINE: He wished us luck.

GRACE: What impertinence! The idea of John Watherstone coming calmly up in Court to wish you luck—I think it's the most disgraceful, cold-blooded——

ARTHUR: Grace—you will be late for the resumption.

GRACE: Oh, will I? Are you ready, Dickie?

DICKIE: Yes, Mother.

GRACE: You don't think that nice, gray suit of yours you paid so much money for——

ARTHUR: What time are they resuming, Kate?

CATHERINE: Two o'clock.

ARTHUR: It's twenty past two now.

GRACE: Oh, dear! We'll be terribly late. Kate—that's your fault. Arthur, you must finish your lunch——

ARTHUR: Yes, Grace.

GRACE: Promise now.

ARTHUR: I promise.

GRACE (*To herself*): I wonder if Violet will remember to pick up those onions. Perhaps I'd better do it on the way back from the Court. (*As she passes* CATHERINE) Kate, dear, I'm so sorry——

CATHERINE: What for, Mother?

GRACE: John proving such a bad hat. I never did like him very much, you know.

CATHERINE: No, I know.

GRACE: Now, Dickie, when you get to the front door put your head down, like me, and just charge through them all.

ARTHUR: Why don't you go out by the garden?

GRACE: I wouldn't like to risk this dress getting through that hedge. Come on, Dickie. I always shout: "I'm the maid and don't know nothing," so don't be surprised.

DICKIE: Right-oh, Mother.

GRACE *goes out.* DICKIE *follows her.*
There is a pause.

ARTHUR: Are we going to lose this case, Kate?

CATHERINE *quietly shrugs her shoulders.*

It's our last chance.

CATHERINE: I know.

ARTHUR (*With sudden violence*): We've got to win it.

CATHERINE *does not reply.*

What does Sir Robert think?

CATHERINE: He seems very worried.

ARTHUR (*Thoughtfully*): I wonder if you were right, Kate. I wonder if we could have had a better man.

CATHERINE: No, Father. We couldn't have had a better man.

ARTHUR: You admit that now, do you?

CATHERINE: Only that he's the best advocate in England and for some reason—prestige, I suppose—he seems genuinely anxious to win this case. I don't go back on anything else I've ever said about him.

ARTHUR: The papers said that he began today by telling the judge he felt ill and might have to ask for an adjournment. I trust he won't collapse——

CATHERINE: He won't. It was just another of those brilliant tricks of his that he's always boasting about. It got him the sympathy of the Court and possibly—no, I won't say that——

ARTHUR: Say it.

CATHERINE (*Slowly*): Possibly provided him with an excuse if he's beaten.

ARTHUR: You don't like him, do you?

CATHERINE (*Indifferently*): There's nothing in him to like or dislike, Father. I admire him.

DESMOND *appears at the garden door. Standing inside the room, he knocks diffidently.* CATHERINE *and* ARTHUR *turn and see him.*

DESMOND: I trust you do not object to me employing this rather furtive entry. The crowds at the front door are most alarming——

ARTHUR: Come in, Desmond. Why have you left the Court?

DESMOND: My partner will be holding the fort. He is perfectly competent, I promise you.

ARTHUR: I'm glad to hear it.

DESMOND: I wonder if I might see Catherine alone. I have a matter of some urgency to communicate to her——

ARTHUR: Oh. Do you wish to hear this urgent matter, Kate?

CATHERINE: Yes, Father.

ARTHUR: Very well. I shall go and finish my lunch.

He wheels his chair to the dining-room door.

DESMOND *flies to help.*

DESMOND: Allow me.

ARTHUR: Thank you. I can manage this vehicle without assistance.

He goes out.

DESMOND: I fear I should have warned you of my visit. Perhaps I have interrupted——

CATHERINE: No, Desmond. Please sit down.

DESMOND: Thank you. I'm afraid I have only a very short time. I must get back to Court for the cross-examination of the judge-advocate.

CATHERINE: Yes, Desmond. Well?

DESMOND: I have a taxicab waiting at the end of the street.

CATHERINE (*Smiling*): How very extravagant of you, Desmond.

DESMOND (*Also smiling*): Yes. But it shows you how rushed this visit must necessarily be. The fact of the matter is—it suddenly occurred to me during the lunch recess that I had far better see you today.

CATHERINE (*Her thoughts far distant*): Why?

DESMOND: I have a question to put to you, Kate, which, if I had postponed putting until after the verdict, you might—who knows—have thought had been prompted by pity—if we had lost. Or—if we had won, your reply might—again who knows—have been influenced by gratitude. Do you follow me, Kate?

CATHERINE: Yes, Desmond. I think I do.

DESMOND: Ah. Then possibly you have some inkling of what the question is I have to put to you?

CATHERINE: Yes. I think I have.

DESMOND (*A trifle disconcerted*): Oh.

CATHERINE: I'm sorry, Desmond. I ought, I know, to have followed the usual practice in such cases, and told you I had no inkling whatever.

DESMOND: No, no. Your directness and honesty are two of the qualities I so much admire in you. I am glad you have guessed. It makes my task the easier——

CATHERINE (*In a matter-of-fact voice*): Will you give me a few days to think it over?

DESMOND: Of course. Of course.

CATHERINE: I need hardly tell you how grateful I am, Desmond.

DESMOND (*A trifle bewildered*): There is no need, Kate. No need at all——

    CATHERINE *has risen brusquely.*

CATHERINE: You mustn't keep your taxi waiting——

DESMOND: Oh, bother my taxi! (*Recovering himself*) Forgive me, Kate, but you see I know very well what your feelings for me really are.

CATHERINE (*Gently*): You do, Desmond?

DESMOND: Yes, Kate. I know quite well they have never amounted to much more than a sort of—well—shall we say, friendliness? A warm friendliness, I hope. Yes, I think perhaps we can definitely say, warm. But no more than that. That's true, isn't it?

CATHERINE (*Quietly*): Yes, Desmond.

DESMOND: I know, I know. Of course, the thing is that even if I proved the most devoted and adoring huband that ever lived—which, I may say—if you give me the chance, I intend to be—your feelings for me would never—could never—amount to more than that. When I was young it might, perhaps, have been a different story. When I played cricket for England——

    He notices the faintest expression of pity that has crossed CATH-ERINE's *face.*

(*Apologetically*) And, of course, perhaps even that would not have made so much difference. Perhaps you feel I cling too much to my past athletic prowess. I feel it myself, sometimes—but the truth is I have not much else to cling to save that and my love for you. The athletic prowess is fading, I'm afraid, with the years and the stiffening of the muscles—but my love for you will never fade.

CATHERINE (*Smiling*): That's very charmingly said, Desmond.

DESMOND: Don't make fun of me, Kate, please. I meant it, every word. (*Clearing his throat*) However, let's take a more mundane approach and examine the facts. Fact one: You don't love me, and never can. Fact two: I love you, always have, and always will. That is the situation—and it is a situation which, after most careful consideration, I am fully prepared to accept. I reached this decision some months ago, but thought at first it would be better to wait until this case, which is so much on all our minds, should be over. Then at lunch today I determined to anticipate the verdict tomorrow, and let you know what was in my mind at once. No matter what you feel or don't feel for me, no matter what you feel for anyone else, I want you to be my wife.

    Pause.

CATHERINE (*At length*): I see. Thank you, Desmond. That makes everything much clearer.

DESMOND: There is much more that I had meant to say, but I shall put
it in a letter.

CATHERINE: Yes, Desmond. Do.

DESMOND: Then I may expect your answer in a few days?

CATHERINE: Yes, Desmond.

DESMOND (*Looking at his watch*): I must get back to Court. (*He collects
his hat, stick, and gloves*) How did you think it went this morning?

CATHERINE: I thought the postmistress restored the Admiralty's case
with that point about Ronnie's looks——

DESMOND: Oh, no, no. Not at all. There is still the overwhelming fact
that she couldn't identify him. What a brilliant cross-examination,
was it not?

CATHERINE: Brilliant.

DESMOND: He is a strange man, Sir Robert. At times, so cold and distant
and—and——

CATHERINE: Fishlike.

DESMOND: Fishlike, exactly. And yet he has a real passion about this
case. A real passion. I happen to know—of course this must on no
account go any further—but I happen to know that he has made a
very, very great personal sacrifice in order to bring it to court.

CATHERINE: Sacrifice? What? Of another brief?

DESMOND: No, no. That is no sacrifice to him. No—he was offered—you
really promise to keep this to yourself?

CATHERINE: My dear Desmond, whatever the Government offered him
can't be as startling as all that; he's in the Opposition.

DESMOND: As it happens it was quite startling, and a most graceful compliment, if I may say so, to his performance as Attorney-General
under the last Government.

CATHERINE: What was he offered, Desmond?

DESMOND: The appointment to Lord Chief Justice. He turned it down
simply in order to be able to carry on with the case of Winslow
versus Rex. Strange are the ways of men are they not? Goodbye, my
dear.

CATHERINE: Goodbye, Desmond.

    Exit DESMOND.

    CATHERINE *turns from the window deep in thought. She has a puz-
zled, strained expression. It does not look as though it were Des-*

mond she was thinking of. ARTHUR *opens dining-room door and peers round.*

ARTHUR: May I come in now?

CATHERINE: Yes, Father. He's gone.

ARTHUR: I'm rather tired of being gazed at from the street while eating my mutton, as though I were an animal at the Zoo.

CATHERINE (*Slowly*): I've been a fool, Father.

ARTHUR: Have you, my dear?

CATHERINE: An utter fool.

Arthur waits for CATHERINE *to make herself plain. She does not do so.*

ARTHUR: In default of further information, I can only repeat, have you, my dear?

CATHERINE: There can be no further information. I'm under a pledge of secrecy.

ARTHUR: Oh. What did Desmond want?

CATHERINE: To marry me.

ARTHUR: I trust the folly you were referring to wasn't your acceptance of him?

CATHERINE (*Smiling*): No, Father. (*She comes and sits on the arm of his chair*) Would it be such folly, though?

ARTHUR: Lunacy.

CATHERINE: Oh, I don't know. He's nice, and he's doing very well as a solicitor.

ARTHUR: Neither very compelling reasons for marrying him.

CATHERINE: Seriously—I shall have to think it over.

ARTHUR: Think it over by all means. But decide against it.

CATHERINE: I'm nearly thirty, you know.

ARTHUR: Thirty isn't the end of life.

CATHERINE: It might be—for an unmarried woman, with not much looks.

ARTHUR: Rubbish.

CATHERINE *shakes her head.*

Better far to live and die an old maid than to marry Desmond.

CATHERINE: Even an old maid must eat. (*Pause.*)

ARTHUR: I am leaving you and your mother everything, you know.

CATHERINE (*Quietly*): Everything?

ARTHUR: There is still a little left. (*Pause*) Did you take my suggestion as regards your Suffrage Association?

CATHERINE: Yes, Father.

ARTHUR: You demanded a salary?

CATHERINE: I asked for one.

ARTHUR: And they're going to give it to you, I trust?

CATHERINE: Yes, Father. Two pounds a week.

ARTHUR (*Angrily*): That's insulting.

CATHERINE: No. It's generous. It's all they can afford. We're not a very rich organization—you know.

ARTHUR: You'll have to think of something else.

CATHERINE: What else? Darning socks? That's about my only other accomplishment.

ARTHUR: There must be something useful you can do.

CATHERINE: You don't think the work I am doing at the W.S.A. is useful?

> ARTHUR *is silent.*

You may be right. But it's the only work I'm fitted for, all the same. (*Pause*) No, Father. The choice is quite simple. Either I marry Desmond and settle down into quite a comfortable and not really useless existence—or I go on for the rest of my life earning two pounds a week in the service of a hopeless cause.

ARTHUR: A hopeless cause? I've never heard you say that before.

CATHERINE: I've never felt it before.

> ARTHUR *is silent.* CATHERINE *leans her head against his chair.*

CATHERINE: John's going to get married next month.

ARTHUR: Did he tell you?

CATHERINE: Yes. He was very apologetic.

ARTHUR: Apologetic!

CATHERINE: He didn't need to be. It's a girl I know slightly. She'll make him a good wife.

ARTHUR: Is he in love with her?

CATHERINE: No more than he was with me. Perhaps, even, a little less.

ARTHUR: Why is he marrying her so soon after—after——

CATHERINE: After jilting me? Because he thinks there's going to be a war. If there is, his regiment will be among the first to go overseas. Besides, his father approves strongly. She's a general's daughter. Very, very suitable.

ARTHUR: Poor Kate!

> *Pause. He takes her hand slowly.*

How I've messed up your life, haven't I?

CATHERINE: No, Father. Any messing-up that's been done has been done by me.

ARTHUR: I'm so sorry, Kate. I'm so sorry.

CATHERINE: Don't be, Father. We both knew what we were doing.

ARTHUR: Did we?

CATHERINE: I think we did.

ARTHUR: Yet our motives seem to have been different all along—yours and mine, Kate? Can we both have been right?

CATHERINE: I believe we can. I believe we have been.

ARTHUR: And yet they've always been so infernally logical, our opponents, haven't they?

CATHERINE: I'm afraid logic has never been on our side.

ARTHUR: Brute stubbornness—a selfish refusal to admit defeat. That's what your mother thinks have been our motives——

CATHERINE: Perhaps she's right. Perhaps that's all they've been.

ARTHUR: But perhaps brute stubbornness isn't such a bad quality in the face of injustice?

CATHERINE: Or in the face of tyranny. (*Pause*) If you could go back, Father, and choose again—would your choice be different?

ARTHUR: Perhaps.

CATHERINE: I don't think so.

ARTHUR: I don't think so, either.

CATHERINE: I still say we both knew what we were doing. And we were right to do it.

> ARTHUR *kisses the top of her head.*

ARTHUR: Dear Kate. Thank you.

> *There is a silence. A newsboy can be heard dimly, shouting from the street outside.*

You aren't going to marry Desmond, are you?

CATHERINE (*With a smile*): In the words of the Prime Minister, Father —wait and see.

> *He squeezes her hand. The newsboy can still be heard—now a little louder.*

ARTHUR: What's that boy shouting, Kate?

CATHERINE: Only—Winslow case—Latest.

ARTHUR: It didn't sound to me like "Latest."

> CATHERINE *gets up to listen at the window. Suddenly we hear it quite plainly: "Winslow Case Result! Winslow Case Result!"*
Result?

CATHERINE: There must be some mistake.

There is another sudden outburst of noise from the hall as the front door is opened. It subsides again. VIOLET *comes in quickly with a broad smile.*

VIOLET: Oh, sir! Oh, sir!

ARTHUR: What's happened?

VIOLET: Oh, Miss Kate, what a shame you missed it! Just after they come back from lunch, and Mrs. Winslow she wasn't there neither, nor Master Ronnie. The cheering and the shouting and the carrying-on—you never heard anything like it in all your life—and Sir Robert standing there at the table with his wig on crooked and the tears running down his face—running down his face they were, and not able to speak because of the noise. Cook and me we did a bit of crying too, we just couldn't help it—you couldn't, you know. Oh, it was lovely! We did enjoy ourselves. And then cook had her hat knocked over her eyes by the man behind who was cheering and waving his arms about something chronic, and shouting about liberty—you would have laughed, miss, to see her, she was that cross—but she didn't mind really, she was only pretending, and we kept on cheering and the judge kept on shouting, but it wasn't any good, because even the jury joined in, and some of them climbed out of the box to shake hands with Sir Robert. And then outside in the street it was just the same—you couldn't move for the crowd, and you'd think they'd all gone mad the way they were carrying on. Some of them were shouting "Good old Winslow!" and singing "For he's a jolly good fellow," and cook had her hat knocked off again. Oh, it was lovely! (*To* ARTHUR) Well, sir, you must be feeling nice and pleased, now it's all over?

ARTHUR: Yes, Violet. I am.

VIOLET: That's right. I always said it would come all right in the end, didn't I?

ARTHUR: Yes. You did.

VIOLET: Two years all but one month it's been, now, since Master Ronnie come back that day. Fancy.

ARTHUR: Yes.

VIOLET: I don't mind telling you, sir, I wondered sometimes whether you and Miss Kate weren't just wasting your time carrying on the way you have all the time. Still—you couldn't have felt that if you'd been in Court today——

She turns to go and stops.

Oh, sir, Mrs. Winslow asked me to remember most particular to pick up some onions from the greengrocer, but——

CATHERINE: That's all right, Violet. Mrs. Winslow is picking them up herself, on her way back——

VIOLET: I see, miss. Poor Madam! What a sell for her when she gets to the Court and finds it's all over. Well, sir—congratulations, I'm sure.

ARTHUR: Thank you, Violet.

Exit VIOLET.

ARTHUR: It would appear, then, that we've won.

CATHERINE: Yes, Father, it would appear that we've won.

She breaks down and cries, her head on her father's lap.

ARTHUR (*Slowly*): I would have liked to have been there.

Pause. Enter VIOLET.

VIOLET (*Announcing*): Sir Robert Morton!

SIR ROBERT *walks calmly and methodically into the room. He looks as spruce and neat as ever, and* VIOLET'S *description of him in Court does not seem to tally with his composed features.*

CATHERINE *jumps up hastily and dabs her eyes.*

Exit VIOLET.

SIR ROBERT: I thought you might like to hear the actual terms of the Attorney-General's statement—— (*He pulls out a scrap of paper*) So I jotted it down for you. (*Reading*) "I say now, on behalf of the Admiralty, that I accept the declaration of Ronald Arthur Winslow that he did not write the name on the postal order, that he did not take it and that he did not cash it, and that consequently he was innocent of the charge which was brought against him two years ago. I make that statement without any reservation of any description, intending it to be a complete acceptance of the boy's statements."

He folds the paper up and hands it to ARTHUR.

ARTHUR: Thank you, sir. It is rather hard for me to find the words I should speak to you.

SIR ROBERT: Pray do not trouble yourself to search for them, sir. Let us take these rather tiresome and conventional expressions of gratitude for granted, shall we? Now, on the question of damages and costs. I fear we shall find the Admiralty rather niggardly. You are likely still to be left considerably out of pocket. However, doubtless we can apply a slight spur to the First Lord's posterior in the House of Commons——

ARTHUR: Please, sir—no more trouble—I beg. Let the matter rest here.

(*He shows the piece of paper*) This is all I have ever asked for.

SIR ROBERT (*Turning to* CATHERINE): A pity you were not in Court, Miss Winslow. The verdict appeared to cause quite a stir.

CATHERINE: So I heard. Why did the Admiralty throw up the case?

SIR ROBERT: It was a foregone conclusion. Once the handwriting expert had been discredited—not for the first time in legal history—I knew we had a sporting chance, and no jury in the world would have convicted on the postmistress's evidence.

CATHERINE: But this morning you seemed so depressed.

SIR ROBERT: Did I? The heat in the courtroom was very trying, you know. Perhaps I was a little fatigued——

    Enter VIOLET.

VIOLET (*To* ARTHUR): Oh, sir, the gentlemen at the front door say please will you make a statement. They say they won't go away until you do.

ARTHUR: Very well, Violet. Thank you.

VIOLET: Yes, sir.

    Exit VIOLET.

ARTHUR: What shall I say?

SIR ROBERT (*Indifferently*): I hardly think it matters. Whatever you say will have little bearing on what they write.

ARTHUR: What shall I say, Kate?

CATHERINE: You'll think of something, Father.

    She begins to wheel his chair towards the door.

ARTHUR (*Sharply*): No! I refuse to meet the Press in this ridiculous chariot. (*To* CATHERINE) Get me my stick!

CATHERINE (*Protestingly*): Father—you know what the doctor——

ARTHUR: Get me my stick!

    CATHERINE, *without more ado, gets his stick for him. She and* SIR ROBERT *help him out of his chair.*

How is this? I am happy to have lived long enough to have seen justice done to my son——

CATHERINE: It's a little gloomy, Father. You're going to live for ages yet——

ARTHUR: Am I? Wait and see. I could say: This victory is not mine. It is the people who have triumphed—as they always will triumph—over despotism. How does that strike you, sir? A trifle pretentious, perhaps.

SIR ROBERT: Perhaps, sir. I should say it, none the less. It will be very popular.

ARTHUR: Hm! Perhaps I had better say what I really feel, which is merely: Thank God we beat 'em.

He goes out. SIR ROBERT *turns abruptly to* CATHERINE.

SIR ROBERT: Miss Winslow—might I be rude enough to ask you for a little of your excellent whisky?

CATHERINE: Of course.

She goes into the dining-room. SIR ROBERT, *left alone, droops his shoulders wearily. He subsides into a chair. When* CATHERINE *comes back with the whisky he straightens his shoulders instinctively, but does not rise.*

SIR ROBERT: That is very kind. Perhaps you would forgive me not getting up? The heat in the courtroom was really so infernal.

He takes the glass from her and drains it quickly. She notices his hand is trembling slightly.

CATHERINE: Are you feeling all right, Sir Robert?

SIR ROBERT: Just a slight nervous reaction—that's all. Besides, I have not been feeling myself all day. I told the Judge so, this morning, if you remember, but I doubt if he believed me. He thought it was a trick. What suspicious minds people have, have they not?

CATHERINE: Yes.

SIR ROBERT (*Handing her back the glass*): Thank you.

CATHERINE *puts the glass down, then turns slowly back to face him as if nerving herself for an ordeal.*

CATHERINE: Sir Robert—I'm afraid I have a confession and an apology to make to you.

SIR ROBERT (*Sensing what is coming*): Dear lady—I am sure the one is rash and the other superfluous. I would far rather hear neither——

CATHERINE (*With a smile*): I am afraid you must. This is probably the last time I shall see you and it is a better penance for me to say this than to write it. I have entirely misjudged your attitude to this case, and if in doing so I have ever seemed to you either rude or ungrateful, I am sincerely and humbly sorry.

SIR ROBERT (*Indifferently*): My dear Miss Winslow, you have never seemed to me either rude or ungrateful. And my attitude to this case has been the same as yours—a determination to win at all costs. Only —when you talk of gratitude—you must remember that those costs were not mine, but yours.

CATHERINE: Weren't they also yours, Sir Robert?

SIR ROBERT: I beg your pardon?

CATHERINE: Haven't you too made a certain sacrifice for the case?

Pause.

SIR ROBERT: The robes of that office would not have suited me.

CATHERINE: Wouldn't they?

SIR ROBERT (*With venom*): And what is more, I fully intend to have Curry expelled from the Law Society.

CATHERINE: Please don't. He did me a great service by telling me.

SIR ROBERT: I must ask you never to divulge it to another living soul, and even to forget it yourself.

CATHERINE: I shall never divulge it. I'm afraid I can't promise to forget it myself.

SIR ROBERT: Very well. If you choose to endow an unimportant incident with a romantic significance, you are perfectly at liberty to do so. I must go. (*He gets up.*)

CATHERINE: Why are you always at such pains to prevent people knowing the truth about you, Sir Robert?

SIR ROBERT: Am I, indeed?

CATHERINE: You know you are. Why?

SIR ROBERT: Perhaps because *I* do not know the truth about myself.

CATHERINE: That is no answer.

SIR ROBERT: My dear Miss Winslow, are you cross-examining me?

CATHERINE: On this point, yes. Why are you so ashamed of your emotions?

SIR ROBERT: Because, as a lawyer, I must necessarily distrust them.

CATHERINE: Why?

SIR ROBERT: To fight a case on emotional grounds, Miss Winslow, is the surest way of losing it. Emotions muddy the issue. Cold, clear logic—and buckets of it—should be the lawyer's only equipment.

CATHERINE: Was it cold, clear logic that made you weep today at the verdict?

Pause.

SIR ROBERT: Your maid, of course, told you that? It doesn't matter. It will be in the papers tomorrow, anyway. (*Fiercely*) Very well, then, if you must have it, here it is. I wept today because right had been done.

CATHERINE: Not justice?

SIR ROBERT: No. Not justice. Right. It is easy to do justice—very hard to do right. Unfortunately, while the appeal of justice is intellectual, the appeal of right appears for some odd reason to induce tears in court. That is my answer and my excuse. And now, may I leave the witness box?

CATHERINE: No. One last question. How can you reconcile your support of Winslow against the Crown with your political beliefs?

SIR ROBERT: Very easily. No one party has a monopoly of concern for individual liberty. On that issue all parties are united.

CATHERINE: I don't think so.

SIR ROBERT: You don't?

CATHERINE: No. Not all parties. Only some people from all parties.

SIR ROBERT: That is a wise remark. We can only hope, then, that those same people will always prove enough people. You would make a good advocate.

CATHERINE: Would I?

SIR ROBERT: Yes. (*Playfully*) Why do you not canalize your feministic impulses towards the law courts, Miss Winslow, and abandon the lost cause of women's suffrage?

CATHERINE: Because I don't believe it *is* a lost cause.

SIR ROBERT: No? Are you going to continue to pursue it?

CATHERINE: Certainly.

SIR ROBERT: You will be wasting your time.

CATHERINE: I don't think so.

SIR ROBERT: A pity. In the House of Commons in days to come I shall make a point of looking up at the Gallery in the hope of catching a glimpse of you in that provocative hat.

> RONNIE *comes in. He is fifteen now, and there are distinct signs of an incipient man-about-town. He is very smartly dressed in lounge suit and homburg hat.*

RONNIE: I say, Sir Robert, I'm awfully sorry. I didn't know anything was going to happen.

SIR ROBERT: Where were you?

RONNIE: At the pictures.

SIR ROBERT: Pictures? What is that?

CATHERINE: Cinematograph show.

RONNIE: I'm most awfully sorry. I say—we won, didn't we?

SIR ROBERT: Yes. We won. Goodbye, Miss Winslow. Shall I see you in the House then, one day?

CATHERINE (*With a smile*): Yes, Sir Robert. One day. But not in the Gallery. Across the floor.

SIR ROBERT (*With a faint smile*): Perhaps. Goodbye. (*He turns to go.*)

CURTAIN

Lewis Carroll

·

THE TRIAL OF THE KNAVE OF HEARTS

from *Alice's Adventures in Wonderland*

WHO STOLE THE TARTS?

The King and Queen of Hearts were seated on their throne when they arrived, with a great crowd assembled about them—all sorts of little birds and beasts, as well as the whole pack of cards: the Knave was standing before them, in chains, with a soldier on each side to guard him; and near the King was the White Rabbit, with a trumpet in one hand, and a scroll of parchment in the other. In the very middle of the court was a table, with a large dish of tarts upon it: they looked so good, that it made Alice quite hungry to look at them—"I wish they'd get the trial done," she thought, "and hand round the refreshments!" But there seemed to be no chance of this, so she began looking about her, to pass away the time.

Alice had never been in a court of justice before, but she had read about them in books, and she was quite pleased to find that she knew the name of nearly everything there. "That's the judge," she said to herself, "because of his great wig."

The judge, by the way, was the King; and as he wore his crown over the wig, he did not look at all comfortable, and it was certainly not becoming.

"And that's the jury-box," thought Alice, "and those twelve creatures," (she was obliged to say "creatures," you see, because some of them were animals, and some were birds,) "I suppose they are the ju-

133

rors." She said this last word two or three times over to herself, being rather proud of it: for she thought, and rightly too, that very few little girls of her age knew the meaning of it at all. However, "jurymen" would have done just as well.

The twelve jurors were all writing very busily on slates. "What are they all doing?" Alice whispered to the Gryphon. "They can't have anything to put down yet, before the trial's begun."

"They're putting down their names," the Gryphon whispered in reply, "for fear they should forget them before the end of the trial."

"Stupid things!" Alice began in a loud, indignant voice, but she stopped hastily, for the White Rabbit cried out "Silence in the court!" and the King put on his spectacles and looked anxiously round, to see who was talking.

Alice could see, as well as if she were looking over their shoulders, that all the jurors were writing down "stupid things!" on their slates, and she could even make out that one of them didn't know how to spell "stupid," and that he had to ask his neighbor to tell him. "A nice muddle their slates will be in before the trial's over!" thought Alice.

One of the jurors had a pencil that squeaked. This, of course, Alice could *not* stand, and she went round the court and got behind him, and very soon found an opportunity of taking it away. She did it so quickly that the poor little juror (it was Bill, the Lizard) could not make out at all what had become of it; so, after hunting all about for it, he was obliged to write with one finger for the rest of the day; and this was of very little use, as it left no mark on the slate.

"Herald, read the accusation!" said the King.

On this the White Rabbit blew three blasts on the trumpet, and then unrolled the parchment scroll, and read as follows:

> "The Queen of Hearts, she made some tarts,
>   All on a summer day:
> The Knave of Hearts, he stole those tarts,
>   And took them quite away!"

"Consider your verdict," the King said to the jury.

"Not yet, not yet!" the Rabbit hastily interrupted. "There's a great deal to come before that!"

"Call the first witness," said the King; and the Rabbit blew three blasts on the trumpet, and called out "First witness!"

The first witness was the Hatter. He came in with a teacup in one hand and a piece of bread-and-butter in the other. "I beg your pardon, your Majesty," he began, "for bringing these in, but I hadn't quite finished my tea when I was sent for."

"You ought to have finished," said the King. "When did you begin?"

The Hatter looked at the March Hare, who had followed him into the court, arm-in-arm with the Dormouse. "Fourteenth of March, I *think* it was," he said.

"Fifteenth," said the March Hare.

"Sixteenth," said the Dormouse.

"Write that down," the King said to the jury, and the jury eagerly wrote down all three dates on their slates, and then added them up, and reduced the answer to shillings and pence.

"Take off your hat," the King said to the Hatter.

"It isn't mine," said the Hatter.

"Stolen!" the King exclaimed, turning to the jury, who instantly made a memorandum of the fact.

"I keep them to sell," the Hatter added as an explanation: "I've none of my own. I'm a hatter."

Here the Queen put on her spectacles, and began staring hard at the Hatter, who turned pale and fidgeted.

"Give your evidence," said the King; "and don't be nervous, or I'll have you executed on the spot."

This did not seem to encourage the witness at all: he kept shifting from one foot to the other, looking uneasily at the Queen, and in his confusion he bit a large piece out of his teacup instead of the bread-and-butter.

Just at this moment Alice felt a very curious sensation, which puzzled her a good deal until she made out what it was: she was beginning to grow larger again, and she thought at first she would get up and leave the court; but on second thought she decided to remain where she was as long as there was room for her.

"I wish you wouldn't squeeze so," said the Dormouse, who was sitting next to her. "I can hardly breathe."

"I can't help it," said Alice very meekly: "I'm growing."

"You've no right to grow *here*," said the Dormouse.

"Don't talk nonsense," said Alice more boldly: "you know you're growing too."

"Yes, but *I* grow at a reasonable pace," said the Dormouse; "not in that ridiculous fashion." And he got up very sulkily and crossed over to the other side of the court.

All this time the Queen had never left off staring at the Hatter, and, just as the Dormouse crossed the court, she said to one of the officers of the court, "Bring me the list of the singers in the last concert!" on which the wretched Hatter trembled so, that he shook off both his shoes.

"Give your evidence," the King repeated angrily, "or I'll have you executed, whether you're nervous or not."

"I'm a poor man, your Majesty," the Hatter began, in a trembling voice, "—and I hadn't begun my tea—not above a week or so—and what with the bread-and-butter getting so thin—and the twinkling of the tea——"

"The twinkling of *what?*" said the King.

"It *began* with the tea," the Hatter replied.

"Of course twinkling *begins* with a T!" said the King sharply. "Do you take me for a dunce? Go on!"

"I'm a poor man," the Hatter went on, "and most things twinkled after that—only the March Hare said——"

"I didn't!" the March Hare interrupted in a great hurry.

"You did!" said the Hatter.

"I deny it!" said the March Hare.

"He denies it," said the King: "leave out that part."

"Well, at any rate, the Dormouse said——" the Hatter went on, looking anxiously round to see if he would deny it too: but the Dormouse denied nothing, being fast asleep.

"After that," continued the Hatter, "I cut some more bread-and-butter——"

"But what did the Dormouse say?" one of the jury asked.

"That I can't remember," said the Hatter.

"You *must* remember," remarked the King, "or I'll have you executed."

The miserable Hatter dropped his teacup and bread-and-butter, and went down on one knee. "I'm a poor man, your Majesty," he began.

"You're a *very* poor *speaker,*" said the King.

Here one of the guinea-pigs cheered, and was immediately suppressed by the officers of the court. (As that is rather a hard word, I will just explain to you how it was done. They had a large canvas bag, which tied up at the mouth with strings: into this they slipped the guinea-pig, head first, and then sat upon it.)

"I'm glad I've seen that done," thought Alice. "I've so often read in the newspapers, at the end of trials, 'There was some attempt at applause, which was immediately suppressed by the officers of the court,' and I never understood what it meant till now."

"If that's all you know about it, you may stand down," continued the King.

"I can't go no lower," said the Hatter: "I'm on the floor, as it is."

"Then you may *sit* down," the King replied.

Here the other guinea-pig cheered, and was suppressed.

"Come, that finishes the guinea-pigs!" thought Alice. "Now we shall get on better."

"I'd rather finish my tea," said the Hatter, with an anxious look at the Queen, who was reading the list of singers.

"You may go," said the King; and the Hatter hurriedly left the court, without even waiting to put his shoes on.

"—and just take his head off outside," the Queen added to one of the officers; but the Hatter was out of sight before the officer could get to the door.

"Call the next witness!" said the King.

The next witness was the Duchess's cook. She carried the pepper-box in her hand, and Alice guessed who it was, even before she got into the court, by the way the people near the door began sneezing all at once.

"Give your evidence," said the King.

"Sha'n't," said the cook.

The King looked anxiously at the White Rabbit, who said in a low voice, "Your Majesty must cross-examine *this* witness."

"Well, if I must, I must," the King said with a melancholy air, and, after folding his arms and frowning at the cook till his eyes were nearly out of sight, he said in a deep voice, "What are tarts made of?"

"Pepper, mostly," said the cook.

"Treacle," said a sleepy voice behind her.

"Collar that Dormouse," the Queen shrieked out. "Behead that Dormouse! Turn that Dormouse out of court! Suppress him! Pinch him! Off with his whiskers."

For some minutes the whole court was in confusion, getting the Dormouse turned out, and, by the time they had settled down again, the cook had disappeared.

"Never mind!" said the King, with an air of great relief. "Call the next witness." And he added in an undertone to the Queen, "Really, my dear, *you* must cross-examine the next witness. It quite makes my forehead ache!"

Alice watched the White Rabbit as he fumbled over the list, feeling very curious to see what the next witness would be like, "—for they haven't got much evidence *yet,*" she said to herself. Imagine her surprise, when the White Rabbit read out, at the top of his shrill little voice, the name "Alice!"

ALICE'S EVIDENCE

"Here!" cried Alice, quite forgetting in the flurry of the moment how large she had grown in the last few minutes, and she jumped up in such a hurry that she tipped over the jury-box with the edge of her skirt, upsetting all the jurymen on to the heads of the crowd below, and there they lay sprawling about, reminding her very much of a globe of goldfish she had accidentally upset the week before.

"Oh, I *beg* your pardon!" she exclaimed in a tone of great dismay, and began picking them up again as quickly as she could, for the accident of the goldfish kept running in her head, and she had a vague sort of idea that they must be collected at once and put back into the jury-box, or they would die.

"The trial cannot proceed," said the King in a very grave voice, "Until all the jurymen are back in their proper places—*all,*" he repeated with great emphasis, looking hard at Alice as he said so.

Alice looked at the jury-box, and saw that, in her haste, she had put the Lizard in head downwards, and the poor little thing was waving its tail about in a melancholy way, being quite unable to move. She soon got it out again, and put it right; "not that it signifies much," she said to herself; "I should think it would be *quite* as much use in the trial one way up as the other."

As soon as the jury had a little recovered from the shock of being upset, and their slates and pencils had been found and handed back to them, they set to work very diligently to write out a history of the accident, all except the Lizard, who seemed too much overcome to do anything but sit with its mouth open, gazing up into the roof of the court.

"What do you know about this business?" the King said to Alice.

"Nothing," said Alice.

"Nothing *whatever?*" persisted the King.

"Nothing whatever," said Alice.

"That's very important," the King said, turning to the jury. They were just beginning to write this down on their slates, when the White Rabbit interrupted: *"Un*important, your Majesty means, of course," he said in a very respectful tone, but frowning and making faces at him as he spoke.

*"Un*important, of course, I meant," the King hastily said, and went on himself in an undertone, "important—unimportant—unimportant—important——" as if he were trying which word sounded best.

Some of the jury wrote it down "important," and some "unimportant." Alice could see this, as she was near enough to look over their slates; "but it doesn't matter a bit," she thought to herself.

At this moment the King, who had been for some time busily writing in his notebook, called out "Silence!" and read out from his book, "Rule Forty-two. *All persons more than a mile high to leave the court.*"

Everybody looked at Alice.

"I'm not a mile high," said Alice.

"You are," said the King.

"Nearly two miles high," added the Queen.

"Well, I sha'n't go, at any rate," said Alice: "besides, that's not a regular rule: you invented it just now."

"It's the oldest rule in the book," said the King.

"Then it ought to be Number One," said Alice.

The King turned pale, and shut his notebook hastily. "Consider your verdict," he said to the jury, in a low trembling voice.

"There's more evidence to come yet, please your Majesty," said the White Rabbit, jumping up in a great hurry: "this paper has just been picked up."

"What's in it?" said the Queen.

"I haven't opened it yet," said the White Rabbit, "but it seems to be a letter, written by the prisoner to—to somebody."

"It must have been that," said the King, "unless it was written to nobody, which isn't usual, you know."

"Who is it directed to?" said one of the jurymen.

"It isn't directed at all," said the White Rabbit; "in fact, there's nothing written on the *outside.*" He unfolded the paper as he spoke, and added, "It isn't a letter after all: it's a set of verses."

"Are they in the prisoner's handwriting?" asked another of the jury-men.

"No, they're not," said the White Rabbit, "and that's the queerest thing about it." (The jury all looked puzzled.)

"He must have imitated somebody else's hand," said the King. (The jury all brightened up again.)

"Please your Majesty," said the Knave, "I didn't write it, and they can't prove I did: there's no name signed at the end."

"If you didn't sign it," said the King, "that only makes the matter worse. You *must* have meant some mischief, or else you'd have signed your name like an honest man."

There was a general clapping of hands at this: it was the first really clever thing the King had said that day.

"That *proves* his guilt, of course," said the Queen: "so, off with——"

"It doesn't prove anything of the sort!" said Alice. "Why, you don't even know what they're about!"

"Read them," said the King.

The White Rabbit put on his spectacles. "Where shall I begin, please your Majesty?" he asked.

"Begin at the beginning," the King said gravely, "and go on till you come to the end: then stop."

There was dead silence in the court, whilst the While Rabbit read out these verses—

> "They told me you had been to her,
>   And mentioned me to him:
> She gave me a good character,
>   But said I could not swim.
>
>
> He sent them word I had not gone,
>   (We know it to be true):
> If she should push the matter on,
>   What would become of you?
>
>
> I gave her one, they gave him two,
>   You gave us three or more;
> They all returned from him to you,
>   Though they were mine before.

If I or she should chance to be
    Involved in this affair,
He trusts to you to set them free,
    Exactly as we were.

My notion was that you had been
    (Before she had this fit)
An obstacle that came between
    Him, and ourselves, and it.

Don't let him know she liked them best,
    For this must ever be
A secret, kept from all the rest,
    Between yourself and me."

"That's the most important piece of evidence we've heard yet," said the King, rubbing his hands; "so now let the jury——"

"If any of them can explain it," said Alice, (she had grown so large in the last few minutes that she wasn't a bit afraid of interrupting him), "I'll give him sixpence. *I* don't believe there's an atom of meaning in it."

The jury all wrote down on their slates, "*She* doesn't believe there's an atom of meaning in it," but none of them attempted to explain the paper.

"If there's no meaning in it," said the King, "that saves a world of trouble, you know, as we needn't try to find any. And yet I don't know," he went on, spreading out the verses on his knee, and looking at them with one eye; "I seem to see some meaning in them after all. '——*said I could not swim*—' you can't swim can you?" he added, turning to the Knave.

The Knave shook his head sadly. "Do I look it?" he said. (Which he certainly did *not,* being made entirely of cardboard.)

"All right, so far," said the King, as he went on muttering over the verses to himself: " '*We know it to be true*—' that's the jury, of course —'*If she should push the matter on*'—that must be the Queen—'*What would become of you?*'—What, indeed!—'*I gave her one, they gave him two*—' why, that must be what he did with the tarts, you know——"

"But it goes on '*they all returned from him to you,*' " said Alice.

"Why, there they are!" said the King triumphantly, pointing to the tarts on the table. "Nothing can be clearer than *that*. Then again— *'before she had this fit—'* you never had *fits,* my dear, I think?" he said to the Queen.

"Never!" said the Queen furiously, throwing an inkstand at the Lizard as she spoke. (The unfortunate little Bill had left off writing on his slate with one finger, as he found it made no mark; but he now hastily began again, using the ink, that was trickling down his face, as long as it lasted.)

"Then the words don't *fit* you," said the King, looking round the court with a smile. There was a dead silence.

"It's a pun!" the King added in an angry tone, and everybody laughed.

"Let the jury consider their verdict," the King said, for about the twentieth time that day.

"No, no!" said the Queen. "Sentence first—verdict afterwards."

"Stuff and nonsense!" said Alice loudly. "The idea of having the sentence first!"

"Hold your tongue!" said the Queen, turning purple.

"I won't!" said Alice.

"Off with her head!" the Queen shouted at the top of her voice. Nobody moved.

"Who cares for *you?*" said Alice (she had grown to her full size by this time). "You're nothing but a pack of cards!"

At this the whole pack rose up into the air, and came flying down upon her: she gave a little scream, half of fright and half of anger, and tried to beat them off, and found herself lying on the bank, with her head in the lap of her sister, who was gently brushing away some dead leaves that had fluttered down from the trees upon her face.

"Wake up, Alice dear!" said her sister. "Why, what a long sleep you've had!"

"Oh, I've had such a curious dream!" said Alice, and she told her sister, as well as she could remember them, all these strange Adventures of hers that you have just been reading about; and when she had finished, her sister kissed her, and said "It *was* a curious dream, dear, certainly: but now run in to your tea: it's getting late." So Alice got up and ran off, thinking while she ran, as well she might, what a wonderful dream it had been.

Guy de Maupassant

.
.

HIPPOLYTE'S CLAIM

The fat Justice of the Peace, with one eye closed and the other half-open, is listening with evident displeasure to the plaintiffs. Once in a while he gives a sort of grunt that foretells his opinion, and in a thin voice resembling that of a child, he interrupts them to ask questions. He has just rendered judgment in the case of Monsieur Joly against Monsieur Petitpas, the contestants having come to court on account of the boundary of a field which had been accidentally over-stepped by Monsieur Petitpas's farmhand, while the latter was plowing.

Now he calls the case of Hippolyte Lacour, vestryman and ironmonger, against Madame Céleste Césarine Luneau, widow of Anthime Isidore Luneau.

Hippolyte Lacour is forty-five years old; he is tall and gaunt, with a clean-shaven face and long hair, and he speaks in a slow, singsong voice.

Madame Luneau appears to be about forty years of age. She is built like a prize-fighter, and her plain dress is stretched tightly over her portly form. Her enormous hips hold up her overflowing bosom in front, while in the back they support the great rolls of flesh that cover her shoulders. Her face, with strongly cut features, rests on a short, fat neck, and her strong voice is pitched at a key that makes the windows and the eardrums of her auditors vibrate. She is about to become a mother and her huge form protrudes like a mountain.

The witnesses for the defense are waiting to be called.

143

HIS HONOR Begins: Hippolyte Lacour, state your complaint.

THE PLAINTIFF Speaks: Your Honor, it will be nine months on Saint-Michael's day that the defendant came to me one evening, after I had rung the Angelus, and began an explanation relating to her barrenness.

THE JUSTICE OF THE PEACE: Kindly be more explicit.

HIPPOLYTE: Very well, your Honor. Well, she wanted to have a child and desired my participation. I didn't raise any objection, and she promised to give me one hundred francs. The thing was all cut and dried, and now she refuses to acknowledge my claim, which I renew before your Honor.

THE JUSTICE: I don't understand in the least. You say that she wanted a child! What kind of child! Did she wish to adopt one?

HIPPOLYTE: No, your Honor, she wanted a new one.

THE JUSTICE: What do you mean by a new one?

HIPPOLYTE: I mean a newborn child, one that we were to beget as if we were man and wife.

THE JUSTICE: You astonish me. To what end did she make this abnormal proposition?

HIPPOLYTE: Your Honor, at first I could not make out her reasons, and was taken a little aback. But as I don't do anything without thoroughly investigating beforehand, I called on her to explain matters to me, which she did. You see, her husband, Anthime Isidore, whom you knew as well as you know me, had died the week before, and his money reverted to his family. This greatly displeased her on account of the loss it meant, so she went to a lawyer who told her all about what might happen if a child should be born to her after ten months. I mean by this that if she gave birth to a child inside of the ten months following the death of Anthime Isidore, her offspring would be considered legitimate and would entitle her to the inheritance. She made up her mind at once to run the risk, and came to me after church, as I have already had the honor of telling you, seeing that I am the father of eight living children, the eldest of whom is a grocer in Caen, department of Calvados, and legitimately married to Victoire-Elisabeth Rabou—

THE JUSTICE: These details are superfluous. Go back to the subject.

HIPPOLYTE: I am getting there, your Honor. So she said to me: "If you succeed, I'll give you one hundred francs as soon as I get the doctor's report." Well, your Honor, I made ready to give entire satisfaction, and after eight weeks or so I learned with pleasure that I had succeeded. But when I asked her for the hundred francs she refused to pay me. I renewed my demands several times, never getting so much as a pin. She even called me a liar and a weakling, a libel which can be destroyed by glancing at her.

THE JUSTICE: Defendant, what have you to say?

MADAME LUNEAU: Your Honor, I say that this man is a liar.

THE JUSTICE: How can you prove this assertion?

MADAME LUNEAU (*red in the face, choking and stammering*): How can I prove it? What proofs have I? I haven't a single real proof that the child isn't his. But, your Honor, it isn't his, I swear it on the head of my dead husband.

THE JUSTICE: Well, whose is it, then?

MADAME LUNEAU (stammering with rage): How do I know? How do— do I know? Everybody's, I suppose. Here are my witnesses, your Honor, they're all here, the six of them. Now make them testify, make them testify. They'll tell—

THE JUSTICE: Collect yourself, Madame Luneau, collect yourself and reply calmly to my questions. What reasons have you to doubt that this man is the father of the child you are carrying?

MADAME LUNEAU: What reasons? I have a hundred to one, a hundred? No, two hundred, five hundred, ten thousand, a million and more reasons to believe he isn't. After the proposal I made to him, with the promise of one hundred francs, didn't I learn that he wasn't the father of his own children, your Honor, not the father of one of 'em?

HIPPOLYTE (calmly): That's a lie.

MADAME LUNEAU (exasperated): A lie! A lie, is it? I guess his wife has been seen by everybody around here. Call my witnesses, your Honor, and make them testify.

HIPPOLYTE (calmly): It's a lie.

MADAME LUNEAU: It's a lie, is it? How about the red-haired ones, then? I suppose they're yours, too?

THE JUSTICE: Kindly refrain from personal attacks, or I shall be obliged to call you to order.

MADAME LUNEAU: Well, your Honor, I had my doubts about him, and said I to myself, two precautions are better than one, so I explained my position to Césaire Lepic, the witness who is present. Says he to me, "At your disposal, Madame Luneau," and he lent me his assistance in case Hippolyte should turn out to be unreliable. But as soon as the other witnesses heard that I wanted to make sure against any disappointment, I could have had more than a hundred, your Honor, if I had wanted them. That tall one over there, Lucas Chandelier, swore at the time that I oughtn't to give Hippolyte Lacour a cent, for he hadn't done more than the rest of them who had obliged me for nothing.

HIPPOLYTE: What did you promise for? I expected the money, your Honor. No mistake with me—a promise given, a promise kept.

MADAME LUNEAU (beside herself): One hundred francs! One hundred francs! One hundred francs for that, you liar! The others there didn't ask a red cent! Look at 'em, all six of 'em! Make them testify, your Honor, they'll tell sure. (To Hippolyte.) Look at 'em, you liar! they're as good as you. They're only six, but I could have had one, two, three, five hundred of 'em for nothing, too, you robber!

HIPPOLYTE: Well, even if you'd had a hundred thousand—

MADAME LUNEAU: I could, if I'd wanted 'em.

HIPPOLYTE: I did my duty, so it doesn't change matters.

MADAME LUNEAU (slapping her protuberant form with both hands): Then prove that it's you that did it, prove it, you robber! I defy you to prove it!

HIPPOLYTE (calmly): Maybe I didn't do any more than anybody else. But you promised me a hundred francs for it. What did you ask the others for, afterward? You had no right to. I guess I could have done it alone.

MADAME LUNEAU: It is not true, robber! Call my witnesses, your Honor; they'll answer, sure.

The Justice called the witnesses in behalf of the defense. Six red, awkward individuals appeared.

THE JUSTICE: Lucas Chandelier, have you any reason to suppose that you are the father of the child Madame Luneau is carrying?

LUCAS CHANDELIER: Yes, sir.

THE JUSTICE: Célestin-Pierre Sidoine, have you any reason to suppose that you are the father of the child Madame Luneau is carrying?

CÉLESTIN-PIERRE SIDOINE: Yes, sir.

The four other witnesses testified to the same effect.

The Justice, after a pause, pronounced judgment: Whereas the plaintiff has reasons to believe himself the father of the child which Madame Luneau desired, Lucas Chandelier, Célestin-Pierre Sidoine, and others, have similar, if not conclusive reasons to lay claim to the child.

But whereas Mme. Luneau had previously asked the assistance of Hippolyte Lacour for a duly stated consideration:

And whereas one may not question the absolute good faith of Hippolyte Lacour, though it is questionable whether he had a perfect right to enter such an agreement, seeing that the plaintiff is married, and compelled by law to remain faithful to his lawful spouse:

Therefore the Court condemns Madame Luneau to pay an indemnity of twenty-five francs to Hippolyte Lacour for loss of time and unjustifiable abduction.

Guy de Maupassant

:

THE ASSASSIN

The guilty man was defended by a very young lawyer, a beginner, who spoke thus:

"The facts are undeniable, gentlemen of the jury. My client, an honest man, an irreproachable employee, gentle and timid, assassinated his employer in a moment of anger which seems to me incomprehensible. If you will allow me, I would like to look into the psychology of the crime, so to speak, without wasting any time or attempting to excuse anything. We shall then be able to judge better.

"John Nicholas Lougère is the son of very honorable people, who made of him a simple, respectful man.

"That is his crime: respect! It is a sentiment, gentlemen, which we of today no longer know, of which the name alone seems to exist while its power has disappeared. It is necessary to enter certain old, modest families to find this severe tradition, this religion of a thing or of a man, this sentiment where belief takes on a sacred character, this faith which doubts not, nor smiles, nor entertains a suspicion.

"One cannot be an honest man, a truly honest man in the full force of the term, and be respectful. The man who respects has his eyes closed. He believes. We others, whose eyes are wide open upon the world, who live here in this hall of justice, this purger of society, where all infamy runs aground, we others who are the confidants of shame, the devoted defenders of all human meanness, the support, not to say the supporters, of male and female sharpers, from a prince to a tramp,

148

we who welcome with indulgence, with complacence, with a smiling benevolence all the guilty and defend them before you, we who, if we truly love our profession, measure our legal sympathy by the size of the crime, we could never have a respectful soul. We see too much of this river of corruption, which catches the chiefs of power as well as the lowest scamp; we know too much of how it gives and takes and sells itself. Places, offices, honors brutally exchanged for a little money, or skillfully exchanged for titles and interests in industrial enterprises, or sometimes, simply for the kiss of a woman.

"Our duty and our profession force us to be ignorant of nothing, to suspect everybody, because everybody is doubtful; and we are taken by surprise when we find ourselves face to face with a man, like the assassin seated before you, who possesses the religion of respect to such a degree that he will become a martyr for it.

"We others, gentlemen, have a sense of honor, a certain need of propriety, from a disgust of baseness, from a sentiment of personal dignity and pride; but we do not carry at the bottom of our hearts the blind, inborn, brutal faith of this man.

"Let me tell you the story of his life:

"He was brought up, like many another child, to separate all human acts into two parts: the good and the bad. He was shown the good with an irresistible authority which made him only distinguish the bad, as we distinguish day and night. His father did not belong to the superior race of minds who, looking from a height, see the sources of belief and recognize the social necessities born of these distinctions.

"He grew up, religious and confident, enthusiastic and limited. At twenty-two he married. His wife was a cousin, brought up as he was, simple and pure as he was. His was the inestimable privilege of having for a companion an honest woman with a true heart, the rarest and most respectable thing in the world. He had for his mother that veneration which surrounds mothers in patriarchal families, that profound respect which is reserved for divinities. This religion he reflected somewhat upon his wife, and it became scarcely less as conjugal familiarity increased. He lived in absolute ignorance of double dealing, in a state of constant uprightness and tranquil happiness which made him a being apart from the world. Deceiving no one he had never a suspicion that any one would deceive him.

"Some time before his marriage, he had become cashier in the office of Mr. Langlais, the man who was lately assassinated by him.

"We know, gentlemen of the jury, by the testimony of Mrs. Langlais and of her brother, Mr. Perthuis, a partner of her husband, of all the family and of all the higher employees of the bank, that Lougère was a model employee, upright, submissive, gentle, prompt, and deferential toward his superiors. They treated him with the consideration due to his exemplary conduct. He was accustomed to this homage and to a kind of respect shown to Mrs. Lougère, whose worthiness was upon all lips.

"But she died of typhoid fever in a few days' time. He assuredly felt a profound grief, but the cold, calm grief of a methodical heart. Only from his pallor and from a change in his looks was one able to judge how deeply he had been wounded.

"Then, gentlemen, the most natural thing in the world happened.

"This man had been married ten years. For ten years he had been accustomed to feel the presence of a woman near him always. He was habituated to her care, her familiar voice upon his return, the good night at evening, the cheerful greeting of the morning, the gentle rustle of the dress so dear to the feminine heart, to that caress, at once lover-like and maternal, which renders life pleasant, to that loved presence that made the hours move less slowly. He was also accustomed to being spoiled at table, perhaps, and to all those attentions which become, little by little, so indispensable.

"He could no longer live alone. Then, to pass the interminable evenings, he got into the habit of spending an hour or two in a neighboring wine shop. He would drink a glass and sit there motionless, following, with heedless eye, the billiard balls running after one another under the smoke of the pipes, listening to, without hearing, the discussion of the players, the disputes of his neighbors over politics, and the sound of laughter that sometimes went up from the other end of the room, from some unusual joke. He often ended by going to sleep, from sheer lassitude and weariness. But, at the bottom of his heart and of his flesh, there was the irresistible need of a woman's heart and flesh; and, without thinking, he approached each evening a little nearer to the desk where the cashier, a pretty blonde, sat, attracted to her unconquerably, because she was a woman.

"At first they chatted, and he got into the habit, so pleasant for him, of passing the evening by her side. She was gracious and kind, as one learns in this occupation to smile, and she amused herself by making him renew his order as often as possible, which makes business good.

"But each day Lougère was becoming more and more attached to this woman whom he did not know, whose whole existence he was ignorant of, and whom he loved only because he was in the way of seeing nobody else.

"The little creature was crafty, and soon perceived that she could reap some benefit from this guileless man; she then sought out the best means of exploiting him. The most effective, surely, was to marry him.

"This she accomplished without difficulty.

"Need I tell you, gentlemen of the jury, that the conduct of this girl had been most irregular and that marriage, far from putting a check to her flight, seemed on the contrary to render it more shameless?

"From the natural sport of feminine astuteness, she seemed to take pleasure in deceiving this honest man with all the employees of his office. I said with all. We have letters, gentlemen. There was soon a public scandal, of which the husband alone, as usual, was the only one ignorant.

"Finally, this wretch, with an interest easy to understand, seduced the son of the proprietor, a young man nineteen years old, upon whose mind and judgment she had a deplorable influence. Mr. Langlais, whose eyes had been closed up to that time, through friendship for his employee, resented having his son in the hands, I should say in the arms of this dangerous woman, and was legitimately angry.

"He made the mistake of calling Lougère to him on the spot and of speaking to him of his paternal indignation.

"There remains nothing more for me to say, gentlemen, except to read to you the recital of the crime, made by the lips of the dying man, and submitted as evidence. It says:

" 'I learned that my son had given to this woman, that same night, ten thousand francs, and my anger was stronger on that account. Certainly, I never suspected the honorableness of Lougère, but a certain kind of blindness is more dangerous than positive faults. And so I had him come to me and told him that I should be obliged to deprive myself of his services.

" 'He remained standing before me, terrified, and not comprehending. He ended by demanding, rather excitedly, some explanation. I refused to give him any, affirming that my reasons were wholly personal. He believed then that I suspected him of indelicacy and, very pale, besought, implored me to explain. Held by this idea, he was strong and began to talk loud. As I kept silent, he abused and insulted me, until he arrived at such a degree of exasperation that I was fearful of results.

" 'Then, suddenly, upon a wounding word that struck upon a full heart, I threw the whole truth in his face.

" 'He stood still some seconds, looking at me with haggard eyes. Then I saw him take from my desk the long shears, which I use for making margins to certain registers, I saw him fall upon me with uplifted arm, and I felt something enter my throat just above the breast, without noticing any pain.'

"This, gentleman of the jury, is the simple recital of this murder. What more can be said for his defense? He respected his second wife with blindness because he respected his first with reason."

After a short deliberation, the prisoner was acquitted.

Jack London

.

THE BENEFIT OF THE DOUBT

Carter Watson, a current magazine under his arm, strolled slowly along, gazing about him curiously. Twenty years had elapsed since he had been on this particular street, and the changes were great and stupefying. This Western city of three hundred thousand souls had contained but thirty thousand, when, as a boy, he had been wont to ramble along its streets. In those days the street he was now on had been a quiet residence street in the respectable working-class quarter. On this late afternoon he found that it had been submerged by a vast and vicious tenderloin. Chinese and Japanese shops and dens abounded, all confusedly intermingled with low white resorts and boozing kens. This quiet street of his youth had become the toughest quarter of the city.

He looked at his watch. It was half-past five. It was the slack time of the day in such a region, as he well knew, yet he was curious to see. In all his score of years of wandering and studying social conditions over the world, he had carried with him the memory of his old town as a sweet and wholesome place. The metamorphosis he now beheld was startling. He certainly must continue his stroll and glimpse the infamy to which his town had descended.

Another thing: Carter Watson had a keen social and civic consciousness. Independently wealthy, he had been loath to dissipate his energies in the pink teas and freak dinners of society, while actresses, race-horses, and kindred diversions had left him cold. He had the ethical bee

153

in his bonnet and was a reformer of no mean pretension, though his work had been mainly in the line of contributions to the heavier reviews and quarterlies and to the publication over his name of brightly, cleverly written books on the working classes and the slum-dwellers. Among the twenty-seven to his credit occurred titles such as, "If Christ Came to New Orleans," "The Worked-out Worker," "Tenement Reform in Berlin," "The Rural Slums of England," "The People of the East Side," "Reform Versus Revolution," "The University Settlement as a Hot Bed of Radicalism" and "The Cave Man of Civilization."

But Carter Watson was neither morbid nor fanatic. He did not lose his head over the horrors he encountered, studied, and exposed. No hair-brained enthusiasm branded him. His humor saved him, as did his wide experience and his conservative philosophic temperament. Nor did he have any patience with lightning change reform theories. As he saw it, society would grow better only through the painfully slow and arduously painful processes of evolution. There were no short cuts, no sudden regenerations. The betterment of mankind must be worked out in agony and misery just as all past social betterments had been worked out.

But on this late summer afternoon, Carter Watson was curious. As he moved along he paused before a gaudy drinking place. The sign above read, "The Vendome." There were two entrances. One evidently led to the bar. This he did not explore. The other was a narrow hallway. Passing through this he found himself in a huge room, filled with chair-encircled tables and quite deserted. In the dim light he made out a piano in the distance. Making a mental note that he would come back some time and study the class of persons that must sit and drink at those multitudinous tables, he proceeded to circumnavigate the room.

Now, at the rear, a short hallway led off to a small kitchen, and here, at a table, alone, sat Patsy Horan, proprietor of the Vendome, consuming a hasty supper ere the evening rush of business. Also, Patsy Horan was angry with the world. He had got out of the wrong side of bed that morning, and nothing had gone right all day. Had his barkeepers been asked, they would have described his mental condition as a grouch. But Carter Watson did not know this. As he passed the little hallway, Patsy Horan's sullen eyes lighted on the magazine he carried under his arm. Patsy did not know Carter Watson, nor did he know that what he carried under his arm was a magazine. Patsy, out of the depths of his grouch, decided that this stranger was one of those pests who marred and scarred the walls of his back rooms by tacking up or pasting up advertisements. The color on the front cover of the magazine convinced him that it was such an advertisement. Thus the trouble began. Knife and fork in hand, Patsy leaped for Carter Watson.

"Out wid yeh!" Patsy bellowed. "I know yer game!"

Carter Watson was startled. The man had come upon him like the eruption of a jack-in-the-box.

"A defacin' me walls," cried Patsy, at the same time emitting a string of vivid and vile, rather than virile, epithets of opprobrium.

"If I have given any offense I did not mean to—"

But that was as far as the visitor got. Patsy interrupted.

"Get out wid yeh; yeh talk too much wid yer mouth," quoted Patsy, emphasizing his remarks with flourishes of the knife and fork.

Carter Watson caught a quick vision of that eating-fork inserted uncomfortably between his ribs, knew that it would be rash to talk further with his mouth, and promptly turned to go. The sight of his meekly retreating back must have further enraged Patsy Horan, for that worthy, dropping the table implements, sprang upon him.

Patsy weighed one hundred and eighty pounds. So did Watson. In this they were equal. But Patsy was a rushing, rough-and-tumble saloon-fighter, while Watson was a boxer. In this the latter had the advantage, for Patsy came in wide open, swinging his right in a perilous sweep. All Watson had to do was to straight-left him and escape. But Watson had another advantage. His boxing, and his experience in the slums and ghettos of the world, had taught him restraint.

He pivoted on his feet, and, instead of striking, ducked the other's swinging blow and went into a clinch. But Patsy, charging like a bull, had the momentum of his rush, while Watson, whirling to meet him, had no momentum. As a result, the pair of them went down, with all their three hundred and sixty pounds of weight, in a long crashing fall, Watson underneath. He lay with his head touching the rear wall of the large room. The street was a hundred and fifty feet away, and he did some quick thinking. His first thought was to avoid trouble. He had no wish to get into the papers of this, his childhood town, where many of his relatives and family friends still lived.

So it was that he locked his arms around the man on top of him, held him close, and waited for the help to come that must come in response to the crash of the fall. The help came—that is, six men ran in from the bar and formed about in a semi-circle.

"Take him off, fellows," Watson said. "I haven't struck him, and I don't want any fight."

But the semi-circle remained silent. Watson held on and waited. Patsy, after various vain efforts to inflict damage, made an overture.

"Leggo o' me an' I'll get off o' yeh," said he.

Watson let go, but when Patsy scrambled to his feet he stood over his recumbent foe, ready to strike.

"Get up," Patsy commanded.

His voice was stern and implacable, like the voice of God calling to judgment, and Watson knew there was no mercy there.

"Stand back and I'll get up," he countered.

"If yer a gentleman, get up," quoth Patsy, his pale blue eyes aflame with wrath, his fist ready for a crushing blow.

At the same moment he drew his foot back to kick the other in the face. Watson blocked the kick with his crossed arms and sprang to his feet so quickly that he was in a clinch with his antagonist before the latter could strike. Holding him, Watson spoke to the onlookers:

"Take him away from me, fellows. You see I am not striking him. I don't want to fight. I want to get out of here."

The circle did not move nor speak. Its silence was ominous and sent a chill to Watson's heart. Patsy made an effort to throw him, which culminated in his putting Patsy on his back. Tearing loose from him, Watson sprang to his feet and made for the door. But the circle of men was interposed like a wall. He noticed the white, pasty faces, the kind that never see the sun, and knew that the men who barred his way were the night-prowlers and preying beasts of the city jungle. By then he was thrust back upon the pursuing, bull-rushing Patsy.

Again it was a clinch, in which, in momentary safety, Watson appealed to the gang. And again his words fell on deaf ears. Then it was that he knew fear. For he had known of many similar situations, in low dens like this, when solitary men were man-handled, their ribs and features caved in, themselves beaten and kicked to death. And he knew, further, that if he were to escape he must neither strike his assailant nor any of the men who opposed him.

Yet in him was righteous indignation. Under no circumstances could seven to one be fair. Also, he was angry, and there stirred in him the fighting beast that is in all men. But he remembered his wife and children, his unfinished book, the ten thousand rolling acres of the up-country ranch he loved so well. He even saw in flashing visions the blue of the sky, the golden sun pouring down on his flower-spangled meadows, the lazy cattle knee-deep in the brooks, and the flash of trout in the riffles. Life was good—too good for him to risk it for a moment's sway of the beast. In short, Carter Watson was cool and scared.

His opponent, locked by his masterly clinch, was striving to throw him. Again Watson put him on the floor, broke away, and was thrust back by the pasty-faced circle to duck Patsy's swinging right and effect another clinch. This happened many times. And Watson grew even cooler, while the baffled Patsy, unable to inflict punishment, raged wildly and more wildly. He took to batting with his head in the clinches. The first time, he landed his forehead flush on Watson's nose. After that, the latter, in the clinches, buried his face in Patsy's breast. But the enraged Patsy batted on, striking his own eye and nose and cheek on the top of the other's head. The more he was thus injured, the more and the harder did Patsy bat.

This one-sided contest continued for twelve or fifteen minutes. Watson never struck a blow, and strove only to escape. Sometimes, in the free moments, circling about among the tables as he tried to win the door, the pasty-faced men gripped his coat-tails and flung him back at the swinging right of the on-rushing Patsy. Time upon time, and times without end, he clinched and put Patsy on his back, each time first whirling him around and putting him down in the direction of the door and gaining toward that goal by the length of the fall.

In the end, hatless, dishevelled, with streaming nose and one eye closed, Watson won to the sidewalk and into the arms of a policeman.

"Arrest that man," Watson panted.

"Hello, Patsy," said the policeman. "What's the mix-up?"

"Hello, Charley," was the answer. "This guy comes in—"

"Arrest that man, officer," Watson repeated.

"G'wan! Beat it!" said Patsy.

"Beat it!" added the policeman. "If you don't I'll pull you in."

"Not unless you arrest that man. He has committed a violent and unprovoked assault on me."

"Is it so, Patsy?" was the officer's query.

"Nah. Lemme tell you, Charley, an' I got the witnesses to prove it, so help me God. I was settin' in me kitchen eatin' a bowl of soup, when this guy comes in an' gets gay wid me. I never seen him in me born days before. He was drunk—"

"Look at me, officer," protested the indignant sociologist. "Am I drunk?"

The officer looked at him with sullen, menacing eyes and nodded to Patsy to continue.

"This guy gets gay wid me. 'I'm Tim McGrath,' says he, 'an' I can do the like to you,' says he. 'Put up yer hands.' I smiles, an' wid that, biff biff, he lands me twice an' spills me soup. Look at me eye. I'm fair murdered."

"What are you going to do, officer?" Watson demanded.

"Go on, beat it," was the answer, "or I'll pull you sure."

Then the civic righteousness of Carter Watson flamed up.

"Mr. Officer, I protest—"

But at that moment the policeman grabbed his arm with a savage jerk that nearly overthrew him.

"Come on, you're pulled."

"Arrest him, too," Watson demanded.

"Nix on that play," was the reply. "What did you assault him for, him a peacefully eatin' his soup?"

II

Carter Watson was genuinely angry. Not only had he been wantonly assaulted, badly battered, and arrested, but the morning papers without exception came out with lurid accounts of his drunken brawl with the proprietor of the notorious Vendome. Not one accurate or truthful line was published. Patsy Horan and his satellites described the battle in detail. The one incontestible thing was that Carter Watson had been drunk. Thrice he had been thrown out of the place and into the gutter, and thrice he had come back, breathing blood and fire and announcing that he was going to clean out the place. "EMINENT SOCIOLOGIST JAGGED AND JUGGED," was the first headline he read, on the front page, accompanied by a large portrait of himself. Other headlines were: "CARTER WATSON ASPIRED TO CHAMPIONSHIP HONORS"; "CARTER WATSON GETS HIS"; "NOTED SOCIOLOGIST ATTEMPTS TO CLEAN OUT A TEN-

DERLOIN CAFE"; and "CARTER WATSON KNOCKED OUT BY PATSY HORAN IN THREE ROUNDS."

At the police court, next morning, under bail, appeared Carter Watson to answer the complaint of the People Versus Carter Watson, for the latter's assault and battery on one Patsy Horan. But first, the Prosecuting Attorney, who was paid to prosecute all offenders against the People, drew him aside and talked with him privately.

"Why not let it drop?" said the Prosecuting Attorney. "I tell you what you do, Mr. Watson: Shake hands with Mr. Horan and make it up, and we'll drop the case right here. A word to the Judge, and the case against you will be dismissed."

"But I don't want it dismissed," was the answer. "Your office being what it is, you should be prosecuting me instead of asking me to make up with this—this fellow."

"Oh, I'll prosecute you all right," retorted the Prosecuting Attorney.

"Also you will have to prosecute this Patsy Horan," Watson advised; "for I shall now have him arrested for assault and battery."

"You'd better shake and make up," the Prosecuting Attorney repeated, and this time there was almost a threat in his voice.

The trials of both men were set for a week later, on the same morning, in Police Judge Witberg's court.

"You have no chance," Watson was told by an old friend of his boyhood, the retired manager of the biggest paper in the city. "Everybody knows you were beaten up by this man. His reputation is most unsavory. But it won't help you in the least. Both cases will be dismissed. This will be because you are you. Any ordinary man would be convicted."

"But I do not understand," objected the perplexed sociologist. "Without warning I was attacked by this man and badly beaten. I did not strike a blow. I—"

"That has nothing to do with it," the other cut him off.

"Then what is there that has anything to do with it?"

"I'll tell you. You are now up against the local police and political machine. Who are you? You are not even a legal resident in this town. You live up in the country. You haven't a vote of your own here. Much less do you swing any votes. This dive proprietor swings a string of votes in his precinct—a mighty long string."

"Do you mean to tell me that this Judge Witberg will violate the

sacredness of his office and oath by letting this brute off?" Watson demanded.

"Watch him," was the grim reply. "Oh, he'll do it nicely enough. He
will give an extra-legal, extra-judicial decision, abounding in every
word in the dictionary that stands for fairness and right."

"But there are the newspapers," Watson cried.

"They are not fighting the administration at present. They'll give it to
you hard. You see what they have already done to you."

"Then these snips of boys on the police detail won't write the truth?"

"They will write something so near like the truth that the public will
believe it. They write their stories under instruction, you know. They
have their orders to twist and color, and there won't be much left of
you when they get done. Better drop the whole thing right now. You are
in bad."

"But the trials are set."

"Give the word and they'll drop them now. A man can't fight a machine unless he has a machine behind him."

III

But Carter Watson was stubborn. He was convinced that the machine
would beat him, but all his days he had sought social experience, and this
was certainly something new.

The morning of the trial the Prosecuting Attorney made another attempt to patch up the affair.

"If you feel that way, I should like to get a lawyer to prosecute the
case," said Watson.

"No, you don't," said the Prosecuting Attorney. "I am paid by the
People to prosecute, and prosecute I will. But let me tell you. You have
no chance. We shall lump both cases into one, and you watch out."

Judge Witberg looked good to Watson. A fairly young man, short,
comfortably stout, smooth-shaven and with an intelligent face, he
seemed a very nice man indeed. This good impression was added to by
the smiling lips and the wrinkles of laughter in the corners of his black
eyes. Looking at him and studying him, Watson felt almost sure that his
old friend's prognostication was wrong.

But Watson was soon to learn. Patsy Horan and two of his satellites
testified to a most colossal aggregation of perjuries. Watson could not

have believed it possible without having experienced it. They denied the existence of the other four men. And of the two that testified, one claimed to have been in the kitchen, a witness to Watson's unprovoked assault on Patsy, while the other, remaining in the bar, had witnessed Watson's second and third rushes into the place as he attempted to annihilate the unoffending Patsy. The vile language ascribed to Watson was so voluminously and unspeakably vile, that he felt they were injuring their own case. It was so impossible that he should utter such things. But when they described the brutal blows he had rained on poor Patsy's face, and the chair he demolished when he vainly attempted to kick Patsy, Watson waxed secretly hilarious and at the same time sad. The trial was a farce, but such lowness of life was depressing to contemplate when he considered the long upward climb humanity must make.

Watson could not recognize himself, nor could his worst enemy have recognized him, in the swashbuckling, rough-housing picture that was painted of him. But, as in all cases of complicated perjury, rifts and contradictions in the various stories appeared. The Judge somehow failed to notice them, while the Prosecuting Attorney and Patsy's attorney shied off from them gracefully. Watson had not bothered to get a lawyer for himself, and he was now glad that he had not.

Still, he retained a semblance of faith in Judge Witberg when he went himself on the stand and started to tell his story.

"I was strolling casually along the street, your Honor," Watson began, but was interrupted by the Judge.

"We are not here to consider your previous actions," bellowed Judge Witberg. "Who struck the first blow?"

"Your Honor," Watson pleaded, "I have no witnesses of the actual fray, and the truth of my story can only be brought out by telling the story fully—"

Again he was interrupted.

"We do not care to publish any magazines here," Judge Witberg roared, looking at him so fiercely and malevolently that Watson could scarcely bring himself to believe that this was the same man he had studied a few minutes previously.

"Who struck the first blow?" Patsy's attorney asked.

The Prosecuting Attorney interposed, demanding to know which of the two cases lumped together this was, and by what right Patsy's lawyer, at that stage of the proceedings, should take the witness. Patsy's attorney fought back. Judge Witberg interfered, professing no knowledge of any two cases being lumped together. All this had to be explained. Battle royal raged, terminating in both attorneys apologizing to the Court and to each other. And so it went, and to Watson it had the seeming of a group of pickpockets ruffling and bustling an honest man as they took his purse. The machine was working, that was all.

"Why did you enter this place of unsavory reputation?" was asked him.

"It has been my custom for many years, as a student of economics and sociology, to acquaint myself—"

But this was as far as Watson got.

"We want none of your ologies here," snarled Judge Witberg. "It is a plain question. Answer it plainly. Is it true or not true that you were drunk? That is the gist of the question."

When Watson attempted to tell how Patsy had injured his face in his attempts to bat with his head, Watson was openly scouted and flouted, and Judge Witberg again took him in hand.

"Are you aware of the solemnity of the oath you took to testify to nothing but the truth on this witness stand?" the Judge demanded. "This is a fairy story you are telling. It is not reasonable that a man would so injure himself, and continue to injure himself, by striking the soft and sensitive parts of his face against your head. You are a sensible man. It is unreasonable, is it not?"

"Men are unreasonable when they are angry," Watson answered meekly.

Then it was that Judge Witberg was deeply outraged and righteously wrathful.

"What right have you to say that?" he cried. "It is gratuitous. It has no bearing on the case. You are here as a witness, sir, of events that have transpired. The Court does not wish to hear any expressions of opinion from you at all."

"I but answered your question, your Honor," Watson protested humbly.

"You did nothing of the sort," was the next blast. "And let me warn you, sir, let me warn you, that you are laying yourself liable to contempt by such insolence. And I will have you know that we know how to observe the law and the rules of courtesy down here in this little courtroom. I am ashamed of you."

And, while the next punctilious legal wrangle between the attorneys interrupted his tale of what happened in the Vendome, Carter Watson, without bitterness, amused and at the same time sad, saw rise before him the machine, large and small, that dominated his country, the unpunished and shameless grafts of a thousand cities perpetrated by the spidery and vermin-like creatures of the machines. Here it was before him, a courtroom and a judge, bowed down in subservience by the machine to a dive-keeper who swung a string of votes. Petty and sordid as it was, it was one face of the many-faced machine that loomed colossally, in every city and state, in a thousand guises overshadowing the land.

A familiar phrase rang in his ears: "It is to laugh." At the height of the wrangle, he giggled, once, aloud, and earned a sullen frown from Judge Witberg. Worse, a myriad times, he decided, were these bullying lawyers and this bullying judge than the bucko mates in first quality hellships, who not only did their own bullying but protected themselves as well. These petty rapscallions, on the other hand, sought protection behind the majesty of the law. They struck, but no one was permitted to strike back, for behind them were the prison cells and the clubs of the stupid policemen—paid and professional fighters and beaters-up of men. Yet he was not bitter. The grossness and the sliminess of it was forgotten in the simple grotesqueness of it, and he had the saving sense of humor.

Nevertheless, hectored and heckled though he was, he managed in the end to give a simple, straightforward version of the affair, and, despite a belligerent cross-examination, his story was not shaken in any particular. Quite different it was from the perjuries that had shouted aloud through the stories of Patsy and his two witnesses.

Both Patsy's attorney and the Prosecuting Attorney rested their cases, letting everything go before the Court without argument. Watson protested against this, but was silenced when the Prosecuting Attorney told him that he was the Public Prosecutor and knew his business.

"Patrick Horan has testified that he was in danger of his life and that he was compelled to defend himself," Judge Witberg's verdict began. "Mr. Watson has testified to the same thing. Each has sworn that the other struck the first blow; each has sworn that the other made an unprovoked assault on him. It is an axiom of the law that the defendant should be given the benefit of the doubt. A very reasonable doubt exists. Therefore, in the case of the People Versus Carter Watson the benefit of the doubt is given to said Carter Watson and he is herewith ordered discharged from custody. The same reasoning applies to the case of the People Versus Patrick Horan. He is given the benefit of the doubt and discharged from custody. My recommendation is that both defendants shake hands and make up."

In the afternoon papers the first headline that caught Watson's eye was: "CARTER WATSON ACQUITTED." In the second paper it was: "CARTER WATSON ESCAPES A FINE." But what capped everything was that one beginning: "CARTER WATSON A GOOD FELLOW." In the text he read how Judge Witberg had advised both fighters to shake hands, which they promptly did. Further, he read:

" 'Let's have a nip on it,' said Patsy Horan.

" 'Sure,' said Carter Watson.

"And, arm in arm, they ambled for the nearest saloon."

IV

Now, from the whole adventure, Watson carried away no bitterness. It was a social experience of a new order, and it led to the writing of another book, which he entitled, "POLICE COURT PROCEDURE: A Tentative Analysis."

One summer morning a year later, on his ranch, he left his horse and himself clambered on through a miniature canyon to inspect some rock ferns he had planted the previous winter. Emerging from the upper end of the canyon, he came out on one of his flower-spangled meadows, a delightful isolated spot, screened from the world by low hills and clumps of trees. And here he found a man, evidently on a stroll from the summer hotel down at the little town a mile away. They met face to face and the recognition was mutual. It was Judge Witberg. Also, it was a clear case of trespass, for Watson had trespass signs upon his boundaries, though he never enforced them.

Judge Witberg held out his hand, which Watson refused to see.

"Politics is a dirty trade, isn't it, Judge?" he remarked. "Oh, yes, I see your hand, but I don't care to take it. The papers said I shook hands with Patsy Horan after the trial. You know I didn't, but let me tell you that I'd a thousand times rather shake hands with him and his vile following of curs, than with you."

Judge Witberg was painfully flustered, and as he hemmed and hawed and essayed to speak, Watson, looking at him, was struck by a sudden whim, and he determined on a grim and facetious antic.

"I should scarcely expect any animus from a man of your acquirements and knowledge of the world," the Judge was saying.

"Animus?" Watson replied. "Certainly not. I haven't such a thing in my nature. And to prove it, let me show you something curious, something you have never seen before." Casting about him, Watson picked up a rough stone the size of his fist. "See this. Watch me."

So saying, Carter Watson tapped himself a sharp blow on the cheek. The stone laid the flesh open to the bone and the blood spurted forth.

"The stone was too sharp," he announced to the astounded Police Judge, who thought he had gone mad. "I must bruise it a trifle. There is nothing like being realistic in such matters."

Whereupon Carter Watson found a smooth stone and with it pounded his cheek nicely several times.

"Ah," he cooed. "That will turn beautifully green and black in a few hours. It will be most convincing."

"You are insane," Judge Witberg quavered.

"Don't use such vile language to me," said Watson. "You see my bruised and bleeding face? You did that, with that right hand of yours. You hit me twice—biff biff. It is a brutal and unprovoked assault. I am in danger of my life. I must protect myself."

Judge Witberg backed away in alarm before the menacing fists of the other.

"If you strike me I'll have you arrested," Judge Witberg threatened.

"That is what I told Patsy," was the answer. "And do you know what he did when I told him that?"

"No."

"That!"

And at the same moment Watson's right fist landed flush on Judge Witberg's nose, putting that legal gentleman over on his back on the grass.

"Get up!" commanded Watson. "If you are a gentleman, get up— that's what Patsy told me, you know."

Judge Witberg declined to rise, and was dragged to his feet by the coat collar, only to have one eye blacked and be put on his back again. After that it was a red Indian massacre. Judge Witberg was humanely and scientifically beaten up. His cheeks were boxed, his ears cuffed, and his face was rubbed in the turf. And all the time Watson exposited the way Patsy Horan had done it. Occasionally, and very carefully, the facetious sociologist administered a real bruising blow. Once, dragging the poor Judge to his feet, he deliberately bumped his own nose on the gentleman's head. The nose promptly bled.

"See that!" cried Watson, stepping back and deftly shedding his blood all down his own shirt front. "You did it. With your fist you did it. It is awful. I am fair murdered. I must again defend myself."

And once more Judge Witberg impacted his features on a fist and was sent to grass.

"I will have you arrested," he sobbed as he lay.

"That's what Patsy said."

"A brutal—sniff, sniff—and unprovoked—sniff, sniff—assault."

"That's what Patsy said."

"I will surely have you arrested."

"Speaking slangily, not if I can beat you to it."

And with that, Carter Watson departed down the canyon, mounted his horse, and rode to town.

An hour later, as Judge Witberg limped up the grounds to his hotel, he was arrested by a village constable on a charge of assault and battery preferred by Carter Watson.

v

"Your Honor," Watson said next day to the village Justice, a well-to-do farmer and graduate, thirty years before, from a cow college, "since this Sol Witberg has seen fit to charge me with battery, following upon my charge of battery against him, I would suggest that both cases be lumped together. The testimony and the facts are the same in both cases."

To this the Justice agreed, and the double case proceeded. Watson, as prosecuting witness, first took the stand and told his story.

"I was picking flowers," he testified. "Picking flowers on my own land, never dreaming of danger. Suddenly this man rushed upon me from behind the trees. 'I am the Dodo,' he says, 'and I can do you to a frazzle. Put up your hands.' I smiled, but with that, biff biff, he struck me, knocking me down and spilling my flowers. The language he used was frightful. It was an unprovoked and brutal assault. Look at my cheek. Look at my nose. I could not understand it. He must have been drunk. Before I recovered from my surprise he had administered this beating. I was in danger of my life and was compelled to defend myself. That is all, your Honor, though I must say, in conclusion, that I cannot get over my perplexity. Why did he say he was the Dodo? Why did he so wantonly attack me?"

And thus was Sol Witberg given a liberal education in the art of perjury. Often, from his high seat, he had listened indulgently to police court perjuries in cooked-up cases; but for the first time perjury was directed against him, and he no longer sat above the court, with the bailiffs, the policemen's clubs, and the prison cells behind him.

"Your Honor," he cried, "never have I heard such a pack of lies told by so bare-faced a liar—"

Watson here sprang to his feet.

"Your Honor, I protest. It is for your Honor to decide truth or falsehood. The witness is on the stand to testify to actual events that have transpired. His personal opinion upon things in general, and upon me, has no bearing on the case whatever."

The Justice scratched his head and waxed phlegmatically indignant.

"The point is well taken," he decided. "I am surprised at you, Mr. Witberg, claiming to be a judge and skilled in the practice of the law, and yet being guilty of such unlawyerlike conduct. Your manner, sir, and your methods, remind me of a shyster. This is a simple case of assault and battery. We are here to determine who struck the first blow, and we are not interested in your estimates of Mr. Watson's personal character. Proceed with your story."

Sol Witberg would have bitten his bruised and swollen lip in chagrin, had it not hurt so much. But he contained himself and told a simple, straightforward, truthful story.

"Your Honor," Watson said, "I would suggest that you ask him what he was doing on my premises."

"A very good question. What were you doing, sir, on Mr. Watson's premises?"

"I did not know they were his premises."

"It was a trespass, your Honor," Watson cried. "The warnings are posted conspicuously."

"I saw no warnings," said Sol Witberg.

"I have seen them myself," snapped the Justice. "They are very conspicuous. And I would warn you, sir, that if you palter with the truth in such little matters you may darken your more important statements with suspicion. Why did you strike Mr. Watson?"

"Your Honor, as I have testified, I did not strike a blow."

The Justice looked at Carter Watson's bruised and swollen visage, and turned to glare at Sol Witberg.

"Look at that man's cheek!" he thundered. "If you did not strike a blow how comes it that he is so disfigured and injured?"

"As I testified—"

"Be careful," the Justice warned.

"I will be careful, sir. I will say nothing but the truth. He struck himself with a rock. He struck himself with two different rocks."

"Does it stand to reason that a man, any man not a lunatic, would so injure himself, and continue to injure himself, by striking the soft and sensitive parts of his face with a stone?" Carter Watson demanded.

"It sounds like a fairy story," was the Justice's comment. "Mr. Witberg, had you been drinking?"

"No, sir."

"Do you never drink?"

"On occasion."

The Justice meditated on this answer with an air of astute profundity.

Watson took advantage of the opportunity to wink at Sol Witberg, but that much-abused gentleman saw nothing humorous in the situation.

"A very peculiar case, a very peculiar case," the Justice announced, as he began his verdict. "The evidence of the two parties is flatly contradictory. There are no witnesses outside the two principals. Each claims the other committed the assault, and I have no legal way of determining the truth. But I have my private opinion, Mr. Witberg, and I would recommend that henceforth you keep off of Mr. Watson's premises and keep away from this section of the country—"

"This is an outrage!" Sol Witberg blurted out.

"Sit down, sir!" was the Justice's thundered command. "If you interrupt the Court in this manner again, I shall fine you for contempt. And I warn you I shall fine you heavily—you, a judge yourself, who should be conversant with the courtesy and dignity of courts. I shall now give my verdict:

"It is a rule of law that the defendant shall be given the benefit of the doubt. As I have said, and I repeat, there is no legal way for me to determine who struck the first blow. Therefore, and much to my regret,"— here he paused and glared at Sol Witberg—"in each of these cases I

am compelled to give the defendant the benefit of the doubt. Gentlemen, you are both dismissed."

"Let us have a nip on it," Watson said to Witberg, as they left the
courtroom; but that outraged person refused to lock arms and amble
to the nearest saloon.

Anton Chekhov

.

IN THE COURT

At the district town of N. in the cinnamon-colored government house in which the Zemstvo, the sessional meetings of the justices of the peace, the Rural Board, the Liquor Board, the Military Board, and many others sit by turns, the Circuit Court was in session on one of the dull days of autumn. Of the above-mentioned cinnamon-colored house a local official had wittily observed:

"Here is Justitia, here is Policia, here is Militia—a regular boarding school of high-born young ladies."

But, as the saying is, "Too many cooks spoil the broth," and probably that is why the house strikes, oppresses, and overwhelms a fresh unofficial visitor with its dismal barrack-like appearance, its decrepit condition, and the complete absence of any kind of comfort, external or internal. Even on the brightest spring days it seems wrapped in a dense shade, and on clear moonlight nights, when the trees and the little dwelling-houses merged in one blur of shadow seem plunged in quiet slumber, it alone absurdly and inappropriately towers, an oppressive mass of stone, above the modest landscape, spoils the general harmony, and keeps sleepless vigil as though it could not escape from burdensome memories of past unforgiven sins. Inside it is like a barn and extremely unattractive. It is strange to see how readily these elegant lawyers, members of committees, and marshals of nobility, who in their own homes will make a scene over the slightest fume from the stove, or stain on the floor, resign themselves here to whirring ventilation

170

wheels, the disgusting smell of fumigating candles, and the filthy, forever perspiring walls.

The sitting of the circuit court began between nine and ten. The program of the day was promptly entered upon, with noticeable haste. The
cases came on one after another and ended quickly, like a church
service without a choir, so that no mind could form a complete picture
of all this parti-colored mass of faces, movements, words, misfor-
tunes, true sayings and lies, all racing by like a river in flood. . . . By
two o'clock a great deal had been done: two prisoners had been sentenced to service in convict battalions, one of the privileged class had
been sentenced to deprivation of rights and imprisonment, one had
been acquitted, one case had been adjourned.

At precisely two o'clock the presiding judge announced that the case
"of the peasant Nikolay Harlamov, charged with the murder of his
wife," would next be heard. The composition of the court remained the
same as it had been for the preceding case, except that the place of the
defending counsel was filled by a new personage, a beardless young
graduate in a coat with bright buttons. The president gave the order—
"Bring in the prisoner!"

But the prisoner, who had been got ready beforehand, was already
walking to his bench. He was a tall, thick-set peasant of about fifty-five,
completely bald, with an apathetic, hairy face and a big red beard. He
was followed by a frail-looking little soldier with a gun.

Just as he was reaching the bench the escort had a trifling mishap.
He stumbled and dropped the gun out of his hands, but caught it at
once before it touched the ground, knocking his knee violently against
the butt end as he did so. A faint laugh was audible in the audience.
Either from the pain or perhaps from shame at his awkwardness the
soldier flushed a dark red.

After the customary questions to the prisoner, the shuffling of the
jury, the calling over and swearing in of the witnesses, the reading of
the charge began. The narrow-chested, pale-faced secretary, far too thin
for his uniform, and with sticking plaster on his cheek, read it in a low,
thick bass, rapidly like a sacristan, without raising or dropping his
voice, as though afraid of exerting his lungs; he was seconded by the
ventilation wheel whirring indefatigably behind the judge's table, and
the result was a sound that gave a drowsy, narcotic character to the stillness of the hall.

The president, a short-sighted man, not old but with an extremely exhausted face, sat in his armchair without stirring and held his open hand near his brow as though screening his eyes from the sun. To the droning of the ventilation wheel and the secretary he meditated. When the secretary paused for an instant to take breath on beginning a new page, he suddenly started and looked round at the court with lusterless eyes, then bent down to the ear of the judge next to him and asked with a sigh:

"Are you putting up at Demyanov's, Matvey Petrovitch?"

"Yes, at Demyanov's," answered the other, starting too.

"Next time I shall probably put up there too. It's really impossible to put up at Tipyakov's! There's noise and uproar all night! Knocking, coughing, children crying. . . . It's impossible!"

The assistant prosecutor, a fat, well-nourished, dark man with gold spectacles, with a handsome, well-groomed beard, sat motionless as a statue, with his cheek propped on his fist, reading Byron's "Cain." His eyes were full of eager attention and his eyebrows rose higher and higher with wonder. . . . From time to time he dropped back in his chair, gazed without interest straight before him for a minute, and then buried himself in his reading again. The council for the defense moved the blunt end of his pencil about the table and mused with his head on one side. . . . His youthful face expressed nothing but the frigid, immovable boredom which is commonly seen on the face of schoolboys and men on duty who are forced from day to day to sit in the same place, to see the same faces, the same walls. He felt no excitement about the speech he was to make, and indeed what did that speech amount to? On instructions from his superiors in accordance with long-established routine he would fire it off before the jurymen, without passion or ardor, feeling that he was colorless and boring, and then—gallop through the mud and the rain to the station, thence to the town, shortly to receive instructions to go off again to some district to deliver another speech. . . . It was a bore!

At first the prisoner turned pale and coughed nervously into his sleeve, but soon the stillness, the general monotony and boredom infected him too. He looked with dull-witted respectfulness at the judges' uniforms, at the weary faces of the jurymen, and blinked calmly. The surroundings and procedure of the court, the expectation of which had so weighed on his soul while he was awaiting them in prison, now had the most soothing effect on him. What he met here was not at all what he could have expected. The charge of murder hung over him, and yet here he met with neither threatening faces nor indignant looks nor loud phrases about retribution nor sympathy for his extraordianry fate; not one of those who were judging him looked at him with interest or for long. . . . The dingy windows and walls, the voice of the secretary, the attitude of the prosecutor were all saturated with official indifference and produced an atmosphere of frigidity, as though the murderer were simply an official property, or as though he were not being judged by living men, but by some unseen machine, set going, goodness knows how or by whom. . . .

The peasant, reassured, did not understand that the men here were as accustomed to the dramas and tragedies of life and were as blunted by the sight of them as hospital attendants are at the sight of death, and that the whole horror and hopelessness of his position lay just in this mechanical indifference. It seemed that if he were not to sit quietly but to get up and begin beseeching, appealing with tears for their mercy, bitterly repenting, that if he were to die of despair—it would all be shattered against blunted nerves and the callousness of custom, like waves against a rock.

When the secretary finished, the president for some reason passed his hands over the table before him, looked for some time with his eyes screwed up towards the prisoner, and then asked, speaking languidly:

"Prisoner at the bar, do you plead guilty to having murdered your wife on the evening of the ninth of June?"

"No, sir," answered the prisoner, getting up and holding his gown over his chest.

After this the court proceeded hurriedly to the examination of witnesses. Two peasant women and five men and the village policeman who had made the inquiry were questioned. All of them, mud-bespattered, exhausted with their long walk and waiting in the witnesses' room, gloomy and dispirited, gave the same evidence. They testified that Harlamov lived "well" with his old woman, like anyone else; that he never beat her except when he had had a drop; that on the ninth of June when the sun was setting the old woman had been found in the porch with her skull broken; that beside her in a pool of blood lay an axe. When they looked for Nikolay to tell him of the calamity he was not in his hut or in the streets. They ran all over the village, looking for him. They went to all the pothouses and huts, but could not find him. He had disappeared, and two days later came of his own accord to the police office, pale, with his clothes torn, trembling all over. He was bound and put in the lock-up.

"Prisoner," said the president, addressing Harlamov, "cannot you explain to the court where you were during the three days following the murder?"

"I was wandering about the fields. . . . Neither eating nor drinking. . . ."

"Why did you hide yourself, if it was not you that committed the murder?"

"I was frightened. . . . I was afraid I might be judged guilty. . . ."

"Aha! . . . Good, sit down!"

The last to be examined was the district doctor who had made a post-mortem on the old woman. He told the court all that he remembered of his report at the post-mortem and all that he had succeeded in thinking of on his way to the court that morning. The president screwed up his eyes at his new glossy black suit, at his foppish cravat, at his moving lips; he listened and in his mind the languid thought seemed to spring up of itself:

"Everyone wears a short jacket nowadays, why has he had his made long? Why long and not short?"

The circumspect creak of boots was audible behind the president's back. It was the assistant prosecutor going up to the table to take some papers.

"Mihail Vladimirovitch," said the assistant prosecutor, bending down to the president's ear, "amazingly slovenly the way that Koreisky conducted the investigation. The prisoner's brother was not examined, the village elder was not examined, there's no making anything out of his description of the hut. . . ."

"It can't be helped, it can't be helped," said the president, sinking back in his chair. "He's a wreck . . . dropping to bits!"

"By the way," whispered the assistant prosecutor, "look at the audience, in the front row, the third from the right . . . a face like an actor's . . . that's the local Croesus. He has a fortune of something like fifty thousand."

"Really? You wouldn't guess it from his appearance. . . . Well, dear boy, shouldn't we have a break?"

"We will finish the case for the prosecution, and then. . . ."

"As you think best. . . . Well?" The president raised his eyes to the doctor. "So you consider that death was instantaneous?"

"Yes, in consequence of the extent of the injury to the brain substance. . . ."

When the doctor had finished, the president gazed into the space between the prosecutor and the counsel for the defense and suggested:

"Have you any questions to ask?"

The assistant prosecutor shook his head negatively, without lifting his eyes from "Cain"; the counsel for the defense unexpectedly stirred and, clearing his throat, asked:

"Tell me, doctor, can you from the dimensions of the wound form any theory as to . . . as to the mental condition of the criminal? That is, I mean, does the extent of the injury justify the supposition that the accused was suffering from temporary aberration?"

The president raised his drowsy indifferent eyes to the counsel for the defense. The assistant prosecutor tore himself from "Cain," and looked at the president. They merely looked, but there was no smile, no surprise, no perplexity—their faces expressed nothing.

"Perhaps," the doctor hesitated, "if one considers the force with which . . . er—er—er . . . the criminal strikes the blow. . . . However, excuse me, I don't quite understand your question. . . ."

The counsel for the defense did not get an answer to his question, and indeed he did not feel the necessity of one. It was clear even to himself that that question had strayed into his mind and found utterance simply through the effect of the stillness, the boredom, the whirring ventilator wheels.

When they had got rid of the doctor the court rose to examine the "material evidences." The first thing examined was the full-skirted coat, upon the sleeve of which there was a dark brownish stain of blood. Harlamov on being questioned as to the origin of the stain stated:

"Three days before my old woman's death Penkov bled his horse. I was there; I was helping to be sure, and . . . and got smeared with it. . . ."

"But Penkov has just given evidence that he does not remember that you were present at the bleeding. . . ."

"I can't tell about that."

"Sit down."

They proceeded to examine the axe with which the old woman had been murdered.

"That's not my axe," the prisoner declared.

"Whose is it, then?"

"I can't tell . . . I hadn't an axe. . . ."

"A peasant can't get on for a day without an axe. And your neighbor Ivan Timofeyitch, with whom you mended a sledge, has given evidence that it is your axe. . . ."

"I can't say about that, but I swear before God (Harlamov held out his hand before him and spread out the fingers), before the living God. And I don't remember how long it is since I did have an axe of my own. I did have one like that only a bit smaller, but my son Prohor lost it. Two years before he went into the army, he drove off to fetch wood, got drinking with the fellows, and lost it. . . ."

"Good, sit down."

This systematic distrust and disinclination to hear him probably irritated and offended Harlamov. He blinked and red patches came out on his cheekbones.

"I swear in the sight of God," he went on, craning his neck forward. "If you don't believe me, be pleased to ask my son Prohor. Proshka, what did you do with the axe?" he suddenly asked in a rough voice, turning abruptly to the soldier escorting him. "Where is it?"

It was a painful moment! Everyone seemed to wince and as it were shrink together. The same fearful, incredible thought flashed like lightning through every head in the court, the thought of possibly fatal coincidence, and not one person in the court dared to look at the soldier's face. Everyone refused to trust his thought and believed that he had heard wrong.

"Prisoner, conversation with the guards is forbidden . . ." the president made haste to say.

No one saw the escort's face, and horror passed over the hall unseen as in a mask. The usher of the court got up quietly from his place and tiptoeing with his hand held out to balance himself went out of the court. Half a minute later there came the muffled sounds and footsteps that accompany the change of guard.

All raised their heads and, trying to look as though nothing had happened, went on with their work. . . .

Anton Chekhov

:

WORSE AND WORSE

A lawyer by the name of Kalyakin was sitting with Gradusov, the choirmaster of the cathedral, in the latter's living room. Turning about in his fingers a summons from the justice of the peace addressed to the choirmaster, the lawyer was saying:

"You must admit, Dosifey Petrovich, you are guilty. I respect you, I appreciate your friendly attitude toward me. Nevertheless, I must say, though it hurts me, that you were in the wrong. Yes, sir, in the wrong. You insulted my client, Derevyashkin. . . . Tell me, why on earth did you insult him?"

"Who the devil insulted him?" burst out Gradusov, a tall old man with a low forehead that promised little, heavy eyebrows, and a brass medal in his lapel. "All I did was to talk morals to him, that's all! Fools must be taught! If you don't teach fools, they'll be all over the place."

"But, Dosifey Petrovich, it wasn't a lesson that you gave him. As he states in his petition, you addressed him as an inferior in public, and, what's worse, you called him an ass, a scoundrel, and so forth. . . . And once you even raised your hand, as if you were going to do him bodily injury."

"Well, why not thrash him if he deserves it? I don't understand."

"But realize that you have no right to do it!"

"I have no right? No, excuse me . . . that's a bit thick. Come off of it, and don't pull my leg! After they'd discharged him honorably from

177

the archbishop's choir and kicked him out of there, he sang in my choir for ten years. I'm his benefactor, if you please. If he's sore because I threw him out of the choir, it's his own fault. I threw him out for philosophizing. And if you're a fool with no brains, then you sit in your corner and hold your tongue. . . . Hold your tongue, and listen to what intelligent people say. But he, the blockhead, he'd go out of his way to put his oar in. Here we're rehearsing or a mass is being sung, and he has to have something to say about Bismarck and about all kinds of Gladstones. Will you believe me, the blackguard has actually subscribed for a newspaper! And how many times I punched him in the jaw because of the Russo-Turkish War—that you can't even imagine! Here we have to get on with the singing and he leans over to the tenors and begins telling them how we blew up a Turkish ironclad with dynamite. Is that the way to act? Of course, it's nice that we won a victory. But that doesn't mean you stop singing. You can talk about these things after the mass is over. In one word: a swine."

"So you insulted him even before this?"

"Before this he didn't take offense. He felt that I was doing it for his own good, he understood why I did it. He knew that it is a sin to talk back to your elders and your benefactors, but when he became a clerk in the police station—why, then he got a swelled head and took leave of his senses. 'I'm no choir singer,' says he, 'I'm an official. I'm going to take an examination so as to get the rank of filing clerk.' 'Come,' says I, 'what a fool you are! You should cut down on your philosophizing and wipe your nose a little oftener, and that would be better than to be thinking about ranks. Rank isn't for the likes of you, you just look for humble pie.' He wouldn't hear of it! Or take this very case—why is he dragging me into court? Isn't he the scum of the earth? I was sitting in Samopluyev's tavern, having tea with our churchwarden. The place was jammed, not a table to be had. . . . I looked round and there he was, with the other clerks, swilling beer. Dressed to kill, his snout in the air, shouting and waving his arms. . . . I kept my ears open—he was talking about the cholera epidemic. . . . Well, what can you do with a fellow like that? He was philosophizing! I kept mum, you know, I suffered. . . . Gab away, I thought, gab away. . . . The tongue has no bones. . . . Suddenly, as ill luck would have it, the machine started playing. He got worked up, the hoodlum, got to his feet and harangued his chums: 'Let's drink,' said he, 'to the prosperity of . . . ! I am a son of my fatherland,' said he, 'a born Slavophil! I'll shed my blood so it waves forever! Where's the enemy? Come on out! I'll take on whoever don't agree with me!' And he banged the table with his fist! That was more than I could stand. . . . I went up to him and said politely: 'Listen, Osip . . . If you don't understand anything, you swine, then you'd better shut up and don't hold forth. An educated man may air his opinions, but you should take a back seat. You're a louse, you're scum. . . .' For every word I said, he had ten. . . . And the fat was in the fire. Everything I said, of course, I said for his own good, but with him, it was his stupidity that was talking. . . . He took offense—and now he is haling me into court. . . ."

"Yes," said Kalyakin, sighing. "It's too bad. . . . Something trifling happens, and the devil knows what the results are. . . . You're a family man, well thought of, and here this lawsuit comes along, there's talk, gossip, possible arrest. . . . You must put an end to this business, Dosifey Petrovich. You have one way out, which suits Derevyashkin, too. You will go to Samopluyev's tavern with me today at six o'clock, when the clerks and the actors and the others in whose presence you insulted him gather there, and you'll apologize to him. Then he will withdraw his petition. Understand? I hope you will agree to it. I'm speaking to you as a friend. . . . You insulted Derevyashkin, you shamed him, above all, you cast suspicion on his praiseworthy sentiments, you even . . . disparaged those sentiments. In these times, you know, that's not done. You must be more careful. Briefly, your remarks have been interpreted in a way that in these times, you know . . . It's now a quarter to six. Will you please come with me?"

Gradusov shook his head, but when Kalyakin vividly painted for him the interpretation placed on his words and the consequences which this interpretation could have, Gradusov took fright and consented.

"Now be sure and make your apology properly, in the right way," the lawyer instructed him, as they were walking toward the tavern. "Go up to him and address him politely, say: 'Excuse me, I withdraw my remarks,' and so on, and so forth."

On arriving at the tavern, Gradusov and Kalyakin found a whole crowd there. Merchants were present, and actors, petty officials, police clerks—all the "rabble" that was in the habit of gathering there of evenings to have tea or beer. Sitting with the clerks was Derevyashkin himself, a fellow of uncertain age, with a shaven chin, big, unblinking eyes, a squashed nose, and hair so coarse that looking at it, you conceived the desire to clean your boots. His face was so tellingly built that a glance was sufficient to let you know that he was a drunkard, that he sang in a bass voice, that he was stupid, but not so stupid as to fail to consider himself very intelligent. Seeing the choirmaster, he half rose to his feet and twitched his whiskers like a cat. The crowd, apparently informed beforehand that there would be a public penance, pricked up its ears.

"Here, Mr. Gradusov has agreed," said Kalyakin, entering.

The choirmaster greeted a few people, blew his nose noisily, flushed, and went up to Derevyashkin.

"I apologize," he mumbled, without looking at him, and putting his handkerchief back in his pocket. "In the presence of everyone here, I take back my words."

"I accept your apology," Derevyashkin said in a bass voice, and glancing round triumphantly at the company, he sat down. "I'm satisfied. Mr. Lawyer, please stop the proceedings."

"I apologize," Gradusov continued. "Forgive me . . . I don't like unpleasantnesses. You want me to address you formally—all right, I will. You want me to consider you intelligent—very well. I don't give a damn. I don't bear grudges, brother. Devil take you!"

"But, allow me, you were supposed to apologize to me, not swear at me."

"How else should I apologize? I have apologized! If I wasn't consistent about addressing you formally, that's just a slip of the tongue. I'm not to go down on my knees to you, am I? I apologize, and I even thank the Lord that you have enough sense to drop the case. I've no time to hang around the court. . . . In all my life I never yet went to law, I'm not going to law, and if you listen to your betters, excuse the expression, you'll take my advice and not go to law either."

"Right you are! Won't you have a drink with me on the Peace of San Stephano?"

"I don't mind a drink. Only, Osip, you are a swine, brother. . . . I'm not swearing at you, it's just an expression. You're a swine, brother! Do you remember that time when you were grovelling before me, on your knees, after they kicked you out of the archbishop's choir? Eh? And you dare to hale your benefactor into court! You're a cur, a cur! And you're not ashamed? Gentlemen, I ask you, shouldn't this fellow be ashamed?"

"Allow me! But this is calling names again!"

"Who's calling names? I'm just talking, teaching you how to behave. . . . We've made up, and I'm telling you, for the last time, that I have no intention of swearing at you. . . . Catch me getting mixed up with you, you fiend, after you've tried to hale your benefactor into court! To hell with you! I don't even want to talk to you. And if I happened to call you a swine by accident just now, well, you really are a swine! . . . Instead of praying for your benefactor all your born days, because for ten years he fed you and taught you your notes, you file a stupid complaint against him and set a devil of a lawyer, a whole pack of them, on his trail!"

"Permit me, Dosifey Petrovich," put in Kalyakin, offended. "It was no devil who called on you: it was I. Please be a little more careful."

"Was I talking about you? You can call on me every day and welcome. But what astonishes me is that you, an educated man, a university graduate, instead of instructing this gander, you take his part! If I were you, I would send him to rot in prison! And besides, what are you angry about? I apologized, didn't I? What more do you want of me? I don't understand. Gentlemen, be my witnesses: I have apologized, and I have no intention of apologizing a second time to some idiot!"

"You're an idiot yourself," Osip brought out hoarsely, and struck his chest in an access of indignation.

"I'm an idiot? I! And you can say this to me?" Gradusov turned crimson and trembled. "You dared say it? Then take this! And the slap I just gave you, you scoundrel, isn't all: I'm going to take you to court, I'll show you what it means to insult a man. Gentlemen, be my witnesses. Officer, what's the matter with you, standing there just looking on? I'm being insulted and you don't lift a finger. You get your pay, but when it comes to keeping order, is it your business or not, eh? You think the law can't touch you?"

The police officer crossed over to Gradusov, and then the fun began.

A week later Gradusov was facing the justice of the peace, accused of having insulted Derevyashkin, the lawyer, and the police officer, the last as he was in the course of performing his official duties. At first he did not understand whether he was the plaintiff or the defendant, and when, finally, the justice sentenced him to a term of two months in jail, he smiled bitterly and muttered:

"H'mm, I was insulted and I am to do time! Queer . . . Your Honor, one must try a case according to law and not according to notions. Your dear mama, the late Varvara Sergeyevna, the Kingdom of

Heaven be hers, would have had fellows like Osip flogged, and you back them up. What will be the result? You will acquit these rascals, another judge will acquit them. . . . With whom, then, can one lodge a complaint?"

"You may file an appeal within two weeks. . . . And please watch your tongue. You may go."

"Certainly . . . Everybody knows that nowadays you can't get along on just your salary," Gradusov brought out, with a meaningful wink. "Willy-nilly, if you want to eat, you put an innocent man into the cooler. That's how it is, and you can't blame a person . . ."

"What!"

"Nothing sir. I was just, errh . . . I was talking about *haben Sie gewesen.* . . . You think that because you wear a gold chain you're above the law. Never mind, I'll show you up."

So now Gradusov was facing a charge of contempt of court. But the dean of the cathedral stepped in and somehow it was quashed.

When he appealed to the district court Gradusov was convinced that not only would he be acquitted, but that Osip would be clapped into jail. He clung to this conviction while the case was being tried. Standing before the justices, he behaved peaceably, with restraint, and said little. Only once, when the chairman invited him to sit down, he took offense and said:

"Is it written in the statute books that a choirmaster should sit next to one of his singers?"

When the court confirmed the verdict of the justice of the peace, he screwed up his eyes.

"What, sir? How's that, sir? he asked. "What do you mean, sir?"

"The district court has confirmed the verdict of the justice of the peace. If you're not satisfied, you may appeal to the senate."

"Yes, sir. My heartiest thanks, your Excellency, for this prompt and just verdict. Of course, one can't get along on just his salary nowadays. That I understand perfectly. But excuse me, we shall yet find a court that cannot be bribed."

I shall not repeat everything that Gradusov said to the district court. At present he is on trial again for contempt, but this time of a higher court, and he refuses to listen to friends who try to explain to him that he is to blame. He is convinced of his innocence and believes that, sooner or later, they will thank him for the abuses he has disclosed.

"There's nothing to be done with this fool," declared the dean, throwing up his arms, "he just doesn't understand."

John Galsworthy

:

MANNA

The Petty Sessions Court at Linstowe was crowded. Miracles do not happen every day, nor are rectors frequently charged with larceny. The interest roused would have relieved all those who doubt the vitality of our ancient church. People who never went outside their farms or plots of garden had walked as much as three miles to see the show. Mrs. Gloyn, the sandy-haired little keeper of the shop where soap and herrings, cheese, matches, boot-laces, bull's-eyes, and the other luxuries of a countryside could be procured, remarked to Mrs. Redland, the farmer's wife, " 'Tis quite a gatherin', like." To which Mrs. Redland replied, " 'Most like church of a Sunday."

More women, it is true, than men were present, because of their greater piety, and because most of them had parted with pounds of butter, chickens, ducks, potatoes, or some such offertory in kind during the past two years, at the instance of the rector. They had a vested interest in this matter, and were present, accompanied by their grief at value unreceived. From Trover, their little village on the top of the hill two miles from Linstowe, with the squat church tower, beautifully untouched, and the body of the building ruined by perfect restoration, they had trooped in; some even coming from the shore of the Atlantic a mile beyond, across the Downs, whence other upland square church towers could be viewed on the skyline against the gray January heavens. The occasion was in a sense unique, and its piquancy strengthened by that rivalry which is the essence of religion.

For there was no love lost between church and chapel in Trover, and the rector's flock had long been fortified in their power of "parting" by fear lest "chapel" (also present that day in court) should mock at his impecuniosity. Not that his flock approved of his poverty. It had seemed "silly-like" ever since the news had spread that his difficulties had been caused by a faith in shares. To improve a secure if moderate position by speculation would not have seemed wrong if he had succeeded, but failure had made him dependent on their butter, their potatoes, their eggs and chickens. In that parish, as in others, the saying "Nothing succeeds like success" was true, nor had the villagers any abnormal disposition to question the title-deeds of affluence.

But it is equally true that nothing irritates so much as finding that one of whom you have the right to beg is begging of you. This was why the rector's tall, thin, black figure, down which a ramrod surely had been passed at birth; his narrow, hairless, white and wasted face, with red eyebrows over eyes that seemed now burning and now melting; his grizzled red hair under a hat almost green with age; his abrupt and dictatorial voice; his abrupt and mirthless laugh—all were on their nerves. His barked-out utterances, "I want a pound of butter—pay you Monday!" "I want some potatoes—pay you soon!" had sounded too often in the ears of those who had found his repayments so far purely spiritual. Now and then one of the more cynical would remark, "Ah! I told un *my* butter was all to market." Or, "The man can't 'ave no principles— he didn't get no chicken out o' me." And yet it was impossible to let him and his old mother die on them—it would give too much pleasure "over the way." And they never dreamed of losing him in any other manner, because they knew his living had been purchased. Money had passed in that transaction; the whole fabric of the Church and of society was involved. His professional conduct, too, was flawless; his sermons long and fiery; he was always ready to perform those supernumerary duties—weddings, baptisms, and burials—which yielded him what revenue he had, now that his income from the living was mortgaged up to the hilt. Their loyalty held as the loyalty of people will when some great institution of which they are members is endangered.

Gossip said that things were in a dreadful way at the Rectory; the external prosperity of that red-brick building surrounded by laurels which did not flower, heightened ironically the conditions within. The old lady, his mother, eighty years of age, was reported never to leave her bed this winter, because they had no coal. She lay there, with her three birds flying about dirtying the room, for neither she nor her son would ever let a cage-door be shut—deplorable state of things! The one servant was supposed never to be paid. The tradesmen would no longer leave goods because they could not get their money. Most of the furniture had been sold; and the dust made you sneeze "fit to bust yourself, like."

With a little basket on his arm the rector collected for his household three times a week, pursuing a kind of method, always in the apparent belief that he would pay on Monday and observing the Sabbath as a day of rest. His mind seemed ever to cherish the faith that his shares were on the point of recovery; his spirit never to lose belief in his divine right to be supported. It was extremely difficult to refuse him; the postman had twice seen him standing on the railway line that ran past just below the village, "with 'is 'at off, as if he was in two minds —like!" This vision of him close to the shining metals had powerfully impressed many good souls who loved to make flesh creep. They would say, "I wouldn' never be surprised if someat' 'appened to 'im one of these days!" Others, less romantic, shook their heads, insisting that "he wouldn' never do nothin' while his old mother lived." Others again, more devout, maintained that "he wouldn' never go against the scriptures, settin' an example like that!"

II

The Petty Sessions Court that morning resembled church on the occasion of a wedding, for the villagers of Trover had put on their black clothes and grouped themselves according to their religious faiths—"Church" in the right, "Chapel" in the left-hand aisle. They presented all that rich variety of type and monotony which the remoter country still affords to the observer; their mouths were almost all a little open and their eyes fixed with intensity on the Bench. The three magistrates— Squire Pleydell in the chair, Dr. Becket on his left, and "the Honble" Calmady on his right—were by most seen for the first time in their judicial capacity; and curiosity was divided between their proceedings and observation of the rector's prosecutor, a small baker from the town whence the village of Trover derived its necessaries. The face of this fellow, like that of a white walrus, and the back of his bald head were of interest to everyone until the case was called and the rector himself entered. In his thin black overcoat he advanced and stood as if a little dazed. Then, turning his ravaged face to the Bench, he jerked out:

"Good morning! Lot of people!"

A constable behind him murmured:

"Into the dock, sir, please."

Moving across, he entered the wooden edifice.

"Quite like a pulpit," he said, and uttered his barking laugh.

Through the court ran a stir and shuffle, as it might be of sympathy with his lost divinity, and every eye was fixed on that tall lean figure, with the red, gray-streaked hair.

Entering the witness-box, the prosecutor deposed as follows:

"Last Tuesday afternoon, your Honors, I 'appened to be drivin' my cart meself up through Trover on to the cottages just above the dip, and I'd gone in to Mrs. 'Oney's, the laundress, leavin' my cart standin', same as I always do. I 'ad a bit o' gossip, an' when I come out, I see this gentleman walkin' away in front towards the village street. It so 'appens I 'appened to look in the back o' my cart, and I thinks to meself: 'That's funny! There's only two flat rounds—'ave I left two 'ere by mistake?' I call to Mrs. 'Oney an' I says, 'I 'aven't been absent, 'ave I, an' left ye two?' 'No,' she says, 'only one—'ere 'tis! Why?' she says. 'Well,' I says, 'I 'ad four when I come in to you; there's only two now. 'Tis funny!' I says. ' 'Ave you dropped one?' she says. 'No,' I says, 'I counted 'em.' 'That's funny,' she says; 'perhaps a dog's 'ad it.' ' 'E may 'ave,' I says, 'but the only thing I see on the road is that there.' An' I pointed to this gentleman. 'Oh!' she says, 'that's the rector.' 'Yes,' I says, 'I ought to know that, seein' 'e's owed me money a matter of eighteen months. I think I'll drive on,' I says. Well, I drove on, and come up to this gentleman. 'E turns 'is 'ead and looks at me. 'Good afternoon!' he says—like that. 'Good afternoon, sir,' I says. 'You 'aven't seen a loaf, 'ave you?' 'E pulls the loaf out of 'is pocket. 'On the ground,' 'e says; 'dirty,' 'e says. 'Do for my birds! Ha! ha!' like that. 'Oh!' I says, 'indeed! Now I know!' I says. I kept my 'ead, but I thinks: 'That's a bit too light-'earted. You owes me one pound, eight and tuppence; I've whistled for it gettin' on for two years, but you ain't content with that, it seems! Very well,' I thinks; 'we'll see.' An' I don't give a darn whether you're a parson or not!' I charge 'im with takin' my bread."

Passing a dirty handkerchief over his white face and huge gingery mustache, the baker was silent. Suddenly from the dock the rector called out: "Bit of dirty bread—feed my birds. Ha, ha!"

There was a deathly little silence. Then the baker said slowly:

"What's more, I say he ate it 'imself. I call two witnesses to that."

The chairman, passing his hand over his hard, alert face, that of a master of hounds, asked:

"Did you see any dirt on the loaf? Be careful!"

The baker answered stolidly:

"Not a speck."

Dr. Becket, a slight man with a short gray beard and eyes restive from having to notice painful things, spoke:

"Had your horse moved?"

"'E never moves."

"Ha, ha!" came the rector's laugh.

The chairman said sharply:

"Well, stand down; call the next witness—Charles Stodder, carpenter. Very well! Go on, and tell us what you know."

But before he could speak the rector called out in a loud voice, "Chapel!"

"Hsssh, sir!" But through the body of the court had passed a murmur of challenge, as it were, from one aisle to the other.

The witness, a square man with a red face, gray hair, whiskers, and mustache, and lively, excitable, dark eyes, watering with anxiety, spoke in a fast, soft voice.

"Tuesday afternoon, your worships, it might be about four o'clock, I was passin' up the village, an' I saw the rector at his gate with a loaf in 'is 'and."

"Show us how."

The witness held his black hat to his side, with the rounded top outwards.

"Was the loaf clean or dirty?"

Sweetening his little eyes, the witness answered:

"I should say 'twas clean."

"Lie!"

The chairman said sternly:

"You mustn't interrupt, sir. You didn't see the bottom of the loaf?" The witness's little eyes snapped.

"Not eggzactly."

"Did the rector speak to you?"

The witness smiled. "The rector wouldn' never stop me if I was passin'. I collects the rates."

The rector's laugh, so like a desolate dog's bark, killed the bubble of gaiety rising in the court; and again that deathly little silence followed.

Then the chairman said:

"Do you want to ask him anything?"

The rector turned. "Why d'you tell lies?"

The witness, screwing up his eyes, said excitedly:

"What lies 'ave I told, please?"

"You said the loaf was clean."

"So 'twas clean, so far as I see."

"Come to church and you won't tell lies."

"Reckon I can learn truth faster in chapel."

The chairman rapped his desk.

"That'll do, that'll do! Stand down! Next witness—Emily Bleaker. Yes? What are you? Cook at the rectory? Very well. What do you know about the affair of this loaf last Tuesday afternoon?"

The witness, a broad-faced, brown-eyed girl, answered stolidly, "Nothin', zurr."

"Ha, ha!"

"Hssh! Did you see the loaf?"

"Noa."

"What are you here for, then?"

"Master asked for a plate and a knaife. He an' old missus ate et for dinner. I see the plate after; there wasn't on'y crumbs on et."

"If you never saw the loaf, how do you know they ate it?"

"Because ther warn't nothin' else in the 'ouse."

The rector's voice barked out:

"Quite right!"

The chairman looked at him fixedly.

"Do you want to ask her anything?"

The rector nodded.

"You been paid your wages?"

"Noa, I 'asn't."

"D'you know why?"

"Noa."

"Very sorry—no money to pay you. That's all."

This closed the prosecutor's case and there followed a pause, during which the Bench consulted together and the rector eyed the congregation, nodding to one here and there. Then the chairman, turning to him, said:

"Now, sir, do you call any witnesses?"

"Yes. My bell-ringer. He's a good man. You can believe him."

The bell-ringer, Samuel Bevis, who took his place in the witness-box, was a kind of elderly Bacchus, with permanently trembling hands. He deposed as follows:

"When I passed rector Tuesday afternoon, he calls after me: 'See this!' 'e says, and up 'e held it. 'Bit o' dirrty bread,' 'e says: 'do for my burrds.' Then on he goes walkin'."

"Did you see whether the loaf was dirty?"

"Yaas, I think 'twas dirrty."

"Don't *think!* Do you *know?*"

"Yaas; 'twas dirrty."

"Which side?"

"Which saide? I think 'twas dirrty on the bottom."

"Are you sure?"

"Yaas; 'twas dirrty on the bottom, for zartain."

"Very well. Stand down. Now, sir, will you give us your version of this matter?"

The rector, pointing at the prosecutor and the left-hand aisle, jerked out the words:

"All chapel—want to see me down."

The chairman said stonily:

"Never mind that. Come to the facts, please."

"Certainly! Out for a walk—passed the baker's cart—saw a loaf fallen in the mud—picked it up—do for my birds."

"What birds?"

"Magpie and two starlings; quite free—never shut the cage door; well fed."

"The baker charges you with taking it from his cart."

"Lie! Underneath the cart in a puddle."

"You heard what your cook said about your eating it. Did you?"

"Yes, birds couldn't eat all—nothing in the house—mother and I—hungry."

"Hungry?"

"No money. Hard up—very! Often hungry. Ha, ha!"

Again through the court that queer rustle passed. The three magistrates gazed at the accused. Then "the Honble" Calmady said:

"You say you found the loaf under the cart. Didn't it occur to you to put it back? You could see it had fallen. How else could it have come there?"

The rector's burning eyes seemed to melt.

"From the sky—manna." Staring round the court, he added, "Hungry—God's elect—to the manna born!" And, throwing back his head, he laughed. It was the only sound in a silence as of the grave.

The magistrates spoke together in low tones. The rector stood motionless, gazing at them fixedly. The people in the court sat as if at a play. Then the chairman said:

"Case dismissed."

"Thank you."

Jerking out that short thanksgiving, the rector descended from the dock and passed down the center aisle, followed by every eye.

III

From the Petty Sessions Court the congregation wended its way back to Trover, by the muddy lane, "Church" and "Chapel," arguing the case. To dim the triumph of the "Church" the fact remained that the baker had lost his loaf and had not been compensated. The loaf was worth money; no money had passed. It was hard to be victorious and yet reduced to silence and dark looks at girding adversaries. The nearer they came to home, the more angry with "Chapel" did they grow. Then the bell-ringer had his inspiration. Assembling his three assistants, he hurried to the belfry, and in two minutes the little old tower was belching forth the merriest and maddest peal those bells had ever furnished. Out it swung in the still air of the gray winter day, away to the very sea.

A stranger, issuing from the inn, hearing that triumphant sound, and seeing so many black-clothed people about, said to his driver:

"What is it—a wedding?"

"No, zurr, they say 'tis for the rector, like; he've a just been acquitted for larceny."

*

On the Tuesday following, the rector's ravaged hairless face appeared in Mrs. Gloyn's doorway, and his voice, creaking like a saw, said:

"Can you let me have a pound of butter? Pay you soon."

What else could he do? Not even to God's elect does the sky always send down manna.

Luigi Pirandello

:

SICILIAN HONOR

As soon as prisoner Saru Argentu—known to his friends as Tarara—
was brought into the caged dock of the squalid Court of Assizes he
pulled out of his pocket an immense red cotton handkerchief heavily
over-printed with yellow flowers and spread it with great care on the
bench so as not to dirty the sky-blue colored suit which he had bought
specially for his trial. A brand-new suit and a brand-new handkerchief
they were.

Then—sitting on the bench—he quietly turned his smiling face to
the peasants packing the part of the Court left open to the public. His
flat, fierce-looking face, freshly shaven but wrinkled and angular, with
two heavy golden pendants dangling from his ears, gave him the peculiar appearance of a monkey which could not help being comic even
in the sad atmosphere of a Sicilian Court.

A thick, horrid stench, a mixture of stable and perspiration, a stink of
goats, a fustiness of filthy animals, was filling the room.

Some of the women, shading their eyes with black mantillas, could
not help crying at the sight of the prisoner, but Tarara himself, craning
his neck right and left, went on smiling from his cage, now lifting one of
his heavy rough hands as a salute, now nodding at them as if he were
pleased to see again so many familiar faces of friends and work companions.

It was, in fact, almost a joy for him to be at last able to appear at his
trial after so many months of preventive prison. He was so poor that he

had not even been able to pay for a counsel of his own choice, and he had to accept legal aid of the State; but, as far as his own person was concerned, he had at least been able to come to the trial in a new suit, well groomed and freshly shaven as on a Sunday.

After the first formalities, the jury sworn in, the President ordered the prisoner to stand.

"Your name?"

"Tarara."

"This is a nickname. What's your real name?"

"Well, yes. . . . Argentu, Saru Argentu, Your Honor, but they all know me as 'Tarara'."

"Very well. How old are you?"

"I don't know, Your Honor."

"What, you don't know your own age?"

Tarara shrugged his shoulders, meaning that the question of age was a mere worldly vanity to which no one need attach too much importance.

"I live in the country, Your Honor. Who bothers about age, there?"

A burst of laughter filled the Court, and the President, bending his head, began to consult the papers in front of him.

"You were born in 1873: you are therefore thirty-nine."

Tarara opened both arms as if bending to the inevitable.

"Your Honor knows best."

To prevent fresh laughter, the President avoided putting more formal questions by giving himself the answer: "It is so. . . . It is so. . . ." At last he said:

"Sit down. The Clerk will now read you the charge for which you are being tried."

The Clerk started reading the charge, but he had soon to stop, for the foreman of the jury, overpowered by the stench of the Court, was on the point of fainting. Orders were given for all windows and doors to be left open.

It was then that the prisoner's superiority over those who were going to be his judges appeared as clear and as unquestionable as daylight.

Sitting on his huge scarlet handkerchief, Tarara was entirely indifferent to that nasty stench with which he was so familiar. He could in fact still smile, hardly feeling the heat in his heavy sky-blue Sunday suit. Even the flies—which were upsetting the members of the jury, the public prosecutor, the clerk, the lawyers, the ushers and even the jailers—were not giving him the slightest trouble.

They were resting on his hands, buzzing around his face, sticking to his forehead or even to the corners of his mouth and eyes, but he was not feeling them, nor was he even trying to chase them away. Unconcerned with all this, he was all smiles for his friends. He was sure of his acquittal. He had murdered to defend his honor.

The young barrister briefed by the State for his defense had reassured him that although he was guilty of having murdered his wife, there could be no verdict of guilty, the murder indisputably having been committed on the discovery of her unfaithfulness.

In the blessed unawareness of the beasts, Tarara could therefore ignore even the remotest shadow of remorse. All that was puzzling him was the fact that he had been brought to answer for something which, after all, was no concern of anyone else but himself. All this staging of justice appeared to him as something inevitable, like Fate. Justice was for him like a bad year on land, nothing more. And justice, with all its solemn setting of high benches, bells, robes and uniforms was for Tarara something as mysterious as the great new steam mill of his village which had been opened with great pomp the previous year. One could bring his own grist to that mill, but who could guarantee that the flour one received back was from the same grist? It was a question of accepting with blind eyes and with resignation the flour which it pleased the miller to give.

Comparing the mysterious machinery of the steam mill (which had aroused in him so much diffidence) with the equally complicated and mysterious wheels of justice, Tarara could not help thinking that his case was like the grist brought to the mill: one had to accept the result which would come out of the trial as one had to accept the flour which came out of the mill.

He knew, of course, that he had split open his wife's head with a hatchet because, returning home on a Saturday night soaking with rain and covered with mud, he had found the whole lane astir over a horrible scandal which had broken out in his home. A few hours previously his wife had been discovered in his bedroom with the young Count Agatino Fiorica, the wealthy landowner. It was Fiorica's wife who had informed the police and who had caused the two lovers to be arrested according to the law. It has become impossible for the neighbors to hide the event from Tarara, for his wife had been kept at the police station all night with her lover and next morning, when Tarara saw her creeping back to his door, he had leapt on her holding the hatchet in his hand and splitting her head before anybody had time to stop him.

All this he knew, of course, but how different it seemed from that long story which the Clerk was reading. . . .

When the Clerk finished, the President asked the prisoner to stand again:

"Prisoner at the bar, you have now heard the crime with which you are charged."

Tarara made a slight gesture and with his usual smile he answered:

"To tell you the truth, Your Honor, I did not pay any attention."

The President looked at him sternly:

"You are accused of having willfully murdered with a hatchet your wife, Rosaria Femminella, on the morning of the 10th of December, 1911. What have you to say in your defense? Turn to the jury and speak to them clearly and with the respect due to justice."

Tarara laid a hand on his chest to convey his respect due to justice, but feeling that another burst of laughter might follow his words, he stood silent for a long time unable to find his words, uncertain and shy.

"Well," insisted the President, "what have you to say? Tell the jury all you know. . . ."

Tarara shrugged his shoulders and said:

"Your Honor and you, too, gentlemen, you are learned people who understood all that is written in those papers, but I live in the country. If the writing in those papers says that I have killed my wife, then it is true and let us talk no more about it."

Even the President this time had to join in the general laughter.

"Let us talk no more about it? I am afraid you will soon see that there will be a lot to talk about, on the contrary."

"I mean, Your Honor," explained Tarara, again laying his hand on his chest, "I mean to say that I did it. Yes, I did it, that's all. I did it because I couldn't help it."

"Order, order," shouted the President at the fresh outburst of laughter, furiously ringing his bell. "This is a Court of Justice, where a man is being tried for murder. I shall order to clear the Court if there is more laughter and I must warn the jury on the seriousness of their task."

Then turning sternly to the dock:

"What do you mean by saying you could not help it?"

"I mean, Your Honor, that it wasn't my fault."

"Not your fault? Whose fault then?"

"Allow me to interrupt, Your Honor." The young State counsel jumped up, getting alarmed at the aggressive tone of the President. "It is quite obvious that if we carry on like this we shall be entangling this poor man altogether. I think he is right in saying that the fault was not his but that of his wife, who was betraying him with Count Fiorica. It's as clear as daylight."

"Let the prisoner answer for himself," rebuked the President. Then, turning to Tarara: "Is this what you intended saying?"

Tarara first shook his head, then added:

"No, Your Honor. It wasn't that poor woman's fault either. It was all the fault of that lady, Count Fiorica's wife, who stirred matters up. What business had she, I am asking Your Honor, that woman to raise such a terrible scandal at my doorstep that even the stones of the street had to blush for shame? What business had she to follow that perfect gentleman Count Fiorica to the slum of a dirty peasant? God alone knows, Your Honor, what we poor people have to do to earn a crust of bread."

There were tears in his eyes, while he was clasping both hands on his chest, but all round the Court people were bending in convulsions of laughter. The President alone—and Tarara's counsel—had seen the importance of a statement which seemed to rob the defense of its principal argument: intense provocation.

"You confess, then?" said the President, "that you were aware of your wife's relations with Count Fiorica. Is it so?"

"Your Honor," interrupted the young counsel, jumping to his feet, "I protest. This question should have never been put. I formally object to it being put to my client."

"But I am following your client's own confession . . ." retorted the President.

"My client has never confessed. All he said is that the cause of his action was Signora Fiorica raising such a scandal on his doorstep. . . ."

"Quite right, but you cannot stop me asking the prisoner whether he knew before the day of the crime of the immoral relations of his wife with the Count."

The whole Court was getting restless. From every corner violent signs were made to Tarara that he should deny any knowledge of his wife's unfaithfulness, but Tarara remained shy, uncertain and frightened. He could find no words to answer, turning at times to his counsel and at times to the audience where dozens of hands were making frantic signs of denial.

"Must I. . . . Must I . . . say no?" he muttered to the audience.

"Old turnip," yelled somebody from the bottom of the Court.

"You must tell the truth," admonished the President. "In your own interest."

"Well, Your Honor, I am telling the truth," said Tarara, trembling and crossing both hands on his chest. "I am. And the truth is this: I knew it and yet it was as if I didn't know it. The thing, Your Honor, was on the quiet and nobody could have dared to face me and tell me that I knew it. I am a peasant, gentlemen, and what can a peasant know when he toils like a beast in the fields from Monday morning till Saturday night? What does a peasant know of his troubles at home? Of course, if somebody had come to me and told me: 'Tarara, your wife and Count Fiorica are too friendly,' I would have rushed home and split my wife's head with my hatchet. But nobody had ever come to tell me, Your Honor, and in order not to raise trouble I even sent someone to give warning when I had to return home earlier than the end of the week. This shows, Your Honor, how careful I have been to avoid doing any harm to anybody. Men are what they are and women too. Of course men should know that women have it in their blood to be untrue even if their husband is never away, but women too should know that men cannot so lightly stand the scorn of their friends. . . . There are certain insults which slash your face like a knife. . . . No man can stand them. Now, gentlemen of the jury, you will understand me when I say that my poor wife would have never allowed me to be insulted, and in fact I have never even had a cross word with her, as all my neighbors can witness. But what fault have I, gentlemen of the jury, if that blessed lady, without any warning. . . . Yes, Your Honor, you should get her here, that lady, to face me and I would tell her: If your husband had had a similar affair with a spinster you might have pleased yourself as there was no husband to consider, but by what right have you come to upset me, who have always led a quiet life, who had nothing to do with the matter, who had always refused to see or hear anything, toiling from Monday morning to Saturday night in the fields to earn a living? Do you think you can allow yourself such fun? This scandal may be merely a joke for you: you are sure to take your husband back after a couple of days. But did it ever occur to you that your joke might affect the whole life of another man and that this man could not allow his face to be slashed by the ridicule you aroused and that he would have to act as a man must act? Why didn't you come to me first? I would have told you: Leave them alone. All men are alike. Man is a hunter. Can you really be jealous of a dirty peasant woman? Can you blame your husband if he fancies a bit of brown bread every now and then instead of the white one of every day? This, Your Honor, I would have told the lady and most likely nothing would have happened of what has happened through her fault, as I told you before, through her fault alone. . . ."

Hilarity mixed with loud comments followed the prisoner's long speech. With resounding ringings of the bell the President tried to restore order. Then he said:

"Prisoner at the bar. Is this your defense?"

"No, Your Honor, it is not my defense . . . it is the truth, merely the truth."

But as truth—even so candidly confessed—is not always easy to be accepted, the jury found Tarara guilty of murder with only mild provocation and a sentence of thirteen years' imprisonment followed.

Sholom Aleichem

:

DREYFUS IN KASRILEVKA

I doubt if the Dreyfus case made such a stir anywhere as it did in Kasrilevka.

Paris, they say, seethed like a boiling vat. The papers carried streamers, generals shot themselves, and small boys ran like mad in the streets, threw their caps in the air, and shouted wildly, "Long live Dreyfus!" or "Long live Esterhazy!" Meanwhile the Jews were insulted and beaten, as always. But the anguish and pain that Kasrilevka underwent, Paris will not experience till Judgment Day.

How did Kasrilevka get wind of the Dreyfus case? Well, how did it find out about the war between the English and the Boers, or what went on in China? What do they have to do with China? Tea they got from Wisotzky in Moscow. In Kasrilevka they do not wear the light summer material that comes from China and is called pongee. That is not for their purses. They are lucky if they have a pair of trousers and an undershirt, and they sweat just as well, especially if the summer is a hot one.

So how did Kasrilevka learn about the Dreyfus case? From Zeidel.

Zeidel, Reb Shaye's son, was the only person in town who subscribed to a newspaper, and all the news of the world they learned from him, or rather through him. He read and they interpreted. He spoke and they supplied the commentary. He told what he read in the paper, but they turned it around to suit themselves, because they understood better than he did.

One day Zeidel came to the synagogue and told how in Paris a certain Jewish captain named Dreyfus had been imprisoned for turning over certain government papers to the enemy. This went into one ear and out of the other. Someone remarked in passing, "What won't a Jew do to make a living?"

And another added spitefully, "A Jew has no business climbing so high, interfering with kings and their affairs."

Later when Zeidel came to them and told them a fresh tale, that the whole thing was a plot, that the Jewish Captain Dreyfus was innocent and that it was an intrigue of certain officers who were themselves involved, then the town became interested in the case. At once Dreyfus became a Kasrilevkite. When two people came together, he was the third.

"Have you heard?"

"I've heard."

"Sent away for good."

"A life sentence."

"For nothing at all."

"A false accusation."

Later when Zeidel came to them and told them that there was a possibility that the case might be tried again, that there were some good people who undertook to show the world that the whole thing had been a plot, Kasrilevka began to rock indeed. First of all, Dreyfus was one of *ours*. Secondly, how could such an ugly thing happen in Paris? It didn't do any credit to the French. Arguments broke out everywhere; bets were made. Some said the case would be tried again, others said it would not. Once the decision had been made, it was final. All was lost.

As the case went on, they got tired of waiting for Zeidel to appear in the synagogue with the news; they began to go to his house. Then they could not wait that long, and they began to go along with him to the post office for his paper. There they read, digested the news, discussed, shouted, gesticulated, all together and in their loudest voices. More than once the postmaster had to let them know in gentle terms that the post office was not the synagogue. "This is not your synagogue, you Jews. This is not *kahal shermaki*."

They heard him the way Haman hears the *grager* on *Purim*. He shouted, and they continued to read the paper and discuss Dreyfus.

They talked not only of Dreyfus. New people were always coming into the case. First Esterhazy, then Picquart, then General Mercies, Pellieux Gonse . . .

There were two people whom Kasrilevka came to love and revere. These were Emile Zola and Labori. For Zola each one would gladly have died. If Zola had come to Kasrilevka the whole town would have come out to greet him, they would have borne him aloft on their shoulders.

"What do you think of his letters?"

"Pearls. Diamonds. Rubies."

They also thought highly of Labori. The crowd delighted in him, praised him to the skies, and, as we say, licked their fingers over his speeches. Although no one in Kasrilevka had ever heard him, they were sure he must know how to make a fine speech.

I doubt if Dreyfus' relatives in Paris awaited his return from the Island as anxiously as the Jews of Kasrilevka. They traveled with him over the sea, felt themselves rocking on the waves. A gale arose and tossed the ship up and down, up and down, like a stick of wood. "Lord of Eternity," they prayed in their hearts, "be merciful and bring him safely to the place of the trial. Open the eyes of the judges, clear their brains, so they may find the guilty one and the whole world may know of our innocence. Amen. *Selah.*"

The day when the good news came that Dreyfus had arrived was celebrated like a holiday in Kasrilevka. If they had not been ashamed to do so, they would have closed their shops.

"Have you heard?"

"Thank the Lord."

"Ah, I would have liked to have been there when he met his wife."

"And I would have liked to see the children when they were told, 'Your father has arrived.' "

And the women, when they heard the news, hid their faces in their aprons and pretended to blow their noses so no one could see they were crying. Poor as Kasrilevka was, there was not a person there who would not have given his very last penny to take one look at the arrival.

As the trial began, a great excitement took hold of the town. They tore not only the paper to pieces, but Zeidel himself. They choked on their food, they did not sleep nights. They waited for the next day, the next and the next.

Suddenly there arose a hubbub, a tumult. That was when the lawyer, Labori, was shot. All Kasrilevka was beside itself.

"Why? For what? Such an outrage! Without cause! Worse than in Sodom!"

That shot was fired at their heads. The bullet was lodged in their breasts, just as if the assassin had shot at Kasrilevka itself.

"God in Heaven," they prayed, "reveal thy wonders. Thou knowest how if thou wishest. Perform a miracle, that Labori might live."

And God performed the miracle. Labori lived.

When the last day of the trial came, the Kasrilevkites shook as with a fever. They wished they could fall asleep for twenty-four hours and not wake up till Dreyfus was declared a free man.

But as if in spite, not a single one of them slept a wink that night. They rolled all night from side to side, waged war with the bedbugs, and waited for day to come.

At the first sign of dawn they rushed to the post office. The outer gates were still closed. Little by little a crowd gathered outside and the street was filled with people. Men walked up and down, yawning, stretching, pulling their earlocks and praying under their breath.

When Yadama the janitor opened the gates they poured in after him. Yadama grew furious. He would show them who was master here, and pushed and shoved till they were all out in the street again. There they waited for Zeidel to come. And at last he came.

When Zeidel opened the paper and read the news aloud, there arose such an outcry, such a clamor, such a roar that the heavens could have split open. Their outcry was not against the judges who gave the wrong verdict, not at the generals who swore falsely, not at the French who showed themselves up so badly. The outcry was against Zeidel.

"It cannot be!" Kasrilevka shouted with one voice. "Such a verdict is impossible! Heaven and earth swore that the truth must prevail. What kind of lies are you telling us?"

"Fools!" shouted Zeidel, and thrust the paper into their faces. "Look! See what the paper says!"

"Paper! Paper!" shouted Kasrilevka. "And if you stood with one foot in heaven and the other on earth, would we believe you?"

"Such a thing must not be. It must never be! Never! Never!"

And—who was right?

W. S. Gilbert

:

TRIAL BY JURY

DRAMATIS PERSONAE

THE LEARNED JUDGE
THE PLAINTIFF
THE DEFENDANT
COUNSEL FOR THE PLAINTIFF
USHER
FOREMAN OF THE JURY
ASSOCIATE
FIRST BRIDESMAID

SCENE: *A Court of Justice. Barristers, Attorneys, and Jury-men discovered.*

CHORUS: Hark, the hour of ten is sounding:
    Hearts with anxious fears are bounding,
    Hall of Justice crowds surrounding,
     Breathing hope and fear—
    For to-day in this arena,
    Summoned by a stern subpoena,
    Edwin, sued by Angelina,
     Shortly will appear.

   Enter USHER

SOLO—USHER: Now, Jurymen, hear my advice—
    All kinds of vulgar prejudice
     I pray you set aside:
    With stern judicial frame of mind
    From bias free of every kind,
     This trial must be tried.

CHORUS: From bias free of every kind,
     This trial must be tried.

 (*During Chorus,* USHER *sings fortissimo, "Silence in Court!"*)

USHER: Oh, listen to the plaintiff's case:
    Observe the features of her face—
     The broken-hearted bride.
    Condole with her distress of mind:
    From bias free of every kind,
     This trial must be tried!

CHORUS: From bias free, etc.

USHER: And when amid the plaintiff's shrieks,
    The ruffianly defendant speaks—
     Upon the other side;
    What *he* may say you needn't mind—
    From bias free of every kind,
     This trial must be tried!

CHORUS: From bias free, etc.

Enter DEFENDANT

RECIT—DEFENDANT: Is this the Court of the Exchequer?

ALL: It is!

DEFENDANT (*aside*): Be firm, be firm, my pecker,
　　Your evil star's in the ascendant!

ALL: Who are you?

DEFENDANT: I'm the Defendant!

CHORUS OF JURYMEN (*shaking their fists*):

　　　　　Monster, dread our damages.
　　　　　We're the jury,
　　　　　Dread our fury!

DEFENDANT:　　Hear me, hear me, if you please,
　　　　　These are very strange proceedings—
　　　　For permit me to remark
　　　　　On the merits of my pleadings,
　　　　You're at present in the dark.

DEFENDANT *beckons to* JURYMEN—*they leave the box and gather
round him as they sing the following:*

　　　　　That's a very true remark—
　　　　　　On the merits of his pleadings
　　　　　We're at present in the dark!
　　　　　Ha! ha!—ha! ha!

SONG—DEFENDANT:

　　　　　When first my old, old love I knew,
　　　　　　My bosom welled with joy;
　　　　　My riches at her feet I threw—
　　　　　　I was a love-sick boy!
　　　　　No terms seemed too extravagant
　　　　　　Upon her to employ—
　　　　I used to mope, and sigh, and pant,
　　　　　Just like a love-sick boy!
　　　　　　　Tink-a-Tank—Tink-a-Tank.

　　　　　But joy incessant palls the sense;
　　　　　　And love, unchanged, will cloy,
　　　　And she became a bore intense
　　　　　Unto her love-sick boy!
　　　　With fitful glimmer burnt my flame,
　　　　　And I grew cold and coy,

At last, one morning, I became
Another's love-sick boy.
                    Tink-a-Tank—Tink-a-Tank.

CHORUS OF JURYMEN (*advancing stealthily*):
Oh, I was like that when a lad!
    A shocking young scamp of a rover,
I behaved like a regular cad;
    But that sort of thing is all over.
I'm now a respectable chap
    And shine with a virtue resplendent
And, therefore, I haven't a scrap
    Of sympathy with the defendant!
        He shall treat us with awe,
        If there isn't a flaw,
Singing so merrily—Trial-la-law!
Trial-la-law—Trial-la-law!
Singing so merrily—Trial-la-law!

They enter the Jury-box.

RECIT—USHER (*on Bench*):
Silence in Court, and all attention lend.
Behold your Judge! In due submission bend!

Enter JUDGE *on Bench*

CHORUS:
All hail great Judge!
    To your bright rays
We never grudge
    Ecstatic praise.
            All hail!

May each decree
    As statute rank
And never be
    Reversed in banc.
            All hail!

RECIT—JUDGE:
For these kind words accept my thanks, I pray.
A Breach of Promise we've to try to-day.
But firstly, if the time you'll not begrudge,
I'll tell you how I came to be a Judge.

ALL: He'll tell us how he came to be a Judge!
SONG—JUDGE:

> When I, good friends, was called to the bar,
>> I'd an appetite fresh and hearty,
> But I was, as many young barristers are,
>> An impecunious party.
>
> I'd a swallow-tail coat of a beautiful blue—
>> A brief which I bought of a booby—
> A couple of shirts and a collar or two,
>> And a ring that looked like a ruby!

CHORUS: A couple of shirts, etc.
JUDGE:

> In Westminster Hall I danced a dance,
>> Like a semi-despondent fury;
> For I thought I should never hit on a chance
>> Of addressing a British Jury—
> But I soon got tired of third-class journeys,
>> And dinners of bread and water;
> So I fell in love with a rich attorney's
>> Elderly, ugly daughter.

CHORUS: So he fell in love, etc.
JUDGE:

> The rich attorney, he jumped with joy,
>> And replied to my fond professions:
> "You shall reap the reward of your pluck, my
>> boy
> At the Bailey and Middlesex Sessions.
> You'll soon get used to her looks," said he,
>> "And a very nice girl you'll find her!
> She may very well pass for forty-three
>> In the dusk, with a light behind her!"

CHORUS: She may very well, etc.
JUDGE:

> The rich attorney was good as his word;
>> The briefs came trooping gaily,
> And every day my voice was heard
>> At the Sessions or Ancient Bailey.
> All thieves who could my fees afford
>> Relied on my orations,
> And many a burglar I've restored

To his friends and his relations.

CHORUS: And many a burglar, etc.

JUDGE: At length I became as rich as the Gurneys—
An incubus then I thought her,
So I threw over that rich attorney's
Elderly, ugly daughter.
The rich attorney my character high
Tried vainly to disparage—
And now, if you please, I'm ready to try
This Breach of Promise of Marriage!

CHORUS: And now if you please, etc.

JUDGE: For now I am a Judge!

ALL: And a good Judge too.

JUDGE: Yes, now I am a Judge!

ALL: And a good Judge too!

JUDGE: Though all my law is fudge,
Yet I'll never, never budge,
But I'll live and die a Judge!

ALL: And a good Judge too!

JUDGE (*pianissimo*) : It was managed by a job—

ALL: And a good job too!

JUDGE: It was managed by a job!

ALL: And a good job too!

JUDGE: It is patent to the mob,
That my being made a nob
Was effected by a job.

ALL: And a good job too!

Enter COUNSEL *for* PLAINTIFF. *He takes his place in front row of Counsels' seats.*

RECIT—COUNSEL: Swear thou the Jury!

USHER: Kneel, Jurymen, oh, kneel!

All the JURY *kneel in the Jury-box, and so are hidden from audience.*

USHER: Oh, will you swear by yonder skies,
Whatever question may arise,
'Twixt rich and poor, 'twixt low and high,
That you will well and truly try?

JURY (*raising their hands, which alone are visible*) :
To all of this we make reply

By the dull slate of yonder sky:
That we will well and truly try.

(*All rise with the last note.*)

RECIT—COUNSEL: Where is the Plaintiff?
Let her now be brought.

RECIT—USHER:

Oh, Angelina! Come thou into Court!
Angelina! Angelina!!

Enter the BRIDESMAIDS.

CHORUS OF BRIDESMAIDS:

Comes the broken flower—
Comes the cheated maid—
Though the tempest lower,
Rain and cloud will fade
Take, oh take these posies:
Though thy beauty rare
Shame the blushing roses,
They are passing fair!
Wear the flowers till they fade;
Happy be thy life, oh maid!

The JUDGE, *having taken a great fancy to* FIRST BRIDESMAID, *sends her a note by* USHER, *which she reads, kisses rapturously, and places in her bosom.*

Enter PLAINTIFF.

SOLO—PLAINTIFF:

O'er the season vernal,
Time may cast a shade;
Sunshine, if eternal,
Makes the roses fade!
Time may do his duty;
Let the thief alone—
Winter hath a beauty,
That is all his own.
Fairest days are sun and shade:
I am no unhappy maid!

The JUDGE *having by this time transferred his admiration to* PLAIN-TIFF, *directs the* USHER *to take the note from* FIRST BRIDESMAID *and hand it to* PLAINTIFF, *who reads it, kisses it rapturously, and places it in her bosom.*

CHORUS OF BRIDESMAIDS:
>   Comes the broken flower, etc.

JUDGE: Oh, never, never, never, since I joined the human race,
>   Saw I so exquisitely fair a face.

THE JURY (*shaking their forefingers at him*): Ah, sly dog! Ah, sly dog!

JUDGE (*to* JURY): How say you? Is she not designed for capture?

FOREMAN (*after consulting with the* JURY): We've but one word, my
>   lord, and that is—Rapture.

PLAINTIFF (*curtseying*): Your kindness, gentlemen, quite overpowers!

JURY: We love you fondly and would make you ours!

THE BRIDESMAIDS (*shaking their forefingers at* JURY):
>   Ah, sly dogs! Ah, sly dogs!

RECIT— COUNSEL *for* PLAINTIFF:
>   May it please you, my lud!
>   Gentlemen of the jury!

ARIA
>   With a sense of deep emotion,
>   I approach this painful case;
>   For I never had a notion
>   That a man could be so base,
>   Or deceive a girl confiding,
>   Vows, *etcetera,* deriding.

ALL:
>   He deceived a girl confiding,
>   Vows, *etcetera,* deriding.

> PLAINTIFF *falls sobbing on* COUNSEL's *breast and remains there.*

COUNSEL:
>   See my interesting client,
>   Victim of a heartless wile!
>   See the traitor all defiant
>   Wear a supercilious smile!
>   Sweetly smiled my client on him,
>   Coyly woo'd and gently won him.

ALL:
>   Sweetly smiled, etc.

COUNSEL:
>   Swiftly fled each honeyed hour
>   Spent with this unmanly male!
>   Camberwell became a bower,
>   Peckham an Arcadian Vale,
>   Breathing concentrated otto!—
>   An existence *à la* Watteau.

ALL:
>   Bless, us, concentrated otto! etc.

COUNSEL:
>   Picture, then, my client naming,

And insisting on the day:
Picture him excuses framing—
    Going from her far away;
Doubly criminal to do so,
For the maid had bought her *trousseau!*

ALL: Doubly criminal, etc.

COUNSEL (*to* PLAINTIFF, *who weeps*):
            Cheer up, my pretty—oh, cheer up!

JURY: Cheer up, cheer up, we love you!

> COUNCIL *leads* PLAINTIFF *fondly into Witness-box; he takes a tender leave of her, and resumes his place in Court.*
> PLAINTIFF *reels as if about to faint.*

JUDGE: That she is reeling
                    Is plain to see!

FOREMAN: If faint you're feeling
                    Recline on me!

> *She falls sobbing on to the* FOREMAN's *breast.*

PLAINTIFF (*feebly*):   I shall recover
                    If left alone.

ALL (*shaking their fists at* DEFENDANT):
                    Oh, perjured lover,
                    Atone! atone!

FOREMAN: Just like a father
                    I wish to be.

> *Kissing her.*

JUDGE (*approaching her*):
                    Or, if you'd rather,
                    Recline on me!

> *She jumps on to Bench, sits down by the* JUDGE, *and falls sobbing on his breast.*

COUNSEL: Oh! fetch some water
                    From far Cologne!

ALL: For this sad slaughter
                    Atone! atone!

JURY (*shaking fists at* DEFENDANT):
            Monster, monster, dread our fury—
            There's the Judge, and we're the Jury!
            Come! Substantial damages,
            Dam—

USHER: Silence in Court!
SONG—DEFENDANT:

Oh, gentlemen, listen, I pray,
    Though I own that my heart has been ranging,
Of nature the laws I obey,
    For nature is constantly changing.
The moon in her phases is found,
    The time and the wind and the weather,
The months in succession come round,
    And you don't find two Mondays together.
    Consider the moral, I pray,
        Nor bring a young fellow to sorrow,
    Who loves this young lady to-day,
        And loves that young lady to-morrow.

BRIDESMAIDS (*rushing forward, and kneeling to* JURY):
        Consider the moral, etc.

DEFENDANT:

You cannot eat breakfast all day,
    Nor is it the act of a sinner,
When breakfast is taken away,
    To turn your attention to dinner;
And it's not in the range of belief,
    That you could hold him as a glutton,
Who, when he is tired of beef,
    Determines to tackle the mutton.
    But this I am willing to say,
        If it will appease her sorrow,
    I'll marry this lady to-day,
        And I'll marry that lady to-morrow!

BRIDESMAIDS (*rushing forward as before*):
        But this he is willing to say, etc.

RECIT—JUDGE:

That seems a reasonable proposition,
    To which, I think, your client may agree.
COUNSEL: But, I submit, my lord, with all submission,
    To marry two at once is Burglaree!
    Referring to law book.
    In the reign of James the Second,

It was generally reckoned
As a very serious crime
To marry two wives at one time.
Hands book up to JUDGE, *who reads it.*

ALL: Oh, man of learning!

QUARTETTE

JUDGE: A nice dilemma we have here,
That calls for all our wit:

COUNSEL: And at this stage, it don't appear
That we can settle it.

DEFENDANT (*in Witness-box*):
If I to wed the girl am loth
A breach 'twill surely be—

PLAINTIFF: And if he goes and marries both,
It counts as Burglaree!

ALL: A nice dilemma, etc.

DUET—PLAINTIFF *and* DEFENDANT:

PLAINTIFF (*embracing him rapturously*):
I love him—I love him—with fervor unceasing
I worship and madly adore;
My blind adoration is always increasing,
My loss I shall ever deplore.
Oh, see what a blessing, what love and caressing
I've lost, and remember it, pray,
When you I'm addressing, are busy assessing
The damages Edwin must pay!

DEFENDANT (*repelling her furiously*):
I smoke like a furnace—I'm always in liquor,
A ruffian—a bully—a sot;
I'm sure I should thrash her, perhaps I should kick her,
I am such a very bad lot!
I'm not prepossessing, as you may be guessing,
She couldn't endure me a day;
Recall my professing, when you are assessing
The damages Edwin must pay!

*She clings to him passionately; after a struggle, he throws her off
into arms of* COUNSEL.

JURY: We would be fairly acting,

But this is most distracting!

RECIT—JUDGE:

    The question, gentlemen—is one of liquor;
    You ask for guidance—this is my reply:
    He says, when tipsy, he would thrash and kick her,
    Let's make him tipsy, gentlemen, and try!

COUNSEL: With all respect
                       I do object!

PLAINTIFF: I do object!

DEFENDANT: I don't object!

ALL: With all respect
                       We do object!

JUDGE (*tossing his books and papers about*):

      All the legal furies seize you!
      No proposal seems to please you,
      I can't stop up here all day,
      I must shortly go away.
      Barristers, and you, attorneys,
      Set out on your homeward journeys;
      Gentle, simple-minded Usher,
      Get you, if you like, to Russ*her;*
      Put your briefs upon the shelf,
      I will marry her myself!

He comes down from Bench to floor of Court. He embraces AN-
GELINA.

FINALE

PLAINTIFF: Oh, joy unbounded,
                    With wealth surrounded,
                    The knell is sounded
                       Of grief and woe.

COUNSEL: With love devoted
                    On you he's doated
                    To castle moated
                       Away they go.

DEFENDANT: I wonder whether
                    They'll live together
                    In marriage tether
                     In manner true?

USHER: It seems to me, sir,

> Of such as she, sir,
> A judge is he, sir,
> > And a good judge too.

JUDGE: Yes, I am a Judge.

ALL: And a good Judge too!

JUDGE: Yes, I am a Judge.

ALL: And a good Judge too!

JUDGE: Though homeward as you trudge,
You declare my law is fudge.
Yet of beauty I'm a judge.

ALL: And a good Judge too!

CURTAIN

Frank O'Connor

·

COUNSEL FOR OEDIPUS

To sit in court and watch a case between wife and husband is like seeing a performance of *Oedipus*. You know that no matter what happens the man hasn't a chance. A colt will consider it a matter of conscience to pass a filly, and a court of law is the same. Even the man's own counsel will be ashamed of him and envy counsel for the wife, who, whatever she did or didn't do, has the ear of the court. As for judges—every single one that I've known had a mother fixation.

But the worst thing of all is that even the man is divided against himself. Now, take the day when Mickie Joe Dougherty was defending a big countryman called Lynam, whose wife was suing him for legal separation and accusing him of cruelty and adultery. The adultery was admitted, and all that was needed to prove the cruelty was to put Tom Lynam in the box. He was a big, good-looking man with a stiff, morose manner; one of those men who are deceptively quiet and good-humored for months on end and then lay you out with a stick for a casual remark about politics.

His wife was a trim, mousy little female about half his height and a quarter his weight, with an anxious face and a gentle, bedraggled air. She cocked her little head while she listened to her counsel's questions, as though they were uttered in a foreign language, and replied to them in something of the same way, raising her colorless little voice and illustrating her answers with pathetic, half-completed gestures. It reminded

216

you of fourth-form French. All the same, it gave impressiveness to the picture she drew of her husband, drunk and violent, smashing everything in the kitchen on her. You could see O'Meara, the judge, adored her. "Come over here where we can hear you, ma'am," he said, pointing to a seat on the bench beside him, and he leaned one elbow on the bench, crossed his legs, and studied her. Poor O'Meara was a bad case; he had blood pressure as well as a mother fixation. Once or twice, as she gave her evidence, she glanced sadly and pityingly at her husband, who stared back at her with a gloomy hatred that was awe-inspiring. Most men, hearing how they have beaten and strangled their wives, even if they never laid a finger on them, don't know where to look—the poor devils are wondering what everyone thinks of them—but here was a man who watched his wife as if he was wondering why the blazes he hadn't taken a hatchet and finished the job as he was at it.

"And what did he say then?" asked Kenefick, her counsel.

"He called me—do I have to say that?" she asked with a wistful girlish look at O'Meara.

"Oh, not at all, not at all, ma'am," he said hastily. "Write it down," and pushed pencil and paper towards her. She wrote as she talked, slowly and carefully, raising her eyes sightlessly as she thought of all the cruel things her husband had said to her. Then she passed the paper apologetically to the judge, who glanced at it and passed it down to counsel. Tom Lynam, his face black with fury, leaned forward and whispered something to his solicitor, Matt Quill, but Matt only shook his head. If Matt had had his way, he'd have settled the case out of court.

"Did he say anything else?" asked Kenefick.

"Only if I didn't get out of the house in five minutes, sir, that he'd do to me what the Jews did to Jesus."

"What the Jews did to who?" O'Meara asked incredulously.

"Jesus, my lord," she replied, bowing her head reverently at the Holy Name. "Our Blessed Lord, you know. Crucify me, he meant."

"Huh!" snorted O'Meara with his blood pressure going up several degrees.

"Tell my lord what happened then," prompted Kenefick.

"So then I told him I could not go out at that hour of night, and the state of feebleness I was in," Mrs. Lynam continued with growing animation, "and he dragged me off the sofa and twisted my wrist behind my back." She illustrated "wrist" and "back" with another feeble gesture which she didn't complete.

"And did he know the state you were in?"

"Sure, how could he not know it?" cried Mrs. Lynam with her little hands outspread. "I wasn't able to get up from the sofa the whole day. That was what he had against me, of course. He wouldn't believe I was sick. Shamming he said I was."

"And what did he do?"

"Oh, he kicked me."

"Where was this?"

Her hand went to her back again, and she blushed. "Oh, in the—"

"No, no, no. I don't mean that. Where did this occur? What direction did he kick you in?"

"Oh, out the front door, sir," she replied hastily. "I fell on the path. Tommy—that's our little boy—knelt alongside me and began to cry, and my husband told him if he didn't get to bed, he'd do the same to him."

"He'd do the same to Tommy. How old is the child?"

"Five, sir, the 14th of February."

"And your husband made no effort to see were you injured in the fall?"

"Oh, indeed he didn't, sir," she replied with a smile like a rainbow— an optical illusion between two downpours. "Only to give me another kick off the path and into the flower-bed."

"And didn't you, at any time, make some appeal to him to cease this cruel treatment?" demanded Kenefick, stepping up his voice to indignation.

"Oh, indeed, I did, sir," she replied, responding sadly with a shake of her head. Whatever brand of French she spoke, it was clearly going down well, and she was beginning to enjoy it herself. "I asked him did he think I was in a fit state to go crawling across the fields in the dark to a neighbor's house, but he only used a filthy expression and banged the door in my face."

"And those were the marks that you showed next day to Dr. O'Mahony?"

"They were, sir. The same. A week he made me stop in bed with them."

"Tell me, ma'am," the judge interrupted, "this second kick he gave you—the one that sent you off the path into the flower-bed—where were you when he did that?"

"Oh, on the ground, my lord. I was too bad to get up. Half the way across the fields, I was crawling like that, on my hands and knees."

After this it was scarcely necessary to prove her husband's behavior with Nora MacGee, a woman of notorious bad character, for in fact she had had a child by him and his paternity was not denied. He had even visited her and nursed the child himself.

"And did you ask him to give up seeing this woman?"

"Why then, indeed, I did, sir. A dozen times if I did it once."

"And what did he say?"

"He said he wouldn't give up seeing a Lynam child for all the Hanafeys that were ever pupped, sir. The Hanafeys are my family," she added with her rainbow smile.

At this, Kenefick sat down as though he could not bear to prolong the poor woman's agony further, and Mickie Joe rose. Now, it cannot be pretended that, the best day he ever was, Mickie Joe was much of a lawyer or made a good appearance in court. Mickie Joe had begun life as a schoolmaster, but abandoned it, first for politics and then for the law. He really loved the art of oratory, and his soul filled with emotion whenever he spoke of the great orators of old who swayed vast audiences with the power of their voices, but Mickie Joe's own voice was like the whistle of a train, and the only effect he had ever had on an audience was to make them laugh. He had a long, thin, mournful face, and big, blackberry-colored sunken eyes, and he looked at you over his pince-nez as though at any moment he might burst into tears. Everybody loved Mickie Joe, everybody tried to throw business in his way, but nobody ever took him seriously. He had a tendency which was very obvious in the Lynam case to identify himself with his client, a thing no real lawyer will do. A client is a fact, and a true lawyer hates facts. A lawyer is like an actor who can never bother about what sort of play he appears in, but tells himself some little story to cover as many of the incidents as he can be bothered to remember. The only thing he hates is to be reminded—for instance by the author—what the real story is about.

But Mickie Joe got up bursting with indignation, and even O'Meara smiled at the picture of Mickie Joe, who never said a cross word to anybody, identifying himself with this uproarious, drunken farmer. He felt Tom Lynam had been wronged and was bent on proving it. What made it funnier was that he began with a series of questions which nobody understood, which only reflected further Mrs. Lynam's virtue and his client's beastliness, but which he asked with a bitter reserve. Mrs.

Lynam wasn't afraid of him. No woman was ever afraid of Mickie Joe. She answered steadily and quietly. Yes, she had been educated in a convent. Yes, she was a great friend of Sister Dominic. And of Father O'Regan, the parish priest. Yes, she had asked their advice before beginning proceedings against her husband. Yes, she was a member of the Women's Sodality and the Children of Mary.

Then Mickie Joe began to expand, and it became clear what his purpose had been. But it also looked as though Mickie Joe had lost his reason. It's bad enough to attack a woman, but to attack her because she's a pious woman is to go looking for trouble.

"And when you were at the Women's Sodality," he asked icily, looking at her between the wig and the pince-nez, "who got your husband's supper?"

"Sometimes he got it himself."

"And the children's supper?"

"Of an odd time."

"And when you were out at Mass, he got his breakfast, I suppose?"

"Unless he wanted to wait till I got in."

"But you always got it for him when you came in?"

"Always, except when I wasn't able."

"And I take it you weren't always able?"

"Well, no," she admitted candidly. "Not always." She still didn't take him seriously.

"You were able to go to Mass," he said, drawling every word, "but you were not able to get your husband's breakfast? Is that what you're telling my lord?"

"Sometimes I went to Mass when I wasn't able, either," she replied with a noble pathos which would have silenced another man but not Mickie Joe.

"You went to Mass when you weren't able," he repeated with a bitter smile, "but you didn't get your husband's breakfast when you weren't able. Is that what you mean?"

"I think I ought to explain that," she said, beginning to get flurried. "I'm not strong. I have a pain in my back. I hurted it years ago in a fall I got. Dr. O'Mahony treated me."

"Mrs. Lynam, do you also suffer from headaches?"

"I do. Bilious," she replied, pointing to her stomach.

"Really, Mr. Dougherty," said O'Meara wearily, "if a headache is an offense we're all bad characters."

Of course, by this time O'Meara was champing at the bit, waiting to get on with his judgment. For a judge with a mother fixation to listen to evidence at all when he wants to rush to the rescue of some poor afflicted female is an ordeal in itself, but it made it worse that all there was between himself and it was a poor fish like Mickie Joe. But for once Mickie Joe did not give way. He looked at the judge reprovingly over his pince-nez and replied in a wail:

"My lord, if the petitioner is presented to the court as something out of a medical museum, I have nothing more to say."

"Oh, go on, Mr. Dougherty, go on!" said O'Meara, but all the same he grew red. He was beginning to notice like the rest of us that Mickie Joe had ceased to be a figure of fun, but no more than ourselves did he realize what was happening. The truth was that there is only one person who can stand up to a man with a mother fixation, and that is a woman-hater. Exactly as O'Meara wanted to get at that big hulk of a man in the court, Mickie Joe wanted to get at that gentle, pious little woman sitting up beside the judge with her hands in her lap. And, in a queer way, his dislike was beginning to affect people's opinion. It wasn't only that you couldn't any longer patronize Mickie Joe. You couldn't any longer see her the way you had seen her first. Whether it was right or wrong, another picture was beginning to emerge of a woman who was both ruthless and designing and who ruled her great brute of a husband by her weakness. This was only one stage of his ruin. In the next she would be living in comfort in a terrace house on his earnings, while he dragged out an impoverished and lonely existence.

Lynam himself began to perk up, and, instead of looking at his wife, looked at the people round him. The court had gradually begun to fill up, the way it does when a case gets interesting. He still scowled, but now he seemed to be challenging the people in court to say if he wasn't justified.

"Did you and your husband do much visiting together, Mrs. Lynam?" Mickie Joe asked gently.

"Well, you can't do much with two children, sir, can you?" she asked with soft reproach.

"That depends, ma'am," he said with a mournful smile. "A lot of people seem to be able to do it."

"I dare say they have servants," she said nervously.

"Strange to say, ma'am, friendships have been known to persist even in the humblest homes," sighed Mickie Joe with a smile like a glacier.

"I'm sure I don't know how they manage it, then."

"There are such things as neighbors, ma'am."

"Well, you can't be always asking the neighbors."

"No," he said bitterly. "You can ask them to put you up after a quarrel with your husband, but you can't ask them to mind your children. And how much attention do the children need? What age is your little girl, ma'am?"

"She's ten."

"And she couldn't look after the little fellow and herself?"

"Well, I can explain that," she said with a nervous glance at the judge. "You see, they don't get on, and you couldn't leave little Tommy with her, on account of that."

"You mean, she would beat him?" Mickie Joe asked sternly.

"Well, not beat him exactly," said Mrs. Lynam, getting more rattled than ever. "But she might be tormenting him."

"Mrs. Lynam," he asked gravely, "is it the way you didn't like to ask the neighbors or the neighbors didn't like to be asked?"

"I don't know why you say that," she said, shaking her head. "The children don't like going to strange houses, and you wouldn't blame them."

"Do you mean that, ma'am, or do you mean they did not like going to houses where they would have to behave themselves? Mrs. Lynam, isn't it true that your children are too spoiled and vicious to be left in the home of any reasonable person?"

"No," she replied shrilly, starting in her seat. "Certainly not. I never heard such a thing."

But Tom Lynam himself looked at his counsel with such an expression of astonishment that it was clear to everyone that intuitively Mickie Joe had stumbled on the truth. He knew it himself too, and for the first time a smile of satisfaction played about his thin, mournful lips.

"Did many of your husband's friends visit you?"

"Some of them did, yes."

"He had a lot of friends at the time he married you, hadn't he?"

"He had. A few."

"And at the time of this break-up, how many of them were still coming to the house?"

The witness's eyes sought out one tall man sitting at the back of the court.

"I'm sure I couldn't say," she replied doubtfully. "There was one of them at any rate."

"The local St. Sebastian, I presume?"

"The local—I beg your pardon; I didn't catch."

"Mrs. Lynam, every married man has at least one friend who sticks to him, even in spite of his wife's attempts to separate them," Mickie Joe said savagely. "What happened to his other friends?"

"I'm sure I don't know."

"Mrs. Lynam, why did they stop coming to your house? Was it, for instance, that when they came for a meal, you sent your husband out to do the shopping?"

"Only a couple of times," she said excitedly. "And that is a thing that might happen to anybody. No matter how careful a housekeeper you were, you couldn't remember everything."

"And I dare say that while he was out, you left them there to entertain themselves?" he asked with a wicked smile.

"Only if I was putting the children to bed, sir," she said sanctimoniously.

"And I suppose, too, that when this last remaining friend of your husband—this Last Rose of Summer left blooming alone—came to bring him out, say, to the greyhounds, it sometimes happened that they couldn't go?"

"Well, I explained about my back," she said earnestly.

"You did, ma'am, fully," said Mickie Joe cruelly. "We are now better acquainted with your back than with any other portion of your anatomy. And we may take it that your husband and his friend had to stay at home and mind the children instead of enjoying themselves."

"I'm sure they enjoyed themselves more than I did," she said. "They played cards a lot. They're both very fond of cards."

But Tom Lynam was still staring incredulously at Mickie Joe. The tall man at the back of the court had grown red. He smiled and nodded amiably to the judge, to the counsel, and even to the pressmen. The Last Rose of Summer, a shy, neighborly sort of man, was clearly enjoying the publicity. Lynam leaned forward and whispered something to his solicitor, but Quill only frowned and brushed him off. Quill was beginning to see the power and pathos of the play Mickie Joe was producing and no more than any other man of the theater had he time to spare for the author's views.

"Tell me, ma'am," Mickie Joe asked, "how long is it since you had relations with your husband?"

"Since I what?" she asked in a baby voice, her head raised expectantly.

"Since you went to bed with him, if you like."

"Oh, I forgot to mention that," she said hastily. "He doesn't sleep with me, of course. He has a bedroom of his own."

"Oh, he has a bedroom of his own, has he?" Mickie Joe asked with a new light in his eye. "We'll come back to that. But that wasn't the question I asked just now. The question I asked was how long it was since you had relations with him."

"Well, with my back," she began, raising her hand illustratively to her hip.

"Never mind your back now, ma'am. It's not your back we're talking about at the moment. How long is it?"

"Oh, I suppose about two years," she replied pertly.

"Or more?"

"It could be."

"No doubt it left no impression on your mind," said Mickie Joe. "But when you asked your husband not to have further relations with Mrs. MacGee, you weren't inviting him to have them with you?"

"He never asked me."

"And when he was at Mrs. MacGee's, nursing his child by her, he was in the only decent sort of home he had," said Mickie Joe with a throb of pathos in his voice that, for once, didn't make anybody laugh. "Would it be true to say that you don't think much of married life, ma'am?"

"Oh, I wouldn't say that," she replied vigorously. "The Church, of course, takes a very high view of it."

"I was referring to you, ma'am, not to the Church. Now, weren't you always baaing and bleating to Sister Dominic about the drawbacks of married life?"

"I went to her for advice," Mrs. Lynam replied anxiously. She was beginning to be doubtful of the impression she was creating, and small wonder.

"On your oath, ma'am," shouted Mickie Joe, "didn't you say to Sister Dominic that you never had a happy day after you left the convent?"

"Did I?" Mrs. Lynam asked nervously with a finger to her chin.

"Didn't you?"

"I don't remember. But I might, when I was upset."

"And to Father O'Regan, when you were trying to set him against your unfortunate, decent husband?"

"I never tried to set anyone against him," she retorted indignantly. "All I asked Father O'Regan was to ask him to be more natural."

"Natural?"

"Reasonable, I mean. Ah, 'tis all very well to be talking, Mr. Dougherty. That may be all right for young people, but 'tis no way for people like us to be behaving."

The tables were turned now with a vengeance. Tom Lynam had ceased to look at anyone now but his wife, and at her he looked with an expression of overpowering gravity. He seemed to be saying: "I told you what would happen and you wouldn't believe me. Now look at the result." He knew as everyone else did that she had failed to prove her case, and that even the policemen at the back of the court who had wives of cast iron were looking reproachfully at the gentle, insinuating little woman who was being revealed as a gray, grim, discontented monster with a mania for power.

When the court adjourned, Mickie Joe's cross-examination wasn't over, but he could easily have closed there, for even O'Meara's mother fixation could find nothing to fix on in the petitioner's case. She was probably the only person in court who didn't realize she had lost, but even she was badly shaken. She grabbed her handbag and waddled quickly down the court, looking neither to right nor to left. As she passed, her husband looked reproachfully at her, but she refused to catch his eye. Suddenly to everyone's astonishment he jumped up and followed her. The lawyers followed, too, without delay. They were afraid that in their moment of triumph he would snatch the victory from them by finishing the job in the hall. Instead, when they went out he was standing before her, talking in a low, pleading voice. She, with an actressy air, was listening, but half turned away from him as if caught in flight. Finally he approached Quill and Mickie Joe with a frown on his handsome face.

"Nellie and me are settling this between us," he muttered.

"You're what?" Quill asked in consternation. "But damn it, man, you have it won."

"I know that," Lynam replied in an apologetic mutter, "and I'm very grateful, but I wouldn't like her to have to answer any more questions. She thinks I told you all the things you mentioned. You know yourself I didn't."

Mickie Joe was fit to be tied. He stared at his client over his pince-nez.

"You mean you're going back to live with that woman?" he asked coldly.

"I am."

"And you know that within forty-eight hours she'll be making your life a misery again?"

"If she does itself, we'll settle it between us," Tom Lynam retorted in a low voice, though his anger could be heard rumbling beneath, like a volcano.

"You certainly will," Mickie Joe said with icy fury. "You will not get me to assist you. A man tries to help you, but it is only talent thrown away. Go and commit suicide in your own way. I have nothing further to do with you."

"There's a pair of us there," Lynam exploded. "I don't know where you got your information, but you can go back to the people that told you and tell them to mind their own business. I won't let you or anyone talk to my wife that way."

Quill almost had to separate them. Two madder men he had rarely seen. But from the window of the barristers' room he and Mickie Joe saw the Lynams depart together, she small and sprightly, he tall and morose, and realized that never would they see justice done to a man in a court of law. It was like Oedipus. You couldn't say whether it was the Destiny that pursued the man or the man the Destiny; but you could be quite sure that nothing in the world would ever keep the two of them apart.

Shiga Naoya

:

HAN'S CRIME

Much to everyone's astonishment, the young Chinese juggler, Han, severed his wife's carotid artery with one of his heavy knives in the course of a performance. The young woman died on the spot. Han was immediately arrested.

At the scene of the event were the director of the theater, Han's Chinese assistant, the announcer, and more than three hundred spectators. There was also a policeman who had been stationed behind the audience. Despite the presence of all these witnesses, it was a complete mystery whether the killing had been intentional or accidental.

Han's act was as follows: his wife would stand in front of a wooden board about the size of a door, and from a distance of approximately four yards, he would throw his large knives at her so that they stuck in the board about two inches apart, forming a contour around her body. As each knife left his hand, he would let out a staccato exclamation as if to punctuate his performance.

The examining judge first questioned the director of the theater.

"Would you say that this was a very difficult act?"

"No, Your Honor, it's not as difficult as all that for an experienced performer. But to do it properly, you need steady nerves and complete concentration."

"I see. Then assuming that what happened was an accident, it was an extremely unlikely type of accident?"

"Yes indeed, Your Honor. If accidents were not so very unlikely, I should never have allowed the act in my theater."

"Well then, do you consider that this was done on purpose?"

"No, Your Honor, I do not. And for this reason: an act of this kind performed at a distance of twelve feet requires not only skill but at the same time a certain—well, intuitive sense. It is true that we all thought a mistake virtually out of the question, but after what has happened, I think we must admit that there was always the possibility of a mistake."

"Well then, which do you think it was—a mistake or on purpose?"

"That I simply cannot say, Your Honor."

The judge felt puzzled. Here was a clear case of homicide, but whether it was manslaughter or premeditated murder it was impossible to tell. If a murder, it was indeed a clever one, thought the judge.

Next the judge decided to question the Chinese assistant, who had worked with Han for many years past.

"What was Han's normal behavior?" he asked.

"He was always very correct, Your Honor; he didn't gamble or drink or run after women. Besides, last year he took up Christianity. He studied English and in his free time always seemed to be reading collections of sermons—the Bible and that sort of thing."

"And what about his wife's behavior?"

"Also very correct, Your Honor. Strolling players aren't always the most moral people, as you know. Mrs. Han was a pretty little woman and quite a few men used to make propositions to her, but she never paid the slightest attention to that kind of thing."

"And what sort of temperaments did they have?"

"Always very kind and gentle, sir. They were extremely good to all their friends and acquaintances and never quarreled with anyone. But . . ." He broke off and reflected a moment before continuing. "Your Honor, I'm afraid that if I tell you this, it may go badly for Han. But to be quite truthful, these two people, who were so gentle and unselfish to others, were amazingly cruel in their relations to each other."

"Why was that?"

"I don't know, Your Honor."

"Was that the case ever since you first knew them?"

"No, Your Honor. About two years ago Mrs. Han was pregnant. The child was born prematurely and died after about three days. That marked a change in their relations. They began having terrible rows over the most trivial things, and Han's face used to turn white as a sheet.

He always ended by suddenly growing silent. He never once raised his hand against her or anything like that—I suppose it would have gone against his principles. But when you looked at him, Your Honor, you could see the terrible anger in his eyes! It was quite frightening at times.

"One day I asked Han why he didn't separate from his wife, seeing that things were so bad between them. Well, he told me that he had no real grounds for divorce, even though his love for her had died. Of course, she felt this and gradually stopped loving him too. He told me all this himself. I think the reason he began reading the Bible and all those sermons was to calm the violence in his heart and stop himself from hating his wife, whom he had no real cause to hate. Mrs. Han was really a pathetic woman. She had been with Han nearly three years and had traveled all over the country with him as a strolling player. If she'd ever left Han and gone back home, I don't think she'd have found it easy to get married. How many men would trust a woman who'd spent all that time traveling about? I suppose that's why she stayed with Han, even though they got on so badly."

"And what do you really think about this killing?"

"You mean, Your Honor, do I think it was an accident or done on purpose?"

"That's right."

"Well, sir, I've been thinking about it from every angle since the day it happened. The more I think, the less I know what to make of it. I've talked about it with the announcer, and he also says he can't understand what happened."

"Very well. But tell me this: at the actual moment it did happen, did it occur to you to wonder whether it was accidental or on purpose?"

"Yes, sir, it did. I thought . . . I thought, 'He's gone and killed her.' "

"On purpose, you mean?"

"Yes, sir. However the announcer says that he thought, 'His hand's slipped.' "

"Yes, but he didn't know about their everyday relations as you did."

"That may be, Your Honor. But afterwards I wondered if it wasn't just because I did know about those relations that I thought, 'He's killed her.' "

"What were Han's reactions at the moment?"

"He cried out, 'Ha.' As soon as I heard that, I looked up and saw blood gushing from his wife's throat. For a few seconds she kept standing there, then her knees seemed to fold up under her and her body swayed forward. When the knife fell out, she collapsed on the floor, all crumpled in a heap. Of course there was nothing any of us could do— we just sat there petrified, staring at her. . . . As to Han, I really can't describe his reactions, for I wasn't looking at him. It was only when the thought struck me, 'He's finally gone and killed her,' that I glanced at him. His face was dead white and his eyes closed. The stage manager lowered the curtain. When they picked up Mrs. Han's body she was already dead. Han dropped to his knees then, and for a long time he went on praying in silence."

"Did he appear very upset?"

"Yes, sir, he was quite upset."

"Very well. If I have anything further to ask you, I shall call for you again."

The judge dismissed the Chinese assistant and now summoned Han himself to the stand. The juggler's intelligent face was drawn and pale; one could tell right away that he was in a state of nervous exhaustion.

"I have already questioned the director of the theater and your assistant," said the judge when Han had taken his place in the witness box. "I now propose to examine you."

Han bowed his head.

"Tell me," said the judge, "did you at any time love your wife?"

"From the day of our marriage until the child was born I loved her with all my heart."

"And why did the birth of the child change things?"

"Because I knew it was not mine."

"Did you know who the other man was?"

"I had a very good idea. I think it was my wife's cousin."

"Did you know him personally?"

"He was a close friend. It was he who first suggested that we get married. It was he who urged me to marry her."

"I presume that his relations with her occurred prior to your marriage."

"Yes, sir. The child was born eight months after we were married."

"According to your assistant, it was a premature birth."

"That is what I told everyone."

"The child died very soon after birth, did it not? What was the cause of death?"

"He was smothered by his mother's breasts."

"Did your wife do that on purpose?"

"She said it was an accident."

The judge was silent and looked fixedly at Han's face. Han raised his head but kept his eyes lowered as he awaited the next question. The judge continued.

"Did your wife confess these relations to you?"

"She did not confess, nor did I ever ask her about them. The child's death seemed like retribution for everything and I decided that I should be as magnanimous as possible, but . . ."

"But in the end you were unable to be magnanimous?"

"That's right. I could not help thinking that the death of the child was insufficient retribution. When apart from my wife, I was able to reason calmly, but as soon as I saw her, something happened inside me. When I saw her body, my temper would begin to rise."

"Didn't divorce occur to you?"

"I often thought that I should like to have a divorce, but I never mentioned it to my wife. My wife used to say that if I left her she could no longer exist."

"Did she love you?"

"She did not love me."

"Then why did she say such things?"

"I think she was referring to the material means of existence. Her home had been ruined by her elder brother, and she knew that no serious man would want to marry a woman who had been the wife of a strolling player. Also her feet were too small for her to do any ordinary work."

"What were your physical relations?"

"I imagine about the same as with most couples."

"Did your wife have any real liking for you?"

"I do not think she really liked me. In fact, I think it must have been very painful for her to live with me as my wife. Still, she endured it. She endured it with a degree of patience almost unthinkable for a man. She used to observe me with a cold, cruel look in her eyes as my life gradually went to pieces. She never showed a flicker of sympathy as she saw me struggling in agony to escape into a better, truer sort of existence."

"Why could you not take some decisive action—have it out with her, or even leave her if necessary?"

"Because my mind was full of all sorts of ideals."

"What ideals?"

"I wanted to behave towards my wife in such a way that there would be no wrong on my side. . . . But in the end it didn't work."

"Did you never think of killing your wife?"

Han did not answer and the judge repeated his question. After a long pause, Han replied, "Before the idea of killing her occurred to me, I often used to think it would be a good thing if she died."

"Well, in that case, if it had not been against the law, don't you think you might have killed her?"

"I wasn't thinking in terms of the law, sir. That's not what stopped me. It was just that I was weak. At the same time I had this overmastering desire to enter into a truer sort of life."

"Nevertheless you did think of killing your wife, did you not—later on, I mean?"

"I never made up my mind to do it. But, yes, it is correct to say that I did think about it once."

"How long was that before the event?"

"The previous night. . . . Or perhaps even the same morning."

"Had you been quarreling?"

"Yes, sir."

"What about?"

"About something so petty that it's hardly worth mentioning."

"Try telling me about it."

"It was a question of food. I get rather short-tempered when I haven't eaten for some time. Well, that evening my wife had been dawdling and our supper wasn't ready when it should have been. I got very angry."

"Were you more violent than usual?"

"No, but afterwards I still felt worked up, which was unusual. I suppose it was because I'd been worrying so much during those past weeks about making a better existence for myself, and realizing there was nothing I could do about it. I went to bed but couldn't get to sleep. All sorts of upsetting thoughts went through my mind. I began to feel that whatever I did, I should never be able to achieve the things I really wanted—that however hard I tried, I should never be able to escape from all the hateful aspects of my present life. This sad, hopeless state of affairs all seemed connected with my marriage. I desperately wanted to find a chink of light to lead me out of my darkness, but even this desire was gradually being extinguished. The hope of escape still flickered and sputtered within me, and I knew that if ever it should go out I would to all intents and purposes be a dead person.

"And then the ugly thought began flitting through my mind, 'If only she would die! If only she would die! Why should I not kill her?' The practical consequence of such a crime meant nothing to me any longer. No doubt I would go to prison, but life in prison could not be worse—could only be better—than this present existence. And yet somehow I had the feeling that killing my wife would solve nothing. It would have been a shirking of the issue, in the same way as suicide. I must go through each day's suffering as it came, I told myself; there was no way to circumvent that. That had become my true life: to suffer.

"As my mind raced along these tracks, I almost forgot that the cause of my suffering lay beside me. Utterly exhausted, I lay there unable to sleep. I fell into a blank state of stupefaction, and as my tortured mind turned numb, the idea of killing my wife gradually faded. Then I was overcome by the sad empty feeling that follows a nightmare. I thought of all my fine resolutions for a better life, and realized that I was too weakhearted to attain it. When dawn finally broke I saw that my wife also, had not been sleeping. . . ."

"When you got up, did you behave normally towards each other?"

"We did not say a single word to each other."

"But why didn't you think of leaving her, when things had come to this?"

"Do you mean, Your Honor, that that would have been a solution of my problem? No, no, that too would have been a shirking of the issue! As I told you, I was determined to behave towards my wife so that there would be no wrong on my side."

Han gazed earnestly at the judge, who nodded his head as a sign for him to continue.

"Next day I was physically exhausted and of course my nerves were ragged. It was agony for me to remain still, and as soon as I had got dressed I left the house and wandered aimlessly about the deserted parts of town. Constantly the thought kept returning that I must do something to solve my life, but the idea of killing no longer occurred to me. The truth is that there was a chasm between my thoughts of murder the night before and any actual decision to commit a crime! Indeed, I never even thought about that evening's performance. If I had, I certainly would have decided to leave out the knife-throwing act. There were dozens of other acts that could have been substituted.

"Well, the evening came and finally it was our turn to appear on the stage. I did not have the slightest premonition that anything out of the ordinary was to happen. As usual, I demonstrated to the audience the sharpness of my knives by slicing pieces of paper and thowing some of the knives at the floor boards. Presently my wife appeared, heavily made up and wearing an elaborate Chinese costume; after greeting the audience with her charming smile, she took up her position in front of the board. I picked up one of the knives and placed myself at the distance from her.

"That's when our eyes met for the first time since the previous evening. At once I understood the risk of having chosen this particular act for that night's performance! Obviously I would have to master my nerves, yet the exhaustion which had penetrated to the very marrow of my bones prevented me. I sensed that I could no longer trust my own arm. To calm myself I closed my eyes for a moment, and I sensed that my whole body was trembling.

"Now the time had come! I aimed my first knife above her head; it struck just one inch higher than usual. My wife raised her arms and I prepared to throw my next two knives under each of her arms. As the first one left the ends of my fingers, I felt as if something were holding it back; I no longer had the sense of being able to determine the exact destination of my knives. It was now really a matter of luck if the knife struck at the point intended; each of my movements had become deliberate and self-conscious.

"I threw one knife to the left of my wife's neck and was about to throw another to the right when I saw a strange expression in her eyes. She seemed to be seized by a paroxysm of fear! Did she have a presentiment that this knife, that in a matter of seconds would come hurtling towards her, was going to lodge in her throat? I felt dizzy, as if about to faint. Forcing the knife deliberately out of my hand, I as good as aimed it into space. . . ."

The judge was silent, peering intently at Han.

"All at once the thought came to me, 'I've killed her,' " said Han abruptly.

"On purpose, you mean?"

"Yes. Suddenly I felt that I had done it on purpose."

"After that I understand you knelt down beside your wife's body and prayed in silence."

"Yes, sir. That was a rather cunning device that occurred to me on the spur of the moment. I realized that everyone knew me as a believer in Christianity. But while I was making a pretense of praying, I was in fact carefully calculating what attitude to adopt."

"So you were absolutely convinced that what you had done was on purpose?"

"I was. But I realized at once that I should be able to pretend it had been an accident."

"And why did you think it had been on purpose?"

"I had lost all sense of judgment."

"Did you think you'd succeeded in giving the impression it was an accident?"

"Yes, though when I thought about it afterwards it made my flesh creep. I pretended as convincingly as I could to be grief-stricken, but if there'd been just one really sharp-witted person about, he'd have realized right away that I was only acting. Well, that evening I decided that there was no good reason why I should not be acquitted; I told myself very calmly that there wasn't a shred of material evidence against me. To be sure, everyone knew how badly I got on with my wife, but if I persisted in saying that it was an accident, no one could prove the contrary. Going over in my mind everything that had happened, I saw that my wife's death could be explained very plausibly as an accident.

"And then a strange question came to my mind: why did I myself believe that it had *not* been an accident? The previous night I had thought about killing her, but might it not be that very fact which now caused me to think of my act as deliberate? Gradually I came to the point that I myself did not know what actually had happened! At that I became very happy—almost unbearably happy. I wanted to shout at the top of my lungs."

"Because you had come to consider it an accident?"

"No, that I can't say: because I no longer had the slightest idea as to whether it had been intentional or not. So I decided that my best way of being acquitted would be to make a clean breast of everything. Rather than deceive myself and everyone else by saying it was an accident, why not be completely honest and say I did not know what happened? I cannot declare it was a mistake; on the other hand I can't admit it was intentional. In fact, I can plead neither 'guilty' nor 'not guilty.'"

Han was silent. The judge, too, remained silent for a long moment before saying softly, reflectively, "I believe that what you have told me is true. Just one more question: do you not feel the slightest sorrow for your wife's death?"

"None at all! Even when I hated my wife most bitterly in the past, I never could have imagined I would feel such happiness in talking about her death."

"Very well," said the judge. "You may stand down."

Han silently lowered his head and left the room. Feeling strangely moved, the judge reached for his pen. On the document which lay on the table before him he wrote down the words, "Not guilty."

Anatole France

:

CRAINQUEBILLE

I

In every sentence pronounced by a judge in the name of the sovereign people, dwells the whole majesty of justice. The august character of that justice was brought home to Jérôme Crainquebille, costermonger, when, accused of having insulted a policeman, he appeared in the police court. Having taken his place in the dock, he beheld in the imposing somber hall magistrates, clerks, lawyers in their robes, the usher wearing his chains, gendarmes, and, behind a rail, the bare heads of the silent spectators. He, himself, occupied a raised seat, as if some sinister honor were conferred on the accused by his appearance before the magistrate. At the end of the hall, between two assessors, sat the President Bourriche. The palm leaves of an officer of the Academy decorated his breast. Over the tribune were a bust representing the Republic and a crucifix, as if to indicate that all laws divine and human were suspended over Crainquebille's head. Such symbols naturally inspired him with terror. Not being gifted with a philosophic mind, he did not inquire the meaning of the bust and the crucifix; he did not ask how far Jesus and the symbolical bust harmonized in the law courts. Nevertheless, here was matter for reflection; for, after all, pontifical teaching and canon law are in many points opposed to the constitution of the Republic and to the civil code. So far as we know, the Decretals have not been abolished. Today, as formerly, the Church of Christ teaches

237

that only those powers are lawful to which it has given its sanction. Now the French Republic claims to be independent of pontifical power. Crainquebille might reasonably say:

"Gentlemen and magistrates, in so much as President Loubet has not been anointed, the Christ, whose image is suspended over your heads, repudiates you through the voice of councils and of Popes. Either he is here to remind you of the rights of the Church, which invalidate yours, or His presence has no rational signification."

Whereupon President Bourriche might reply:

"Prisoner Crainquebille, the kings of France have always quarrelled with the Pope. Guillaume de Nogaret was excommunicated, but for so trifling a reason he did not resign his office. The Christ of the tribune is not the Christ of Gregory VII or of Boniface VIII. He is, if you will, the Christ of the Gospels, who knew not one word of canon law, and had never heard of the holy Decretals."

Then Crainquebille might not without reason have answered:

"The Christ of the Gospels was an agitator. Moreover, he was the victim of a sentence, which for nineteen hundred years all Christian peoples have regarded as a grave judicial error. I defy you, *Monsieur le Président,* to condemn me in His name to so much as forty-eight hours' imprisonment."

But Crainquebille did not indulge in any considerations either historical, political or social. He was wrapped in amazement. All the ceremonial, with which he was surrounded, impressed him with a very lofty idea of justice. Filled with reverence, overcome with terror, he was ready to submit to his judges in the matter of his guilt. In his own conscience he was convinced of his innocence; but he felt how insignificant is the conscience of a costermonger in the face of the panoply of the law, and the ministers of public prosecution. Already his lawyer had half persuaded him that he was not innocent.

A summary and hasty examination had brought out the charges under which he labored.

II

CRAINQUEBILLE'S MISADVENTURE

Up and down the town went Jérôme Crainquebille, costermonger, pushing his barrow before him and crying: "Cabbages! Turnips! Carrots!" When he had leeks he cried: "Asparagus!" For leeks are the asparagus of the poor. Now it happened that on October 20, at noon, as he was going down the Rue Montmartre, there came out of her shop the shoemaker's wife, Madame Bayard. She went up to Crainquebille's barrow and scornfully taking up a bundle of leeks, she said:

"I don't think much of your leeks. What do you want a bundle?"

"Sevenpence halfpenny, mum, and the best in the market!"

"Sevenpence halfpenny for three wretched leeks?"

And disdainfully she cast the leeks back into the barrow.

Then it was that Constable 64 came and said to Crainquebille: "Move on."

Moving on was what Crainquebille had been doing from morning till evening for fifty years. Such an order seemed right to him, and perfectly in accordance with the nature of things. Quite prepared to obey, he urged his customer to take what she wanted.

"You must give me time to choose," she retorted sharply.

Then she felt all the bundles of leeks over again. Finally, she selected the one she thought the best, and held it clasped to her bosom as saints in church pictures hold the palm of victory.

"I will give you sevenpence. That's quite enough; and I'll have to fetch it from the shop, for I haven't anything on me."

Still embracing the leeks, she went back into the shop, whither she had been preceded by a customer, carrying a child.

Just at this moment Constable 64 said to Crainquebille for the second time:

"Move on."

"I'm waiting for my money," replied Crainquebille.

"And I'm not telling you to wait for your money; I'm telling you to move on," retorted the constable grimly.

Meanwhile, the shoemaker's wife in her shop was fitting blue slippers on to a child of eighteen months, whose mother was in a hurry. And the green heads of the leeks were lying on the counter.

For the half century that he had been pushing his barrow through the streets, Crainquebille had been learning respect for authority. But now his position was a peculiar one: he was torn asunder between what was his due and what was his duty. His was not a judicial mind. He failed to understand that the possession of an individual's right in no way exonerated him from the performance of a social duty. He attached too great importance to his claim to receive sevenpence, and too little to the duty of pushing his barrow and moving on, forever moving on. He stood still.

For the third time Constable 64 quietly and calmly ordered him to move on. Unlike Inspector Montauciel, whose habit it is to threaten constantly but never to take proceedings, Constable 64 is slow to threaten and quick to act. Such is his character. Though somewhat sly, he is an excellent servant and a loyal soldier. He is as brave as a lion and as gentle as a child. He knows naught save his official instructions.

"Don't you understand when I tell you to move on?"

To Crainquebille's mind his reason for standing still was too weighty for him not to consider it sufficient. Wherefore, artlessly and simply he explained it:

"Good Lord! Don't I tell you that I am waiting for my money."

Constable 64 merely replied:

"Do you want me to summons you? If you do, you have only to say so."

At these words Crainquebille slowly shrugged his shoulders, looked sadly at the constable, and then raised his eyes to heaven, as if he would say:

"I call God to witness! Am I a lawbreaker? Am I one to make light of the bylaws and ordinances which regulate my ambulatory calling? At five o'clock in the morning I was at the market. Since seven, pushing my barrow and wearing my hands to the bone, I have been crying: 'Cabbages! Turnips! Carrots!' I am turned sixty. I am worn out. And you ask me whether I have raised the black flag of rebellion. You are mocking me and your joking is cruel."

Either because he failed to notice the expression on Crainquebille's face, or because he considered it no excuse for disobedience, the constable inquired curtly and roughly whether he had been understood.

Now, just at that moment the block of traffic in the Rue Montmartre was at its worst. Carriages, drays, carts, omnibuses, trucks, jammed one against the other, seemed indissolubly welded together. From their quivering immobility proceeded shouts and oaths. Cabmen and butchers' boys, grandiloquent and drawling, insulted one another from a distance, and omnibus conductors, regarding Crainquebille as the cause of the block, called him "a dirty leek."

Meanwhile, on the pavement the curious were crowding round to listen to the dispute. Then the constable, finding himself the center of attention, began to think it time to display his authority:

"Very well," he said, taking a stumpy pencil and a greasy notebook from his pocket.

Crainquebille persisted in his idea, obedient to a force within. Besides, it was now impossible for him either to move on or to draw back. The wheel of his barrow was unfortunately caught in that of a milkman's cart.

Tearing his hair beneath his cap he cried:

"But don't I tell you I'm waiting for my money! Here's a fix! *Misère de misère! Bon sang de bon sang!*"

By these words, expressive rather of despair than of rebellion, Constable 64 considered he had been insulted. And, because to his mind all insults must necessarily take the consecrated, regular, traditional, liturgical, ritual form so to speak of *Mort aux vaches,** thus the offender's words were heard and understood by the constable.

"Ah! You said: *Mort aux vaches.* Very good. Come along."

Stupefied with amazement and distress, Crainquebille opened his great rheumy eyes and gazed at Constable 64. With a broken voice proceeding now from the top of his head and now from the heels of his boots, he cried, with his arms folded over his blue blouse:

"I said '*Mort aux vaches*'? I? . . . Oh!"

The tradesmen and errand boys hailed the arrest with laughter. It gratified the taste of all crowds for violent and ignoble spectacles. But there was one serious person who was pushing his way through the throng; he was a sad-looking old man, dressed in black, wearing a high hat; he went up to the constable and said to him in a low voice very gently and firmly:

"You are mistaken. This man did not insult you."

"Mind your own business," replied the policeman, but without threatening, for he was speaking to a man who was well dressed.

The old man insisted calmly and tenaciously. And the policeman ordered him to make his declaration to the Police Commissioner.

Meanwhile Crainquebille was explaining:

"Then I did say '*Mort aux vaches!*' Oh! . . ."

As he was thus giving vent to his astonishment, Madame Bayard, the

* It is impossible to translate this expression. It means "down with spies," the word spies being used to indicate the police.

shoemaker's wife, came to him with sevenpence in her hand. But Constable 64 already had him by the collar; so Madame Bayard, thinking that no debt could be due to a man who was being taken to the police station, put her sevenpence into her apron pocket.

Then, suddenly beholding his barrow confiscated, his liberty lost, a gulf opening beneath him, and the sky overcast, Crainquebille murmured:

"It can't be helped!"

Before the Commissioner, the old gentleman declared that he had been hindered on his way by the block in the traffic, and so had witnessed the incident. He maintained that the policeman had not been insulted, and that he was laboring under a delusion. He gave his name and profession: Dr. David Matthieu, chief physician at the Ambroise-Paré Hospital, officer of the Legion of Honor. At another time such evidence would have been sufficient for the Commissioner. But just then men of science were regarded with suspicion in France.

Crainquebille continued under arrest. He passed the night in the lockup. In the morning he was taken to the police court in the prison van.

He did not find prison either sad or humiliating. It seemed to him necessary. What struck him as he entered was the cleanliness of the walls and of the brick floor.

"Well, for a clean place, yes, it is a clean place. You might eat off the floor."

When he was left alone, he wanted to draw out his stool; but he perceived that it was fastened to the wall. He expressed his surprise aloud:

"That's a queer idea! Now there's a thing I should never have thought of, I'm sure."

Having sat down, he twiddled his thumbs and remained wrapped in amazement. The silence and the solitude overwhelmed him. The time seemed long. Anxiously he thought of his barrow, which had been confiscated with its load of cabbages, carrots, celery, dandelion and corn-salad. And he wondered, asking himself with alarm: "What have they done with my barrow?"

On the third day he received a visit from his lawyer, Maître Lemerle, one of the youngest members of the Paris Bar, president of a section of La Ligue de la Patrie Française.

Crainquebille endeavored to tell him his story; but it was not easy, for he was not accustomed to conversation. With a little help he might perhaps have succeeded. But his lawyer shook his head doubtfully at everything he said; and, turning over his papers, muttered:

"Hm! Hm! I don't find anything about all this in my brief."

Then, in a bored tone, twirling his fair mustache he said:

"In your own interest it would be advisable, perhaps, for you to confess. Your persistence in absolute denial seems to me extremely unwise."

And from that moment Crainquebille would have made confession if he had known what to confess.

III

CRAINQUEBILLE BEFORE THE MAGISTRATES

President Bourriche devoted six whole minutes to the examination of Crainquebille. This examination would have been more enlightening if the accused had replied to the questions asked him. But Crainquebille was unaccustomed to discussion; and in such a company his lips were sealed by reverence and fear. So he was silent: and the President answered his own question; his replies were staggering. He concluded: "Finally, you admit having said, *'Mort aux vaches.'* "

"I said, *'Mort aux vaches!'* because the policeman said, *'Mort aux vaches!'* so then I said, *'Mort aux vaches!'* "

He meant that, being overwhelmed by the most unexpected of accusations, he had in his amazement merely repeated the curious words falsely attributed to him, and which he had certainly never pronounced. He had said, *"Mort aux vaches!"* as he might have said, "I capable of insulting anyone! How could you believe it?"

President Bourriche put a different interpretation on the incident.

"Do you maintain," he said, "that the policeman was, himself, the first to utter the exclamation?"

Crainquebille gave up trying to explain. It was too difficult.

"You do not persist in your statement. You are quite right," said the President.

And he had the witness called.

Constable 64, by name Bastien Matra, swore he spoke the truth and nothing but the truth. Then he gave evidence in the following terms:

"I was on my beat on October 20, at noon, when I noticed in the Rue Montmartre a person who appeared to be a hawker, unduly blocking the traffic with his barrow opposite No. 328. Three times I intimated to him the order to move on, but he refused to comply. And when I gave him warning that I was about to charge him, he retorted by crying: *'Mort aux vaches!'* Which I took as an insult."

This evidence, delivered in a firm and moderate manner, the magistrates received with obvious approbation. The witnesses for the defense were Madame Bayard, shoemaker's wife, and Dr. David Matthieu, chief physician to the Hospital Ambroise Paré, officer of the Legion of Honor. Madame Bayard had seen nothing and heard nothing. Dr. Matthieu was in the crowd which had gathered round the policeman, who was ordering the costermonger to move on. His evidence led to a new episode in the trial.

"I witnessed the incident," he said. "I observed that the constable had made a mistake; he had not been insulted. I went up to him and called his attention to the fact. The officer insisted on arresting the costermonger, and told me to follow him to the Commissioner of Police. This I did. Before the Commissioner, I repeated my declaration."

"You may sit down," said the President. "Usher, recall witness Matra."

"Matra, when you proceeded to arrest the accused, did not Dr. Matthieu point out to you that you were mistaken?"

"That is to say, *Monsieur le Président,* that he insulted me."

"What did he say?"

"He said, *'Mort aux vaches!'* "

Uproarious laughter arose from the audience.

"You may withdraw," said the President hurriedly.

And he warned the public that if such unseemly demonstrations occurred again he would clear the court. Meanwhile, counsel for the defense was haughtily fluttering the sleeves of his gown, and for the moment it was thought that Crainquebille would be acquitted.

Order having being restored, Maître Lemerle rose. He opened his pleading with a eulogy of policemen: "those unassuming servants of society who, in return for a trifling salary, endure fatigue and brave incessant danger with daily heroism. They were soldiers once, and soldiers they remain; soldiers, that word expresses everything. . . ."

From this consideration Maître Lemerle went on to descant eloquently on the military virtues. He was one of those, he said, who would not allow a finger to be laid on the army, on that national army, to which he was so proud to belong.

The President bowed. Maître Lemerle happened to be lieutenant in the Reserves. He was also nationalist candidate for Les Vieilles Haudriettes. He continued:

"No, indeed, I do not esteem lightly the invaluable services unassumingly rendered, which the valiant people of Paris receive daily from the guardians of the peace. And had I beheld in Crainquebille, gentlemen, one who had insulted an ex-soldier, I should never have consented to represent him before you. My client is accused of having said: *'Mort aux vaches!'* The meaning of such an expression is clear. If you consult *Le Dictionnaire de la Langue Verte* (slang) you will find: *'Vachard,* a sluggard, an idler, one who stretches himself out lazily like a cow instead of working. *Vache,* one who sells himself to the police; spy.' *Mort aux vaches* is an expression employed by certain people. But the question resolves itself into this: how did Crainquebille say it? And, further, did he say it at all? Permit me to doubt it, gentlemen.

"I do not suspect Constable Matra of any evil intention. But, as we have said, his calling is arduous. He is sometimes harassed, fatigued, overdone. In such conditions he may have suffered from an aural hallucination. And, when he comes and tells you, gentlemen, that Dr. David Matthieu, officer of the Legion of Honor, chief physician at the Ambroise-Paré Hospital, a gentlemen and a prince of science, cried: *'Mort aux vaches,'* then we are forced to believe that Matra is obsessed, and if the term be not too strong, suffering from the mania of persecution.

"And even if Crainquebille did cry: *'Mort aux vaches,'* it remains to be proved whether such words on his lips can be regarded as an offense. Crainquebille is the natural child of a costermonger, depraved by years of drinking and other evil courses. Crainquebille was born alcoholic. You behold him brutalized by sixty years of poverty. Gentlemen, you must conclude that he is irresponsible."

Maître Lemerle sat down. Then President Bourriche muttered a sentence condemning Jérôme Crainquebille to pay fifty francs fine and to go to prison for a fortnight. The magistrates convicted him on the strength of the evidence given by Constable Matra.

As he was being taken down the long dark passage of the Palais, Crainquebille felt an intense desire for sympathy. He turned to the municipal guard who was his escort and called him three times:

" 'Cipal! . . . 'cipal! . . . Eh! 'cipal!" And he sighed:

"If anyone had told me only a fortnight ago that this would happen!"

Then he reflected:

"They speak too quickly, these gentlemen. They speak well, but they speak too quickly. You can't make them understand you. . . . 'cipal, don't you think they speak too quickly?"

But the soldier marched straight on without replying or turning his head.

Crainquebille asked him:

"Why don't you answer me?"

The soldier was silent. And Crainquebille said bitterly:

"You would speak to a dog. Why not to me? Do you never open your mouth? Is it because your breath is foul?"

I V

AN APOLOGY FOR PRESIDENT
BOURRICHE

After the sentence had been pronounced, several members of the audience and two or three lawyers left the hall. The clerk was already calling another case. Those who went out did not reflect on the Crainquebille affair, which had not greatly interested them; and they thought no more about it. Monsieur Jean Lermite, an etcher, who happened to be at the Palais, was the only one who meditated on what he had just seen and heard. Putting his arm on the shoulder of Maître Joseph Aubarrée, he said:

"President Bourriche must be congratulated on having kept his mind free from idle curiosity, and from the intellectual pride which is determined to know everything. If he had weighed one against the other the contradictory evidence of Constable Matra and Dr. David Matthieu, the magistrate would have adopted a course leading to nothing but doubt and uncertainty. The method of examining facts in a critical spirit would be fatal to the administration of justice. If the judge were so imprudent as to follow that method, his sentences would depend on his personal sagacity, of which he has generally no very great store, and on human infirmity which is universal. Where can he find a criterion? It cannot be denied that the historical method is absolutely incapable of providing him with the certainty he needs. In this connection you may recall a story told of Sir Walter Raleigh.

" 'One day, when Raleigh, a prisoner in the Tower of London, was working, as was his wont, at the second part of his "History of the World," there was a scuffle under his window. He went and looked at the brawlers; and when he returned to his work, he thought he had observed them very carefully. But on the morrow, having related the incident to one of his friends who had witnessed the affair and had even taken part in it, he was contradicted by his friend on every point. Reflecting, therefore, that if he were mistaken as to events which passed beneath his very eyes, how much greater must be the difficulty of ascertaining the truth concerning events far distant, he threw the manuscript of his history into the fire.'

"If the judges had the same scruples as Sir Walter Raleigh, they would throw all their notes into the fire. But they have no right to do so. They would thus be flouting justice; they would be committing a crime. We may despair of knowing, we must not despair of judging. Those who demand that sentences pronounced in law courts should be founded upon a methodical examination of facts, are dangerous sophists, and perfidious enemies of justice both civil and military. President Bourriche has too judicial a mind to permit his sentences to depend on reason and knowledge, the conclusions of which are eternally open to question. He founds them on dogma and molds them by tradition, so that the authority of his sentences is equal to that of the Church's commandments. His sentences are indeed canonical. I mean that he derives them from a certain number of sacred canons. See, for example, how he classifies evidence, not according to the uncertain and deceptive qualities of appearances and of human veracity, but according to intrinsic, permanent and manifest qualities. He weighs them in the scale, using weapons of war for weights. Can anything be at once simpler and wiser? Irrefutable for him is the evidence of a guardian of the peace, once his humanity be abstracted, and he conceived as a registered number, and according to the categories of an ideal police. Not that Matra (Bastien), born at Cinto-Monte in Corsica, appears to him incapable of error. He never thought that Bastien Matra was gifted with any great faculty of observation, nor that he applied any secret and vigorous method to the examination of facts. In truth it is not Bastien Matra he is considering, but Constable 64. A man is fallible, he thinks. Peter and Paul may be mistaken. Descartes and Gassendi, Leibnitz and Newton, Bichat and

Claude Bernard were capable of error. We may all err and at any moment. The causes of error are innumerable. The perceptions of our senses and the judgment of our minds are sources of illusion and causes of uncertainty. We dare not rely on the evidence of a single man: *Testis unus, testis nullus.* But we may have faith in a number. Bastien Matra, of Cinto-Monte, is fallible. But Constable 64, when abstraction has been made of his humanity, cannot err. He is an entity. And entity has nothing in common with a man; it is free from all that confuses, corrupts and deceives men. It is pure, unchangeable and unalloyed. Wherefore the magistrates did not hesitate to reject the evidence of the mere man, Dr. David Matthieu, and to admit that of Constable 64, who is the pure idea, an emanation from divinity come down to the judgment bar.

"By following such a line of argument, President Bourriche attains to a kind of infallibility, the only kind to which a magistrate may aspire. When the man who bears witness is armed with a sword, it is the sword's evidence that must be listened to, not the man's. The man is contemptible and may be wrong. The sword is not contemptible and is always right. President Bourriche has seen deeply into the spirit of laws. Society rests on force; force must be respected as the august foundation of society. Justice is the administration of force. President Bourriche knows that Constable 64 is an integral part of the Government. The Government is immanent in each one of its officers. To slight the authority of Constable 64 is to weaken the State. To eat the leaves of an artichoke is to eat the artichoke, as Bossuet puts it in his sublime language. (*Politique tirée de l'Ecriture sainte, passim.*)

"All the swords of the State are turned in the same direction. To oppose one to the other is to overthrow the Republic. For that reason, Crainquebille, the accused, is justly condemned to a fortnight in prison and a fine of fifty francs, on the evidence of Constable 64. I seem to hear President Bourriche, himself, explaining the high and noble considerations which inspired his sentence. I seem to hear him saying:

" 'I judged this person according to the evidence of Constable 64, because Constable 64 is the emanation of public force. And if you wish to prove my wisdom, imagine the consequences had I adopted the opposite course. You will see at once that it would have been absurd. For if my judgments were in opposition to force, they would never be executed. Notice, gentlemen, that judges are only obeyed when force is on their side. A judge without policemen would be but an idle dreamer. I should be doing myself an injury if I admitted a policeman to be in the wrong. Moreover, the very spirit of laws is in opposition to my doing so. To disarm the strong and to arm the weak would be to subvert that social order which it is my duty to preserve. Justice is the sanction of established injustice. Was justice ever seen to oppose conquerors and usurpers? When an unlawful power arises, justice has only to recognize it and it becomes lawful. Form is everything; and between crime and innocence there is but the thickness of a piece of stamped paper. It was for you, Crainquebille, to be the strongest. If, after having cried: *"Mort aux vaches!"* you had declared yourself emperor, dictator, President of the Republic or even town councillor, I assure you, you would not have been sentenced to pass a fortnight in prison, and to pay a fine of fifty francs. I should have acquitted you. You may be sure of that.'

"Such would have doubtless been the words of President Bourriche; for he has a judicial mind, and he knows what a magistrate owes to society. With order and regularity he defends social principles. Justice is social. Only wrong-headed persons would make justice out to be human and reasonable. Justice is administered upon fixed rules, not in obedience to physical emotions and flashes of intelligence. Above all things do not ask justice to be just, *it has no need to be just since it is justice,* and I might even say that the idea of just justice can have only arisen in the brains of an anarchist. True, President Magnaud pronounces just sentences; but if they are reversed, that is still justice.

"The true judge weighs his evidence with weights that are weapons. So it was in the Crainquebille affair, and in other more famous cases."

Thus said Monsieur Jean Lermite as he paced up and down the Salle des Pas Perdus.

Scratching the tip of his nose, Maître Joseph Aubarrée, who knows the Palais well, replied:

"If you want to hear what I think, I don't believe that President Bourriche rose to so lofty a metaphysical plane. In my opinion, when he received as true the evidence of Constable 64, he merely acted according to precedent. Imitation lies at the root of most human actions. A respectable person is one who conforms to custom. People are called good when they do as others do."

v

CRAINQUEBILLE SUBMITS TO THE LAWS
OF THE REPUBLIC

Having been taken back to his prison, Crainquebille sat down on his chained stool, filled with astonishment and admiration. He, himself, was not quite sure whether the magistrates were mistaken. The tribunal had concealed its essential weakness beneath the majesty of form. He could not believe that he was in the right, as against magistrates whose reasons he had not understood: it was impossible for him to conceive that anything could go wrong in so elaborate a ceremony. For, unaccustomed to attending Mass or frequenting the Elysée, he had never in his life witnessed anything so grand as a police court trial. He was perfectly aware that he had never cried, *"Mort aux vaches!"* That for having said it he should have been sentenced to a fortnight's imprisonment seemed to him an august mystery, one of those articles of faith to which believers adhere without understanding them, an obscure, striking, adorable and terrible revelation.

This poor old man believed himself guilty of having mystically offended Constable 64, just as the little boy learning his first Catechism believes himself guilty of Eve's sin. His sentence had taught him that he had cried: *"Mort aux vaches!"* He must, therefore, have cried: *"Mort aux vaches!"* in some mysterious manner, unknown to himself. He was transported into a supernatural world. His trial was his apocalypse.

If he had no very clear idea of the offense, his idea of the penalty was still less clear. His sentence appeared to him a solemn and superior ritual, something dazzling and incomprehensible, which is not to be discussed, and for which one is neither to be praised nor pitied. If at that moment he had seen President Bourriche, with white wings and a halo round his forehead, coming down through a hole in the ceiling, he would not have been surprised at this new manifestation of judicial glory. He would have said: "This is my trial continuing!"

On the next day his lawyer visited him:

"Well, my good fellow, things aren't so bad after all! Don't be discouraged. A fortnight is soon over. We have not much to complain of."

"As for that, I must say the gentlemen were very kind, very polite: not a single rude word. I shouldn't have believed it. And the *cipal* was wearing white gloves. Did you notice?"

"Everything considered, we did well to confess."

"Perhaps."

"Crainquebille, I have a piece of good news for you. A charitable person, whose interest I have elicited on your behalf, gave me fifty francs for you. The sum will be used to pay your fine."

"When will you give me the money?"

"It will be paid into the clerk's office. You need not trouble about it."

"It does not matter. All the same I am very grateful to this person." And Crainquebille murmured meditatively: "It's something out of the common that's happening to me."

"Don't exaggerate, Crainquebille. Your case is by no means rare, far from it."

"You couldn't tell me where they've put my barrow?"

VI

CRAINQUEBILLE IN THE LIGHT OF
PUBLIC OPINION

After his discharge from prison, Crainquebille trundled his barrow along the Rue Montmartre, crying: "Cabbages, turnips, carrots!" He was neither ashamed nor proud of his adventure. The memory of it was not painful. He classed it in his mind with dreams, travels and plays. But, above all things, he was glad to be walking in the mud, along the paved streets, and to see overhead the rainy sky as dirty as the gutter, the dear sky of the town. At every corner he stopped to have a drink; then, gay and unconstrained, spitting in his hands in order to moisten his horny palms, he would seize the shafts and push on his barrow. Meanwhile a flight of sparrows, as poor and as early as he, seeking their livelihood in the road, flew off at the sound of his familiar cry: "Cabbages, turnips, carrots!" An old housewife, who had come up, said to him as she felt his celery:

"What's happened to you, Père Crainquebille? We haven't seen you for three weeks. Have you been ill? You look rather pale."

"I'll tell you, M'ame Mailloche, I've been doing the gentleman."

Nothing in his life changed, except that he went oftener to the pub, because he had an idea it was a holiday and that he had made the acquaintance of charitable folk. He returned to his garret rather gay. Stretched on his mattress he drew over him the sacks borrowed from the chestnut seller at the corner which served him as blankets and he pondered: 'Well, prison is not so bad; one has everything one wants there. But all the same one is better at home.' "

His contentment did not last long. He soon perceived that his customers looked at him askance.

"Fine celery, M'ame Cointreau!"

"I don't want anything."

"What! Nothing! Do you live on air then?"

And M'ame Cointreau without deigning to reply returned to the large bakery of which she was the mistress. The shopkeepers and caretakers, who had once flocked round his barrow all green and blooming, now turned away from him. Having reached the shoemaker's, at the sign of l'Ange Gardien, the place where his adventures with justice had begun, he called:

"M'ame Bayard, M'ame Bayard, you owe me sevenpence halfpenny from last time."

But M'ame Bayard, who was sitting at her counter, did not deign to turn her head.

The whole of the Rue Montmartre was aware that Père Crainquebille had been in prison, and the whole of the Rue Montmartre gave up his acquaintance. The rumor of his conviction had reached the Faubourg and the noisy corner of the Rue Richer. There, about noon, he perceived Madame Laure, a kind and faithful customer, leaning over the barrow of another costermonger, young Martin. She was feeling a large cabbage. Her hair shone in the sunlight like masses of golden threads loosely twisted. And young Martin, a nobody, a good-for-nothing, was protesting with his hand on his heart that there were no finer vegetables than his. At this sight Crainquebille's heart was rent. He pushed his barrow up to young Martin's, and in a plaintive broken voice said to Madame Laure: "It's not fair of you to forsake me."

As Madame Laure herself admitted, she was no duchess. It was not in society that she had acquired her ideas of the prison van and the police station. But can one not be honest in every station in life? Every one has his self-respect; and one does not like to deal with a man who has just come out of prison. So the only notice she took of Crainquebille was to give him a look of disgust. And the old costermonger resenting the affront shouted:

"Dirty wench, go along with you."

Madame Laure let fall her cabbage and cried:

"Eh! Be off with you, you bad penny. You come out of prison and then insult folk!"

If Crainquebille had had any self-control, he would never have reproached Madame Laure with her calling. He knew only too well that one is not master of one's fate, that one cannot always choose one's occupation, and that good people may be found everywhere. He was accustomed discreetly to ignore her customers' business with her; and he despised no one. But he was beside himself. Three times he called Madame Laure drunkard, wench, harridan. A group of idlers gathered round Madame Laure and Crainquebille. They exchanged a few more insults as serious as the first; and they would soon have exhausted their vocabulary, if a policeman had not suddenly appeared, and at once, by his silence and immobility, rendered them as silent and as motionless as himself. They separated. But this scene put the finishing touch to the discrediting of Crainquebille in the eyes of the Faubourg Montmartre and the Rue Richer.

VII

RESULTS

The old man went along mumbling: "For certain she's a hussy, and none more of a hussy than she."

But at the bottom of his heart that was not the reproach he brought against her. He did not scorn her for being what she was. Rather he esteemed her for it, knowing her to be frugal and orderly. Once they had liked to talk together. She used to tell him of her parents who lived in the country. And they had both resolved to have a little garden and keep poultry. She was a good customer. And then to see her buying cabbages from young Martin, a dirty, good-for-nothing wretch; it cut him to the heart; and when she pretended to despise him, that put his back up, and then . . . !

But she, alas, was not the only one who shunned him as if he had the plague. Everyone avoided him. Just like Madame Laure, Madame Cointreau the baker, Madame Bayard of l'Ange Gardien scorned and repulsed him. Why, the whole of society refused to have anything to do with him!

So because one had been put away for a fortnight one was not good enough even to sell leeks! Was it just? Was it reasonable to make a decent chap die of starvation because he had got into difficulties with a copper? If he was not to be allowed to sell vegetables, then it was all over with him. Like a badly doctored wine he turned sour. After having had words with Madame Laure, he now had them with everyone. For a mere nothing he would tell his customers what he thought of them and in no ambiguous terms, I assure you. If they felt his wares too long, he would call them to their faces chatterer, soft head. Likewise at the wineshop he bawled at his comrades. His friend, the chestnut seller, no longer recognized him; old Père Crainquebille, he said, had turned into a regular porcupine. It cannot be denied: he was becoming rude, disagreeable, evil-mouthed, loquacious. The truth of the matter was that he was discovering the imperfections of society; but he had not the facilities of a Professor of Moral and Political Science for the expression of his ideas concerning the vices of the system and the reforms necessary; and his thoughts evolved devoid of order and moderation.

Misfortune was rendering him unjust. He was taking his revenge on those who did not wish him ill and sometimes on those who were weaker than he. One day he boxed Alphonse, the wine seller's little boy, on the ear, because he had asked him what it was like to be sent away. Crainquebille struck him and said:

"Dirty brat! It's your father who ought to be sent away instead of growing rich by selling poison."

A deed and a speech which did him no honor; for, as the chestnut seller justly remarked, one ought not to strike a child, neither should one reproach him with a father whom he has not chosen.

Crainquebille began to drink. The less money he earned the more brandy he drank. Formerly frugal and sober, he himself marvelled at the change.

"I never used to be a waster," he said. "I suppose one doesn't improve as one grows old."

Sometimes he severely blamed himself for his misconduct and his laziness:

"Crainquebille, old chap, you ain't good for anything but liftin' your glass."

Sometimes he deceived himself and made out that he needed the drink.

"I must have it now and then; I must have a drop to strengthen me and cheer me up. It seems as if I had a fire in my inside; and there's nothing like the drink for quenching it."

It often happened that he missed the auction in the morning and so had to provide himself with damaged fruit and vegetables on credit. One day, feeling tired and discouraged, he left his barrow in its shed, and spent the livelong day hanging round the stall of Madame Rose, the tripe seller, or lounging in and out of the wineshops near the market. In the evening, sitting on a basket, he meditated and became conscious of his deterioration. He recalled the strength of his early years: the achievements of former days, the arduous labors and the glad evenings: those days quickly passing, all alike and fully occupied; the pacing in the darkness up and down the market pavement, waiting for the early auction; the vegetables carried in armfuls and artistically arranged in the barrow; the piping hot black coffee of Mère Théodore swallowed standing, and at one gulp; the shafts grasped vigorously; and then the loud cry, piercing as cock crow, rending the morning air as he passed through the crowded streets. All that innocent, rough life of the human pack-horse came before him. For half a century, on his travelling stall, he had borne to townsfolk worn with care and vigil the fresh harvest of kitchen gardens. Shaking his head he sighed:

"No! I'm not what I was. I'm done for. The pitcher goes so often to the well that at last it comes home broken. And then I've never been the same since my affair with the magistrates. No, I'm not the man I was."

In short he was demoralized. And when a man reaches that condition he might as well be on the ground and unable to rise. All the passers-by tread him under foot.

VIII

THE FINAL RESULT

Poverty came, black poverty. The old costermonger who used to come back from the Faubourg Montmartre with a bag full of five-franc pieces, had not a single coin now. Winter came. Driven out of his garret, he slept under the carts in a shed. It had been raining for days; the gutters were overflowing, and the shed was flooded.

Crouching in his barrow, over the pestilent water, in the company of spiders, rats and half-starved cats, he was meditating in the gloom. Having eaten nothing all day and no longer having the chestnut seller's sacks for a covering, he recalled the fortnight when the Government had provided him with food and clothing. He envied the prisoners' fate. They suffer neither cold nor hunger, and an idea occurred to him:

"Since I know the trick why don't I use it?"

He rose and went out into the street. It was a little past eleven. The night was dark and chill. A drizzling mist was falling, colder and more penetrating than rain. The few passers-by crept along under cover of the houses.

Crainquebille went past the Church of Saint-Eustache and turned into the Rue Montmartre. It was deserted. A guardian of the peace stood on the pavement, by the apse of the church. He was under a gas lamp, and all around fell a fine rain looking reddish in the gaslight. It fell on to the policeman's hood. He looked chilled to the bone; but, either because he preferred to be in the light or because he was tired of walking he stayed under the lamp, and perhaps it seemed to him a friend, a companion. In the loneliness of the night the flickering flame was his only entertainment. In his immobility he appeared hardly human. The reflection of his boots on the wet pavement, which looked like a lake, prolonged him downwards and gave him from a distance the air of some amphibious monster half out of water. Observed more closely he had at once a monkish and a military appearance. The coarse features of his countenance, magnified under the shadow of his hood, were sad and placid. He wore a thick mustache, short and gray. He was an old copper, a man of some two-score years. Crainquebille went up to him softly, and in a weak hesitating voice, said: *"Mort aux vaches!"*

Then he awaited the result of those sacred words. But nothing came of them. The constable remained motionless and silent, with his arms folded under his short cloak. His eyes were wide open; they glistened in the darkness and regarded Crainquebille with sadness, vigilance and scorn.

Crainquebille, astonished, but still resolute, muttered:

"Mort aux vaches! I tell you."

There was a long silence in the chill darkness and the falling of the fine penetrating rain. At last the constable spoke:

"Such things are not said. . . . For sure and for certain they are not said. At your age you ought to know better. Pass on."

"Why don't you arrest me?" asked Crainquebille.

The constable shook his head beneath his dripping hood:

"If we were to take up all the addlepates who say what they

oughtn't to, we should have our work cut out! . . . And what would be the use of it?"

Overcome by such magnanimous disdain, Crainquebille remained for some time stolid and silent, with his feet in the gutter. Before going, he tried to explain:

"I didn't mean to say: *Mort aux vaches!* to you. It was not for you more than for another. It was only an idea."

The constable replied sternly but kindly:

"Whether an idea or anything else it ought not to be said, because when a man does his duty and endures much, he ought not to be insulted with idle words. . . . I tell you again to pass on."

Crainquebille, with head bent and arms hanging limp, plunged into the rain and the darkness.

Agatha Christie

.

THE WITNESS FOR THE PROSECUTION

Mr. Mayherne adjusted his pince-nez and cleared his throat with a little dry-as-dust cough that was wholly typical of him. Then he looked again at the man opposite him, the man charged with willful murder.

Mr. Mayherne was a small man, precise in manner, neatly, not to say foppishly, dressed, with a pair of very shrewd and piercing gray eyes. By no means a fool. Indeed, as a solicitor, Mr. Mayherne's reputation stood very high. His voice, when he spoke to his client, was dry but not unsympathetic.

"I must impress upon you again that you are in very grave danger, and that the utmost frankness is necessary."

Leonard Vole, who had been staring in a dazed fashion at the blank wall in front of him, transferred his glance to the solicitor.

"I know," he said hopelessly. "You keep telling me so. But I can't seem to realize yet that I'm charged with murder—*murder*. And such a dastardly crime too."

Mr. Mayherne was practical, not emotional. He coughed again, took off his pince-nez, polished them carefully, and replaced them on his nose. Then he said, "Yes, yes, yes. Now, my dear Mr. Vole, we're going to make a determined effort to get you off—and we shall succeed —we shall succeed. But I must have all the facts. I must know just how damaging the case against you is likely to be. Then we can fix the best line of defense."

Still the young man looked at him in the same dazed, hopeless fashion. To Mr. Mayherne the case had seemed black enough, and the guilt of the prisoner assured. Now, for the first time, he felt a doubt.

"You think I'm guilty," said Leonard Vole, in a low voice. "But, by God, I swear I'm not! It looks pretty black against me, I know that. I'm like a man caught in a net—the meshes of it all round me, entangling me whichever way I turn. But I didn't do it, Mr. Mayherne, I didn't do it!"

In such a position a man was bound to protest his innocence. Mr. Mayherne knew that. Yet, in spite of himself, he was impressed. It might be, after all, that Leonard Vole was innocent.

"You are right, Mr. Vole," he said gravely. "The case does look very black against you. Nevertheless, I accept your assurance. Now, let us get to facts. I want you to tell me in your own words exactly how you came to make the acquaintance of Miss Emily French."

"It was one day in Oxford Street. I saw an elderly lady crossing the road. She was carrying a lot of parcels. In the middle of the street she dropped them, tried to recover them, found a bus was almost on top of her and just managed to reach the curb safely, dazed and bewildered by people having shouted at her. I recovered her parcels, wiped the mud off them as best I could, retied the string of one, and returned them to her."

"There was no question of your having saved her life?"

"Oh! dear me, no. All I did was to perform a common act of courtesy. She was extremely grateful, thanked me warmly, and said something about my manners not being those of most of the younger generation—I can't remember the exact words. Then I lifted my hat and went on. I never expected to see her again. But life is full of coincidences. That very evening I came across her at a party at a friend's house. She recognized me at once and asked that I should be introduced to her. I then found out that she was a Miss Emily French and that she lived at Cricklewood. I talked to her for some time. She was, I imagine, an old lady who took sudden and violent fancies to people. She took one to me on the strength of a perfectly simple action which anyone might have performed. On leaving, she shook me warmly by the hand, and asked me to come and see her. I replied, of course, that I should be very pleased to do so, and she then urged me to name a day. I did not want particularly to go, but it would have seemed churlish to refuse, so I fixed on the following Saturday. After she was gone, I learned something about her from my friends. That she was rich, eccentric, lived alone with one maid and owned no less than eight cats."

"I see," said Mr. Mayherne. "The question of her being well off came up as early as that?"

"If you mean that I inquired—" began Leonard Vole hotly, but Mr. Mayherne stilled him with a gesture.

"I have to look at the case as it will be presented by the other side. An ordinary observer would not have supposed Miss French to be a lady of means. She lived poorly, almost humbly. Unless you had been told the contrary, you would in all probability have considered her to be in poor circumstances—at any rate to begin with. Who was it exactly who told you that she was well off?"

"My friend, George Harvey, at whose house the party took place."

"Is he likely to remember having done so?"

"I really don't know. Of course it is some time ago now."

"Quite so, Mr. Vole. You see, the first aim of the prosecution will be to establish that you were in low water financially—that is true, is it not?"

Leonard Vole flushed.

"Yes," he said, in a low voice. "I'd been having a run of infernal bad luck just then."

"Quite so," said Mr. Mayherne again. "That being, as I say, in low water financially, you met this rich old lady and cultivated her acquaintance assiduously. Now if we are in a position to say that you had no idea she was well off, and that you visited her out of pure kindness of heart—"

"Which is the case."

"I dare say. I am not disputing the point. I am looking at it from the outside point of view. A great deal depends on the memory of Mr. Harvey. Is he likely to remember that conversation or is he not? Could he be confused by counsel into believing that it took place later?"

Leonard Vole reflected for some minutes. Then he said steadily enough, but with a rather paler face, "I do not think that that line would be successful, Mr. Mayherne. Several of those present heard his remark, and one or two of them chaffed me about my conquest of a rich old lady."

The solicitor endeavored to hide his disappointment with a wave of the hand.

"Unfortunate," he said. "But I congratulate you upon your plain speaking, Mr. Vole. It is to you I look to guide me. Your judgment is quite right. To persist in the line I spoke of would have been disastrous. We must leave that point. You made the acquaintance of Miss French, you called upon her, the acquaintanceship progressed. We want a clear reason for all this. Why did you, a young man of thirty-three, good-looking, fond of sport, popular with your friends, devote so much of your time to an elderly woman with whom you could hardly have anything in common?"

Leonard Vole flung out his hands in a nervous gesture.

"I can't tell you—I really can't tell you. After the first visit, she pressed me to come again, spoke of being lonely and unhappy. She made it difficult for me to refuse. She showed so plainly her fondness and affection for me that I was placed in an awkward position. You see, Mr. Mayherne, I've got a weak nature—I drift—I'm one of those people who can't say 'No.' And believe me or not, as you like, after the third or fourth visit I paid her I found myself getting genuinely fond of the old thing. My mother died when I was young, an aunt brought me up, and she too died before I was fifteen. If I told you that I genuinely enjoyed being mothered and pampered, I dare say you'd only laugh."

Mr. Mayherne did not laugh. Instead he took off his pince-nez again and polished them, a sign with him that he was thinking deeply.

"I accept your explanation, Mr. Vole," he said at last. "I believe it to be psychologically probable. Whether a jury would take that view of it is another matter. Please continue your narrative. When was it that Miss French first asked you to look into her business affairs?"

"After my third or fourth visit to her. She understood very little of money matters, and was worried about some investments."

Mr. Mayherne looked up sharply.

"Be careful, Mr. Vole. The maid, Janet Mackenzie, declares that her mistress was a good woman of business and transacted all her own affairs, and this is borne out by the testimony of her bankers."

"I can't help that," said Vole earnestly. "That's what she said to me."

Mr. Mayherne looked at him for a moment or two in silence. Though he had no intention of saying so, his belief in Leonard Vole's innocence was at that moment strengthened. He knew something of the mentality of elderly ladies. He saw Miss French, infatuated with the good-looking young man, hunting about for pretexts that should bring him to the house. What more likely than that she should plead ignorance of business, and beg him to help her with her money affairs? She was enough of a woman of the world to realize that any man is slightly flattered by such an admission of his superiority. Leonard Vole had been flattered. Perhaps, too, she had not been averse to letting this young man know that she was wealthy. Emily French had been a strong-willed old woman, willing to pay her price for what she wanted. All this passed rapidly through Mr. Mayherne's mind, but he gave no indication of it, and asked instead a further question.

"And you did handle her affairs for her at her request?"

"I did."

"Mr. Vole," said the solicitor, "I am going to ask you a very serious question, and one to which it is vital I should have a truthful answer. You were in low water financially. You had the handling of an old lady's affairs—an old lady who, according to her own statement, knew little or nothing of business. Did you at any time, or in any manner, convert to your own use the securities which you handled? Did you engage in any transaction for your own pecuniary advantage which will not bear the light of day?" He quelled the other's response. "Wait a minute before you answer. There are two courses open to us. Either we can make a feature of your probity and honesty in conducting her affairs whilst pointing out how unlikely it is that you would commit murder to obtain money which you might have obtained by such infinitely easier means. If, on the other hand, there is anything in your dealings which the prosecution will get hold of—if, to put it baldly, it can be proved that you swindled the old lady in any way, we must take the line that you had no motive for the murder, since she was already a profitable source of income to you. You perceive the distinction. Now, I beg of you, take your time before you reply."

But Leonard Vole took no time at all.

"My dealings with Miss French's affairs were all perfectly fair and above board. I acted for her interests to the very best of my ability, as any one will find who looks into the matter."

"Thank you," said Mr. Mayherne. "You relieve my mind very much. I pay you the compliment of believing that you are far too clever to lie to me over such an important matter."

"Surely," said Vole eagerly, "the strongest point in my favor is the lack of motive. Granted that I cultivated the acquaintanceship of a rich old lady in the hopes of getting money out of her—that, I gather, is the substance of what you have been saying—surely her death frustrates all my hopes?"

The solicitor looked at him steadily. Then, very deliberately, he repeated his unconscious trick with his pince-nez. It was not until they were firmly replaced on his nose that he spoke.

"Are you not aware, Mr. Vole, that Miss French left a will under which you are the principal beneficiary?"

"What?" The prisoner sprang to his feet. His dismay was obvious and unforced. "My God! What are you saying? She left her money to me?"

Mr. Mayherne nodded slowly. Vole sank down again, his head in his hands.

"You pretend you know nothing of this will?"

"Pretend? There's no pretense about it. I knew nothing about it."

"What would you say if I told you that the maid, Janet Mackenzie, swears that you *did* know? That her mistress told her distinctly that she had consulted you in the matter, and told you of her intentions?"

"Say? That she's lying! No, I go too fast. Jane is an elderly woman. She was a faithful watchdog to her mistress, and she didn't like me. She was jealous and suspicious. I should say that Miss French confided her intentions to Janet, and that Janet either mistook something she said, or else was convinced in her own mind that I had persuaded the old lady into doing it. I dare say that she believes herself now that Miss French actually told her so."

"You don't think she dislikes you enough to lie deliberately about the matter?"

Leonard Vole looked shocked and startled.

"No, indeed! Why should she?"

"I don't know," said Mr. Mayherne thoughtfully. "But she's very bitter against you."

The wretched young man groaned again.

"I'm beginning to see," he muttered. "It's frightful. I made up to her, that's what they'll say, I got her to make a will leaving her money to me, and then I go there that night, and there's nobody in the house—they find her the next day—oh! My God, it's awful!"

"You are wrong about there being nobody in the house," said Mr. Mayherne. "Janet, as you remember, was to go out for the evening. She went, but about half-past nine she returned to fetch the pattern of a blouse sleeve which she had promised to a friend. She let herself in by the back door, went upstairs and fetched it, and went out again. She heard voices in the sitting-room, though she could not distinguish what they said, but she will swear that one of them was Miss French's and one was a man's."

"At half-past nine," said Leonard Vole. "At half-past nine. . . ." He sprang to his feet. "But then I'm saved—saved—"

"What do you mean, saved?" cried Mr. Mayherne, astonished.

"By half-past nine I was at home again! My wife can prove that. I left Miss French about five minutes to nine. I arrived home about twenty past nine. My wife was there waiting for me. Oh! Thank God—thank God! And bless Janet Mackenzie's sleeve pattern."

In his exuberance, he hardly noticed that the grave expression of the solicitor's face had not altered. But the latter's words brought him down to earth with a bump.

"Who, then, in your opinion, murdered Miss French?"

"Why, a burglar, of course, as was thought at first. The window was forced, you remember. She was killed with a heavy blow from a crowbar, and the crowbar was found lying on the floor beside the body. And several articles were missing. But for Janet's absurd suspicions and dislike of me, the police would never have swerved from the right track."

"That will hardly do, Mr. Vole," said the solicitor. "The things that were missing were mere trifles of no value, taken as a blind. And the marks on the window were not at all conclusive. Besides, think for yourself. You say you were no longer in the house by half-past nine. Who, then, was the man Janet heard talking to Miss French in the sitting-room? She would hardly be having an amicable conversation with a burglar?"

"No," said Vole. "No—" He looked puzzled and discouraged. "But anyway," he added with reviving spirit, "it lets me out. I've got an *alibi*. You must see Romaine—my wife—at once."

"Certainly," acquiesced the lawyer. "I should already have seen Mrs. Vole but for her being absent when you were arrested. I wired to Scotland at once, and I understand that she arrives back to-night. I am going to call upon her immediately I leave here."

Vole nodded, a great expression of satisfaction settling down over his face.

"Yes, Romaine will tell you. My God! It's a lucky chance that."

"Excuse me, Mr. Vole, but you are very fond of your wife?"

"Of course."

"And she of you?"

"Romaine is devoted to me. She'd do anything in the world for me."

He spoke enthusiastically, but the solicitor's heart sank a little lower. The testimony of a devoted wife—would it gain credence?

"Was there anyone else who saw you return at nine-thirty? A maid, for instance?"

"We have no maid."

"Did you meet anyone in the street on the way back?"

"Nobody I knew. I rode part of the way in a bus. The conductor might remember."

Mr. Mayherne shook his head doubtfully.

"There is no one, then, who can confirm your wife's testimony?"

"No. But it isn't necessary, surely?"

"I dare say not. I dare say not," said Mr. Mayherne hastily. "Now there's just one thing more. Did Miss French know that you were a married man?"

"Oh, yes."

"Yet you never took your wife to see her. Why was that?"

For the first time, Leonard Vole's answer came halting and uncertain.

"Well—I don't know."

"Are you aware that Janet Mackenzie says her mistress believed you to be single, and contemplated marrying you in the future?"

Vole laughed.

"Absurd! There was forty years' difference in age between us."

"It has been done," said the solicitor drily. "The fact remains. Your wife never met Miss French?"

"No—" Again the constraint.

"You will permit me to say," said the lawyer, "that I hardly understand your attitude in the matter."

Vole flushed, hesitated, and then spoke.

"I'll make a clean breast of it. I was hard up, as you know. I hoped that Miss French might lend me some money. She was fond of me, but she wasn't at all interested in the struggles of a young couple. Early on, I found that she had taken it for granted that my wife and I didn't get on—were living apart. Mr. Mayherne—I wanted the money—for Romaine's sake. I said nothing, and allowed the old lady to think what she chose. She spoke of my being an adopted son to her. There was never any question of marriage—that must be just Janet's imagination."

"And that is all?"

"Yes—that is all."

Was there just a shade of hesitation in the words? The lawyer fancied so. He rose and held out his hand.

"Good-bye, Mr. Vole." He looked into the haggard young face and spoke with an unusual impulse. "I believe in your innocence in spite of the multitude of facts arrayed against you. I hope to prove it and vindicate you completely."

Vole smiled back at him.

"You'll find the alibi is all right," he said cheerfully.

Again he hardly noticed that the other did not respond.

"The whole thing hinges a good deal on the testimony of Janet Mackenzie," said Mr. Mayherne. "She hates you. That much is clear."

"She can hardly hate me," protested the young man.

The solicitor shook his head as he went out.

"Now for Mrs. Vole," he said to himself.

He was seriously disturbed by the way the thing was shaping.

The Voles lived in a small shabby house near Paddington Green. It was to this house that Mr. Mayherne went.

In answer to his ring, a big slatternly woman, obviously a charwoman, answered the door.

"Mrs. Vole? Has she returned yet?"

"Got back an hour ago. But I dunno if you can see her."

"If you will take my card to her," said Mr. Mayherne quietly, "I am quite sure that she will do so."

The woman looked at him doubtfully, wiped her hand on her apron and took the card. Then she closed the door in his face and left him on the step outside.

In a few minutes, however, she returned with a slightly altered manner.

"Come inside, please."

She ushered him into a tiny drawing-room. Mr. Mayherne, examining a drawing on the wall, started up suddenly to face a tall pale woman who had entered so quietly that he had not heard her.

"Mr. Mayherne? You are my husband's solicitor, are you not? You have come from him? Will you please sit down?"

Until she spoke he had not realized that she was not English. Now, observing her more closely, he noticed the high cheekbones, the dense blue-black of the hair, and an occasional very slight movement of the hands that was distinctly foreign. A strange woman, very quiet. So quiet as to make one uneasy. From the very first Mr. Mayherne was conscious that he was up against something that he did not understand.

"Now, my dear Mrs. Vole," he began, "you must not give way—"

He stopped. It was so very obvious that Romaine Vole had not the slightest intention of giving way. She was perfectly calm and composed.

"Will you please tell me all about it?" she said. "I must know everything. Do not think to spare me. I want to know the worst." She hesitated, then repeated in a lower tone with a curious emphasis which the lawyer did not understand, "I want to know the worst."

Mr. Mayherne went over his interview with Leonard Vole. She listened attentively, nodding her head now and then.

"I see," she said, when he had finished. "He wants me to say that he came in at twenty minutes past nine that night?"

"He did come in at that time?" said Mr. Mayherne sharply.

"That is not the point," she said coldly. "Will my saying so acquit him? Will they believe me?"

Mr. Mayherne was taken aback. She had gone so quickly to the core of the matter.

"That is what I want to know," she said. "Will it be enough? Is there anyone else who can support my evidence?"

There was a suppressed eagerness in her manner that made him vaguely uneasy.

"So far there is no one else," he said reluctantly.

"I see," said Romaine Vole.

She sat for a minute or two perfectly still. A little smile played over her lips.

The lawyer's feeling of alarm grew stronger and stronger.

"Mrs. Vole—" he began. "I know what you must feel—"

"Do you?" she said. "I wonder."

"In the circumstances—"

"In the circumstances—I intend to play a lone hand."

He looked at her in dismay.

"But, my dear Mrs. Vole—you are overwrought. Being so devoted to your husband—"

"I beg your pardon?"

The sharpness of her voice made him start. He repeated in a hesitating manner, "Being so devoted to your husband—"

Romaine Vole nodded slowly, the same strange smile on her lips.

"Did he tell you that I was devoted to him?" she asked softly. "Ah! Yes, I can see he did. How stupid men are! Stupid—stupid—stupid—"

She rose suddenly to her feet. All the intense emotion that the lawyer had been conscious of in the atmosphere was now concentrated in her tone.

"I hate him, I tell you! I hate him. I hate him. I hate him! I would like to see him hanged by the neck till he is dead."

The lawyer recoiled before her and the smoldering passion in her eyes.

She advanced a step nearer, and continued vehemently, "Perhaps I *shall* see it. Supposing I tell you that he did not come in that night at twenty past nine, but at twenty past *ten?* You say that he tells you he knew nothing about the money coming to him. Supposing I tell you he knew all about it, and counted on it, and committed murder to get it? Supposing I tell you that he admitted to me that night when he came in what he had done? That there was blood on his coat? What then? Supposing that I stand up in court and say all these things?"

Her eyes seemed to challenge him. With an effort, he concealed his growing dismay, and endeavored to speak in a rational tone.

"You cannot be asked to give evidence against your husband—"

"He is not my husband!"

The words came out so quickly that he fancied he had misunderstood her.

"I beg your pardon? I—"

"He is not my husband."

The silence was so intense that you could have heard a pin drop. "I was an actress in Vienna. My husband is alive but in a mad house. So we could not marry. I am glad now."

She nodded defiantly.

"I should like you to tell me one thing," said Mr. Mayherne. He contrived to appear as cool and unemotional as ever. "Why are you so bitter against Leonard Vole?"

She shook her head, smiling a little.

"Yes, you would like to know. But I shall not tell you. I will keep my secret. . . ."

Mr. Mayherne gave his dry little cough and rose.

"There seems no point in prolonging the interview," he remarked. "You will hear from me again after I have communicated with my client."

She came closer to him, looking into his eyes with her own wonderful dark ones.

"Tell me," she said, "did you believe—honestly—that he was innocent when you came here to-day?"

"I did," said Mr. Mayherne.

"You poor little man." She laughed.

"And I believe so still," finished the lawyer. "Good evening, madam."

He went out of the room, taking with him the memory of her startled face.

"This is going to be the devil of a business," said Mr. Mayherne to himself as he strode along the street.

Extraordinary, the whole thing. An extraordinary woman. A very dangerous woman. Women were the devil when they got their knife into you.

What was to be done? That wretched young man hadn't a leg to stand upon. Of course, possibly he did commit the crime. . . .

"No," said Mr. Mayherne to himself. "No—there's almost too much evidence against him. I don't believe this woman. She was trumping up the whole story. But she'll never bring it into court."

He wished he felt more conviction on the point.

The police court proceedings were brief and dramatic. The principal witnesses for the prosecution were Janet Mackenzie, maid to the dead woman, and Romaine Heilger, Austrian subject, the mistress of the prisoner.

Mr. Mayherne sat in court and listened to the damning story that the latter told. It was on the lines she had indicated to him in their interview.

The prisoner reserved his defense and was committed for trial.

Mr. Mayherne was at his wits' end. The case against Leonard Vole was black beyond words. Even the famous K.C. who was engaged for the defense held out little hope.

"If we can shake that Austrian woman's testimony, we might do something," he said dubiously. "But it's a bad business."

Mr. Mayherne had concentrated his energies on one single point. Assuming Leonard Vole to be speaking the truth, and to have left the murdered woman's house at nine o'clock, who was the man Janet heard talking to Miss French at half-past nine?

The only ray of light was in the shape of a scapegrace nephew who had in bygone days cajoled and threatened his aunt out of various sums of money. Janet Mackenzie, the solicitor learned, had always been attached to this young man, and had never ceased urging his claims upon her mistress. It certainly seemed possible that it was this nephew who had been with Miss French after Leonard Vole left, especially as he was not to be found in any of his old haunts.

In all other directions, the lawyer's researches had been negative in their result. No one had seen Leonard Vole entering his own house, or leaving that of Miss French. No one had seen any other man enter or leave the house in Cricklewood. All inquiries drew blanks.

It was the eve of the trial when Mr. Mayherne received the letter which was to lead his thoughts in an entirely new direction.

It came by the six o'clock post. An illiterate scrawl, written on common paper and enclosed in a dirty envelope with the stamp stuck on crooked.

Mr. Mayherne read it through once or twice before he grasped its meaning.

"DEAR MISTER:

"Youre the lawyer chap wot acks for the young feller. If you want that painted foreign hussy showd up for wot she is an her pack of lies you come to 16 Shaw's Rents Stepney to-night It ull cawst you 2 hundred quid Arsk for Missis Mogson."

The solicitor read and re-read this strange epistle. It might, of course, be a hoax, but when he thought it over, he became increasingly convinced that it was genuine, and also convinced that it was the one hope for the prisoner. The evidence of Romaine Heilger damned him completely, and the line the defense meant to pursue, the line that the evidence of a woman who had admittedly lived an immoral life was not to be trusted, was at best a weak one.

Mr. Mayherne's mind was made up. It was his duty to save his client at all costs. He must go to Shaw's Rents.

He had some difficulty in finding the place, a ramshackle building in an evil-smelling slum, but at last he did so, and on inquiry for Mrs. Mogson was sent up to a room on the third floor. On this door he knocked, and getting no answer, knocked again.

At this second knock, he heard a shuffling sound inside, and presently the door was opened cautiously half an inch and a bent figure peered out.

Suddenly the woman, for it was a woman, gave a chuckle and opened the door wider.

"So it's you, dearie," she said, in a wheezy voice. "Nobody with you, is there? No playing tricks? That's right. You can come in—you can come in."

With some reluctance the lawyer stepped across the threshold into the small dirty room, with its flickering gas jet. There was an untidy unmade bed in a corner, a plain deal table and two rickety chairs. For the first time Mr. Mayherne had a full view of the tenant of this unsavory apartment. She was a woman of middle age, bent in figure, with a mass of untidy gray hair and a scarf wound tightly round her face. She saw him looking at this and laughed again, the same curious toneless chuckle.

"Wondering why I hide my beauty, dear? He, he, he. Afraid it may tempt you, eh? But you shall see—you shall see."

She drew aside the scarf and the lawyer recoiled involuntarily before the almost formless blur of scarlet. She replaced the scarf again.

"So you're not wanting to kiss me, dearie? He, he, I don't wonder. And yet I was a pretty girl once—not so long ago as you'd think, either. Vitriol, dearie, vitriol—that's what did that. Ah! But I'll be even with 'em—"

She burst into a hideous torrent of profanity which Mr. Mayherne tried vainly to quell. She fell silent at last, her hands clenching and unclenching themselves nervously.

"Enough of that," said the lawyer sternly. "I've come here because I have reason to believe you can give me information which will clear my client, Leonard Vole. Is that the case?"

Her eyes leered at him cunningly.

"What about the money, dearie?" she wheezed. "Two hundred quid, you remember."

"It is your duty to give evidence and you can be called upon to do so."

"That won't do, dearie. I'm an old woman, and I know nothing. But you give me two hundred quid, and perhaps I can give you a hint or two. See?"

"What kind of hint?"

"What should you say to a letter? A letter from *her*. Never mind how I got hold of it. That's my business. It'll do the trick. But I want my two hundred quid."

Mr. Mayherne looked at her coldly, and made up his mind.

"I'll give you ten pounds, nothing more. And only that if this letter is what you say it is."

"Ten pounds?" She screamed and raved at him.

"Twenty," said Mr. Mayherne, "and that's my last word."

He rose as if to go. Then, watching her closely, he drew out a pocketbook, and counted out twenty one-pound notes.

"You see," he said. "That is all I have with me. You can take it or leave it."

But already he knew that the sight of the money was too much for her. She cursed and raved impotently, but at last she gave in. Going over to the bed she drew something out from beneath the tattered mattress.

"Here you are, damn you!" she snarled. "It's the top one you want."

It was a bundle of letters that she threw to him, and Mr. Mayherne untied them and scanned them in his usual cool, methodical manner. The woman, watching him eagerly, could gain no clue from his impassive face.

He read each letter through, then returned again to the top one and read it a second time. Then he tied the whole bundle up again carefully.

They were love letters, written by Romaine Heilger, and the man they were written to was not Leonard Vole. The top letter was dated the day of the latter's arrest.

"I spoke true, dearie, didn't I?" whined the woman. "It'll do for her, that letter?"

Mr. Mayherne put the letters in his pocket, then he asked a question.

"How did you get hold of this correspondence?"

"That's telling," she said with a leer. "But I know something more. I heard in court what that hussy said. Find out where *she* was at twenty past ten, the time she says she was at home. Ask at the Lion Road Cinema. They'll remember—a fine upstanding girl like that— curse her!"

"Who is the man?" asked Mr. Mayherne. "There's only a Christian name here."

The other's voice grew thick and hoarse, her hands clenched and unclenched. Finally she lifted one to her face.

"He's the man that did this to me. Many years ago now. She took him away from me—a chit of a girl she was then. And when I went after him—and went for him too—he threw the cursed stuff at me! And she laughed—damn her! I've had it in for her for years. Followed her, I have, spied upon her. And now I've got her! She'll suffer for this, won't she, Mr. Lawyer? She'll suffer?"

"She will probably be sentenced to a term of imprisonment for perjury," said Mr. Mayherne quietly.

"Shut away—that's what I want. You're going, are you? Where's my money? Where's that good money?"

Without a word, Mr. Mayherne put down the notes on the table. Then, drawing a deep breath, he turned and left the squalid room. Looking back, he saw the old woman crooning over the money.

He wasted no time. He found the cinema in Lion Road easily enough, and, shown a photograph of Romaine Heilger, the commissionaire recognized her at once. She had arrived at the cinema with a man some time after ten o'clock on the evening in question. He had not noticed her escort particularly, but he remembered the lady who had spoken to him about the picture that was showing. They stayed until the end, about an hour later.

Mr. Mayherne was satisfied. Romaine Heilger's evidence was a tissue of lies from beginning to end. She had evolved it out of her passionate hatred. The lawyer wondered whether he would ever know what lay behind that hatred. What had Leonard Vole done to her? He had seemed dumbfounded when the solicitor had reported her attitude to him. He had declared earnestly that such a thing was incredible—yet it had seemed to Mr. Mayherne that after the first astonishment his protests had lacked sincerity.

He *did* know. Mr. Mayherne was convinced of it. He knew, but he had no intention of revealing the fact. The secret between those two remained a secret. Mr. Mayherne wondered if some day he should come to learn what it was.

The solicitor glanced at his watch. It was late, but time was everything. He hailed a taxi and gave an address.

"Sir Charles must know of this at once," he murmured to himself as he got in.

The trial of Leonard Vole for the murder of Emily French aroused widespread interest. In the first place the prisoner was young and good-looking, then he was accused of a particularly dastardly crime, and there was the further interest of Romaine Heilger, the principal witness for the prosecution. There had been pictures of her in many papers, and several fictitious stories as to her origin and history.

The proceedings opened quietly enough. Various technical evidence came first. Then Janet Mackenzie was called. She told substantially the same story as before. In cross-examination counsel for the defense succeeded in getting her to contradict herself once or twice over her account of Vole's association with Miss French; he emphasized the fact that though she had heard a man's voice in the sitting-room that night, there was nothing to show that it was Vole who was there, and he managed to drive home a feeling that jealousy and dislike of the prisoner were at the bottom of a good deal of her evidence.

Then the next witness was called.

"Your name is Romaine Heilger?"

"Yes."

"You are an Austrian subject?"

"Yes."

"For the last three years you have lived with the prisoner and passed yourself off as his wife?"

Just for a moment Romaine Heilger's eyes met those of the man in the dock. Her expression held something curious and unfathomable.

"Yes."

The questions went on. Word by word the damning facts came out. On the night in question the prisoner had taken out a crowbar with him. He had returned at twenty minutes past ten, and had confessed to having killed the old lady. His cuffs had been stained with blood, and he had burned them in the kitchen stove. He had terrorized her into silence by means of threats.

As the story proceeded, the feeling of the court which had, to begin with, been slightly favorable to the prisoner, now set dead against him. He himself sat with downcast head and moody air, as though he knew he were doomed.

Yet it might have been noted that her own counsel sought to restrain

Romaine's animosity. He would have preferred her to be more un-biased.

Formidable and ponderous, counsel for the defense arose.

He put it to her that her story was a malicious fabrication from start to finish, that she had not even been in her own house at the time in question, that she was in love with another man and was deliberately seeking to send Vole to his death for a crime he did not commit.

Romaine denied these allegations with superb insolence.

Then came the surprising denouement, the production of the letter. It was read aloud in court in the midst of a breathless stillness.

"Max, beloved, the Fates have delivered him into our hands! He has been arrested for murder—but, yes, the murder of an old lady! Leonard who would not hurt a fly! At last I shall have my revenge. The poor chicken! I shall say that he came in that night with blood upon him—that he confessed to me. I shall hang him, Max—and when he hangs he will know and realize that it was Romaine who sent him to his death. And then—happiness, Beloved! Happiness at last!"

There were experts present ready to swear that the handwriting was that of Romaine Heilger, but they were not needed. Confronted with the letter, Romaine broke down utterly and confessed everything. Leonard Vole had returned to the house at the time he said, twenty past nine. She had invented the whole story to ruin him.

With the collapse of Romaine Heilger, the case for the Crown collapsed also. Sir Charles called his few witnesses, the prisoner himself went into the box and told his story in a manly straight-forward manner, unshaken by cross-examination.

The prosecution endeavored to rally, but without great success. The judge's summing up was not wholly favorable to the prisoner, but a reaction had set in and the jury needed little time to consider their verdict.

"We find the prisoner not guilty."

Leonard Vole was free!

Little Mr. Mayherne hurried from his seat. He must congratulate his client.

He found himself polishing his pince-nez vigorously, and checked himself. His wife had told him only the night before that he was getting a habit of it. Curious things, habits. People themselves never knew they had them.

An interesting case—a very interesting case. That woman, now, Romaine Heilger.

The case was dominated for him still by the exotic figure of Romaine Heilger. She had seemed a pale, quiet woman in the house at Paddington, but in court she had flamed out against the sober background, flaunting herself like a tropical flower.

If he closed his eyes he could see her now, tall and vehement, her exquisite body bent forward a little, her right hand clenching and unclenching itself unconsciously all the time.

Curious things, habits. That gesture of hers with the hand was her habit, he supposed. Yet he had seen someone else do it quite lately. Who was it now? Quite lately—

He drew in his breath with a gasp as it came back to him. *The woman in Shaw's Rents. . . .*

He stood still, his head whirling. It was impossible—impossible— Yet, Romaine Heilger was an actress.

The K.C. came up behind him and clapped him on the shoulder.

"Congratulated our man yet? He's had a narrow shave, you know. Come along and see him."

But the little lawyer shook off the other's hand.

He wanted one thing only—to see Romaine Heilger face to face.

He did not see her until some time later, and the place of their meeting is not relevant.

"So you guessed," she said, when he had told her all that was in his mind. "The face? Oh! that was easy enough, and the light of that gas jet was too bad for you to see the make-up."

"But why—why—"

"Why did I play a lone hand?" She smiled a little, remembering the last time she had used the words.

"Such an elaborate comedy!"

"My friend—I had to save him. The evidence of a woman devoted to him would not have been enough—you hinted as much yourself. But I know something of the psychology of crowds. Let my evidence be wrung from me, as an admission, damning me in the eyes of the law, and a reaction in favor of the prisoner would immediately set in."

"And the bundle of letters?"

"One alone, the vital one, might have seemed like a—what do you call it?—put-up job."

"Then the man called Max?"

"Never existed, my friend."

"I still think," said little Mr. Mayherne, in an aggrieved manner, "that we could have got him off by the—er—normal procedure."

"I dared not risk it. You see you *thought* he was innocent—"

"And you *knew* it? I see," said little Mr. Mayherne.

"My dear Mr. Mayherne," said Romaine, "you do not see at all. I knew—he was guilty!"

Arthur C. Train

:

THE DOG ANDREW

"EVERY DOG IS ENTITLED TO ONE
BITE."

"Now see here!" shouted Mr. Appleboy, coming out of the boathouse, where he was cleaning his morning's catch of perch, as his neighbor Mr. Tunnygate crashed through the hedge and cut across Appleboy's parched lawn to the beach. "See here, Tunnygate, I won't have you trespassing on my place! I've told you so at least a dozen times! Look at the hole you've made in that hedge, now! Why can't you stay in the path?"

His ordinarily good-natured countenance was suffused with anger and perspiration. His irritation with Mr. Tunnygate had reached the point of explosion. Tunnygate was a thankless friend and he was a great cross to Mr. Appleboy. Aforetime, the two had been intimate in the fraternal, taciturn intimacy characteristic of fat men, an attraction perhaps akin to that exerted for one another by celestial bodies of great mass, for it is a fact that stout people do gravitate toward one another —and hang or float in placid juxtaposition, perhaps merely as a physical result of their avoirdupois.

So Appleboy and Tunnygate had swum into each other's spheres of influence, either blown by the dallying winds of chance or drawn by some mysterious animal magnetism, and, being both addicted to the delights of the soporific sport sanctified by Izaak Walton, had raised unto themselves portable temples upon the shores of Long Island Sound in that part of the geographical limits of the Greater City known as Throggs Neck.

Every morn during the heat of the summer months Appleboy would rouse Tunnygate or, conversely, Tunnygate would rouse Appleboy, and each in his own wobbly skiff would row out to the spot which seemed most propitious to the piscatorial art. There, under two green umbrellas, like two fat rajahs in their shaking howdahs upon the backs of two white elephants, the friends would sit in solemn equanimity awaiting the evasive cunner, the vagrant perch or cod or the occasional flirtatious eel. They rarely spoke and when they did, the edifice of their conversation—their Tower of Babel, so to speak—was monosyllabic. Thus:

"Huh! Ain't had a bite!"

"Huh!"

"Huh!"

Silence for forty minutes. Then: "Huh! Had a bite?"

"Nope!"

"Huh!"

That was generally the sum total of their interchange. Yet it satisfied them, for their souls were in harmony. To them it was pregnant of unutterable meanings, of philosophic mysteries more subtle than those of the esoterics, of flowers and poetry, of bird-song and twilight, of all the nuances of softly whispered avowals, of the elusive harmonies of love's half-fainting ecstasy.

"Huh!"

"Huh!"

And then into this Eden—only not by virtue of the excision of any skeletal tissue such as was originally necessary in the case of Adam—burst woman. There was silence no longer. The air was rent with clamor; for both Appleboy and Tunnygate, within a month of one another, took unto themselves wives. Wives after their own image!

For a while things went well enough; it takes ladies a few weeks to find out each other's weak points. But then the new Mrs. Tunnygate unexpectedly yet undeniably began to exhibit the serpent's tooth. For no obvious reason at all she conceived a violent hatred of Mrs. Appleboy, a hatred that waxed all the more virulent on account of its object's innocently obstinate refusal to comprehend or recognize it. Indeed Mrs. Tunnygate found it so difficult to rouse Mrs. Appleboy into a state of belligerency sufficiently interesting that she soon transferred her energies to the more worthy task of making Appleboy's life a burden to him.

To this end she devoted herself with a truly Machiavellian ingenuity, devising all sort of insults, irritations and annoyances, and adding to the venom of her tongue the inventive cunning of a Malayan witch doctor. The Appleboys' flowerpots mysteriously fell off the piazza, their thole-pins disappeared, their milk bottles vanished, Mr. Appleboy's fish lines acquired a habit of derangement equalled only by barbed-wire entanglements, and his clams went bad! But these things might have been borne had it not been for the crowning achievement of her malevolence, the invasion of the Appleboys' cherished lawn, upon which they lavished all that anxious tenderness which otherwise they might have devoted to a child.

It was only about twenty feet by twenty, and it was bordered by a hedge of moth-eaten privet, but anyone who has ever attempted to induce a blade of grass to grow upon a sand-dune will fully appreciate the deviltry of Mrs. Tunnygate's malignant mind. Already there was a horrid rent where Tunnygate had floundered through at her suggestion, in order to save going round the pathetic grass-plot which the Appleboys had struggled to create where Nature had obviously intended a floral vacuum.

Undoubtedly it had been the sight of Mrs. Appleboy with her small watering-pot patiently encouraging the recalcitrant blades that had suggested the malicious thought to Mrs. Tunnygate that maybe the Appleboys didn't own that far up the beach. They didn't—that was the mockery of it. Like many others they had built their porch on their boundary line, and, as Mrs. Tunnygate pointed out, they were claiming to own something that wasn't theirs. So Tunnygate, in daily obedience to his spouse, forced his way through the hedge to the beach, and daily the wrath of the Appleboys grew until they were driven almost to desperation.

Now, when the two former friends sat fishing in their skiffs, they either contemptuously ignored one another or, if they "Huh-Huhed!" at all, the "huhs!" resembled the angry growls of infuriated beasts. The worst of it was that the Appleboys couldn't properly do anything about it. Tunnygate had, as Mrs. Tunnygate sneeringly pointed out, a perfect legal right to push his way through the hedge and tramp across the lawn, and she didn't propose to allow the Appleboys to gain any rights by proscription, either. Not much!

Therefore, when Mr. Appleboy addressed to Mr. Tunnygate the remarks with which this story opens, the latter insolently replied in words, form or substance, that Mr. Appleboy could go to hell. Moreover, as he went by Mr. Appleboy, he took pains to kick over a clod of transplanted sea-grass, nurtured by Mrs. Appleboy as the darling of her bosom, and designed to give an air of verisimilitude to an otherwise bare and unconvincing surface of sand. Mr. Appleboy almost cried with vexation. "Oh!" he ejaculated, struggling for words to express the full content of his feeling. "Gosh, but you're—mean!"

He hit it! Curiously enough, that was exactly the word! Tunnygate was mean—and his meanness was second only to that of the fat hippopotama, his wife.

Then, without knowing why, for he had no formulated ideas as to the future, and probably only intended to try to scare Tunnygate with vague threats, Appleboy added: "I warn you not to go through that hedge again! Understand—I warn you! And if you do, I won't be responsible for the consequences!"

He really didn't mean a thing by the words, and Tunnygate knew it.

"Huh!" retorted the latter contemptuously. "You!"

Mr. Appleboy went inside the shack and banged the door. Mrs. Appleboy was peeling potatoes in the kitchen-living room.

"I can't stand it!" he cried weakly. "He's driving me wild!"

"Poor lamb!" soothed Mrs. Appleboy, peeling an interminable rind. "Ain't that just a sweetie? Look! It's most as long as your arm!"

She held it up dangling between her thumb and forefinger. Then, with a groan, she dropped it at his feet. "I know it's a real burden to you, deary!" she sighed.

Suddenly they both bent forward with startled eyes, hypnotized by the peel upon the floor.

Unmistakably it spelled "dog"! They looked at one another significantly.

"It is a symbol!" breather Mrs. Appleboy in an awed whisper.

"Whatever it is, it's some grand idea!" exclaimed her husband. "Do you know anybody who's got one? I mean a—a———"

"I know just what you mean," she agreed, "I wonder we never thought of it before! But there wouldn't be any use in getting *any* dog!"

"Oh, no!" he concurred. "We want a real—dog!"

"One you know about!" she commented.

"The fact is," said he, rubbing his forehead, "if they know about 'em, they do something to 'em. It ain't so easy to get the right kind."

"Oh, we'll get one!" she encouraged him. "Now Aunt Eliza up to Livornia used to have one. It made a lot of trouble and they ordered her—the selectmen did—to do away with it. But she only pretended she had—she didn't really—and I think she's got him yet."

"Gee!" said Mr. Appleboy tensely. "What sort was it?"

"A bull!" she replied. "With a big white face."

"That's the kind!" he agreed excitedly. "What was its name?"

"Andrew," she answered.

"That's a queer name for a dog!" he commented. "Still, I don't care what his name is, so long as he's the right kind of dog! Why don't you write to Aunt Eliza to-night?"

"Of course Andrew may be dead," she hazarded. "Dogs do die."

"Oh, I guess Andrew isn't dead!" he said hopefully. "That tough kind of dog lasts a long time. What will you say to Aunt Eliza?"

Mrs. Appleboy went to the dresser and took a pad and pencil from one of the shelves.

"Something like this," she answered, poising the pencil over the pad in her lap:

"Dear Aunt Eliza: I hope you are quite well. It is sort of lonely living down here on the beach and there are a good many rough characters, so we are looking for a dog for companionship and protection. Almost any kind of healthy dog would do and you may be sure he would have a good home. Hoping to see you soon. Your affectionate niece, Bashemath."

"I hope she'll send us Andrew," said Appleboy fervently.

"I guess she will!" nodded Bashemath.

"What on earth is that sign?" wrathfully demanded Mrs. Tunnygate one morning about a week later as she looked across the Appleboys' lawn from her kitchen window. "Can you read it, Herman?"

Herman stopped trying to adjust his collar and went out on the piazza.

"Something about 'dog,' " he declared finally.

"Dog!" she exclaimed. "They haven't got a dog!"

"Well," he remarked, "that's what the sign says: 'Beware of the dog!' And there's something above it. Oh! 'No crossing this property. Trespassing forbidden.' "

"What impudence!" avowed Mrs. Tunnygate. "Did you ever know

such people! First they try and take land that don't belong to them, and then they go and lie about having a dog. Where are they, anyway?"

"I haven't seen 'em this morning," he answered. "Maybe they've gone away and put up the sign so we won't go over. Think that'll stop us!"

"In that case, they've got another think comin'!" she retorted. "I've got a good mind to have you go over and tear up the whole place!"

" 'N pull up the hedge?" he concurred eagerly. "Good chance!"

Indeed, to Mr. Tunnygate it seemed the supreme opportunity both to distinguish himself in the eyes of his blushing bride and to gratify that perverse instinct, inherited from our cave-dwelling ancestors, to destroy utterly—in order, perhaps, that they may never seek to avenge themselves upon us—those whom we have wronged.

Accordingly, Mr. Tunnygate girded himself with his suspenders, and with a gleam of fiendish exultation in his eye, stealthily descended from his porch and crossed to the hole in the hedge. No one was in sight except two barefooted searchers after clams a few hundred yards farther up the beach and a man working in a field half a mile away. The bay shimmered in the broiling August sun and from a distant grove came the rattle and wheeze of locusts. Throggs Neck blazed in silence, and utterly silent was the house of Appleboy.

With an air of bravado, but with a slightly accelerated heartbeat, Tunnygate thrust himself through the hole in the hedge and looked scornfully about the Appleboy lawn. A fierce rage worked through his veins. A lawn! What effrontery! What business had these condescending second-raters to presume to improve a perfectly good beach which was satisfactory to other folks? He'd show 'em! He took a step in the direction of the transplanted sea-grass. Unexpectedly the door of the Appleboy kitchen opened.

"I warned you!" enunciated Mr. Appleboy with unnatural calmness, which with another background might have struck almost anybody as suspicious.

"Huh!" returned the startled Tunnygate, forced under the circumstances to assume a nonchalance that he did not altogether feel. "You!"

"Well," repeated Mr. Appleboy, "don't ever say I didn't."

"Pshaw!" ejaculated Mr. Tunnygate disdainfully.

With premeditation and deliberation, and with undeniable malice aforethought, he kicked the nearest bunch of sea-grass several feet in the air. His violence carried his leg high and he partially lost his equilibrium. Simultaneously a white streak shot from beneath the porch and something like a red-hot poker thrust itself savagely into an extremely tender part of his anatomy.

"Ouch! O—o—oh!" he yelled in agony. "Oh!"

"Come here, Andrew!" said Mr. Appleboy mildly. "Good doggy! Come here!"

But Andrew paid no attention. He had firmly affixed himself to the base of Mr. Tunnygate's personality without any intention of being immediately detached. And he had selected that place, taken aim, and discharged himself with an air of confidence and skill begotten of lifelong experience.

"Oh! O—o—oh!" screamed Tunnygate, turning wildly and clawing through the hedge, dragging Andrew after him. "Oh! O—oh!"

Mrs. Tunnygate rushed to the door in time to see her spouse lumbering up the beach with a white object gyrating in the air behind him.

"What's the matter?" she called out languidly. Then perceiving the *matter,* she hastily followed. The Appleboys were standing on their lawn, viewing the whole proceeding with ostentatious indifference.

Up the beach fled Tunnygate, his cries becoming fainter and fainter. The two clam-diggers watched him curiously, but made no attempt to go to his assistance. The man in the field leaned luxuriously upon his hoe and surrendered himself to unalloyed delight. Tunnygate was now but a white flicker against the distant sand. His wails had a dying fall: "O—o—oh!"

"Well, we warned him!" remarked Mr. Appleboy to Bashemath with a smile in which, however, lurked a slight trace of apprehension.

"We certainly did!" she replied. Then, after a moment, she added a trifle anxiously: "I wonder what will happen to Andrew!"

Tunnygate did not return. Neither did Andrew. Secluded in their kitchen-living room the Appleboys heard a motor arrive and, through a crack in the door, saw it carry Mrs. Tunnygate away bedecked as for some momentous ceremonial. At four o'clock, while Appleboy was digging bait, he observed another motor making its wriggly way along the dunes. It was fitted longitudinally with seats, had a wire grating and was marked, "N.Y.P.D." Two policemen in uniform sat in front. Instinctively Appleboy realized that the gods had called him. His heart sank among the clams. Slowly he made his way back to the lawn where the wagon had stopped outside the hedge.

"Hey there!" called out the driver. "Is your name Appleboy?"

Appleboy nodded.

"Put your coat on, then, and come along," directed the other. "I've got a warrant for you."

"Warrant?" stammered Appleboy dizzily.

"What's that?" cried Bashemath, appearing at the door. "Warrant for what?"

The officer slowly descended and handed Appleboy a paper.

"For assault," he replied. "I guess you know what for, all right!"

"We haven't assaulted anybody," protested Mrs. Appleboy heatedly. "Andrew——"

"You can explain all that to the judge," retorted the cop. "Meantime put on your duds and climb in. If you don't expect to spend the night at the station, you'd better bring along the deed of your house so you can give bail."

"But who's the warrant for?" persisted Mrs. Appleboy.

"For Enoch Appleboy," retorted the cop wearily. "Can't you read?"

"But Enoch didn't do a thing!" she declared. "It was Andrew!"

"Who's Andrew?" inquired the officer of the law mistrustfully.

"Andrew's a dog," she explained.

"Mr. Tutt," announced Tutt, leaning against his senior partner's doorjamb, with a formal-looking paper in his hand, "I have landed a case that will delight your legal soul."

"Indeed?" queried the elder lawyer. "I have never differentiated between my legal soul and any other I may possess. However, I assume from your remark that we have been retained in a matter presenting some peculiarly absurd, archaic or otherwise interesting doctrine of law?"

"Not directly," responded Tutt, "though you will doubtless find it entertaining enough; but indirectly—atmospherically, so to speak—it touches upon doctrines of jurisprudence, of religion and of philosophy, replete with historic fascination."

"Good!" exclaimed Mr. Tutt, laying down his stogy. "What kind of a case is it?"

"It's a dog case!" said the junior partner, waving the paper. "The dog bit somebody!"

"Ah!" exclaimed Mr. Tutt, perceptibly brightening. "Doubtless we shall find a precedent in Oliver Goldsmith's famous elegy:

"And in that town a dog was found,
As many dogs there be,
Both mongrel, puppy, whelp, and hound,
And curs of low degree."

"Only," explained Tutt, "in this case, though the man recovered of the bite, the dog refused to die!"

"And so they want to prosecute the dog? It can't be done. An animal hasn't been brought to the bar of justice for several centuries."

"No, no!" interrupted Tutt. "They don't——"

"There was a case," went on Mr. Tutt reminiscently, "let me see—at Sauvigny, I think it was—about 1457, when they tried a sow and three pigs for killing a child. The court assigned a lawyer to defend her, but like many an assigned counsel he couldn't think of anything to say in her behalf. As regards the little pigs, he did enter the plea that no animus was shown, that they had merely followed the example of their mother, and that at worst they were under age and irresponsible. However, the court found them all guilty, and the sow was publicly hanged in the market place."

"What did they do with the three little pigs?" inquired Tutt with some interest.

"They were pardoned on account of their extreme youth," said Mr. Tutt, "and turned loose again—with a warning."

"I'm glad of that!" sighed Tutt. "Is that a real case?"

"Absolutely," replied his partner. "I've read it in the Sauvigny records."

"I'll be hanged!" exclaimed Tutt. "I never knew that animals were ever held personally responsible."

"Why, of course they were!" said Mr. Tutt. "Why shouldn't they be? If animals have souls, why shouldn't they be responsible for their acts?"

"But they haven't any souls!" protested Tutt.

"Haven't they, now?" remarked the elder lawyer. "I've seen many an old horse that had a great deal more conscience than his master. And, on general principles, wouldn't it be far more just and humane to have the law deal with a vicious animal that had injured somebody than to leave its punishment to an irresponsible and arbitrary owner, who might be guilty of extreme brutality?"

"If the punishment would do any good—yes!" agreed Tutt.

"Well, who knows?" meditated Mr. Tutt. "I wonder if it ever does any good? But anybody would have to agree that responsibility for one's acts should depend upon the degree of one's intelligence—and from that point of view many of our friends are really much less responsible than sheep."

"Which, as you so sagely point out, would, however, be a poor reason for letting their families punish them in case they did wrong. Just think how such a privilege might be abused! If Uncle John didn't behave himself as his nephews thought proper, they could simply set upon him and briskly beat him up."

"Yes, of course, the law even to-day recognizes the right to exercise physical discipline within the family. Even homicide is excusable, under Section 1054 of our code, when committed in lawfully correcting a child or servant."

"That's a fine relic of barbarism!" remarked Tutt. "But the child soon passes through that dangerous zone and becomes entitled to be tried for his offenses by a jury of his peers; the animal never does."

"Well, an animal couldn't be tried by a jury of his peers, anyhow," said Mr. Tutt.

"I've seen juries that were more like nanny goats than men!" commented Tutt. "I'd like to see some of our clients tried by juries of geese or woodchucks."

"The field of criminal responsibility is the No Man's Land of the law," mused Mr. Tutt. "Roughly, mental capacity to understand the nature of one's acts is the test, but it is applied arbitrarily in the case of human beings and a mere point of time is taken beyond which, irrespective of his actual intelligence, a man is held accountable for whatever he does. Of course that is theoretically unsound. The more intelligent a person is, the more responsible he should be held to be and the higher the quality of conduct demanded of him by his fellows. Yet, after twenty-one, all are held equally responsible—unless they're actually insane. It isn't equity! In theory, no man or animal should be subject to the power of discretionary punishment on the part of another—even his own father or master. But I've seen animals that were shrewder than men, and men who were vastly less intelligent than animals."

"Right-o!" assented Tutt. "Take Scraggs, for instance. He's no more responsible than a chipmunk."

"Nevertheless, the law has always been consistent," said Mr. Tutt, "and has never discriminated between animals any more than it has between men on the ground of varying degrees of intelligence. They used to try 'em all, big and little, wild and domesticated, mammals and invertebrates."

"Oh, come!" exclaimed Tutt. "I may not know much law, but——"

"Between 1120 and 1740 they prosecuted in France alone no less than ninety-two animals. The last one was a cow."

"A cow hasn't much intelligence," observed Tutt.

"And they tried fleas," added Mr. Tutt.

"They have a lot!" commented his junior partner. "I knew a flea once, who——"

"They had a regular form of procedure," continued Mr. Tutt, brushing the flea aside, "which was adhered to with the utmost technical accuracy. You could try an individual animal, either in person or by proxy, or you could try a whole family, swarm or herd. If a town was infested by rats, for example, they first assigned counsel—an advocate, he was called—and then the defendants were summoned three times publicly to appear. If they didn't show up on the third and last call, they were tried *in absentia,* and if convicted were ordered out of the country before a certain date under penalty of being exorcised."

"What happened if they were exorcised?" asked Tutt curiously.

"It depended a good deal on the local power of Satan," answered the old lawyer dryly. "Sometimes they became even more prolific and destructive than they were before, and sometimes they promptly died. All the leeches were prosecuted at Lausanne in 1451. A few selected representatives were brought into court, tried, convicted and ordered to depart within a fixed period. Maybe they didn't fully grasp their obligations or perhaps were just acting contemptuously, but they didn't depart and so were promptly exorcised. Immediately they began to die off and before long there were none left in the country."

"I know some rats and mice I'd like to have exorcised," mused Tutt.

"At Autun, in the fifteenth century, the rats won their case," said Mr. Tutt.

"Who got 'em off?" asked Tutt.

"M. Chassensée, the advocate appointed to defend them. They had been a great nuisance and were ordered to appear in court. But none of them turned up. M. Chassensée therefore argued that a default should not be taken because *all* the rats had been summoned, and some were either so young or so old and decrepit that they needed more time. The court thereupon granted him an extension. However, they didn't arrive on the day set, and this time their lawyer claimed that they were under duress and restrained by bodily fear—of the townspeople's cats: that all these cats, therefore, should first be bound over to keep the peace! The court admitted the reasonableness of this, but the townsfolk refused to be responsible for their cats and the judge dismissed the case!"

"What did Chassensée get out of it?" inquired Tutt.

"There is no record of who paid him or what was his fee."

"He was a pretty slick lawyer," observed Tutt. "Did they ever try birds?"

"Oh, yes!" answered Mr. Tutt. "They tried a cock at Basel in 1474 —for the crime of laying an egg."

"Why was that a crime?" asked Tutt. "I should call it a *tour de force.*"

"Be that as it may," said his partner, "from a cock's egg is hatched the cockatrice, or basilisk, the glance of whose eye turns the beholder to stone. Therefore they tried the cock, found him guilty and burned him and his egg together at the stake. That is why cocks don't lay eggs now."

"I'm glad to know that," said Tutt. "When did they give up trying animals?"

"Nearly two hundred years ago," answered Mr. Tutt. "But for some time after that they continued to try inanimate objects for causing injury to people. I've heard they tried one of the first locomotives that ran over a man and declared it forfeit to the crown as a deodand."

"I wonder if you couldn't get 'em to try Andrew," hazarded Tutt, "and maybe declare him forfeited to somebody as a deodand."

"*Deodand* means 'given to God,' " explained Mr. Tutt.

"Well, I'd give Andrew to God—if God would take him," declared Tutt devoutly.

"But who is Andrew?" asked Mr. Tutt.

"Andrew is a dog," said Tutt, "who bit one Tunnygate, and now the Grand Jury have indicted not the dog, as it is clear from your historical disquisition they should have done, but the dog's owner, Mr. Enoch Appleboy."

"What for?"

"Assault in the second degree with a dangerous weapon."

"What was the weapon?" inquired Mr. Tutt simply.

"The dog."

"What are you talking about?" cried Mr. Tutt. "What nonsense!"

"Yes, it is nonsense!" agreed Tutt. "But they've done it all the same. Read it for yourself!" And he handed Mr. Tutt the indictment.

"The Grand Jury of the County of New York by this indictment accuse Enoch Appleboy of the crime of assault in the second degree, committed as follows:

"Said Enoch Appleboy, late of the Borough of Bronx, City and County aforesaid, on the 21st day of July, in the year of our Lord one thousand nine hundred and twenty-nine, at the Borough and County aforesaid, with force and arms in and upon one Herman Tunnygate, in the peace of the State and People then and there being, feloniously did willfully and wrongfully make an assault in and upon the legs and body of him the said Herman Tunnygate, by means of a certain dangerous weapon, to wit: one dog, of the form, style and breed known as 'bull,' being of the name of 'Andrew,' then and there being within control of the said Enoch Appleboy, which said dog, being of the name of 'Andrew,' the said Enoch Appleboy did then and there feloniously, willfully and wrongfully incite, provoke, and encourage, then and there being, to bite him, the said Herman Tunnygate, by means whereof said dog 'Andrew' did then and there grievously bite the said Herman Tunnygate in and upon the legs and body of him, the said Herman Tunnygate, and the said Enoch Appleboy thus then and there feloniously did willfully and wrongfully cut, tear, lacerate and bruise, and did then and there by means of the dog 'Andrew' aforesaid feloniously, willfully and wrongfully inflict grievous bodily harm upon the said Herman Tunnygate, against the form of the statute in such case made and provided, and against the peace of the People of the State of New York and their dignity."

"That," asserted Mr. Tutt, wiping his spectacles, "is a document worthy of preservation in the Congressional Library. Who drew it?"

"Don't know," answered Tutt; "but whoever he was he was a humorist!"

"It's no good. There isn't any allegation of *scienter* in it," affirmed Mr. Tutt.

"What of it? It says he assaulted Tunnygate with a dangerous weapon. You don't have to set forth that he knew it was a dangerous weapon, if you assert that he did it willfully. You don't have to allege in an indictment charging an assault with a pistol that the defendant knew it was loaded."

"But a dog is different!" reasoned Mr. Tutt. "A dog is not *per se* a dangerous weapon. Saying so doesn't make it so, and that part of the indictment is bad on its face—unless, to be sure, it means that he hit him with a dead dog, which it is clear from the context that he didn't.

The other part—that he set the dog on him—lacks the allegation that the dog was vicious and that Appleboy knew it; in other words an allegation of *scienter*. It ought to read that said Enoch Appleboy "well knowing that said dog Andrew was a dangerous and ferocious animal and would, if incited, provoked and encouraged, bite the legs and body of him the said Herman—did then and there feloniously, willfully and wrongfully incite, provoke and encourage the said Andrew, and so forth.'"

"I get you!" exclaimed Tutt enthusiastically. "Of course an allegation of *scienter* is necessary! In other words, you could demur to the indictment for insufficiency?"

Mr. Tutt nodded.

"But in that case, they'd merely go before the Grand Jury and find another—a good one. It's much better to try and knock the case out on the trial, once and for all."

"Well, the Appleboys are waiting to see you," said Tutt. "They are in my office. Bonnie Doon got the case for us off his local district leader, who's a member of the same lodge of the Abyssinian Mysteries—and he's pulled in quite a lot of good stuff, not all dog cases either! Appleboy's an Abyssinian too."

"I'll see them," consented Mr. Tutt, "but I'm going to have you try the case. I shall insist upon acting solely in an advisory capacity. Dog trials aren't in my line. There are some things which are *infra dig*—even for Ephraim Tutt."

Mr. Appleboy sat stolidly at the bar of justice, pale but resolute. Beside him sat Mrs. Appleboy, also pale but even more resolute. A jury had been selected, without much manifest attention, by Tutt, who had nevertheless managed to slip in an Abyssinian brother on the back row, and an ex-dog fancier for Number Six. Also "among those present" were a delicatessen man from East Houston Street, a dealer in rubber novelties, a plumber and the editor of *Baby's World*. The foreman was almost as fat as Mr. Appleboy, but Tutt regarded this as an even break on account of the size of Tunnygate. As Tutt confidently whispered to Mrs. Appleboy, it was as rotten a jury as he could get.

Mrs. Appleboy didn't understand why Tutt should want a rotten jury, but she nevertheless imbibed some vicarious confidence from this statement and squeezed Appleboy's hand encouragingly. For Appleboy, in spite of his apparent calm, was a very much frightened man, and under the creases of his floppy waistcoat his heart was beating like a tom-tom. The penalty for assault in the second degree was ten years in State's Prison, and life with Bashemath, even in the vicinity of the Tunnygates, seemed sweet. The thought of breaking stones under the summer sun—it was a peculiarly hot summer—was awful. Ten years! He could never live through it! And yet as his glance fell upon the Tunnygates, arrayed in their best finery and sitting with an air of importance upon the front bench of the courtroom, he told himself that he would do the whole thing all over again—yes, he would! He had only stood up for his rights, and Tunnygate's blood was upon his own head—or wherever it was. So he squeezed Bashemath's hand tenderly in response.

Upon the bench Judge Witherspoon, assigned from somewhere up-state to help keep down the ever-lengthening criminal calendar of the Metropolitan District, finished the letter he was writing to his wife in Genesee County, sealed it and settled back in his chair. An old war-horse of the country bar, he had in his time been mixed up in almost every kind of litigation, but as he looked over the indictment he with difficulty repressed a smile. Thirty years ago he'd had a dog case him-self; also of the form, style and breed known as bull.

"You may proceed, Mister District Attorney!" he announced, and Mr. William Montague Pepperill arose with serious mien, and with a high piping voice opened the prosecution.

It was, he told them, a most unusual and hence most important case. The defendant Appleboy had maliciously procured a savage dog of the most vicious sort and loosed it upon the innocent complainant as he was on his way to work, with the result that the latter had nearly been torn to shreds. It was a horrible, dastardly, incredible, fiendish crime, he would expect them to do their full duty in the premises, and they should hear Mr. Tunnygate's story from his own lips.

Mr. Tunnygate limped with difficulty to the stand, and having been sworn, gingerly sat down—partially. Then turning his broadside to the gaping jury he recounted his woes with indignant gasps.

"Have you the trousers which you wore upon that occasion?" inquired Pepperill.

Mr. Tunnygate bowed solemnly and lifted from the floor a paper parcel, which he untied and from which he drew what remained of that now historic garment.

"These are they," he announced dramatically.

"I offer them in evidence," exclaimed Pepperill, "and I ask the jury to examine them with great care."

They did so.

Tutt waited until the trousers had been passed from hand to hand and returned to their owner; then, rotund, chipper and birdlike as ever, began his cross-examination much like a woodpecker attacking a stout stump. The witness had been an old friend of Mr. Appleboy's, had he not? Tunnygate admitted it, and Tutt pecked him again. Never had done him any wrong, had he? Nothing in particular. Well, *any* wrong? Tunnygate hesitated. Why, yes, Appleboy had tried to fence in the public beach that belonged to everybody. Well, did that do the witness any harm? The witness declared that it did; compelled him to go round when he had a right to go across. "Oh!" Tutt put his head on one side and glanced at the jury. "How many feet?" "About twenty feet." Then Tutt pecked a little harder.

"Didn't you tear a hole in the hedge and stamp down the grass when, by taking a few extra steps, you could have reached the beach without difficulty?"

"I—I simply tried to remove an illegal obstruction!" declared Tunnygate indignantly.

"Didn't Mr. Appleboy ask you to keep off?"

"Sure—yes!"

"Didn't you obstinately refuse to do so?"

Mr. Pepperill objected to "obstinately" and it was stricken out.

"I wasn't going to stay off, where I had a right to go," asserted the witness.

"And didn't you have warning that the dog was there?"

"Look here!" suddenly burst out Tunnygate. "You can't hector me into anything. Appleboy never had a dog before. He got a dog just to sic him on me! He put up a sign 'Beware of the dog,' but he knew that I'd think it was just a bluff. It was a plant, that's what it was! And just as soon as I got inside the hedge, that dog went for me and nearly tore me to bits. It was a rotten thing to do and you know it!"

He subsided, panting. Tutt bowed complacently.

"I move the witness' remarks be stricken out on the grounds first, that they are unresponsive; second, that they are irrelevant, incompetent and immaterial; third, that they contain expressions of opinion and hearsay; and fourth, that they are abusive and generally improper."

"Strike them out!" directed Judge Witherspoon. Then he turned to

Tunnygate. "The essence of your testimony is that the defendant set dog on you, is it not? You had quarreled with the defendant, with whom you had formerly been on friendly terms. You entered on premises claimed to be owned by him, though a sign warned you to beware of a dog. The dog attacked and bit you. That's the case, isn't it?"

"Yes, Your Honor."

"Had you ever seen that dog before?"

"No, sir."

"Do you know where he got it?"

"My wife told me——"

"Never mind what your wife told you. Do you——"

"He don't know where the dog came from, judge!" suddenly called out Mrs. Tunnygate in strident tones from where she was sitting. "But I know!" she added venomously. "That woman of his got it from——"

Judge Witherspoon fixed her coldly with an impassive and judicial eye.

"Will you kindly be silent, madam? You will no doubt be given an opportunity to testify as fully as you wish. That is all, sir, unless Mr. Tutt has some more questions."

Tutt waved the witness from the stand contemptuously.

"Well, I'd like a chance to testify!" shrilled Mrs. Tunnygate, rising in full panoply.

"This way, madam," said the clerk, motioning her round the back of the jury box. And she swept ponderously into the offing like a full-rigged bark and came to anchor in the witness chair, her chin rising and falling upon her heaving bosom like the figurehead of a vessel upon a heavy swell.

Now it has never been satisfactorily explained just why the character of an individual should in any way be deducible from such irrelevant attributes as facial anatomy, bodily structure or the shape of the cranium. Perhaps it is not, and in reality we discern disposition from something far more subtle—the tone of the voice, the expression of the eyes, the lines of the face or even from an aura unperceived by the senses. However that may be, the wisdom of the Constitutional safeguard guaranteeing that every person charged with crime shall be confronted by the witnesses against him was instantly made apparent when Mrs. Tunnygate took the stand, for without hearing a word from her firmly compressed lips the jury simultaneously swept her with one comprehensive glance and turned away. Students of women, experienced adventurers in matrimony, these plumbers, bird-merchants, "delicatessens" and the rest looked, perceived and comprehended that here was the very devil of a woman—a virago, a shrew, a termagant, a natural-born trouble-maker; and they shivered and thanked God that she was Tunnygate's and not theirs; their unformulated sentiment best expressed in Pope's immortal couplet:

> *"Oh woman, woman! when to ill thy mind*
> *Is bent, all hell contains no fouler fiend."*

She had said no word. Between the judge and jury nothing had passed, and yet, through the alpha rays of that mysterious medium of communication by which all men are united where woman is concerned the thought was directly transmitted and unanimously acknowledged that here for sure was a hell-cat!

It was as naught to them that she testified to the outrageous illegality of the Appleboys' territorial ambitions, the irascibility of the wife, the violent threats of the husband; or that Mrs. Appleboy had been observed to mail a suspicious letter shortly before the date of the canine assault. They disregarded her. And when Tutt upon cross-examination sought to attack her credibility by asking her various pertinent questions, they unhesitatingly accepted his implied accusations as true, though under the rules of evidence he was bound by her denials.

Peck 1: "Did you not knock Mrs. Appleboy's flower pots off the piazza?" he demanded significantly.

"Never! I never did!" she declared passionately.

But they knew in their hearts that she had.

Peck 2: "Didn't you steal her milk bottles?"

"What a lie! It's absolutely false!"

Yet they knew that she did.

Peck 3: "Didn't you tangle up their fish lines and take their tholepins?"

"Well, I never! You ought to be ashamed to ask a lady such questions!"

They found her guilty.

"I move to dismiss, Your Honor," chirped Tutt blithely at the conclusion of her testimony.

Judge Witherspoon shook his head.

"I want to hear the other side," he remarked. "The mere fact that the defendant put up a sign warning the public against the dog may be taken as some evidence that he had knowledge of the animal's vicious propensities. I shall let the case go to the jury unless this evidence is contradicted or explained. Reserve your motion."

"Very well, Your Honor," agreed Tutt, patting himself upon the abdomen. "I will follow your suggestion and call the defendant. Mr. Appleboy, take the stand."

Mr. Appleboy heavily rose, and the heart of every fat man upon the jury, and particularly that of the Abyssinian brother upon the back row, went out to him. For just as they had known without being told that the new Mrs. Tunnygate was a vixen, they realized that Appleboy was a kind, good-natured man—a little soft, perhaps, like his clams, but no more dangerous. Moreover, it was plain that he had suffered and was, indeed, still suffering, and they had pity for him.

Appleboy's voice shook and so did the rest of his person as he recounted his ancient friendship for Tunnygate and their piscatorial association, their common matrimonial experiences, the sudden change in the temperature of the society of Throggs Neck, the malicious destruction of their property, and the unexplained aggressions of Tunnygate upon the lawn. And the jury, believing, understood.

Then like the sword of Damocles the bessemer voice of Pepperill severed the general atmosphere of amiability: "Where did you get that dog?"

Mr. Appleboy looked round helplessly, distress pictured in every feature.

"My wife's aunt lent it to us."

"How did she come to lend it to you?"

"Bashemath wrote and asked for it."

"Oh! Did you know anything about the dog before you sent for it?"

"Of your own knowledge?" interjected Tutt sharply.

"Oh, no!" returned Appleboy.

"Didn't you know it was a vicious beast?" sharply challenged Pepperill.

"Of your own knowledge?" again warned Tutt.

"I'd never seen the dog."

"Didn't your wife tell you about it?"

Tutt sprang to his feet, wildly waving his arms:

"I object; on the ground that what passed between husband and wife upon this subject must be regarded as confidential."

"I will so rule," said Judge Witherspoon, smiling. "Excluded."

Pepperill shrugged his shoulders.

"I would like to ask a question," interpolated the editor of *Baby's World*.

"Do!" exclaimed Tutt eagerly.

The editor, who was a fat editor, rose in an embarrassed manner.

"Mr. Appleboy!" he began.

"Yes, sir!" responded Appleboy.

"I want to get this straight. You and your wife had a row with the Tunnygates. He tried to tear up your front lawn. You warned him off. He kept on doing it. You got a dog and put up a sign and when he disregarded it you sicked the dog on him. Is that right?"

He was manifestly friendly, merely a bit cloudy in the cerebellum. The Abyssinian brother pulled him sharply by the coat-tails.

"Sit down," he whispered hoarsely. "You're gumming it all up."

"I didn't sic Andrew on him!" protested Appleboy.

"But I say, why shouldn't he have?" demanded the baby's editor. "That's what anybody would do!"

Pepperill sprang frantically to his feet.

"Oh, I object! This juryman is showing bias. This is entirely improper."

"I am, am I?" sputtered the fat editor angrily.

"You want to be fair, don't you?" whined Pepperill. "I've proved that the Appleboys had no right to hedge in the beach!"

"Oh, pooh!" sneered the Abyssinian, now also getting to his feet. "Supposing they hadn't? Who cares a damn? This man Tunnygate deserved all he's got!"

"Gentlemen! Gentlemen!" expostulated the judge firmly. "Take your seats or I shall declare a mistrial. Go on, Mr. Tutt. Call your next witness."

"Mrs. Appleboy," called out Tutt, "will you kindly take the chair?" And that good lady, looking as if all her adipose existence had been devoted to the production of the sort of pies that mother used to make, placidly made her way to the witness stand.

"Did you know that Andrew was a vicious dog?" inquired Tutt.

"No!" answered Mrs. Appleboy firmly. "I didn't."

O woman!

"That is all," declared Tutt with a triumphant smile.

"Then," snapped Pepperill, "why did you send for him?"

"I was lonely," answered Bashemath unblushingly.

"Do you mean to tell this jury you didn't know that that dog was one of the worst biters in Livornia?"

"I do!" she replied. "I only knew Aunt Eliza had a dog. I didn't know anything about the dog personally."

"What did you say to your aunt in your letter?"

"I said I was lonely and wanted protection."

"Didn't you hope the dog would bite Mr. Tunnygate?"

"Why, no!" she declared. "I didn't want him to bite anybody."

At that the delicatessen man poked the plumber in the ribs and they both grinned happily at one another.

Pepperill gave her a last disgusted look and sank back in his seat.

"That is all!" he ejaculated feebly.

"One question, if you please, madam," said Judge Witherspoon. "May I be permitted to"—he coughed as a suppressed snicker ran around the court—"that is—may I not—er—oh, look here! How did you happen to have the idea of getting a dog?"

Mrs. Appleboy turned the full moon of her homely countenance upon the court.

"The potato peel came down that way!" she explained blandly.

"What!" exploded the dealer in rubber novelties.

"The potato peel—it spelled 'dog,' " she repeated artlessly.

"Lord!" deeply suspirated Pepperill. "What a case! Carry me out!"

"Well, Mr. Tutt," said the judge, "now I will hear what you may wish to say upon the question of whether this issue should be submitted to the jury. However, I shall rule that the indictment is sufficient."

Tutt elegantly rose.

"Having due respect to Your Honor's ruling as to the sufficiency of the indictment, I shall address myself simply to the question of *scienter*. I might, of course, dwell upon the impropriety of charging the defendant with criminal responsibility for the act of another free agent even if that agent be an animal—but I will leave that, if necessary, for the Court of Appeals. If anybody were to be indicted in this case, I hold it should have been the dog Andrew. Nay, I do not jest! But I can see by Your Honor's expression that any argument upon that score would be without avail."

"Entirely," remarked Witherspoon. "Kindly go on!"

"Well," continued Tutt, "the law of this matter needs no elucidation. It has been settled since the time of Moses."

"Of whom?" inquired Witherspoon. "You don't need to go back farther than Chief Justice Marshall, so far as I am concerned."

Tutt bowed.

"It is an established doctrine of the common law both of England and
America that it is wholly proper for one to keep a domestic animal for
his use, pleasure or protection, until, as Dykeman, J., says in Muller vs.
McKesson, 10 Hun., 45, 'some vicious propensity is developed and
brought out to the knowledge of the owner.' Up to that time the man
who keeps a dog or other animal cannot be charged with liability for
his acts. This has always been the law.

"In the twenty-first chapter of Exodus at the twenty-eighth verse
it is written: 'If an ox gore a man or a woman, that they die; then the ox
shall be surely stoned, and his flesh shall not be eaten; but the owner
of the ox shall be quit. But if the ox were wont to push with his horn in
time past, and it hath been testified to his owner, and he hath not kept
him in, but that he hath killed a man or a woman; the ox shall be stoned,
and his owner also shall be put to death.'

"In the old English case of Smith vs. Pehal, 2 Strange, 1264, it was
said by the court: 'If a dog has once bit a man, and the owner having
notice thereof keeps the dog, and lets him go about or lie at his door,
an action will lie against him at the suit of a person who is bit, though
it happened by such person's treading on the dog's toes; for it was owing to his not hanging the dog on the first notice. And the safety of the
king's subjects ought not afterwards to be endangered.' That is sound
law; but it is equally good law that 'if a person with full knowledge of
the evil propensities of an animal wantonly excites him or voluntarily
and unnecessarily puts himself in the way of such an animal he would
be adjudged to have brought the injury upon himself, and ought not to
be entitled to recover. In such a case it cannot be said in a legal sense
that the keeping of the animal, which is the gravamen of the offense,
produced the injury.'

"Now in the case at bar, first there is clearly no evidence that this defendant knew or ever suspected that the dog Andrew was otherwise
than of a mild and gentle disposition. That is, there is no evidence
whatever of *scienter*. In fact, except in this single instance there is no
evidence that Andrew ever bit anybody. Thus, in the word of Holy
Writ, the defendant Appleboy should be *quit,* and in the language of
our own courts, 'he must be held harmless.' Secondly, moreover, it ap-

pears that the complainant deliberately put himself in the way of the dog Andrew, after full warning. I move that the jury be directed to return a verdict of not guilty."

"Motion granted," nodded Judge Witherspoon, burying his nose in his handkerchief. "I hold that every dog is entitled to one bite."

"Gentlemen of the jury," chanted the clerk: "How say you? Do you find the defendant guilty or not guilty?"

"Not guilty," returned the foreman eagerly, amid audible evidences of satisfaction from the Abyssinian brother, the *Baby's World* editor and the others. Mr. Appleboy clung to Tutt's hand, overcome by emotion.

"Adjourn court!" ordered the judge. Then he beckoned to Mr. Appleboy. "Come up here!" he directed.

Timidly Mr. Appleboy approached the dais.

"Don't do it again!" remarked His Honor shortly.

"Eh? Beg pardon, Your Honor, I mean——"

"I said: 'Don't do it again!' " repeated the judge. Then, lowering his voice, he whispered: "You see, I come from Livornia, and I've known Andrew for a long time."

As Tutt guided the Appleboys out into the corridor the party came face to face with Mr. and Mrs. Tunnygate.

"Huh!" sneered Tunnygate.

"Huh!" retorted Appleboy.

Karel Čapek

:

MR. HAVLENA'S VERDICT

"Talking about newspapers," said Mr. Beran, "what I think is this: Most people turn first of all to the police reports. It's hard to say whether they're so keen on reading them because of a suppressed desire to commit crime, or for their moral satisfaction and to increase their knowledge of law. What is certain is that they just gloat over them. That's why the papers have to publish police reports every day. But now suppose, for example, the court vacations are on; the courts aren't sitting, but there's got to be a column of reports about them just the same. Or often enough there are no sensational cases on at any of the courts and the police-news reporter has got to have a sensational case, by hook or by crook. When things are like that, the reporters simply have to hatch out a sensational case for themselves. There's a regular market for these sham cases and they're bought, lent or exchanged at the rate of twenty cigarettes or so per item. I know all about it, because I used to share diggings with a police-news reporter; he was fond of booze and he was a slacker, but apart from that he was a fellow who had all his wits about him and who had a miserable screw.

"Now one day a queer sort of chap, down-at-heels, dirty and bloated, turned up in the café where the police-news reporters used to meet; his name was Havlena, he'd studied law but never finished it and he had altogether gone to the dogs; nobody knew exactly how he made a living—in fact, he didn't quite know himself. Well, this fellow Havlena, this loafer was quite well up in criminal or legal matters; when this pressman I knew gave him a cigar and some beer, he would close his eyes, take a few puffs and begin to give the details of the finest and strangest criminal cases you could imagine; then he'd mention the chief points in the defense and quote the public prosecutor's speech in reply, after which he'd pass sentence in the name of the Republic. Then he'd open his eyes, as if he had just woken up, and growl: 'Lend me five crowns.' Once they put him through a test: At one sitting he invented twenty-one criminal cases, each one better than the one before it; but when he got to the twenty-second he stopped short and said: 'Wait a bit, this isn't a case for the petty sessions or even a bench of magistrates; it'd have to go before a jury; and I don't do juries.' You see he was against juries on principle. But to be fair to him, I must say that the sentences he passed, though a bit severe, were models of their kind from a legal point of view; he particularly prided himself on that.

"When the reporters discovered Havlena and saw that the cases he supplied them with were not so hackneyed and dull as those which actually came up before the courts, they formed a sort of trust. For every case which he thought out, Havlena got what they called a court fee, consisting of ten crowns and a cigar, and besides that, two crowns for every month's imprisonment which he imposed; you see, the heavier the sentence, the more difficult the case. The newspaper readers had never before got such a kick out of the police news as when Havlena was supplying his sham criminal cases. No, sir, and now the papers aren't nearly as good as they were in his time; now it's nothing but politics and lawsuits—Heaven alone knows who reads the stuff.

"Now one day Havlena thought out a case, which wasn't by far one of his best, and though up till then none of them had ever caused any trouble, this time the gaff was blown. Reduced to its lowest terms, the case was like this: An old bachelor had a row with a respectable widow who lived opposite him; so he got a parrot and trained it up, so that whenever the lady appeared on her balcony, it screeched out at the top of its voice: 'You slut!' The widow brought an action against him for defamation of character. The district court decided that the defendant, through the agency of his parrot, had made a public laughingstock of the prosecutrix, and in the name of the Republic, sentenced him to fourteen days' imprisonment with costs. 'Eleven crowns and a cigar, please,' said Havlena as a conclusion to the proceedings.

"This particular case appeared in about six newspapers, although it was written up in various ways. In one paper the heading was: 'Far

From The Madding Crowd.' In another: 'Landlord and Poor Widow.'
A third paper called it: 'Accusation against Parrot.' And so on. But
suddenly all these papers received a communication from the Ministry
of Justice asking for particulars of the district court before which the
charge of defamation of character, reported in number so-and-so of
your esteemed journal, had been tried; the verdict and sentence should
be appealed against, since the incriminating words had been uttered,
not by the defendant, but by the parrot; that it could not be regarded as
proven that the words uttered by the said parrot indubitably referred to
the prosecutrix; that hence the words in question could not be regarded
as defamation of character, but at the very utmost as disorderly conduct or a breach of the peace, which could have been dealt with by
binding the defendant over, by duly imposing a fine, or by issuing a
court order for the removal of the bird in question. The Ministry of
Justice accordingly desired to know which district court had dealt with
the case, in order that it might institute appropriate inquiries and so
forth; in fact it was a regular official rumpus.

" 'Good Lord, Havlena, you haven't half landed us in a mess,' the
reporters protested to their retailer. 'Look here, that sentence you
passed in the parrot case is illegal.'

"Havlena went as white as a sheet. 'What,' he shouted, 'the sentence
I passed is illegal. Holy Moses, the Ministry of Justice has got the cheek
to tell me that? Me, Havelena?' The reporters said they'd never seen
a man so offended and angry. 'I'll give them what for,' shouted Havlena, flying into a temper. 'I'll show them whether my verdict's illegal
or not! I'm not going to take this lying down.'—In his vexation and excitement he got terribly drunk; then he took a sheet of paper and for
the benefit of the Ministry of Justice drew up a detailed legal statement to vindicate the verdict; in it he said by teaching his parrot to insult the lady the defendant had manifested his deliberate intention to
insult and disparage her; that hence this was a clear case of unlawful
intent; that the parrot was not the perpetrator of, but only the instrument for, the offense in question; and so forth. As a matter of fact, it
was the most subtle and brilliant piece of legal reasoning which those
reporters had ever seen. Whereupon he signed it with his full name,
Václav Havlena, and sent it to the Ministry of Justice. 'That's that,' he
said, 'and until the matter's dealt with, I'm not going to give any more
judgments; I must get satisfaction first.'

"As you can imagine, the Ministry of Justice took no notice whatever of Havlena's communication; meanwhile Havlena went about looking disgruntled and down in the mouth; he looked seedier than ever and got very thin. When he saw that he had no chance of getting any answer from the Ministry, he quite lost heart; he would spit silently or talk treason, and at last he declared: 'Just you wait, I'll show 'em yet who's in the right.'

"For two months they saw nothing of him; then he turned up again, beaming and smirking, and announced: 'Well, I've been served with a writ at last! Whew, damn that old woman, I had the deuce of a job before I could persuade her to do it. You wouldn't believe that an old girl like that could be so inoffensive; she made me sign a paper that whatever happened I'd foot the bill for her. Anyhow, boys, now it's going to be settled in court.'

" 'What is?' the reporters asked.

" 'Why, that affair with the parrot,' said Havlena. 'I told you I wouldn't let it slide. You see, I bought a parrot and taught it to say: "You slut! You wicked old geezer!" And a deuce of a job it was too, I tell you. For six weeks I didn't set foot outside the house and never uttered a word but: "You slut!" Anyway, now the parrot says it very nicely; the only thing is that the damned stupid bird keeps on shouting it the whole blessed day; it just wouldn't get into the way of only shouting at the woman who lives on the other side of the yard. She's an old girl who gives music lessons; she's seen better days, quite a good sort; but as there aren't any other females in the house, I had to pick on her for the defamation of character. I tell you, it's easy enough to think out an offense like that, but, holy Moses, when it comes to committing it, that's a very different thing. I just couldn't teach that brute of a parrot to call only her names. It calls everyone names. If you ask me, it does that out of sheer cussedness.'

"Then Havlena had a long drink and went on: 'So I tried a different wheeze; whenever the old lady showed her face at the window or in the yard I opened the window in double-quick time so as the parrot could shout at her: "You slut! You wicked old geezer!" And I'm blowed if the old girl didn't start laughing and called over to me: "Well I never, Mr. Havlena, what a nice little bird you've got!" 'Damn the old woman,' growled Mr. Havlena. 'I had to keep pegging away at her for a fortnight, before she'd bring an action against me; but I've got witnesses from all over the house. Aha, and now it's going to be settled in court,' and Havlena rubbed his hands. "I'll eat my hat if I'm not convicted for defamation of character. Those jacks-in-office won't get much change out of me!'

"Until the day when the case came on, Mr. Havlena drank like a fish; he was nervy and restless. In court he was quite the little gentleman; he made a biting speech against himself, referring to the evidence of all the people in the house that the insult was a disgraceful and flagrant one, and demanded the most exemplary penalty. The magistrate, quite a decent old fellow, stroked his beard and said that he would like to hear the parrot. So he adjourned the proceedings and instructed the defendant at the next hearing to bring the bird with him as an exhibit or, should the need arise, as a witness.

"Mr. Havlena appeared at the next hearing with the parrot in a cage. The parrot goggled its eyes at the frightened lady clerk and began to shriek with all its might: 'You slut! You wicked old geezer!'

" 'That's enough,' said the magistrate. 'The evidence of the parrot Lora makes it plain that the expression it used did not refer directly and unequivocally to the prosecutrix."

"The parrot looked at him and yelled: 'You slut!'—'But it is obvious,' continued his worship, 'that it makes use of the expression in question toward all persons, irrespective of their sex. Accordingly there is an absence of contumelious intent, Mr. Havlena.'

"Havlena darted up as if he had been stung. 'Your worship,' he protested excitedly, 'the unlawful intent to cause annoyance is shown by the fact that I was in the habit of opening the window which gave access to the prosecutrix for the purpose of causing the parrot to bring her into contempt.'

" 'That's a moot point,' said his worship. 'The opening of the window possibly indicates some degree of unlawful intent, but in itself it is not a contumelious action. I cannot convict you for opening the window from time to time. You cannot prove that your parrot had the prosecutrix in mind, Mr. Havlena.'

" 'But *I* had her in mind,' urged Havlena in self-defense.

" 'We have no evidence as to that,' demurred the magistrate. 'Nobody heard you utter the incriminating expression. It's no use, Mr. Havlena, I shall have to acquit you.' Whereupon he pronounced judgment accordingly.

" 'And I beg to give notice of appeal against the acquittal,' Havlena burst forth, snatched up the cage containing the bird and rushed out of court, nearly weeping with rage.

"After that they used to come across him here and there, fuddled and devil-may-care. 'Do you call that justice?' he would scream. 'Is there any chance for a man to get his rights anywhere at all? But I won't let matters rest there. I'll have it brought up before the high court. I've got to get my own back for the way I've been made a fool of, even if I have to spend the rest of my life bringing actions. I'm not fighting for my cause, but for justice.'

"I don't exactly know what happened in the appeal court; all I know is that Mr. Havlena's appeal against his acquittal was dismissed. Then Havlena vanished into thin air; there were people who said they'd seen him loitering about the streets like a lost soul and muttering something to himself; I have also heard that to this very day the Ministry of Justice still receives several times a year, a long and furious petition headed: *Defamation of character committed by a parrot.* But Mr. Havlena has, once and for all, stopped supplying police-news reporters with cases; most likely because his faith in law and order has been rudely shaken."

Mark Twain

:

SCIENCE vs. LUCK

At that time, in Kentucky (said the Hon. Mr. K——), the law was very strict against what is termed "games of chance." About a dozen of the boys were detected playing "seven-up" or "old sledge" for money, and the grand jury found a true bill against them. Jim Sturgis was retained to defend them when the case came up, of course. The more he studied over the matter, and looked into the evidence, the plainer it was that he must lose a case at last—there was no getting around that painful fact. Those boys had certainly been betting money on a game of chance. Even public sympathy was roused in behalf of Sturgis. People said it was a pity to see him mar his successful career with a big prominent case like this, which must go against him.

But after several restless nights an inspired idea flashed upon Sturgis, and he sprang out of bed delighted. He thought he saw his way through. The next day he whispered around a little among his clients and a few friends, and then when the case came up in court he acknowledged the seven-up and the betting, and, as his sole defense, had the astounding effrontery to put in the plea that old sledge was not a game of chance! There was the broadest sort of a smile all over the faces of that sophisticated audience. The judge smiled with the rest. But Sturgis maintained a countenance whose earnestness was even severe. The opposite counsel tried to ridicule him out of his position, and did not succeed. The judge jested in a ponderous judicial way about the thing, but did not move him. The matter was becoming grave. The judge lost a little of his patience, and said the joke had gone far enough. Jim Sturgis said he knew of no joke in the matter—his clients could not be punished for indulging in what some people chose to consider a game of chance until it was *proven* that it was a game of chance. Judge and counsel said that would be an easy matter, and forthwith called Deacons Job, Peters, Burke, and Johnson, and Dominies Wirt and Miggles, to testify; and they unanimously and with strong feeling put down the legal quibble of Sturgis by pronouncing that old sledge *was* a game of chance.

"What do you call it *now?*" said the judge.

"I call it a game of science!" retorted Sturgis; "and I'll prove it, too!"

They saw his little game.

He brought in a cloud of witnesses, and produced an overwhelming mass of testimony, to show that old sledge was not a game of chance but a game of science.

Instead of being the simplest case in the world, it had somehow turned out to be an excessively knotty one. The judge scratched his head over it awhile, and said there was no way of coming to a determination, because just as many men could be brought into court who would testify on one side as could be found to testify on the other. But he said he was willing to do the fair thing by all parties, and would act upon any suggestion Mr. Sturgis would make for the solution of the difficulty.

Mr. Sturgis was on his feet in a second.

"Impanel a jury of six of each, Luck *versus* Science. Give them candles and a couple of decks of cards. Send them into the jury room, and just abide by the result!"

There was no disputing the fairness of the proposition. The four deacons and the two dominies were sworn in as the "chance" jurymen, and six inveterate old seven-up professors were chosen to represent the "science" side of the issue. They retired to the jury room.

In about two hours Deacon Peters sent into court to borrow three dollars from a friend. [Sensation.] In about two hours more Dominie Miggles sent into court to borrow a "stake" from a friend. [Sensation.] During the next three or four hours the other dominie and the other deacons sent into court for small loans. And still the packed audience waited, for it was a prodigious occasion in Bull's Corners, and one in which every father of a family was necessarily interested.

The rest of the story can be told briefly. About daylight the jury came in, and Deacon Job, the foreman, read the following

VERDICT

We, the jury in the case of the Commonwealth of Kentucky vs. John Wheeler *et al.*, have carefully considered the points of the case, and tested the merits of the several theories advanced, and do hereby unanimously decide that the game commonly known as old sledge or seven-up is eminently a game of science and not of chance. In demonstration whereof it is hereby and herein stated, iterated, reiterated, set forth, and made manifest that, during the entire night, the "chance" men never won a game or turned a jack, although both feats were common and frequent to the opposition; and furthermore, in support of this our verdict, we call attention to the significant fact that the "chance" men are all busted, and the "science" men have got the money. It is the deliberate opinion of this jury, that the "chance" theory concerning seven-up is a pernicious doctrine, and calculated to inflict untold suffering and pecuniary loss upon any community that takes stock in it.

"That is the way that seven-up came to be set apart and particularized in the statute-books of Kentucky as being a game not of chance but of science, and therefore not punishable under the law," said Mr. K———. "That verdict is of record, and holds good to this day."

John Mortimer

:

THE DOCK BRIEF

A cell. The walls are gray and fade upwards into the shadows so that the ceiling is not seen, and it might even be possible to escape upwards. The door is Right. Backstage is a high, barred window through which the sky looks very blue. Under the window is a stool. Against the Left wall is a bench with a wooden cupboard next to it. On the cupboard a washbasin, a towel and a Bible.

A small fat man is standing on the stool on tiptoes, his hands in his pockets. His eyes are on the sky.

Bolts shoot back. The door opens. MORGENHALL *strides in. He is dressed in a black gown and bands, an aged barrister with the appearance of a dusty vulture. He speaks off stage, to the warder.*

MORGENHALL (*To an unseen warder*): Is this where . . . you keep Mr. Fowle? Good, excellent. Then leave us alone like a kind fellow. Would you mind closing the door? These old places are so drafty.

(*The door closes. The bolts shoot back*)

Mr. Fowle . . . Where are you, Mr. Fowle? Not escaped, I pray. Good heavens man, come down. Come down, Mr. Fowle.

(*He darts at him, and there is a struggle as he pulls down the bewildered* FOWLE)

I haven't hurt you?

(FOWLE, *negative sounding noise*)

I was suddenly anxious. A man in your unfortunate position. Desperate measures. And I couldn't bear to lose you. . . . No, don't stand up. It's difficult for you without braces, or a belt, I can see. And no tie, no shoelaces. I'm so glad they're looking after you. You must forgive me if I frightened you just a little, Mr. Fowle. It was when I saw you by that window . . .

FOWLE (*A hoarse and sad voice*): Epping Forest.

MORGENHALL: What did you say?

FOWLE: I think you can see Epping Forest.

MORGENHALL: No doubt you can. But why, my dear chap, why should you want to?

FOWLE: It's the home stretch.

MORGENHALL: Very well.

FOWLE: I thought I could get a glimpse of the green. Between the chimneys and that shed . . .

(FOWLE *starts to climb again. A brief renewed struggle.*)

MORGENHALL: No, get down. It's not wise to be up there, forever trying to look out. There's a drafty, sneeping wind. Treacherous.

FOWLE: Treacherous?

MORGENHALL: I'm afraid so. You never know what a mean, sneeping wind can do. Catch you by the throat, start a sneeze, then a dry tickle on the chest. I don't want anything to catch you like that before . . .

FOWLE: Before what?

MORGENHALL: You're much better sitting quietly down there in the warm. Just sit quietly and I'll introduce myself.

FOWLE: I am tired.

MORGENHALL: I'm Wilfred Morgenhall.

FOWLE: Wilfred?

MORGENHALL: Morgenhall. The barrister.

FOWLE: The barrister?

MORGENHALL: Perfectly so . . .

FOWLE: I'm sorry.

MORGENHALL: Why?

FOWLE: A barrister. That's very bad.

MORGENHALL: I don't know. Why's it so bad?

FOWLE: When a gentleman of your stamp goes wrong. A long fall.

MORGENHALL: What can you mean?

FOWLE: Different for an individual like me. I only kept a small seed shop.

MORGENHALL: Seed shop? My poor fellow. We mustn't let this unfortunate little case confuse us. We're going to remain very calm, very lucid. We're going to come to important decisions. Now, do me a favor, Mr. Fowle, no more seed shops.

FOWLE: Birdseed, of course. Individuals down our way kept birds mostly. Canaries and budgies. The budgies talked. Lot of lonely people down our way. They kept them for the talk.

MORGENHALL: Mr. Fowle, I'm a barrister.

FOWLE: Tragic.

MORGENHALL: I know the law.

FOWLE: It's trapped you.

MORGENHALL: I'm here to help you.

FOWLE: We'll help each other.

(*Pause.*)

MORGENHALL (*Laughs uncontrollably*): I see. Mr. Fowle, I see where you've been bewildered. You think I'm in trouble as well. Then I've got good news for you at last. I'm free. Oh yes, I can leave here when I like.

FOWLE: You can?

MORGENHALL: The police are my friends.

FOWLE: They are?

MORGENHALL: And I've never felt better in my life. There now, that's relieved you, hasn't it? I'm not in any trouble.

FOWLE: Family all well?

MORGENHALL: I never married.

FOWLE: Rent paid up?

MORGENHALL: A week or two owing perhaps. Temporary lull in business. This case will end all that.

FOWLE: Which case?

MORGENHALL: Your case.

FOWLE: My . . . ?

MORGENHALL: Case.

FOWLE: Oh that—it's not important.

MORGENHALL: Not?

FOWLE: I don't care about it to any large extent. Not as at present advised.

MORGENHALL: Mr. Fowle. How could you say that?

FOWLE: The flavor's gone out of it.

MORGENHALL: But we're only at the beginning.

FOWLE: I can't believe it's me concerned . . .

MORGENHALL: But it is you, Mr. Fowle. You mustn't let yourself forget that. You see, that's why you're here . . .

FOWLE: I can't seem to bother with it.

MORGENHALL: Can you be so busy?

FOWLE: Slopping in, slopping out. Peering at the old forest. It fills in the day.

MORGENHALL: You seem, if I may say so, to have adopted an unpleasantly selfish attitude.

FOWLE: Selfish?

MORGENHALL: Dog in the manger.

FOWLE: In the—?

MORGENHALL: Unenthusiastic.

FOWLE: You're speaking quite frankly, I well appreciate . . .

MORGENHALL: I'm sorry, Fowle. You made me say it. There's so much of this about nowadays. There's so much ready-made entertainment. Free billiards. National Health, television. There's not the spirit abroad there used to be.

FOWLE: You feel that?

MORGENHALL: Whatever I've done I've always been mustard keen on my work. I've never lost the vision, Fowle. In all my disappointments I've never lost the love of the job.

FOWLE: The position in life you've obtained to.

MORGENHALL: Years of study I had to put in. It didn't just drop in my lap.

FOWLE: I've never studied . . .

MORGENHALL: Year after year, Fowle, my window at college was alight until two A.M. There I sat among my books. I fed mainly on herrings . . .

FOWLE: Lean years?

MORGENHALL: And black tea. No subsidized biscuits then, Fowle, no County Council tobacco, just work . . .

FOWLE: Book work, almost entirely? I'm only assuming that of course.

MORGENHALL: Want to hear some Latin?

FOWLE: Only if you have time.

MORGENHALL: *Actus non sit reus nisi mens sit rea. Filius Nullius. In flagrante delictu.* Understand it?

FOWLE: I'm no scholar.

MORGENHALL: You most certainly are not. But I had to be, we all had to be in my day. Then we'd sit for the examinations, mods, smalls, greats, tripos, little goes, week after week, rowing men fainting, Indian students vomiting with fear, and no creeping out for a peep at the book under the pretext of a pump ship or getting a glance at the other fellow's celluloid cuff . . .

FOWLE: That would be very unheard of?

MORGENHALL: Then weeks, months of waiting. Nerve-racking. Go up to the Lake District. Pace the mountains, play draughts, forget to huff. Then comes the fatal post card.

FOWLE: What's it say?

MORGENHALL: Satisfied the examiners. Don't rejoice so soon. True enough I felt I'd turned a corner, got a fur hood, bumped on the head with a Bible. Bachelor of Law sounded sweet in my ears. I thought of celebrating, a few kindred spirits round for a light ale. Told the only lady in my life that in five years' time perhaps . . .

FOWLE: You'd arrived.

MORGENHALL: That's what I thought when they painted my name up on my London chambers. I sat down to fill in the time until they sent my first brief in a real case. I sat down to do the crossword puzzle while I waited. Five years later, Fowle, what was I doing . . . ?

FOWLE: A little charge of High Treason?

MORGENHALL: I was still doing the crossword puzzle.

FOWLE: But better at it.

MORGENHALL: Not much. Not very much. As the years pass there come to be clues you no longer understand.

FOWLE: So all that training?

MORGENHALL: Wasted. The talents rust.

FOWLE: And the lady?

MORGENHALL: Drove an ambulance in the 1914. A stray piece of shrapnel took her. I don't care to talk of it.

FOWLE: Tragic.

MORGENHALL: That was.

FOWLE: Tragic my wife was never called up.

MORGENHALL: You mustn't talk like that, Fowle, your poor wife.

FOWLE: Don't let's carry on about me.

MORGENHALL: But we must carry on about you. That's what I'm here for.

FOWLE: You're here to?

MORGENHALL: Defend you.

FOWLE: Can't be done.

MORGENHALL: Why ever not?

FOWLE: I know who killed her.

MORGENHALL: Who?

FOWLE: Me.

(*Pause.*)

MORGENHALL (*Considerable thought before he says*): Mr. Fowle, I have all the respect in the world for your opinions, but we must face this. You're a man of very little education . . .

FOWLE: That's true.

MORGENHALL: One has only to glance at you. At those curious lobes to your ears. At the line of your hair. At the strange way your eyebrows connect in the middle, to see that you're a person of very limited intelligence.

FOWLE: Agreed, quite frankly.

MORGENHALL: You think you killed your wife.

FOWLE: Seems so to me.

MORGENHALL: Mr. Fowle. Look at yourself objectively. On questions of birdseed I have no doubt you may be infallible—but on a vital point like this might you not be mistaken? . . . Don't answer . . .

FOWLE: Why not, sir?

MORGENHALL: Before you drop the bomb of a reply, consider who will be wounded. Are the innocent to suffer?

FOWLE: I only want to be honest.

MORGENHALL: But you're a criminal, Mr. Fowle. You've broken through the narrow fabric of honesty. You are free to be kind, human, to do good.

FOWLE: But what I did to her . . .

MORGENHALL: She's passed, you know, out of your life. You've set up new relationships. You've picked out me.

FOWLE: Picked out?

MORGENHALL: Selected.

FOWLE: But I didn't know . . .

MORGENHALL: No, Mr. Fowle. That's the whole beauty of it. You didn't know me. You came to me under a system of chance invented, like the football pools, to even out the harsh inequality of a world where you have to deserve success. You, Mr. Fowle, are my first Dock Brief.

FOWLE: Your Dock?

MORGENHALL: Brief.

FOWLE: You couldn't explain?

MORGENHALL: Of course. Prisoners with no money and no friends exist. Luckily, you're one of them. They're entitled to choose any barrister sitting in Court to defend them. The barrister, however old, gets a brief, and is remunerated on a modest scale. Busy lawyers, wealthy lawyers, men with other interests, creep out of Court bent double when the Dock Brief is chosen. We regulars who are not busy sit on. I've been a regular for years. It's not etiquette, you see, even if you want the work, to wave at the prisoner, or whistle, or try to catch his eye by hoisting any sort of little flag.

FOWLE: Didn't know.

MORGENHALL: But you *can* choose the most advantageous seat. The seat any criminal would naturally point at. It's the seat under the window and for ten years my old friend, Tuppy Morgan, bagged it each day at ten. He sat there reading Horace, and writing to his innumerable aunts, and almost once a year a criminal pointed him out. Oh, Mr. Fowle, Tuppy was a limpet on that seat. But, this morning, something, possibly a cold, perhaps death, kept him indoors. So I had his place. And you spotted me, no doubt.

FOWLE: Spotted you?

MORGENHALL: My glasses polished. My profile drawn and learned in front of the great window.

FOWLE: I never noticed.

MORGENHALL: But when they asked you to choose a lawyer?

FOWLE: I shut my eyes and pointed—I've picked horses that way and football teams. Never did me any good, though, by any stretch of the imagination.

MORGENHALL: So even you, Mr. Fowle, didn't choose me?

FOWLE: Not altogether.

MORGENHALL: The law's a haphazard business.

FOWLE: It does seem chancy.

MORGENHALL: Years of training and then to be picked out like a football pool.

FOWLE: Don't take it badly, sir.

MORGENHALL: Of course, you've been fortunate.

FOWLE: So unusual. I was never one to draw the free bird at Christmas, or guess the weight of the cake. Now, I'm sorry I told you.

MORGENHALL: Never mind. You hurt me temporarily, Fowle, I must confess. It might have been kinder to have kept me in ignorance. But now it's done. Let's get down to business. And, Fowle—

FOWLE: Yes, sir.

MORGENHALL: Remember you're dealing with a fellow man. A man no longer young. Remember the hopes I've pinned on you and try . . .

FOWLE: Try?

MORGENHALL: Try to spare me more pain.

FOWLE: I will, sir. Of course I will.

MORGENHALL: Now. Let's get our minds in order.

FOWLE: Sort things out.

MORGENHALL: Exactly. Now, this wife of yours.

FOWLE: Doris?

MORGENHALL: Doris. A bitter unsympathetic woman?

FOWLE: She was always cheerful. She loved jokes.

MORGENHALL: Oh Fowle, do be very careful.

FOWLE: I will, sir. But if you'd known Doris . . . She laughed harder than she worked. Thank God, she'd say, for my old English sense of fun.

MORGENHALL: What sort of jokes, Fowle, did this Doris appreciate?

FOWLE: All sorts. Pictures in the paper. Jokes on the wireless set. Laughs out of crackers. She'd keep them from Christmas to Christmas and trot them out in August.

MORGENHALL: You couldn't share it?

FOWLE: Not to that extent. I often missed the funny point.

MORGENHALL: Then you'd quarrel?

FOWLE: "Don't look so miserable, it may never happen." She said that every night when I came home. "Where'd you get that miserable expression from?"

MORGENHALL: I can see it now. There is a kind of Sunday evening appearance to you.

FOWLE: I was quite happy. But it was always "Cat got your tongue?" "Where's the funeral?" "Play us a tune on that old fiddle face of yours. Lucky there's one of us here that can see the funny side." Then we had to have our tea with the wireless on so that she'd pick up the phrases.

MORGENHALL: You're not a wireless lover?

FOWLE: I couldn't always laugh. And she'd be doubled up across the table, gasping as if her lungs were full of water. "Laugh," she'd call, "laugh, damn you. What've you got to be so miserable about?" Then she'd go under, bubbling like a drowning woman.

MORGENHALL: Made meals difficult?

FOWLE: Indigestible. I would have laughed, but the jokes never tickled me.

MORGENHALL: They tickled her?

FOWLE: Anything did. Anything a little comic. Our names were misfortunate.

MORGENHALL: Your names?

FOWLE: Fowle. Going down the aisle she said: "Now we're cock and hen, aren't we, old bird?" Coming away it was, "Now I'm Mrs. Fowle, you'll have to play fair with me." She laughed so hard we couldn't get her straightened up for the photograph.

MORGENHALL: Fond of puns, I gather you're trying to say.

FOWLE: Of any sort of joke. I had a little aviary at the bottom of my garden. As she got funnier so I spent more time with my birds. Budgerigars are small parrots. Circles round their eyes give them a sad, tired look.

MORGENHALL: You found them sympathetic?

FOWLE: Restful. Until one of them spoke out at me.

MORGENHALL: Spoke—what words?

FOWLE: "Don't look so miserable, it may never happen."

MORGENHALL: The bird said that?

FOWLE: She taught it during the day when I was out at work. It didn't mean to irritate.

MORGENHALL: It was wrong of her, of course. To lead on your bird like that.

FOWLE: But it wasn't him that brought me to it. It was Bateson, the lodger.

MORGENHALL: Another man?

FOWLE: At long last.

MORGENHALL: I can see it now. A crime of passion. An unfaithful wife. In flagrante. . . . Of course, you don't know what that means. We'll reduce it to manslaughter right away. A wronged husband and there's never a dry eye in the jury box. You came in and caught them.

FOWLE: Always laughing together.

MORGENHALL: Maddening.

FOWLE: He knew more jokes than she did.

MORGENHALL: Stealing her before your eyes?

FOWLE: That's what I thought. He was a big man. Ex-police. Said he'd been the scream of the station. I picked him for her specially. In the chitty I put up in the local sweet shop, I wrote: "Humorous type of lodger wanted."

MORGENHALL: But wasn't that a risk?

FOWLE: Slight, perhaps. But it went all right. Two days after he came he poised a bag of flour to fall on her in the kitchen. Then she sewed up the legs of his pajamas. They had to hold on to each other so as not to fall over laughing. "Look at old misery standing there," she said. "He can never see anything subtle."

MORGENHALL: Galling for you. Terribly galling.

FOWLE: I thought all was well. I spent more time with the birds. I'd come home late and always be careful to scrunch the gravel at the front door. I went to bed early and left them with the Light Program. On Sunday mornings I fed the budgies and suggested he take her tea in bed. Laughter, she read out from her horoscope, leads to love, even for those born under the sign of the Virgin.

MORGENHALL: You trusted them. They deceived you.

FOWLE: They deceived me all right. And I trusted them. Especially after I'd seen her on his knee and them both looking at the cartoons from one wrapping of chips.

MORGENHALL: Mr. Fowle, I'm not quite getting the drift of your evidence. My hope is—your thought may not prove a shade too involved for our literal-minded judge. Old Tommy Banter was a Rugger blue in '98. He never rose to chess and his draughts had a brutal, unintelligent quality.

FOWLE: When he'd first put his knee under her I thought he'd do the decent thing. I thought I'd have peace in my little house at last. The wireless set dead silent. The end of all that happy laughter. No sound but the twitter from the end of the garden and the squeak of my own foot on the linoleum.

MORGENHALL: You wanted . . .

FOWLE: I heard them whispering together and my hopes raised high. Then I came back and he was gone.

MORGENHALL: She'd . . .

FOWLE: Turned him out. Because he was getting overly familiar. "I couldn't have that," she said. "I may like my laugh, but thank God, I'm still respectable. No thank you, there's safety in marriage. So I'm stuck with you, fiddle face. Let's play a tune on it, shall we?" She'd sent him away, my last hope.

MORGENHALL: So you . . .

FOWLE: I realize I did wrong.

MORGENHALL: You could have left.

FOWLE: Who'd have fed the birds? That thought was uppermost.

MORGENHALL: So it's not a crime of passion?

FOWLE: Not if you put it like that.

MORGENHALL: Mr. Fowle, I've worked and waited for you. Now, you're the only case I've got, *and* the most difficult.

FOWLE: I'm sorry.

MORGENHALL: A man could crack his head against a case like you and still be far from a solution. Can't you see how twelve honest hearts will snap like steel when they learn you ended up your wife because she *wouldn't* leave you?

FOWLE: If she had left, there wouldn't have been the need.

MORGENHALL: There's no doubt about it. As I look at you now, I see you're an unsympathetic figure.

FOWLE: There it is.

MORGENHALL: It'll need a brilliant stroke to save you. An unexpected move—something pulled out of a hat— I've got it. Something really exciting. The surprise witness.

FOWLE: Witness?

MORGENHALL: Picture the scene, Mr. Fowle. The courtroom silent. The jury about to sink you. The prosecution flushed with victory. And then I rise, my voice a hoarse whisper, exhausted by that long trial. "My Lord. If your Lordship pleases."

FOWLE: What are you saying?

MORGENHALL: Do you expect me to do this off the cuff, Fowle, with no sort of rehearsal?

FOWLE: No . . .

MORGENHALL: Take the stool and co-operate, man. Now, that towel over your head, please, to simulate the dirty gray wig—already you appear anonymous and vaguely alarming.

(MORGENHALL *arranges* FOWLE *on the stool. Drapes the towel over his head*)

Now, my dear Fowle, forget your personality. You're Sir Tommy Banter, living with a widowed sister in a drafty great morgue on Wimbledon Common. Digestion, bad. Politics, an independent moral conservative. Favorite author, doesn't read. Diversions, snooker in the basement of the morgue, peeping at the lovers on the Common and money being given away on the television. In love with capital punishment, corporal punishment, and a younger brother who is accomplished at embroidery. A small, alarmed man, frightened of the great dog he lives with to give him the air of a country squire. Served with distinction in the Great War at sentencing soldiers to long terms of imprisonment. A man without friends, unexpectedly adored by a great-niece, three years old.

FOWLE: I am?

MORGENHALL: Him.

FOWLE: It feels strange.

MORGENHALL: Now, my Lord. I ask your Lordship's leave to call the surprise witness.

FOWLE: Certainly.

MORGENHALL: What?

FOWLE: Certainly.

MORGENHALL: For Heaven's sake, Fowle, this is like practicing bull-fights with a kitten. Here's an irregular application by the defense, something that might twist the trial in the prisoner's favor and prevent you catching the connection at Charing Cross. Your breakfast's like a loadweight on your chest, your sister, plunging at Spot last night, ripped the cloth. The dog bit your ankle on the way downstairs. No, blind yourself with rage and terrible justice.

FOWLE: No. You can't call the surprise witness.

MORGENHALL: That's better. Oh, my Lord. If your Lordship would listen to me.

FOWLE: Certainly not. You've had your chance. Let's get on with it.

MORGENHALL: My Lord. Justice must not only be done, but must clearly be seen to be done. No one knows, as yet, what my surprise witness will say. Perhaps he'll say the prisoner is guilty in his black heart as your Lordship thinks. But, perhaps, gentlemen of the jury, we have trapped an innocent. If so, shall we deny him the one door through which he might walk to freedom? The public outcry would never die down.

FOWLE (*Snatching off the towel and rising angrily to his feet*): Hear, hear!

MORGENHALL: What's that?

FOWLE: The public outcry.

MORGENHALL: Excellent. Now, towel back on. You're the judge.

FOWLE (*As the judge*): Silence! I'll have all those noisy people put out. Very well. Call the witness. But keep it short.

MORGENHALL: Wonderful. Very good. Now. Deathly silence as the witness walks through the breathless crowds. Let's see the surprise witness. Take the towel off.

FOWLE (*Moves from the stool and standing very straight says*): I swear to tell the truth . . .

MORGENHALL: You've got a real feeling for the Law. A pity you came to it so late in life.

FOWLE: The whole truth.

MORGENHALL: Now, what's your name?

FOWLE (*Absent-minded*): Herbert Fowle.

MORGENHALL: No, no. You're the witness.

FOWLE: Martin Jones.

MORGENHALL: Excellent. Now, you know Herbert Fowle?

FOWLE: All my life.

MORGENHALL: Always found him respectable?

FOWLE: Very quiet spoken man, and clean living.

MORGENHALL: Where was he when this crime took place?

FOWLE: He was . . .

MORGENHALL: Just a moment. My Lord, will you sharpen a pencil and note this down.

FOWLE: You'd dare to say that? To him?

MORGENHALL: Fearlessness, Mr. Fowle. The first essential in an advocate. Is your Lordship's pencil poised?

FOWLE (*As judge*): Yes, yes. Get on with it.

MORGENHALL: Where was he?

FOWLE (*As witness*): In my house.

MORGENHALL: All the evening?

FOWLE: Playing whist. I went to collect him and we left Mrs. Fowle well and happy. I returned with him and she'd been removed to the Country and General.

MORGENHALL: Panic stirs the prosecution benches. The prosecutor tries a few fumbling questions. But you stand your ground, don't you?

FOWLE: Certainly.

MORGENHALL: My Lord, I demand the prisoner be released.

FOWLE (*As judge*): Certainly. Can't think what all this fuss has been about. Release the prisoner, and reduce all police officers in Court to the rank of P.C.

(*Pause.*)

MORGENHALL: Fowle.

FOWLE: Yes, sir.

MORGENHALL: Aren't you going to thank me?

FOWLE: I don't know what I can say.

MORGENHALL: Words don't come easily to you, do they?

FOWLE: Very hard.

MORGENHALL: You could just stand and stammer in a touching way and offer me that old gold watch of your father's.

FOWLE: But . . .

MORGENHALL: Well, I think we've pulled your chestnut out of the fire. We'll just have to make sure of this fellow Jones.

FOWLE: But . . .

MORGENHALL: Fowle, you're a good simple chap, but there's no need to interrupt my thinking.

FOWLE: I was only reminding you . . .

MORGENHALL: Well, what?

FOWLE: We have no Jones.

MORGENHALL: Carried off in a cold spell? Then we can get his statement in under the Evidence Act.

FOWLE: He never lived. We made him up.

(*Pause.*)

MORGENHALL: Fowle.

FOWLE: Yes, sir.

MORGENHALL: It's a remarkable thing, but with no legal training I think you've put your finger on a fatal weakness in our defense.

FOWLE: I was afraid it might be so.

MORGENHALL: It is so.

FOWLE: Then we'd better just give in.

MORGENHALL: Give in? We do not give in. When my life depends on this case.

FOWLE: I forgot. Then, we must try.

MORGENHALL: Yes. Brain! Brain! Go to work. It'll come to me, you know, in an illuminating flash. Hard, relentless brain work. This is the way I go at the crosswords and I never give up. I have it. Bateson!

FOWLE: The lodger?

MORGENHALL: Bateson, the lodger. I never liked him. Under a ruthless cross-examination, you know, he might confess that it was he. Do you see a flash?

FOWLE: You look much happier.

MORGENHALL: I am much happier. And when I begin my ruthless cross-examination . . .

FOWLE: Would you care to try it?

MORGENHALL: Mr. Fowle, you and I are learning to muck in splendidly together over this. Mr. Bateson.

FOWLE (*As Bateson, lounging in an imaginary witness box with his hands in his pockets*): Yes, sir.

MORGENHALL: Perhaps, when you address the Court, you'd be good enough to take your hands out of your pockets. Not you, Mr Fowle, of course. You became on very friendly terms with the prisoner's wife?

FOWLE: We had one or two good old laughs together.

MORGENHALL: Was the association entirely innocent?

FOWLE: Innocent laughs. Jokes without offense. The cracker or Christmas card variety. No jokes that would have shamed a post card.

MORGENHALL: And to tell those innocent jokes, did you have to sit very close to Mrs. Fowle?

FOWLE: How do you mean?

MORGENHALL: Did you have to sit beneath her?

FOWLE: I don't understand.

MORGENHALL: Did she perch upon your knee?

FOWLE (*Horrified intake of breath*)

MORGENHALL: What was that?

FOWLE: Shocked breathing from the jury, sir.

MORGENHALL: Having its effect, eh? Now, Mr. Bateson. Will you kindly answer my question.

FOWLE: You're trying to trap me.

MORGENHALL: Not trying, Bateson, succeeding.

FOWLE: Well, she may have rested on my knee. Once or twice.

MORGENHALL: And you loved her, guiltily?

FOWLE: I may have done.

MORGENHALL: And planned to take her away with you?

FOWLE: I did ask her.

MORGENHALL: And when she refused . . .

FOWLE (*As judge*): Just a moment. Where's all this leading?

MORGENHALL: Your Lordship asks me! My Lord, it is our case that it was this man, Bateson, enraged by the refusal of the prisoner's wife to follow him, who struck . . . You see where we've got to?

FOWLE: I do.

MORGENHALL: Masterly. I think you'll have to agree with me.

FOWLE: Of course.

MORGENHALL: No flaws in this one?

FOWLE: Not really a flaw, sir. Perhaps a little hitch.

MORGENHALL: A hitch. Go on. Break it down.

FOWLE: No, sir, really. Not after you've been so kind.

MORGENHALL: Never mind. All my life I've stood against the winds of criticism and neglect. My gown may be a little tattered, my cuffs frayed. There may be a hole in my sock for the drafts to get at me.

Quite often, on my way to Court, I notice that my left shoe lets in water. I am used to hardship. Speak on, Mr. Fowle.

FOWLE: Soon as he left my house, Bateson was stopped by an officer. He'd lifted an alarm clock off of me, and the remains of a bottle of port. They booked him in straight away.

MORGENHALL: You mean, there wasn't time?

FOWLE: Hardly. Two hours later the next door observed Mrs. Fowle at the washing. Then I came home.

MORGENHALL: Do you want to help me?

FOWLE: Of course. Haven't I shown it?

MORGENHALL: But you will go on putting all these difficulties in my way.

FOWLE: I knew you'd be upset.

MORGENHALL: Not really. After all, I'm a grownup, even an old man. At my age one expects little gratitude. There's a cat I feed each day at my lodgings, a waitress in the lunch room here who always gets that sixpence under my plate. In ten, twenty years' time, will they remember me? Oh, I'm not bitter. But a little help, just a very little encouragement . . .

FOWLE: But you'll win this case. A brilliant mind like yours.

MORGENHALL: Yes. Thank God. It's very brilliant.

FOWLE: And all that training.

MORGENHALL: Years of it. Hard, hard training.

FOWLE: You'll solve it, sir.

(*Pause.*)

MORGENHALL: Fowle, do you know what I've heard Tuppy Morgan say? After all, he's sat here, year in, year out, as long as anyone can remember, in Court, waiting for the Dock Brief himself. Wilfred, he's frequently told me, if they ever give you a brief, old fellow, attack the medical evidence. Remember, the jury's full of rheumatism and arthritis and shocking gastric troubles. They love to see a medical man put through it. Always go for a doctor.

FOWLE (*Eagerly*): You'd like to try?

MORGENHALL: Shall we?

FOWLE: I'd enjoy it.

MORGENHALL: Doctor, did you say the lady died of heart failure?

FOWLE (*As doctor*): No.

MORGENHALL: Come, Doctor. Don't fence with me. Her heart wasn't normal when you examined her, was it?

FOWLE: She was dead.

MORGENHALL: So it had stopped.

FOWLE: Yes.

MORGENHALL: Then her heart had failed?

FOWLE: Well . . .

MORGENHALL: So she died of heart failure?

FOWLE: But . . .

MORGENHALL: And heart failure might have been brought on by a fit. I say a fit of laughter at a curiously rich joke on the wireless?

FOWLE: Whew.

(FOWLE *claps softly. Pause.*)

MORGENHALL: Thank you, Fowle. It was kind but I thought, hollow. I don't believe my attack on the doctor was convincing.

FOWLE: Perhaps a bit unlikely. But clever . . .

MORGENHALL: Too clever. No. We're not going to win this on science, Fowle. Science must be thrown away. As I asked those questions, I saw I wasn't even convincing you of your own innocence. But you respond to emotion, Fowle, as I do, the magic of oratory, the wonderful power of words.

FOWLE: Now you're talking.

MORGENHALL: I'm going to talk.

FOWLE: I wish I could hear some of it. Words as grand as print.

MORGENHALL: A golden tongue. A voice like a lyre to charm you out of hell.

FOWLE: Now you've commenced to wander away from all I've understood.

MORGENHALL: I was drawing on the riches of my classical education which comforts me on buses, waiting at surgeries, or in prison cells. But I shall speak to the jury simply, without classical allusions. I shall say . . .

FOWLE: Yes.

MORGENHALL: I shall say . . .

FOWLE: What?

MORGENHALL: I had it on the tip of my tongue.

FOWLE: Oh.

MORGENHALL: I shan't disappoint you. I shall speak for a day, perhaps two days. At the end I shall say . . .

FOWLE: Yes. Just the closing words.

MORGENHALL: The closing words.

FOWLE: To clinch the argument.

MORGENHALL: Yes. The final, irrefutable argument.

FOWLE: If I could only hear.

MORGENHALL: You shall, Fowle. You shall hear it. In Court. It'll come out in Court, and when I sink back in my seat, trembling, and wipe the real tears off my glasses . . .

FOWLE: The judge's summing up.

MORGENHALL: What will Tommy say . . . ?

FOWLE (*As judge*): Members of the jury . . .

MORGENHALL: Struggling with emotion as well.

FOWLE: I can't add anything to the words of the barrister. Go out and consider your verdict.

MORGENHALL: Have they left the box?

FOWLE: Only a formality.

MORGENHALL: I see. I wonder how long they'll be out.

(*Pause*)

They're out a long time.

FOWLE: Of course, it must seem long to you. The suspense.

MORGENHALL: I hope they won't disagree.

FOWLE: I don't see how they can.

(*Pause.*)

MORGENHALL: Fowle.

FOWLE: Yes, sir.

MORGENHALL: Shall we just take a peep into the jury room?

FOWLE: I wish we could.

MORGENHALL: Let's. Let me see, you're the foreman?

FOWLE: I take it we're all agreed, chaps. So let's sit here and have a short smoke.

(*They sit on the bench together.*)

MORGENHALL: An excellent idea. The barrister saved him.

FOWLE: That wonderful speech. I had a bit of doubt before I heard the speech.

MORGENHALL: No doubt now, have you?

FOWLE: Certainly not.

(*They light imaginary pipes*)

Care for a fill of mine?

MORGENHALL: Thank you so much. Match?

FOWLE: Here you are.

MORGENHALL: I say, you don't think the poor fellow's in any doubt, do you?

FOWLE: No. He must know he'll get off. After the speech I mean.

MORGENHALL: I mean, I wouldn't like him to be on pins . . .

FOWLE: Think we ought to go back and reassure him?

> (*They move out of the bench.*)

MORGENHALL: As you wish. Careful that pipe doesn't start a fire in your pocket.

> (*As clerk of Court*)

Gentlemen of the jury. Have you considered your verdict?

FOWLE: We have.

MORGENHALL: And do you find the prisoner guilty or not guilty?

FOWLE: Not guilty, my Lord.

MORGENHALL: Hooray!

FOWLE (*As judge*): Now, if there's any sort of Mafeking around, I'll have the Court closed.

MORGENHALL: So I'm surrounded, mobbed. Tuppy Morgan wrings my hand and says it was lucky he left the seat. The judge sends me a letter of congratulation. The journalists dart off to their little telephones. And what now: "Of course they'd make you a judge but you're probably too busy . . ." There's a queue of solicitors on the stairs . . . My old clerk writes on my next brief, a thousand guineas to divorce a duchess. There are questions of new clothes, laying down the port. Oh, Mr. Fowle, the change in life you've brought me.

FOWLE: It will be your greatest day.

MORGENHALL: Yes, Mr. Fowle. My greatest day.

> (*The bolts shoot back, the door opens slowly*)

What's that? I said we weren't to be interrupted. It's drafty in here with that door open. Close it, there's a good chap, do.

FOWLE: I think, you know, they must want us for the trial.

> (FOWLE *goes out through the door.* MORGENHALL *follows with a dramatic sweep of his gown.*)

THE CURTAIN FALLS

SCENE II

When the Curtain rises again, the sky through the windows shows that it is late afternoon. The door is unlocked and MOR-GENHALL *enters. He is without his wig and gown, more agitated than ever. He speaks to the warder, off stage.*

MORGENHALL: He's not here at the moment—he's not . . . ? Oh, I'm so glad. Just out temporarily? With the governor? Then, I'll wait for him. Poor soul. How's he taking it? You're not allowed to answer questions? The regulations, I suppose. Well, you must obey the regulations. I'll just sit down here, and wait for Mr. Fowle.

    (*The door closes. He whistles. Whistling stops*)

May it please you, my Lord, *members* of the jury. I should have said, may it please you, my *Lord,* members of the jury. I should have said . . .

    (*He begins to walk up and down*)

Members of the jury. Is there one of you who doesn't crave for peace . . . crave for peace. The silence of an undisturbed life, the dignity of an existence without dependents . . . without jokes. Have you never been tempted?

I should have said . . .

Members of the *jury*. You and I are men of the world. If your Lordship would kindly not interrupt my speech to the jury. I'm obliged. Members of the jury, before I was so rudely interrupted.

I might have said . . .

Look at the prisoner, members of the jury. Has he hurt you, done you the slightest harm? Is he not the mildest of men? He merely took it upon himself to regulate his domestic affairs. An Englishman's home is his castle. Do any of you feel a primitive urge, members of the jury, to be revenged on this gentle bird fancier . . .

Members of the jury, I see I'm affecting your emotions, but let us consider the weight of the evidence . . .

Might have said that!

I might have said . . .

    (*With distress*)

I might have said something . . .

    (*The door opens.* FOWLE *enters. He is smiling to himself, but as soon as he sees* MORGENHALL *he looks serious and solicitous.*)

FOWLE: I was hoping you'd find time to drop in, sir. I'm afraid you're upset.

MORGENHALL: No, no, my dear chap. Not at all upset.

FOWLE: The result of the trial's upset you.

MORGENHALL: I feel a little dashed. A little out of sorts.

FOWLE: It was disappointing for you.

MORGENHALL: A touch of disappointment. But there'll be other cases. There may be other cases.

FOWLE: But you'd built such high hopes on this particular one.

MORGENHALL: Well, there it is, Fowle.

FOWLE: It doesn't do to expect too much of a particular thing.

MORGENHALL: You're right, of course.

FOWLE: Year after year I used to look forward keenly to the Feathered Friends Fanciers' annual do. Invariably took the form of a dinner.

MORGENHALL: Your yearly treat?

FOWLE: Exactly. All I had in the enjoyment line. Each year I built high hopes on it. June 13th, I'd say, now there's an evening to look forward to.

MORGENHALL: Something to live for?

FOWLE: In a way. But when it came, you know, it was never up to it. Your collar was always too tight, or the food was inadequate, or someone had a nasty scene with the fancier in the chair. So, on June 14th, I always said to myself: Thank God for a night at home.

MORGENHALL: It came and went and your life didn't change?

FOWLE: No, quite frankly.

MORGENHALL: And this case has left me just as I was before.

FOWLE: Don't say that.

MORGENHALL: Tuppy Morgan's back in his old seat under the window. The judge never congratulated me. No one's rung up to offer me a brief. I thought my old clerk looked coldly at me, and there was a titter in the luncheon room when I ordered my usual roll and tomato soup.

FOWLE: But I . . .

MORGENHALL: And you're not left in a very favorable position.

FOWLE: Don't say that, sir. It's not so bad for me. After all, I had no education.

MORGENHALL: So many years before I could master the Roman Law relating to the ownership of chariots . . .

FOWLE: Wasted, you think?

MORGENHALL: I feel so.

FOWLE: But without that rich background, would an individual have been able to sway the Court as you did?

MORGENHALL: Sway?

FOWLE: The Court.

MORGENHALL: Did I do that?

FOWLE: It struck me you did.

MORGENHALL: Indeed . . .

FOWLE: It's turned out masterly.

MORGENHALL: Mr. Fowle, you're trying to be kind. When I was a child I played French cricket with an uncle who deliberately allowed the ball to strike his legs. At the age of seven that irked me. At sixty-three, I can face the difficulties of accurate batting . . .

FOWLE: But no, sir. I really mean it. I owe it all to you. Where I am.

MORGENHALL: I'm afraid near the end.

FOWLE: Just commencing.

MORGENHALL: I lost, Mr. Fowle. You may not be aware of it. It may not have been hammered home to you yet. But your case is lost.

FOWLE: But there are ways and ways of losing.

MORGENHALL: That's true, of course.

FOWLE: I noticed your artfulness right at the start, when the policeman gave evidence. You pulled out that red handkerchief, slowly and deliberately, like a conjuring trick.

MORGENHALL: And blew?

FOWLE: A sad, terrible trumpet.

MORGENHALL: Unnerved him, I thought.

FOWLE: He never recovered. There was no call to ask questions after that.

MORGENHALL: And then they called that doctor.

FOWLE: You were right not to bother with him.

MORGENHALL: Tactics, you see. We'd decided not to trouble with science.

FOWLE: So we had. And with Bateson . . .

MORGENHALL: No, Fowle. I must beware of your flattery. I think I might have asked Bateson . . .

FOWLE: It wouldn't have made a farthing's difference. A glance told them he was a demon.

MORGENHALL: He stood there, so big and red, with his no tie and dirty collar. I rose up to question him and suddenly it seemed as if there were no reason for us to converse. I remembered what you said about his jokes, his familiarity with your wife. What had he and I in common? I turned from him in disgust. I think that jury guessed the reason for my silence with friend Bateson.

FOWLE: I think they did!

MORGENHALL: But when it came to the speech . . .

FOWLE: The best stroke of all.

MORGENHALL: I can't agree. You no longer carry me with you.

FOWLE: Said from the heart.

MORGENHALL: I'm sure of it. But not, dare I say, altogether justified. We can't pretend, can we, Mr. Fowle, that the speech was a success.

FOWLE: It won the day.

MORGENHALL: I beg you not to be under any illusions. They found you guilty.

FOWLE: I was forgetting. But that masterly speech . . .

MORGENHALL: I can't be hoodwinked.

FOWLE: But you don't know . . .

MORGENHALL: I stood up, Mr. Fowle, and it was the moment I'd waited for. Ambition had driven me to it, the moment when I was alone with what I wanted. Everyone turned to me, twelve blank faces in the jury box, eager to have the grumpy looks wiped off them. The judge was silent. The prosecutor courteously pretended to be asleep. I only had to open my mouth and pour words out. What stopped me?

FOWLE: What?

MORGENHALL: Fear. That's what's suggested. That's what the clerks tittered to the waitresses in Friday's luncheon room. Old Wilf Morgenhall was in a funk.

FOWLE: More shame on them . . .

MORGENHALL: But it wasn't so. Nor did my mind go blank. When I rose I knew exactly what I was going to say.

FOWLE: Then, why?

MORGENHALL: Not say it—you were going to ask?

FOWLE: It had struck me—

MORGENHALL: It must have, Fowle. It must have struck many people. You'll forgive a reminiscence . . .

FOWLE: Glad of one.

MORGENHALL: The lady I happened to mention yesterday. I don't of course often speak of her . . .

FOWLE: She, who, in the 1914 . . . ?

MORGENHALL: Exactly. But I lost her long before that. For years, you know, Mr. Fowle, this particular lady and I met at tea parties, tennis, and so on. Then, one evening, I walked home with her. We stood on Vauxhall Bridge, a warm summer night, and silence fell. It was the moment when I should have spoken, the obvious moment. Then, something overcame me, it wasn't shyness or fear then, but a tremendous exhaustion. I was tired out by the long wait, and when the opportunity came—all I could think of was sleep.

FOWLE: It's a relief . . .

MORGENHALL: To go home alone. To undress, clean your teeth, knock out your pipe, not to bother with failure or success.

FOWLE: So yesterday . . .

MORGENHALL: I had lived through that moment so many times. It happened every day in my mind, daydreaming on buses, or in the doctor's surgery. When it came, I was tired of it. The exhaustion came over me. I wanted it to be all over. I wanted to be alone in my room in the darkness, with a soft pillow round my ears . . . So I failed.

FOWLE: Don't say it.

MORGENHALL: Being too tired to make my daydream public. It's a nice day. Summer's coming.

FOWLE: No, don't, sir. Not too near the window.

MORGENHALL: Why not, Mr. Fowle?

FOWLE: I was concerned. A man in your position might be desperate . . .

MORGENHALL: You say you can see the forest?

FOWLE: Just a splash of it.

MORGENHALL: I think I shall retire from the bar.

FOWLE: Don't say it, sir. After that rigorous training.

MORGENHALL: Well, there it is. I think I shall retire.

FOWLE: But cheer up, sir. As you said, other cases, other days. Let's take this calmly, sir. Let's be very lucid, as you put it in your own statement.

MORGENHALL: Other cases? I'm getting on, you know. Tuppy Morgan's back in his place. I doubt if the Dock Brief will come round again.

FOWLE: But there'll be something.

MORGENHALL: What can there be? Unless?

FOWLE: Yes, sir?

MORGENHALL: There would be another brief if . . .

FOWLE: Yes?

MORGENHALL: I advised you to appeal . . .

FOWLE: Ah, now that, misfortunately . . .

MORGENHALL: There's a different atmosphere there, up in the Appeal Court, Fowle. It's far from the rough and tumble, question and answer, swear on the Bible and lie your way out if it. It's quiet up there, pure

Law, of course. Yes. I believe I'm cut out for the Court of Appeal . . .

FOWLE: But you see . . .

MORGENHALL: A big, quiet Court in the early summer afternoon. Piles of books, and when you put one down, the dust and powdered leather rises and makes the ushers sneeze. The clock ticks. Three old judges in scarlet take snuff with trembling hands. You'll sit in the dock and not follow a legal word. And I'll give them all my Law and get you off on a technicality.

FOWLE: But today . . .

MORGENHALL: Now, if I may remind your Lordships of Prickle against the Haverfordwest Justices ex parte Anger, reported in 96 Moor's Ecclesiastical at page a thousand and three. Have your Lordships the report? Lord Bradwell C.J. says, at the foot of the page, "The guilty intention is a deep foundation stone in the wall of our jurisprudence. So if it be that Prickle did run the bailiff through with his poignard taking him for a stray dog or cat, it seems there would be well raised the plea of autrefois mistake. But contra if he thought him to be his neighbor's cat, then, as my Brother Broadwinkle has well said in Lord Roche and Anderson, there might fall out a constructive larceny and *felo in rem*." Oh, Mr. Fowle, I have some of these fine cases by heart.

FOWLE: Above me, I'm afraid, you're going now.

MORGENHALL: Of course I am. These cases always bore the prisoner until they're upheld or overruled and he comes out dead or alive at the end of it all.

FOWLE: I'd like to hear you reading them, though . . .

MORGENHALL: You would. I'll be followed to Court by my clerk, an old tortoise burdened by the weight of authorities. Then he'll lay them out in a fine buff and half calf row, a letter from a clergyman I correspond with in Wales torn to mark each place. A glass of water, a dry cough and then "My respectful submission."

FOWLE: And that, of course, is . . .

MORGENHALL: That the judge misdirected himself. He forgot the rule in Rimmer's case, he confused his *mens sana,* he displaced the burden of proof, he played fast and loose with all reasonable doubt, he kicked the presumption of innocence round like a football.

FOWLE: Strong words.

MORGENHALL: I shan't let Tommy Banter off lightly.

336 : The Law IN Literature

FOWLE: The judge?

MORGENHALL: Thoroughly unscholarly. Not a word of Latin in the whole summing up.

FOWLE: Not up to you, of course.

MORGENHALL: Thank God, I kept my books. There have been times, Fowle, when I was tempted, pricked and harried for rent perhaps, to have my clerk barter the whole lot away for the few pounds they offer for centuries of entombed law. But I stuck to them. I still have my Swabey and Tristram, my Pod'd Privy Council, my Spinks Prize Cases. I shall open them up and say . . . I shall say . . .

FOWLE: It's no good.

MORGENHALL: What's no good?

FOWLE: It's no good appealing.

MORGENHALL: No good?

FOWLE: No good at all.

MORGENHALL: Mr. Fowle. I've worked hard for you.

FOWLE: True enough.

MORGENHALL: And I mean to go on working.

FOWLE: It's a great comfort . . .

MORGENHALL: In the course of our close, and may I say it? Yes, our happy collaboration on this little crime of yours, I've become almost fond of you.

FOWLE: Thank you, sir.

MORGENHALL: At first, I have to admit it, I was put off by your some-what furtive and repulsive appearance. It's happened before. I saw, I quite agree, only the outer husk, and what I saw was a small man marked by all the physical signs of confirmed criminality.

FOWLE: No oil painting?

MORGENHALL: Let's agree on that at once.

FOWLE: The wife thought so, too.

MORGENHALL: Enough of her, poor woman.

FOWLE: Oh, agreed.

MORGENHALL: My first solicitude for your well-being, let's face up to this as well, had a selfish element. You were my own very case, and I didn't want to lose you.

FOWLE: Natural feelings. But still . . .

MORGENHALL: I haven't wounded you?

FOWLE: Nothing fatal.

MORGENHALL: I'm glad. Because, you know, as we worked on this case together, an affection sprang up . . .

FOWLE: Mutual.

MORGENHALL: You seemed to have a real desire to help, and, if I may say so, an instinctive taste for the Law.

FOWLE: A man can't go through this sort of thing without getting legal interests.

MORGENHALL: Quite so. And of course, as a self-made man, that's to your credit. But I did notice, just at the start, some flaws in you as a client.

FOWLE: Flaws?

MORGENHALL: You may not care to admit it. But let's be honest. After all, we don't want to look on the dreary side; but you may not be with us for very long . . .

FOWLE: That's what I was trying to say . . .

MORGENHALL: Please, Mr. Fowle, no interruptions until we've cleared this out of the way. Now didn't you, just at the beginning, put unnecessary difficulties before us?

FOWLE: Did I?

MORGENHALL: I well remember, before I got a bit of keenness into you, that you seemed about to admit your guilt.

FOWLE: Oh . . .

MORGENHALL: Just a little obstinate, wasn't it?

FOWLE: I dare say . . .

MORGENHALL: And now, when I've worked for fifty years to get the Law at my finger tips, I hear you mutter, "No appeal."

FOWLE: No appeal!

MORGENHALL: Mr. Fowle . . .

FOWLE: Yesterday you asked me to spare you pain, sir. This is going to be very hard for me.

MORGENHALL: What?

FOWLE: As you say, we've worked together, and I've had the pleasure of watching the ticking over of a legal mind. If you'd call any afternoon I'd be pleased to repay the compliment by showing you my birds . . .

MORGENHALL: Not in this world you must realize, unless we appeal.

FOWLE: You see. This morning I saw the governor.

MORGENHALL: You had some complaint?

FOWLE: I don't want to boast, but the truth is . . . he sent for me.

MORGENHALL: You went in fear . . .

FOWLE: And trembling. But he turned out a very gentlemanly sort of individual. Ex-Army, I should imagine. All the ornaments of a gentleman. Wife and children in a tinted photo framed on the desk, handsome oil painting of a prize pig over the mantelpiece. Healthy red face. Strong smell of scented soap . . .

MORGENHALL: But go to the point . . .

FOWLE: I'm telling you. "Well, Fowle," he says, "sit down do. I'm just finishing this letter." So I sat and looked out of his windows. Big wide windows in the governor's office, and the view . . .

MORGENHALL: Fowle, if this anecdote has any point, be a good little chap, reach it.

FOWLE: Of course it has, where was I?

MORGENHALL: Admiring the view as usual.

FOWLE: Panoramic it was. Well, this governor individual, finishing his letter, lit up one of those flat type of Egyptian cigarettes. "Well, Fowle," he said . . .

MORGENHALL: Yes, yes. It's not necessary, Fowle, to reproduce every word of this conversation. Give us the gist, just the meat, you understand. Leave out the trimmings.

FOWLE: Trimmings there weren't. He put it quite bluntly.

MORGENHALL: What did he put?

FOWLE: "Well, Fowle, this may surprise you. But the Home Office was on the telephone about you this morning." Isn't that a Government department?

MORGENHALL: Yes, yes, and well . . .

FOWLE: It seems they do, in his words, come through from time to time, and just on business, of course, on that blower. And quite frankly, he admitted he was as shocked as I was. But the drill is, as he phrased it, a reprieve.

MORGENHALL: A . . . ?

FOWLE: It's all over. I'm free. It seems that trial was no good at all . . .

MORGENHALL: No good. But why?

FOWLE: Oh, no particular reason.

MORGENHALL: There must be a reason. Nothing passes in the Law without a reason.

FOWLE: You won't care to know.

MORGENHALL: Tell me.

FOWLE: You're too busy to wait . . .

MORGENHALL: Tell me, Mr. Fowle. I beg of you. Tell me directly why this governor, who knows nothing of the Law, should have called our one and only trial together "No good."

FOWLE: You yourself taught me not to scatter information like bombs.

MORGENHALL: Mr. Fowle. You must answer my question. My legal career may depend on it. If I'm not to have wasted my life on useless trials.

FOWLE: You want to hear?

MORGENHALL: Certainly.

FOWLE: He may not have been serious. There was a twinkle, most likely, in his eye.

MORGENHALL: But he said . . .

FOWLE: That the barrister they chose for me was no good. An old crock, in his words. No good at all. That he never said a word in my defense. So my case never got to the jury. He said the whole business was ever so null and void, but I'd better be careful in the future . . .

> (MORGENHALL *runs across the cell, mounts the stool, begins to undo his tie*)

No! Mr. Morgenhall! Come down from there! No, sir! Don't do it.

> (*They struggle.* FOWLE *brings* MORGENHALL *to earth*)

Don't you see? If I'd had a barrister who asked questions and made clever speeches I'd be as dead as mutton. Your artfulness saved me . . .

MORGENHALL: My . . .

FOWLE: The artful way you handled it. The dumb tactics. They paid off! I'm alive!

MORGENHALL: There is that . . .

FOWLE: And so are you.

MORGENHALL: We both are?

FOWLE: I'm free.

MORGENHALL: To go back to your birds. I suppose . . .

FOWLE: Yes, Mr. Morgenhall?

MORGENHALL: It's unlikely you'll marry again.

FOWLE: Unlikely.

> (*Long pause.*)

MORGENHALL: But you have the clear appearance of a criminal. I suppose it's not impossible that you might commit some rather more trivial offense.

FOWLE: A man can't live, Mr. Morgenhall, without committing some trivial offenses. Almost daily.

MORGENHALL: Then we may meet again. You may need my services . . .

FOWLE: Constantly.

MORGENHALL: The future may not be so black . . .

FOWLE: The sun's shining.

MORGENHALL: Can we go?

FOWLE: I think the door's been open some time.

(*He tries it. It is unbolted and swings open*)

After you, Mr. Morgenhall, please.

MORGENHALL: No, no.

FOWLE: A man of your education should go first.

MORGENHALL: I think you should lead the way, Mr. Fowle, and as your legal adviser I will follow, at a discreet distance, to straighten out such little tangles as you may hope to leave in your wake. Let's go.

(MORGENHALL, *whistles his fragment of tune*)

(FOWLE, *his whistles join* MORGENHALL's)

(*Whistling they leave the cell,* MORGENHALL *executing, as he leaves, the steps of a small, delighted dance.*)

SLOW CURTAIN

Herman Wouk

:

THE COURT-MARTIAL

from *The Caine Mutiny*

FIRST DAY

Naval Courts and Boards opens with a melancholy section entitled "Charges and Specifications." It is only a hundred twenty-three pages long; not half as long as a twenty-five-cent mystery novel; and within that small compass the Navy has discussed all the worst errors, vices, follies, and crimes into which men may fall. It begins with Making a Mutiny and ends with Unlawful Use of a Distilling Apparatus. In between are such bloody offenses as Adultery, Murder, Rape, and Maiming, and also such nasty peccadilloes as Exhibiting an Obscene Photograph. These are sad, wearying, grisly pages, the more so for their matter-of-fact, systematic tone.

This shopper's list of crime, however, did not provide a charge or specification for the peculiar offense of Lieutenant Stephen Maryk. Captain Breakstone had quickly perceived that, though the affair was more like a mutiny than anything else, Maryk's invoking of Article 184 and his subsequent legalistic conduct made a conviction for mutiny unlikely. It was the queerest sort of twilight situation. In the end he fixed on the catch-all charge provided for rare or complicated offenses, "Conduct to the Prejudice of Good Order and Discipline," and with much care he drew up the following specification:

In that Lieutenant Stephen Maryk, USNR, on or about December 18, 1944, aboard the U.S.S. Caine, willfully, without proper authority, and with-

341

out justifiable cause, did relieve from his duty as commanding officer Lieu-
tenant Commander Philip Francis Queeg, USN, the duly assigned command-
ing officer of said ship, who was then and there in lawful exercise of his
command, the United States then being in a state of war.

The judge advocate, Lieutenant Commander Challee, expected no
difficulty at all in proving this specification. He was an earnest, bright
young officer, holding his high rank on a temporary war promotion. A
slight undercurrent of guilt was running through his days in San Francisco. He had requested the legal duty after several years at sea, because he wanted to spend time with his beautiful wife, a photographer's
model; and he was a little ashamed of having had his request granted.
He therefore pursued his duties with exceptional zeal, and he honestly
regarded the conviction of Maryk, at the moment, as his personal war
aim.

Challee estimated that the prosecution had a prima facie case. A
charge of mutiny, he knew, would have been harder to prove. But Captain Breakstone's mild specification, in his view, was a plain description of the plain facts. The defense could not possibly deny that the
event had occurred; Maryk had signed logs describing it. The key
words were *without proper authority and without justifiable cause.* To
establish their truth, Challee simply had to prove that Queeg was not
and had never been a madman. He had the deposition of Captain Wey-
land in Ulithi, who had interviewed the captain of the *Caine* right
after the mutiny. Three Navy psychiatrists of the San Francisco hospital, who had examined Queeg for weeks, were ready to testify in court
that he was a sane, normal, intelligent man. At the investigation twenty
chiefs and enlisted men of the *Caine* had averred that they had never
seen Queeg do anything crazy or questionable. Not one officer or man,
except the two parties to the mutiny, Keith and Stilwell, had spoken
unfavorably of the captain. Challee had arranged for the appearance of
several presentable sailors and chiefs to repeat their testimony.

Against this array there was only Maryk's so-called medical log. The
board of investigation had dismissed it as "a whining collection of trivial
gripes," commenting that all it proved was Maryk's latent and long-
standing disloyalty. Challee was confident that the court would feel the
same way. Every officer past the rank of junior-grade lieutenant had
served, at one time or another, under an oppressive eccentric. It was
simply a hazard of military life. Challee was fond of telling anecdotes
which topped anything in Maryk's log.

The judge advocate knew that Greenwald had only one good point of attack: the question of criminal intent. He anticipated an eloquent harping on the fact that Maryk had acted for the good of the service, however mistaken his diagnosis of Queeg had been. Challee was fully prepared to demolish the specious sophistry which would follow, that Maryk was innocent of any offense.

He reasoned that Maryk, by willfully ignoring the whole weight of military tradition, and summoning up the mutinous effrontery to depose his commanding officer on the basis of such a wild error of judgment, had ipso facto convicted himself of "conduct to the prejudice of good order and discipline." If this were not true, if the precedent set by Maryk were to go unpunished, the entire Navy chain of command was in jeopardy! Any commanding officer who seemed queer to his exec was in danger of being summarily relieved. Challee was certain that a court of officers, especially a court headed by the austere martinet, Captain Blakely, would see that point. He counted, therefore, on a quick, satisfying victory over Barney Greenwald.

His estimate of the case was a good one. He erred only in his guess of Greenwald's probable strategy.

Willie Keith returned to the *Chrysanthemum* about eleven o'clock in the morning. He dropped his bags in his room and looked through the other rooms for *Caine* officers, but found only empty rumpled bunks. Then he heard faintly from the shower a bellowing of

> *"Parlez-moi d'amour*
> *Rrrrrredites-moi des choses tendres . . ."*

and he knew that Keefer was back. He found the novelist drying himself before a mirror, standing on wooden clogs. " *'Ja vous aim—uh——*—' Willie, you old Dickens lover! How are you, my lad?"

They shook hands. Keefer's tanned body was scrawny, and his face was drawn as though he had not eaten in a week, but he was gay, and his large eyes gleamed oddly.

"Where's everybody, Tom?"

"Hither and yon. Ship's leaving drydock today so most of the boys are aboard. Steve's out with his defense counsel somewhere——"

"Whom did he get?"

"Some lieutenant off a carrier. Used to be a lawyer."

"Good?"

"Can't tell. Steve seems to like him. Mumbling, shambling kind of guy—all kinds of hell breaking loose, Willie. Do you know about your pal Stilwell? He's gone crazy." Keefer flipped the towel around his shoulders and seesawed it briskly.

"What!"

"Diagnosis is acute melancholia. He's up at the base hospital. He was getting kind of funny there aboard ship, you know——"

Willie remembered very well Stilwell's brooding, sallow, pained face. Twice on the homeward voyage the sailor had asked to be relieved of the helm because of a blinding headache. "What happened, Tom?"

"Well, I wasn't here. The story is that he took to his sack and just stayed there for three days, not answering musters, not going up for meals. Said he had a headache. Finally they had to carry him to the hospital. He was all limp and foul, Bellison says——" Willie wrinkled his face in horror. "Well, it was in the cards, Willie. One look at him and you know he's one of these tense burning-up-inside ones. And no education, and a year of riding by Queeg, and the mixed-up emotional background, and on top of it all a general court for mutiny hanging over him—it isn't mutiny, any more, by the way. That's another thing —— Got a cigarette? . . . Thanks."

Keefer wrapped the towel around his middle and clacked out to the saloon, exhaling a gray cloud. Willie followed, saying eagerly, "What's all this about the mutiny?"

"Steve's going to be tried on a charge of conduct to prejudice of good order and discipline. I told you that dried-up captain was out of his head, recommending trial for mutiny. I still don't think you guys have anything to worry about. The legal boys know they have a damn shaky case——"

"What about Stilwell? Is he going to appear, or what?"

"Willie, the guy's a vegetable. They're going to give him electric-shock therapy, I hear—— How'd you make out on leave? Did you marry the girl?"

"No."

"I had a pretty good leave," said the novelist, pulling on white drawers. "I think I've sold my novel."

"Hey, Tom! That's swell! What publisher?"

"Chapman House. Nothing signed yet, you know. But it looks okay——"

"Gosh, it wasn't finished yet, was it?"

"They read twenty chapters and an outline. First publishers I showed it to." The gunnery officer spoke casually, but powerful pride rayed out of his face. Willie regarded him with round eyes. The growing pile of yellow manuscript in Keefer's desk had been half a joke, after all. Novelists were mythical figures to Willie—dead giants like Thackeray, or impossibly remote, brilliant rich men like Sinclair Lewis and Thomas Mann.

"Will—will they give you a big advance, Tom?"

"Well, as I say, nothing's definite. If it all works out, five hundred or a thousand dollars." Willie whistled. "It's not much," Keefer said, "but for an incomplete first novel, well——"

"It's marvelous, Tom, marvelous! I hope it's a huge best seller! It will be, too. I told you long ago I wanted the millionth copy, autographed. That still goes."

Keefer's face relaxed in a foolish rosy smile. "Well, don't rush things, Willie—nothing's signed——"

Steve Maryk's spirit failed him in the very first moments of the court-martial, when the members of the court were sworn. Seven officers stood on a dais in a semicircle behind a polished red-brown bench, their right arms raised, staring with religious gravity at Challee as he intoned the oath from a battered copy of *Courts and Boards*. Behind them on the wall between the wide windows was a large American flag. Outside, green-gray tops of eucalyptus trees stirred in the morning sunlight, and beyond them the blue bay danced with light. It is a cruel unconscious trick of planning that has placed the court-martial room of Com Twelve on Yerba Buena Island, in such fair surroundings, with such a beckoning view. The square gray room seems all the more confining. The flag hangs between the eyes of the accused and the free sunlight and water, and its red and white bars are bars indeed.

Maryk's eyes were drawn to the face of the president of the court, Captain Blakely, who stood at the center of the bench, squarely in front of the flag. It was an alarming face; a sharp nose, a mouth like a black line, and small far-seeing eyes under heavy eyebrows, with a defiant, distrustful glare. Blakely was quite gray, and he had a sagging dry pouch under his jaw, bloodless lips, and shadowy wrinkles around the eyes. Maryk knew his reputation: a submariner, up from the ranks, beached by a heart condition, the toughest disciplinarian of Com Twelve. Maryk was shaking when he sat down after the oath, and it was the face of Blakely that had made him shake.

One regular lieutenant commander and five lieutenants made up the rest of the board. They had the look of any six naval officers passing at random in a BOQ lobby. Two of the lieutenants were reserve doctors; two of them were regulars of the line; one was a reserve of the line.

The large wall clock over Challee's desk ticked around from ten o'clock to quarter of eleven while various legal ceremonies, incomprehensible to Maryk, were performed. For his first witness, Challee called Lieutenant Commander Philip Francis Queeg.

The orderly went out. Everyone in the room watched the door. The ex-captain of the *Caine* entered, tanned, clear-eyed, in a new blue uniform, the sleeve stripes bright gold. Maryk had not seen him for almost two months. The change was startling. His last vivid recollection was of a little stooped potbellied figure in a gray life jacket and wet khakis, clinging to the engine telegraph, the bristly face green and twisted with fear. The man before him was erect, confident, and good-looking—and youthful, despite the few blond strands over a pink scalp. Maryk's nerves were jolted.

Queeg took his seat on a raised platform in the center of the room. His manner during the opening questions was courteous and firm. Never once did he glance in Maryk's direction, though the exec sat to the right of him, only a few feet away, behind the defense desk.

Challee went quickly to the morning of the typhoon, and asked the ex-captain to narrate the events in his own words. The reply of Queeg was a coherent, rapid sketch, in formal language, of the mutiny. Maryk admitted to himself that the facts were presented correctly; the external facts. Slight shadings of what had been said and done, and, of course, a complete omission of any details of how the captain had looked and behaved, sufficed to turn the whole picture inside out. As Queeg told the story, he had simply made every effort to hold fleet course and speed, and in face of worsening weather had managed to do so right up to the moment when his executive officer had unexpectedly run amuck and seized command. Thereafter, by staying on the bridge and judiciously suggesting necessary maneuvers to the frenzied exec, he had brought the ship safely through the storm.

The court members followed the account with sympathetic interest.

Once Captain Blakely transferred a long ominous stare to the defendant. Before Queeg was finished Maryk had totally despaired. He looked to his counsel with frightened eyes. Greenwald doodled with a red crayon on a pad, drawing multitudes of little fat pink pigs.

"Commander," said Challee, "can you account in any way for your executive officer's act?"

"Well," said Queeg calmly, "it was a rather serious situation. The wind was force 10 to 12, the waves were mountainous, and the ship naturally was laboring very badly. Mr. Maryk had shown evidences of growing nervousness and instability all morning. I think when we took that last bad roll he simply went into panic and proceeded to act irrationally. He acted under the delusion that he and he alone could save the ship. His worst weakness was conceit about his seamanship."

"Was the *Caine* in grave danger at that moment?"

"I wouldn't say so, no sir. Of course a typhoon is an extreme hazard at all times, but the ship had ridden well up to that moment and continued to ride well afterward."

"Have you ever been mentally ill, sir?"

"No, sir."

"Were you ill in any way when Mr. Maryk relieved you?"

"I was not."

"Did you protest the relief?"

"As forcefully as I could."

"Did you attempt to resume command?"

"Repeatedly."

"Did you warn your executive officer of the consequences of his act?"

"I told him he was performing a mutinous act."

"What was his reply?"

"That he expected to be court-martialed, but was going to retain command anyway."

"What was the attitude of Lieutenant Junior Grade Keith, the officer of the deck?"

"He was in a state of panic as bad as Maryk's or worse. He consistently backed up Maryk."

"What was the attitude of the rest of the officers?"

"They were perplexed and submissive. Under the circumstances I don't suppose they had any alternative."

"What was the attitude of the helmsman?"

"Stilwell I considered the worst troublemaker on the ship. He was emotionally unbalanced, and for some reason was very devoted to Lieutenant Junior Grade Keith. He gladly participated in defying my orders."

"Where is Stilwell at present?"

"I understand he is in the psychiatric ward of the hospital here, with a diagnosis of acute melancholia."

Challee glanced at the court. "Is there anything else, Commander Queeg, that you care to state in connection with the events of 18 December aboard the *Caine?*"

"Well, I have thought a lot about it all, of course. It's the gravest occurrence in my career, and the only questionable one that I'm aware of. It was an unfortunate freak accident. If the OOD had been anyone but Keith, and the helmsman anyone but Stilwell, it would not have happened. Keefer or Harding or Paynter would have repudiated Maryk's orders and probably snapped him out of it in a hurry. A normal sailor at the helm would have disregarded both officers and obeyed me. It was just bad luck that those three men—Maryk, Keith, and Stilwell—were combined against me at a crucial time. Bad luck for me, and worse luck for them."

Maryk took the crayon from Greenwald's hand as Queeg spoke and scribbled on the pad, *I can prove I wasn't panicky.* The lawyer wrote underneath, *Okay. May not be necessary,* and around both statements he drew a large pig.

"The court would like to question the witness," said Blakely. "Commander Queeg, how long have you been in the naval service?"

"I am completing my fourteenth year, sir."

"In that time you have taken all the prescribed physical and mental examinations incident to entrance to the Academy, graduation, commissioning, promotion, and so forth?"

"Yes, sir."

"Does your medical record contain any entry reflecting in any way any history of illness, mental or physical?"

"It does not, sir. My tonsils were removed in the fall of 1938. That is the only entry that isn't routine."

"Have you ever had an unsatisfactory fitness report, or any letter of reprimand or admonishment, Commander Queeg?"

"Negative, sir. I have one letter of commendation in my jacket."

"Now Commander, the court would like you to account if you can for Lieutenant Maryk's opinion that you were mentally ill, in view of your background and service record." Challee looked quickly at Green-wald, expecting an objection to the question. The defense counsel sat head down, drawing on the pad. He was left-handed; his scarred wrist and hand curved around the moving crayon.

"Well, sir, I will have to point out that I assumed the command of an extremely disorganized and dirty ship. I saw I was in for a long tough grind. I was determined to bring that ship up to snuff, no matter how unpleasant the process might be. I took many stern measures. Lieutenant Maryk, I may say, from the first opposed my will in this regard. He didn't see eye to eye with me at all on this idea of bringing the ship up to snuff, and maybe he thought I was crazy to keep trying. His questionable loyalty and slackness forced me to bear down all the harder, of course, and—well, I guess that's the picture, sir. And as I say, I'll stand on the *Caine*'s battle record under my command, despite all the trouble Maryk gave me."

There was an exchange of looks among the president, Challee, and Greenwald. The defense counsel rose for cross-examination. "Commander Queeg," he said respectfully, looking down at the crayon in his hand, "I should like to ask you whether you have ever heard the expression, 'Old Yellowstain.' "

"In what connection?" Queeg looked genuinely puzzled.

"In any connection."

"Old Yellowstone?"

"Old Yellowstain, sir."

"I have not."

"You aren't aware, then, that all the officers of the *Caine* habitually referred to you as Old Yellowstain?"

The judge advocate jumped to his feet. "I object to the question! It is impertinent badgering of the witness."

Blakely said frostily, "How does defense counsel justify this line of questioning?"

"If the court please, it is the assigned duty of defense counsel to disprove the words in the specification—I quote—*without authority, and without justifiable cause*. It will be the contention of the defense that the authority of Lieutenant Maryk was Articles 184, 185, and 186 of the *Navy Regulations,* and that his justifiable cause was the conduct, demeanor, and decisions of Commander Queeg during his command of the *Caine*. The sobriquet 'Old Yellowstain' used by the officers of the *Caine,* and the facts out of which that sobriquet arose, will be extremely relevant. I quote Article 185: *the conclusion to relieve his commanding officer must be one which a reasonable, prudent and experienced officer would regard as necessary from the facts thus determined to exist."*

The president of the court worked his eyebrows while Greenwald spoke. "The court will be cleared," he said.

In the corridor, Greenwald lounged against the wall and remarked to Maryk, "Captain Blakely doesn't like Jews. Intonations on the name 'Greenwald.' I have absolute pitch for those harmonies."

"Jesus," said Maryk miserably.

"It won't make any difference. You're not supposed to love Jews necessarily, just to give them a fair shake. I've always had a fair shake in the Navy, and I'll get it from Blakely, too, despite the eyebrows."

"I don't think I have a chance at this point," mourned the exec.

"Queeg's doing nobly," said Greenwald. The orderly summoned them back to the courtroom.

"Before ruling, the court wishes to caution defense counsel," Blakely said, staring very hard at Greenwald. "This is a most unusual and delicate case. The honor and career of an officer with an unblemished military record of fourteen years' standing, including long combatant duty, is involved. The court recognizes that the defense is compelled to try to challenge the competence of that officer. Nevertheless, all requirements of legal ethics and military respect and subordination remain in force. The defense counsel will have to bear full responsibility for the conduct of his case, including indiscretions and abuses of his cross-examination privileges." The president halted, and intensified his stare at Greenwald, who stood behind his desk, looking down at his array of pigs. "Subject to the foregoing comment, the judge advocate's objection is overruled. Court stenographer will repeat the question."

The little yeoman in whites said tonelessly, "You aren't aware then that all the officers of the *Caine* habitually referred to you as Old Yellowstain?"

Queeg's head was down between his shoulders, and he squinted up at the air in front of him. He suddenly looked much more familiar to Maryk. "I am not aware of it."

"Commander," said Greenwald, "how many fitness reports did you write on Lieutenant Maryk, disregarding the one after he relieved you?"

"Two, I believe."

"One in January, and one in July?"

"That is correct."

"Do you remember their contents?"

"Well, they weren't bad fitness reports, as I recall."

"Did you give him the highest classification—Outstanding—in both of them?"

"Well, that was at the beginning. I may have."

"Photostats of the reports are available to refresh your memory, Commander."

"I can say definitely, yes, I was still classifying him as outstanding that early in the game."

"Isn't that inconsistent with your statement that from the first he opposed your wishes regarding the *Caine?*"

"No, there's no inconsistency, it's all how you interpret it. I don't use fitness reports to revenge myself on officers who disagree with me, and Maryk did know his job and—maybe I shouldn't have said from the first. In fact he started off at first like a house afire but he funked off very fast. That morning-glory type is quite common and I'm not the first captain who was fooled at first."

"Did you state in your report of 1 July that he was qualified for command?"

"Well, as I say, he started off like a house afire. If you want to know how he ended up why don't you bring up his last fitness report?"

"You wrote that report, Commander, did you not, after he relieved you on the grounds of mental illness?"

"That made no difference at all," exclaimed Queeg, with a touch of the old nasal voice. "The fitness report is not an instrument of retaliation or revenge—not in my hands, it isn't!"

"No further questions at this time." Greenwald turned to the court. "Commander Queeg will be called as a witness for the defense." The eyebrows of the president signaled astonishment followed by resignation. Queeg was excused. He walked out of the room hurriedly.

"Call Lieutenant Thomas Keefer," said Challee. The novelist came marching in, shoulders thrown back, head tilted a little to one side, his eyes looking blankly ahead. After being sworn he sat in the witness chair and crossed his gangling legs. His elbows lay on the arm rests and his fingers were laced across his stomach. His foot danced slightly all the time he testified.

Challee brushed through the opening questions in a monotone, then said, "Now, Lieutenant Keefer, coming to the morning of 18 December —where were you at the time Captain Queeg was relieved?"

"In the charthouse on the bridge."

"What were you doing?"

"Well, the weather was pretty terrible. Several of us were there, officers and men. We wanted to be on hand in case an emergency arose, but naturally we stayed out of the pilothouse, not wanting to clutter it up."

"Describe how you learned that the captain had been relieved."

"Mr. Maryk passed the word for all officers to lay up to the wheelhouse. When we got there he told us that the captain was sick and he had assumed command."

"Where was Commander Queeg at the time?"

"In the wheelhouse."

"Did he concur with Maryk's statement?"

"He did not. He continually protested and warned us that if we complied with Maryk's orders we'd be guilty of collusion in mutiny."

"Did Captain Queeg show any external signs of being sick?"

"Well——" Keefer shifted in his seat and for a moment encountered Maryk's painfully intense glance. Maryk looked away angrily. "Well, I have to say that at the height of a typhoon nobody aboard a four-piper looks very well. He was wet, and tired, and very tense-looking——"

"Was he raving, or foaming, or giving any other common indications of insanity?"

"No."

"Did he speak incoherently or gibberingly when he protested being relieved?"

"No, he spoke clearly."

"Did he look any worse than, say, Lieutenant Keith?"

"No, sir."

"Or Maryk?"

"I guess not. We were all tired, dripping, and knocked about."

"What was your response to Maryk's announcement?"

"Well, things were happening very fast and in a confused way. Captain Queeg was talking to us when the capsized *George Black* was sighted. Maryk began to maneuver to pick up survivors and for an hour that was all anyone thought about."

"Did you make any effort to persuade Maryk to restore Queeg to command?"

"I did not."

"Were you next senior officer to Maryk?"

"I was."

"Didn't you feel the seriousness of the situation?"

"I certainly did, sir."

"Didn't you realize that Captain Queeg's warning about collusion in mutiny was well founded?"

"I did."

"Why did you take no remedial action?"

"I wasn't present when the captain was relieved. I didn't know what he might have done in a critical moment to convince the executive officer that he was sick. And everyone was concentrating on saving first the *Black* survivors and then our own ship. There was no time for arguing. By the time the storm subsided the situation had crystallized. Maryk was in full command. The entire ship was obeying his orders. To oppose him at that point might have been a mutinous act on my part. I decided that for the safety of the ship my best course was to obey his orders until such time as higher authority endorsed or overruled his action. That was what I did."

"Lieutenant Keefer, were you aboard the *Caine* throughout the period when Captain Queeg was in command?"

"Yes."

"Did you ever observe evidences of insanity in him?"

Keefer hesitated, wetted his lips, and looked toward Maryk, who was gnawing a knuckle and staring out of the window at the sunlit trees. "I don't—I can't answer that question intelligently, not being a psychiatrist."

Challee said sternly, "Mr. Keefer, if you saw a man rolling on the deck and foaming at the mouth, or rushing up and down passageways screaming that a tiger was after him, would you venture to say that that man was temporarily deranged?"

"I would."

"Did Commander Queeg ever exhibit such behavior?"

"No. Nothing like that."

"Did you ever think he might be insane?"

"Objection," said Greenwald, rising. "Witness isn't an expert. Matters of opinion are not admissible evidence."

"Question is withdrawn," said Challee with a slight smile, and Blakely ordered it stricken from the record.

When Greenwald sat, Maryk slid the pad under his eyes, with a crimson scrawl all over the pigs: *Why, why, WHY??* Greenwald printed rapidly on a fresh sheet, *Implicating Keefer harms you. Two disgruntled bastards instead of one heroic exec. Take an even strain.*

"Mr. Keefer," said the judge advocate, "at any time prior to 18 December were you informed that Maryk suspected Queeg of being mentally ill?"

"Yes."

"Describe how you learned this fact."

"At Ulithi, about two weeks before the typhoon, Maryk showed me a medical log he'd kept on Queeg's behavior. He asked me to come with him to the *New Jersey* to report the situation to Admiral Halsey."

"What was your reaction to the medical log?"

"I was dumfounded to learn that Maryk had kept it."

"Did you consent to go with him?"

"Yes."

"Why?"

"Well, I was stunned. And I—that is, he was my superior officer and also my close friend. I didn't consider refusing."

"Did you believe that the log justified the relief of Queeg?"

"No. When we arrived aboard the *New Jersey,* I told him as forcibly as I could that in my opinion the log would not justify the action, and that both of us would be liable to a charge of combining to make a mutiny."

"What was his response?"

"He followed my advice. We returned to the *Caine* and no further reference was made by either of us to the log or to Queeg's mental condition."

"Did you inform the captain of Maryk's log?"

"I did not."

"Why not?"

"It would have been disloyal and contrary to the best interests of the ship to stir up my captain against my executive officer. Maryk had evidently abandoned his intention to pursue the matter. I considered the matter closed."

"Were you surprised, two weeks later, when he relieved the captain?"

"I was flabbergasted."

"Were you pleased, Mr. Keefer?"

Keefer squirmed in his chair, peered at the fierce face of Blakely,

and said, "I've said that Maryk was my close friend. I was badly disturbed. I anticipated that at best he would be involved in grave difficulties, and I thought all of us might also be. I thought it was a terrible
situation. I was very far from pleased."

"No further questions." Challee nodded at Greenwald.

The defense counsel rose. "No questions." All seven members of the
court turned to look at Greenwald. Blakely, his eyebrows at maximum
altitude, said, "Does the defense intend to recall the witness at a later
time?"

"No, sir."

"No cross-examination?"

"No, sir."

"Court stenographer will affirmatively note," said Blakely, "that the
accused did not desire to cross-examine Lieutenant Keefer. The court
will question the witness. . . . Mr. Keefer, the court desires that you
describe any factual occurrences you observed which might have led
a prudent and experienced officer to conclude that Captain Queeg might
be mentally ill."

"Sir, as I've said, I'm not a psychiatrist." Keefer was now quite pale.

"Now as to this so-called medical log. You did read this log, Mr.
Keefer. Were the facts contained in it known to you?"

"For the most part, yes, sir."

"But these same facts, which convinced Lieutenant Maryk that he
ought to report the captain to Admiral Halsey, did not convince you, is
that correct?"

"They did not, sir."

"Why not?"

Keefer paused, looked up at the clock, and back at Blakely. "Sir, it's
not something a layman can intelligently discuss——"

"You have stated you were a close friend of Mr. Maryk. This court
is trying to find out among other things any possible extenuating circumstances in his decision to relieve his captain. Did these facts contained in the log merely indicate to you, as a layman, that Captain
Queeg was a highly normal and competent officer?"

There was an edge of irony in the tone. Keefer quickly said, "Speaking from ignorance, sir, my understanding is that mental disability is a
relative thing. Captain Queeg was a very strict disciplinarian, and extremely meticulous in hunting down the smallest matters, and quite in-
sistent in having his own way in all things. He was not the easiest per-

son in the world to reason with. It wasn't my place to question his judgments, but there were several occasions when I thought he bore down too hard and spent excessive time on small matters. Those are the things that were recorded in the medical log. They were very unpleasant. But to jump from them to a conclusion that the captain was a maniac—I was compelled in all honesty to warn Maryk against doing that."

Blakely beckoned to the judge advocate and whispered with him, then said, "No further questions. Witness excused." Keefer stepped down, turned, and walked out rapidly. Maryk looked after him with a small dismal smile.

In the afternoon session Challee began by calling Harding and Paynter. They were sullen witnesses. Once Paynter was admonished by the court for evasiveness. Challee pressed out of both of them a corroboration of Keefer's testimony: the captain had not seemed crazy after being relieved, and they did not know what had prompted the exec's decision. It became obvious in the questioning that they both disliked Queeg. But one after the other they were driven to admit that they had never observed him commit any acts of madness during his entire time of command.

In cross-examining Harding, Greenwald brought out that Stilwell had been restricted to the ship for half a year for reading on watch, and that the whole crew had been docked five days' leave in the States because some sailors had appeared at general quarters without life jackets. He drew from Paynter a description of Stilwell's court-martial.

Challee, in a belligerent re-examination, crowded the engineering officer hard. "Mr. Paynter, did Captain Queeg direct you to find Stilwell guilty?"

"He didn't order me to, no. The way he explained the law, though, he left no doubt what verdict he wanted."

"What verdict did you think he wanted?"

"Guilty, and a bad-conduct discharge."

"What verdict did the court hand down?"

"Guilty and deprived of six liberties."

"Did Captain Queeg attempt to have you change the sentence?"
"No."

"Did he give letters of admonition to the court?"
"No."

"Did he punish you in any way?"

"Well, yes. He said there would be no sleeping after 0800 in the wardroom. And he started keeping a black book on errors we made in writing logs."

"In other words, this cruel punishment consisted of orders to write accurate logs and not to sleep during ship's working hours, is that correct?"

"Well, at the time we were standing a one-in-three watch, and not to be able to sleep in——"

"Answer the question, please. Was that the extent of your so-called punishment?"

"Yes."

"No further questions."

Greenwald rose. "Mr. Paynter, what was the ship doing during that period?"

"Convoy duty in the forward area."

"Were you at sea much?"

"Practically constantly."

"Who were the OOD's?"

"Keefer, Keith, and Harding. I was mostly off the bill because of engine breakdown."

"Were they all department heads?"

"Yes."

"And they were standing OOD watches, four hours on and twelve off, around the clock, week in and week out. How many hours of sleep could they average?"

"Well, see, two nights out of three you lose four hours—either the graveyard or the morning watch. And GQ at dawn—I guess about four or five hours—assuming no night GQ's."

"Were there many night GQ's?"

"Maybe a couple every week."

"Did Captain de Vriess ever restrict daytime sleeping of OOD's?"

"No. He used to urge us to grab sleep when we could. He said he didn't want any foggy zombies conning his ship."

The judge advocate re-examined briefly. "Mr. Paynter, did any of the OOD's die of overstrain?"

"No."

"Did they suffer nervous breakdown?"

"No."

"As a result of this terrible persecution of not being allowed to sleep in working hours, were there any mishaps to the ship?"

"No."

The next witness was Urban. The little signalman's right hand trembled when he was sworn, and his voice quavered. The judge advocate led him to state that he had been the only person in the wheelhouse beside Queeg, Maryk, Keith, and Stilwell when the captain was relieved.

"What were your duties?"

"Kept the quartermaster's notebook, sir."

"Describe in your own words how it happened that Lieutenant Maryk relieved the captain."

"Well, he relieved him at five minutes to ten. I noted it in my book——"

"How did he relieve him?"

"He said, 'I relieve you, sir.' "

"Didn't he do anything else?"

"I don't remember for sure."

"Why did he relieve him? What was happening at the time?"

"The ship was rolling very bad."

Challee looked up at the court in exasperation. "Urban, describe everything that happened in the ten minutes before Captain Queeg was relieved."

"Well, like I say, we were rolling very bad."

Challee waited, his eyes intent on the sailor. After a long silence he burst out, "That's all? Did the exec say anything? Did the captain say anything? Did the OOD say anything? Did the ship just roll in silence for ten minutes?"

"Well, sir, it was a typhoon. I don't remember too well."

Blakely leaned forward, scowling over his clasped fingers at the signalman. "Urban, you're under oath. Evasive answers in a court-martial constitute contempt of court, which is a very bad business. Now think over your answer."

Urban said desperately, "Well, I think the captain wanted to come left and the exec wanted to come right, or something like that."

"Why did the captain want to come left?"

"I don't know, sir."

"Why did the exec want to come right?"

"Sir, I'm a signalman. I was keeping the quartermaster's log. I kept a good log even though we were rolling so bad. I didn't know what it was all about and I still don't."

"Did the captain act crazy?"

"No, sir."

"Did the exec?"

"No, sir."

"Did the exec seem scared?"

"No, sir."

"Did the captain?"

"No, sir."

"Did anyone?"

"I was goddamn scared, sir. I beg your pardon, sir."

A member of the court, a reserve lieutenant with an Irish face and bright red curly hair, chuckled out loud. Blakely turned on him. The lieutenant began writing busily on a yellow pad. "Urban," said Challee, "you are the only witness to this whole affair who is not directly involved. Your testimony is of the utmost importance——"

"I wrote everything in the quartermaster's log, sir, just the way it happened."

"Logs are not supposed to contain conversations. I am trying to find out what was said."

"Well, sir, like I said, one wanted to come right and one wanted to come left. Then Mr. Maryk relieved the captain."

"But the captain definitely did not act queer or crazy in any way at any time that morning—correct?"

"The captain was the same as always, sir."

Challee yelled, "Crazy, or sane, Urban?"

Urban shrank back in his chair, staring at Challee. "Of course he was sane, sir, so far as I knew."

"You don't remember anything that was said by anybody the whole morning?"

"I was busy keeping the log, sir. Except something about coming left or right, and about the storm being bad and all."

"What about ballasting?"

"Well, there was some talk about ballasting."

"To what effect?"

"Just talk about whether to ballast."

"Who wanted to ballast?"

"Well, the captain, or Mr. Maryk, I don't know which."

"It's of the greatest importance that you remember which, Urban."

"I don't know nothing about ballasting, sir. All I know is they talked about it."

"Was the ship ever ballasted that morning?"

"Yes, sir, because I remember I made a note in my log."

"Who gave the order to ballast?"

"I don't remember, sir."

"You don't remember much!"

"I kept a good log, sir. That was what I was there for."

Challee turned to Blakely, exclaiming, "I do not believe this witness is heeding the admonition of the court."

"Urban," said Blakely, "how old are you?"

"Twenty, sir."

"What schooling have you had?"

"One year in high school."

"Have you been telling the whole truth here, or haven't you?"

"Sir, the quartermaster isn't supposed to listen to arguments between the captain and the exec. He's supposed to keep his log. I don't know why Mr. Maryk relieved the captain."

"Did you ever see the captain do anything crazy?"

"No, sir."

"Did you like the captain?"

Urban said miserably, "*Sure* I liked him, sir."

"Continue your examination," said the court to Challee.

"No further questions."

Greenwald approached the witness platform, flipping the red crayon against his palm. "Urban, were you aboard when the *Caine* cut its own tow cable outside Pearl Harbor?"

"Yes, sir."

"What were you doing at the time that it happened?"

"I was—that is, the captain was eating me out—bawling me out—on the bridge."

"What for?"

"My shirttail was out."

"And while the captain was discussing your shirttail the ship steamed over its own towline?"

Challee had been regarding the defense counsel with wrinkled brows. He jumped up. "Object to this line of questioning and request the entire cross-examination so far be stricken from the record. Counsel has tricked the witness with leading questions into asserting as a fact that the *Caine* cut a towline, a material point that was not touched upon in direct examination."

Greenwald said, "The witness stated he had never seen the captain do anything crazy. I am attempting to refute this. *Courts and Boards* 282 says leading questions may be freely used on cross-examination."

The court was cleared. When all the parties returned Blakely said, "Defense counsel will have the opportunity to originate evidence later, and can recall the witness at that time. Objection sustained. Cross-examination thus far will be stricken from the record."

During the rest of the afternoon Challee called twelve chiefs and sailors of the *Caine,* all of whom testified briefly and glumly that Queeg had seemed much like any other captain, and had never to their knowledge done anything insane, either before the typhoon, during it, or afterward. The first of these was Bellison. Greenwald's cross-examination of him consisted of three questions and answers.

"Chief Bellison, what is a paranoid personality?"

"I don't know, sir."

"What is the difference between a psychoneurosis and a psychosis?"

"I don't know, sir." Bellison wrinkled up his face.

"Could you recognize a neurotic person as such if you encountered one?"

"No, sir."

To each of the twelve members of the crew, Greenwald put the same three questions and received the same answers. This litany, repeated twelve times, had a cumulating effect of irritation on Challee and on the court. They glared at Greenwald and fidgeted each time he went through the formula.

The court was adjourned after the testimony of the last sailor, Meatball. Maryk and his lawyer walked silently out of the court-martial building together. The last orange rays of a sinking sun were slanting across the bay, and the air was cool and sweet after the stale varnish-and-linoleum smell of the courtroom. They walked to Greenwald's gray Navy jeep. The gravel walk crunched loudly under their steps. "Have they got us on the run?" Maryk said quietly.

"Who knows?" Greenwald said. "We haven't gone to bat yet. You know this town. Where can we eat good?"

"I'll drive."

Greenwald drank a great many highballs during dinner. He evaded any talk about the court-martial, and filled the conversation with rambling dull information about Indians. He told Maryk that his real ambition had been to become an anthropologist, but he had gone into law out of crusading fervor, figuring that Indians needed to be defended more than to be studied. He said he had regretted the choice often.

He seemed queerer and queerer to Maryk. The exec abandoned hope—with his mind; he was convinced that Queeg, Keefer, and Urban had finished him off in the first day. But he clung to a shred of irrational faith in his strange defender. The prospect of being convicted was so awful that he had to believe in something. The maximum penalty was dismissal and fifteen years' imprisonment.

SECOND DAY, MORNING

"Okay, Lieutenant Keith," said an orderly, opening the door to the anteroom at two minutes past ten.

Willie followed him blindly. They passed through several doors, and suddenly they were in the courtroom, and Willie felt the shooting tingles in his arms and legs that he had felt when the *Caine* approached an invasion beach. The room was a frightening blur of solemn faces; the American flag seemed gigantic, and its red, white, and blue terribly vivid, like a flag in a color movie. He found himself in the witness platform, being sworn, and could not have told how he got there. Challee's face was gray and forbidding. "Mr. Keith, were you officer of the deck of the *Caine* during the forenoon watch on 18 December?"

"I was."

"Was the captain relieved of command by the executive officer during that watch?"

"Yes."

"Do you know why the executive officer took the action he did?"

"Yes. The captain had lost control of himself and the ship, and we were in imminent danger of foundering."

"How many years have you served at sea, Lieutenant?"

"One year and three months."

"Have you ever been in a ship that foundered?"

"No."

"Do you know how many years Commander Queeg has served at sea?"

"No."

"As a matter of fact, Commander Queeg has served over eight years. Which of you is better qualified to judge whether a ship is foundering or not?"

"Myself, sir, if I'm in possession of my faculties and Commander Queeg isn't."

"What makes you think he isn't in possession of his faculties?"

"He wasn't on the morning of December 18."

"Have you studied medicine or psychiatry?"

"No."

"What qualifies you to judge whether your commanding officer was in possession of his faculties on December 18?"

"I observed his behavior."   ·

"Very well, Lieutenant. Describe to the court everything about your captain's behavior which indicated loss of his faculties."

"He froze to the engine-room telegraph. His face showed petrified terror. It was green. His orders were sluggish and vague, and not appropriate."

"Is it for the officer of the deck, Mr. Keith, a junior with one year at sea, to judge whether or not his captain's orders are appropriate?"

"Not ordinarily. But when the ship is in danger of going down and the captain's ship handling is increasing the danger instead of countering it, the OOD can't help observing it."

"Did Captain Queeg foam, or rave, or make nonsensical statements, or insane gestures?"

"No. He seemed to be paralyzed with terror."

"Paralyzed, yet he issued orders?"

"As I say, the orders were not helping matters, but making them worse."

"Be specific, Lieutenant. In what way were his orders making things worse?"

"Well, he kept insisting on going down-wind, when the ship was yawing so badly it was broaching to. And he refused to ballast."

"Refused? Who asked him to ballast?"

"Mr. Maryk."

"Why did the captain refuse?"

"He said he didn't want to contaminate the tanks with salt water."

"After being relieved, did Captain Queeg go violently crazy?"

"No."

"Describe the captain's manner after being relieved of command."

"Well, actually, he seemed better afterward. I think he felt better as soon as he no longer had the responsibility——"

"No opinions, Mr. Keith. Tell the court not what you think, but what you observed, please. What did the captain do?"

"Well, he stayed in the wheelhouse. Several times he tried to resume command."

"In an orderly, sensible way, or in a wild, raving way?"

"The captain was never wild or raving, either before or after being relieved. There are other forms of mental illness."

"Tell us about some others, Mr. Keith." Challee's tone was coarsely sarcastic.

"Well, little as I know about psychiatry, I do know—well, for instance, extreme depression and vagueness, and divorcement from reality, and inaccessibility to reason—things like that——" Willie felt that he was stumbling badly. "Besides, I never said Captain Queeg issued rational orders that morning. They were rational only in so far as they were phrased in correct English. They showed no awareness of reality."

"In your expert opinion, as ship handler and psychiatrist, that is? Very well. Are you aware that Captain Queeg has been pronounced perfectly rational by professional psychiatrists?"

"Yes."

"Do you think these psychiatrists are also mentally ill, Lieutenant Keith?"

"They weren't on the bridge of the *Caine* during the typhoon."

"Were you a loyal officer?"

"I think I was."

"Were you wholeheartedly behind the captain, or antagonistic to him, at all times prior to 18 December?"

Willie knew Queeg had appeared on the first day, but he had no idea of what the testimony had been. He calculated his answer carefully. "I was antagonistic to Captain Queeg at certain isolated times. Otherwise I maintained a loyal and respectful attitude."

"At what isolated times were you antagonistic?"

"Well, it was usually the same basic trouble. When Captain Queeg oppressed or maltreated the men I opposed him. Not very successfully."

"When did the captain ever maltreat the men?"

"Well, I don't know where to begin. Well, first he systematically persecuted Gunner's Mate Second Class Stilwell."

"In what way?"

"First he restricted him to the ship for six months for reading on watch. He refused to grant him leave in the States when there was a grave crisis in Stilwell's family life. Maryk gave Stilwell a seventy-two-hour emergency leave and he returned a few hours over leave. And for all that the captain gave Stilwell a summary court."

"Wasn't Stilwell tried for sending a fraudulent telegram?"

"Yes, and acquitted."

"But the summary court was for fraud, not merely for being AWOL?"

"Yes. I'm sorry, I spoke hastily."

"Take your time and be accurate. Do you think reading on watch in wartime is a negligible offense?"

"I don't think it warrants six months' restriction."

"Are you qualified to pass judgment on matters of naval discipline?"

"I'm a human being. In Stilwell's circumstances, the restriction was inhuman."

Challee paused for a moment. "You say Maryk gave Stilwell a pass. Did Maryk know that the captain had denied leave to Stilwell?"

"Yes."

"Are you testifying, Mr. Keith," the judge advocate said, with the air of having stumbled on something unexpected and good, "that Maryk, as far back as December '43, deliberately violated his captain's orders?"

Willie became rattled. It hadn't occurred to him that he would be disclosing this injurious fact for the first time. "Well, I mean it was my fault actually. I begged him to. I was morale officer, and I thought the man's morale—in fact, I think his present mental collapse is due to the captain's persecution——"

Challee turned to Blakely. "I ask the court to warn this witness against answering with immaterial opinions."

"Stick to facts, Mr. Keith," growled Blakely. Willie shifted in his chair, and felt his clothes all clammy inside. Challee said, "We now have your testimony, Mr. Keith, that you and Maryk and Stilwell connived to circumvent an express order of your commanding officer, a whole year before the typhoon of 18 December——"

"I would do it again, given the same circumstances."

"Do you believe loyalty consists in obeying only such orders as you approve of, or all orders?"

"All orders, except irrational persecution."

"Do you think there is no recourse in the Navy against what *you* think is irrational persecution, except disobedience of orders?"

"I know you can forward a letter to higher authority—via the captain."

"Why didn't you do that in this case?"

"I had to sail with Queeg for another year. The important thing was to get Stilwell home."

"It's an unlucky coincidence, isn't it, that the same insubordinate trio —Maryk, Stilwell, and yourself—combined in the deposing of your captain?"

"Stilwell and I just happened to be on duty when the captain went to pieces. Any other OOD and helmsman would have done the same."

"Maybe. Now, please tell the court any other instances of oppression and maltreatment that occur to you."

Willie hesitated for several seconds, feeling the weight of the court members' unfriendly looks like a pressure on his forehead. "Maybe you can make them all sound silly and trivial here, sir, but at the time they were serious. He cut off the movies for six months just because he wasn't invited to a showing by mistake—he cut off the water at the equator because he was annoyed by the detachment of an officer—he called midnight conferences on insignificant details with department heads who were standing a one-in-three deck watch. And he forbade sleeping by day so there was no chance to catch up on sleep———"

"We've had a lot of testimony on that sleep business. The officers of the *Caine* certainly wanted their sleep, war or no war, didn't they?"

"I said it's easy to poke fun at these things. But it isn't easy to conn a ship in formation in a rain squall when you've been up for seventy-two hours with maybe four hours' consecutive sleep."

"Mr. Keith, did Captain Queeg ever use physical torture on officers or men?"

"No."

"Did he starve them, beat them, or in any way cause anybody injury that will appear in the medical records of the *Caine?*"

"No."

"Did he ever issue punishments not allowed by regulations?"

"He never did anything not allowed by regulations, or if he did he backtracked immediately. He demonstrated how much can be done to oppress and maltreat within regulations."

"You didn't like Captain Queeg, did you, Lieutenant?"

"I did at first, very much. But I gradually realized that he was a petty tyrant and utterly incompetent.

"Did you think he was insane too?"

"Not until the day of the typhoon."

"Did Maryk ever show you his medical log on Queeg?"

"No."

"Did he ever discuss the captain's medical condition with you?"

"No. Mr. Maryk never permitted criticism of the captain in his presence."

"What! Despite the insubordination back in December '43?"

"He would walk out of the wardroom if anything derogatory was said of the captain."

"There were derogatory remarks about the captain in the wardroom? Who uttered them?"

"Every officer except Maryk."

"Would you say that Captain Queeg had a loyal wardroom of officers?"

"All his orders were carried out."

"Except those you thought ought to be circumvented. . . . Mr. Keith, you have stated you disliked the captain."

"That is the truth."

"Come to the morning of 18 December. Was your decision to obey Maryk based on your judgment that the captain had gone mad, or was it based on your dislike of Captain Queeg?"

Willie stared for long seconds at Challee's livid face. There were sharp steel teeth in the question. Willie knew what the true answer was; and he knew that it would probably destroy himself and Maryk. But he felt unable to carry off a lie. "I can't answer," he said at last, in a low voice.

"On what grounds, Lieutenant Keith?"

"Must I state grounds?"

"It is contempt of court to refuse to answer a question except on sufficient grounds, Lieutenant Keith."

Willie said thickly, "I'm not sure. I just don't remember my state of mind that long ago."

"No more questions," said Challee. He turned on his heel and sat down.

*

Willie was absolutely certain, in that instant, staring at the surgically cold faces of the court, that he had convicted Maryk and himself with his own mouth. He shook with boiling impotent rage at the flummery of court routine which prevented him from breaking out and shouting his self-justification; and at the same time he realized that he could never quite justify himself in the Navy's eyes. In plain truth, he had obeyed Maryk for two reasons, first, because he thought the exec was more likely to save the ship, and second, because he hated Queeg. It had never occurred to him, until Maryk took command, that Queeg might be really insane. And he knew, deep down, that he never had believed the captain was crazy. Stupid, mean, vicious, cowardly, incompetent, yes—but sane. The insanity of Queeg was Maryk's only possible plea (and Willie's too); and it was a false plea; and Challee knew it, and the court knew it; and now Willie knew it.

Greenwald rose to cross-examine. "Mr. Keith, you have stated you disliked Captain Queeg."

"I did dislike him."

"Did you state under direct examination all your reasons for disliking him?"

"Not at all. I wasn't given the chance to state half the reasons."

"Please state the rest of your reasons, now, if you will."

Words formed in Willie's mind which, he knew, would change the course of several lives and land him in trouble from which he might never extricate himself. He spoke; it was like punching his fist through a glass door. "My chief reason for disliking Captain Queeg was his cowardice in battle."

Challee started getting to his feet. Greenwald said quickly, "What cowardice?"

"He repeatedly ran from shore batteries——"

"Objection!" shouted the judge advocate. "Counsel is originating evidence beyond the scope of direct examination. He is leading the witness into irresponsible libels of an officer of the Navy. I request that the court admonish defense counsel and strike the cross-examination thus far from the record."

"Please the court," said Greenwald, facing into Blakely's glare, "the witness's dislike of Queeg was not only in the scope of the direct examination, it was the key fact brought out. The background of this dislike is of the utmost consequence. The witness has confessed ignorance of medicine and psychiatry. Things Queeg did, which caused the witness in his ignorance to dislike him, may in fact have been the helpless acts of a sick man. Defense will present material corroboration of all statements of the witness in this connection, and will in fact show that Queeg's acts stemmed from illness——"

Challee flared at Greenwald, "This is not the time for defense to present its case or make a closing argument——"

"The judge advocate has opened the question of Lieutenant Keith's admitted dislike of Captain Queeg," Greenwald shot back. "Evidence is tested as it arises——"

Blakely rapped his gavel. "Defense counsel and the judge advocate are admonished for unseemly personal exchanges. The court will be cleared."

When the parties of the trial came back into the room, Blakely had a copy of *Navy Regulations* open before him on the bench. He wore thick black-rimmed glasses which gave him an oddly peaceful professorial look. "For the benefit of all parties, court will read from Article 4, Sections 13 and 14 of the Articles for the Government of the Navy, before announcing its ruling.

"The punishment of death, or such other punishment as a court-martial may adjudge, may be inflicted on any person in the naval service, who, in time of battle, displays cowardice, negligence, or disaffection, or withdraws from or keeps out of danger to which he should expose himself . . . or in time of battle, deserts his duty or station, or induces others to do so."

Blakely took off his glasses and closed the book. He went on in a grave, tired tone, "The court has said this is a delicate case. Defense counsel and the witness are warned that they are on the most dangerous possible ground. In charging an officer of the United States Navy with an offense punishable by death, and that the most odious offense in military life, equal to murder, they take on themselves the heaviest responsibility, and face consequences the seriousness of which cannot be overstated. The court now asks defense counsel in view of the foregoing whether he desires to withdraw his questions."

Greenwald said, "I do not so desire, sir."

"The court asks the witness to consider carefully the implications of his answers and state whether he desires to withdraw his answers."

Willie, his teeth chattering a little, said, "I do not so desire, sir."

"Subject to the foregoing," said Blakely, with an audible sigh, pushing aside the book, "the objection is overruled. Defense counsel will proceed with his cross-examination."

Willie told about Queeg's running from the Saipan shore battery which had fired on the *Stanfield*. He narrated in detail the episode at Kwajalein which had resulted in Queeg's being nicknamed "Old Yellowstain." He saw for the first time a change in the expressions of the court as he spoke. The frigid solemnity with which they had peered at him gave way slowly, and instead there were seven faces of men listening with interest to an amazing tale. Challee, frowning bitterly, scribbled pages of notes.

"Mr. Keith, who coined this name, 'Old Yellowstain'?" said Greenwald.

"I'm not sure, sir. It just sprang into existence."

"What did it imply?"

"Well, cowardice, of course. But it also referred to the yellow marker. It was one of those naturals. It stuck."

"Have you told all the incidents of cowardice that you recall?"

"Well, in any combat situation Captain Queeg inevitably would be found on the side of the bridge away from the firing. When we were patrolling near a beach, every time the ship reversed course the captain changed wings. Everyone noticed it. It was a common joke. All the bridge personnel will corroborate what I say, if they're not afraid to talk."

Greenwald said, "Besides these incidents of cowardice, what further reasons had you for disliking Queeg?"

"Well—I guess I've told the characteristic ones—well, for one thing, he extorted a hundred dollars from me——"

Challee stood wearily. "Objection. How long will these irrelevant unproven allegations be permitted by the court? The issue in this case is not whether Captain Queeg was a model officer, but whether he was insane on 18 December. Defense counsel has not even touched this issue. I suggest there is strong indication of collusion between defense counsel and witness to recklessly smear Commander Queeg and thus confuse the issue——"

Greenwald said, "The objection is identical with the last one court overruled. I repudiate the charge of collusion. Facts are facts, and need no collusion to be brought out. All these facts bear directly on the mental fitness of Captain Queeg to command a naval vessel, and as evidence they are nothing but clarification of Keith's dislike of his commanding officer, a fact established by the judge advocate at great pains in direct examination."

"The objection is identical," said Blakely, rubbing his eyes, "and it is overruled. Proceed with cross-examination."

"Describe this so-called extortion, Mr. Keith."

Willie told of the loss of the crate of liquor in San Francisco Bay. Captain Blakely began grimacing horribly. Greenwald said, "Did the captain order you to pay for the liquor?"

"Oh, no. He didn't order me. He made me admit that I was responsible for all acts of the working party because I was boat officer—although he had issued all the orders to the working party—and then he asked me to think over what I ought to do about it. That was all. But I was supposed to go on leave next day. My fiancée had flown out from New York to be with me. So I went to the captain. I apologized for my stupidity, and said I'd like to pay for the liquor. He took my money gladly, and signed my leave papers."

"No further questions," Greenwald said, and went to his seat. He felt a powerful grip on his knee under the table. He quickly sketched a revolting cross-eyed pig in a steaming cauldron, labeled it "Queeg," showed it to Maryk, and shredded it into the wastebasket.

Challee re-examined Willie for twenty minutes, probing for contradictions and misstatements in his stories about Queeg; he got off a great deal of sarcasm at Willie's expense, but he did not manage to shake the testimony.

Willie looked at the clock as he left the stand. It was ten minutes of eleven. He was amazed, just as he had been on the morning of the typhoon, by the slow passage of time. He imagined he had been in the witness chair for four hours.

Challee called Captain Randolph P. Southard, a dapper, lean officer with a hard-bitten face and close-cropped head, whose ribbons and medals made three colorful rows over his breast pocket. The judge advocate quickly brought out that Southard was the commander of Destroyer Squadron Eight, and had commanded destroyers of several types, including World War I four-pipers, for ten years. He was Challee's expert witness on ship handling.

Southard testified that under typhoon conditions a destroyer rode just as well going down-wind as up-wind. In fact, he said, because of a destroyer's high freeboard forward it tended to back into the wind,

Therefore, if anything, it was more manageable with the wind astern. He asserted that Queeg's efforts to stay on the fleet's southerly course had been the soundest possible procedure for getting out of the typhoon danger; and that Maryk's decision to turn north had been a dubious and dangerous one, because it had kept the ship in the direct path of the storm.

Greenwald opened his cross-examination by saying, "Captain Southard, have you ever conned a ship through the center of a typhoon?"

"Negative. Been on the fringes often but always managed to avoid the center."

"Have you ever commanded a destroyer-minesweeper, sir?"

"Negative."

"This case, sir, concerns a destroyer-minesweeper at the center of a typhoon——"

"I'm aware of that," Southard said frostily. "I've had DMS's under my command in screens, and I've read the book on 'em. They don't differ from destroyers except in details of topside weight characteristics."

"I ask these questions, Captain, because you are the only expert witness on ship handling and the extent of your expert knowledge should be clear to the court."

"That's all right. I've handled destroyer types in almost every conceivable situation for ten years. Haven't handled a DMS at the center of a typhoon, no, but I don't know who has besides the skipper of the *Caine*. It's a thousand-to-one shot."

"Will you state without reservation that the rules of destroyer handling would hold for a DMS in the center of a typhoon?"

"Well, at the center of a typhoon there are no hard-and-fast rules. That's one situation where it's all up to the commanding officer. Too many strange things happen too fast. But seamanship is seamanship."

"A hypothetical question, Captain. Assuming you are conning a destroyer in winds and seas worse than any you have ever experienced. You are wallowing broadside. You actually believe your ship is foundering. You are in the last extremity. Would you try to bring your ship head into wind, or stern to wind?"

"That's a mighty hypothetical question."

"Yes, sir. Don't you wish to answer it?"

"I'll answer it. In the last extremity I'd head into the wind if I could. *Only* in the last extremity."

"Why, sir?"

"Why, because your engines and rudder have the best purchase that way, that's all, and it's your last chance to keep control of your ship."

"But suppose heading into the wind would mean remaining in the path of a storm instead of escaping?"

"First things first. If you're on the verge of foundering you're as bad off as you can get. Mind you, you said the *last extremity*."

"Yes, sir. No further questions."

Challee stood at once. "Captain, in your opinion who is the best judge as to whether a ship is in its last extremity?"

"There is only one judge. The commanding officer."

"Why?"

"The Navy has made him captain because his knowledge of the sea and of ships is better than anyone else's on the ship. It's very common for subordinate officers to think the ship is a goner when all they're going through is a little weather."

"Don't you think, though, sir, that when his subordinates all agree that the ship is going down the captain ought to listen to them?"

"Negative! Panic is a common hazard at sea. The highest function of command is to override it and to listen to nothing but the voice of his own judgment."

"Thank you, Captain."

SECOND DAY, AFTERNOON

Dr. Forrest Lundeen was a stout, pink-faced commander with gold-rimmed glasses, and straight blond hair fading to gray. He was chief of psychiatry at the Navy hospital, and had headed the medical board which had examined Queeg. He sat comfortably in the witness chair, answering Challee's questions with good-humored alertness.

"How long did your examination last, Doctor?"

"We had the commander under constant observation and testing for three weeks."

"Who comprised the board?"

"Myself, Dr. Bird, and Dr. Manella."

"All three practicing psychiatrists?"

"Dr. Bird and Dr. Manella have been civilian psychiatrists. They are reserve officers. I have specialized in psychiatry in the Navy for fifteen years."

"What was the finding of the board?"

"Commander Queeg was discharged with a clean bill of health."

"No evidence of insanity was found?"

"None whatever."

"Does that mean that Commander Queeg is absolutely normal?"

"Well, normality, you know, is a fiction in psychiatry. It's all relative. No adult is without problems except a happy imbecile. Commander Queeg is a well-adjusted personality."

"Do you consider it possible that two weeks before you began your examination Commander Queeg was insane?"

"It is utterly impossible. The commander is sane now and has always been sane. A psychotic collapse leaves trauma that can always be detected."

"You found no such trauma in Commander Queeg?"

"None."

"Commander Queeg was summarily relieved of command of the U.S.S. *Caine* on December 18, 1944, by his executive officer, who stated that the captain was mentally ill. Do you consider it possible that on that date Commander Queeg was in such a state of psychotic collapse that the executive officer's act was justified?"

"Absolutely impossible."

"Is it possible for a sane man to perform offensive, disagreeable, foolish acts?"

"It happens every day."

"Assuming for a moment—this is a hypothetical question—that the conduct of Commander Queeg throughout his command was harsh, ill-tempered, nasty, oppressive, and often showed bad judgment. Would that be inconsistent with your board's findings?"

"No. We did not find that he was a perfect officer. We found an absence of mental illness."

"From your knowledge of the commander, would you say he is capable of ill temper and harshness?"

"Yes. It's in the picture."

"Having discovered all that, you still say that the act of the executive officer in relieving him was unjustified?"

"From a psychiatric standpoint, completely unjustified. That was the unanimous conclusion of the board."

"Describe the background of your colleagues."

"Bird has special training in Freudian technique. He's a recent honor graduate of Harvard Medical School. Manella is one of the best-known psychosomatic men on the West Coast."

"State their present whereabouts."

"Bird is still on my staff. Manella was detached last week and is en route to the Philippines."

"We will place our report in evidence and hear Dr. Bird. Thank you, Doctor."

The judge advocate allowed himself a direct glance into Greenwald's eyes, and a thin cold grin. Greenwald came shuffling toward the witness platform, rubbing his nose with the back of his hand, looking down at his feet, and presenting a general picture of flustered embarrassment. "Dr. Lundeen, my background is legal, not medical. I hope you will bear with me if I try to clarify technical terms. I'll probably ask some elementary questions."

"Perfectly all right."

"You said Commander Queeg, like all adults, had problems, to which he was adjusted. Can you describe the problems?"

"Well, most of that information comes under the heading of clinical confidences."

"Yes, sir. Suppressing all confidential information, can you still describe in general the problems?"

Challee called out, "I object. Commander Queeg is not on trial. Lieutenant Maryk is. The question constitutes irrelevant probing of medical confidences."

Blakely looked to Greenwald. The pilot shrugged. "I rely on the judgment of the court. Evidence regarding disturbing factors in Commander Queeg's mental make-up is of the utmost importance to the issue, obviously."

With an annoyed glance at the judge advocate, Blakely ordered the court cleared. The parties were summoned back in less than a minute. Blakely said, "The question is material. Objection overruled. The doctor has the privilege of medical discretion in answering." Challee flushed, and slouched in his chair. The stenographer repeated the question.

"Well, you might say the over-all problem is one of inferiority feelings," said Lundeen, "generated by an unfavorable childhood and aggravated by some adult experiences."

"Unfavorable childhood in what way?"

"Disturbed background. Divorced parents, financial trouble, schooling problems."

"And the aggravating factors in adult life?"

"Well, I can't go into those too much. In general, the commander is rather troubled by his short stature, his low standing in his class, and such factors. Apparently the hazing at the Academy was a scarring experience." Lundeen paused. "That's about what I can say."

"How about his present family life?"

The doctor said reluctantly, "Well, you begin to tread on clinical ground there."

"But there are tensions, without describing them?"

"I won't answer further questions in that direction. As I say, the commander is well adjusted to all these things."

"Can you describe the nature of the adjustment?"

"Yes, I can. His identity as a naval officer is the essential balancing factor. It's the key to his personal security and therefore he's excessively zealous to protect his standing. That would account for the harshness and ill temper I spoke about before."

"Would he be disinclined to admit to mistakes?"

"Well, there's a tendency that way. The commander has a fixed anxiety about protecting his standing. Of course there's nothing unbalanced in that."

"Would he be a perfectionist?"

"Such a personality would be."

"Inclined to hound subordinates about small details?"

"He prides himself on meticulousness. Any mistake of a subordinate is intolerable because it might endanger him."

"Is such a personality, with such a zeal for perfection, likely to avoid all mistakes?"

"Well, we all know that reality is beyond the hundred-per-cent control of any human being——"

"Yet he will not admit mistakes when made. Is he lying?"

"Definitely not! He—you might say he revises reality in his own mind so that he comes out blameless. There's a tendency to blame others——"

"Doctor, isn't distorting reality a symptom of mental illness?"

"Certainly not, in itself. It's all a question of degree. None of us wholly faces reality."

"But doesn't the commander distort reality more than, say, you do, or any other person not under his tensions?"

"That's his weakness. Other people have other weaknesses. It's definitely not disabling."

"Would such a personality be inclined to feel that people were against him, hostile to him?"

"It's all part of it. Such a man by nature is constantly on the alert to defend his self-esteem."

"Would he be suspicious of subordinates, and inclined to question their loyalty and competence?"

"Maybe somewhat. It's all part of the anxiety for perfection."

"If criticized from above, would he be inclined to think he was being unjustly persecuted?"

"Well, as I say, it's all one pattern, all stemming from one basic premise, that he must try to be perfect."

"Would he be inclined to stubbornness?"

"Well, you'll have a certain rigidity of personality in such an individual. The inner insecurity checks him from admitting that those who differ with him may be right."

Greenwald suddenly switched from his fumbling manner to clicking preciseness. "Doctor, you've testified that the following symptoms exist in the commander's behavior: rigidity of personality, feelings of persecution, unreasonable suspicion, withdrawal from reality, perfectionist anxiety, an unreal basic premise, and an obsessive sense of self-righteousness."

Dr. Lundeen looked startled. "All mild, sir, all well compensated."

"Yes, Doctor. Is there an inclusive psychiatric term—one label—for this syndrome?"

"Syndrome? Who said anything about a syndrome? You're misusing a term. There's no syndrome, because there's no disease."

"Thank you for the correction, Doctor. I'll rephrase it. Do the symptoms fall into a single pattern of neurotic disturbance—a common psychiatric class?"

"I know what you're driving at, of course. It's a paranoid personality, of course, but that is not a disabling affliction."

"What kind of personality, Doctor?"

"Paranoid."

"Paranoid, Doctor?"

"Yes, paranoid."

Greenwald glanced at Challee, then looked around slowly, one by one, at the faces of the court. He started back to his desk. Challee rose. The pilot said, "I haven't finished cross-examination, I want to consult my notes." Challee sank into his seat. There was a minute of silence. Greenwald shuffled papers at his desk. The word "paranoid" hung in the air.

"Doctor, in a paranoid personality like Commander Queeg's, how do you distinguish between illness and adjustment?"

"As I've said repeatedly"—there was a tired, irritated note in Lundeen's voice—"it's a question of degree. Nobody's absolutely normal. Perhaps you're a mild manic-depressive. Perhaps I'm a mild schizoid. Millions of people live normal lives with these compensated conditions. Their physical analogues are a sway back, a heart murmur, something that is an individual weakness but not a disabling factor. You have to look for the disabling factor."

"Is this disabling factor an absolute or a relative thing, Doctor?"

"How do you mean that?"

"Well, could a man have a paranoid personality which would not disable him for any subordinate duties, but would disable him for command?"

"Conceivably."

"Then as a communications officer he would not be mentally ill—but as captain of the ship he would be mentally ill, isn't that right?"

"You're jumbling up a lot of medical language which you use very loosely," Lundeen said huffily.

"I'm sorry, Doctor."

"In the case of Captain Queeg my board did *not* find him disabled for command."

"I remember that testimony, sir. Can you describe, Doctor, the point at which the paranoid personality becomes disabling?"

"When the man loses control of himself and of the reality around him."

"What are the symptoms of the disabled paranoid who finds reality too much for him?"

"Well, there can be various reactions. Withdrawal into torpor, or frenzy, or nervous collapse—it all depends on circumstances."

"Is the disabling factor likely to show up in personal interviews?"

"With a skilled psychiatrist, yes."

"You mean the patient would go into frenzy or torpor?"

"No. I mean the psychiatrist could detect the disabling mechanisms, the rigidity, persecution feelings, fixed ideas, and so forth."

"Why is a psychiatrist needed, Doctor? Can't an educated intelligent person, like myself, or the judge advocate, or the court, detect a paranoid?"

Dr. Lundeen said sarcastically, "You evidently are not too well acquainted with the pattern. The distinguishing mark of this neurosis is extreme plausibility and a most convincing normal manner on the surface. Particularly in self-justification."

Greenwald looked at the floor for half a minute. There was a rustle at the bench as all the court members, by a common impulse, shifted in their chairs. "A hypothetical question, Doctor, about a commanding officer with a paranoid personality . . . Assuming he does the following things: he becomes bewildered or frightened under fire, and runs away; he damages government property and denies it; he falsifies official records; he extorts money from his subordinates; he issues excessive punishments for small offenses. Is he disabled for command?"

After a long wait, with the court members staring hard at him, Lundeen said, "It's an incomplete question. Does he perform his duties satisfactorily otherwise?"

"Hypothetically, let us say so."

"Well, then, he—he is not necessarily disabled, no. He is obviously not very desirable. It's a question of your level of officer procurement. If you have other men as qualified as him for command, well, they would be preferable. If you're in a war and command personnel is stretched thin, well, you may have to use him. It's another war risk."

"Dr. Lundeen, would you, as an expert witness, say that Commander Queeg should be restored to command of a United States naval vessel?"

"Well, I—— The question's pointless. That's the province of the Bureau of Personnel. The man is not mentally ill. I've repeatedly stated that a paranoid disturbance, however mild, is a distorting condition and exceedingly unpleasant for associates. In war you make do with what you have. He isn't disabled."

"Would you care to have your son under Captain Queeg in battle?" Lundeen glanced unhappily at the judge advocate, who jumped to his feet. "Objection. It is a personal emotional reaction that is being asked for, not an expert opinion."

"I withdraw the question," said Greenwald. "Thank you, Dr. Lundeen. Defense is finished."

Captain Blakely said, "The court wishes to clear up one point." The other court members looked tensely at the president. "Doctor, is such a thing possible—a temporary disability under stress, not amounting to a full collapse? Or—well, let me put it this way. Let's say a man with a mild condition is not disabled for all the usual stresses of command. Now let's say the stresses are multiplied manifold by a most extreme emergency. Would there be a loss in efficiency? A tendency to get confused and rattled, to make erroneous judgments?"

"Well, there might be. Extreme stress does that to almost anybody, sir."

"It's not supposed to do it to commanding officers."

"No, but practically speaking, sir, they're human, too."

"Very well, Doctor, thank you."

Challee resumed direct examination, and led Lundeen to assert several times, in different ways, that Queeg was not and had never been disabled. The doctor made these statements with aggrieved emphasis, occasionally looking sidewise at the defense lawyer.

"Dr. Bird will be my last witness, sir," Challee said to the court, as the orderly went out to call the second psychiatrist.

"Very well," said Blakely, glancing at the clock. It was five minutes past two. The lieutenant who came in was an extremely slender, youthful-looking man with dark hair, sallow skin, and sharp sensitive features. His eyes were brown, deep-set, large, and penetrating. There was something of the fanatic in his look. He was quite handsome.

Under Challee's questioning he confirmed everything that Dr. Lundeen had said about Queeg. In crisp, clear, yet gentle tones, he asserted that Queeg was fit for command now and had never been unfit. Challee said, "Did Dr. Manella concur with you and Dr. Lundeen in this opinion?"

"He did."

Challee paused, then said, "Did you find any indication that the commander had what is known as a paranoid personality?"

"Well, I would prefer to call it an obsessive personality with paranoid features."

"But this did not indicate mental unfitness?"

"No, it did not."

"Do the terms 'paranoid personality' or 'obsessive personality' occur in your board's report?"

"No."

"Why not, Doctor?"

"Well, terminology is far from exact in psychiatry. The same terms may mean different things even to men of the same school. 'Paranoid personality' sounds disabling and really isn't, at least not for me or Dr. Lundeen or Dr. Manella."

"Then Commander Queeg was pronounced fit from three different psychiatric viewpoints?"

"Yes."

"You unanimously agreed, Doctor, that Commander Queeg is mentally fit now and must have been mentally fit on 18 December, when he was summarily relieved on the grounds of mental illness?"

"That was our unanimous conclusion."

"No further questions."

Greenwald approached the witness. "Doctor, in the Freudian analysis is there such a thing as mental illness?"

"Well, there are disturbed people and adjusted people."

"But *disturbed* and *adjusted* correspond roughly, don't they, to the terms *sick* and *well* as laymen use them?"

"Very roughly, yes."

"Would you say Commander Queeg suffers from inferiority feelings?"

"Yes."

"Based on what?"

"Very severe childhood trauma. But they are well compensated."

"Is there a difference between *compensated* and *adjusted?*"

"Most definitely."

"Can you explain it?"

"Well——" Bird smiled and settled back in his chair. "Let's say a man has some deep-seated psychological disturbance buried in his unconscious. It will drive him to do strange things and will keep him in a constant state of tension, but he'll never know why. He can *compensate* by finding outlets for his peculiar drives, by will power, by day dreams, by any one of a thousand conscious devices. He can never *adjust* without undergoing psychoanalysis and bringing the disturbance up from the unconscious to the light of day."

"Has Commander Queeg ever been psychoanalyzed?"

"No."

"He is, then, a disturbed person?"

"Yes, he is. Not disabled, however, by the disturbance."

"Dr. Lundeen testified that he was adjusted."

Bird smiled. "Well, you're in terminology again. Adjustment has a special meaning in Freudian technique. Dr. Lundeen used it roughly to mean that the patient has compensated for his disturbance."

"Can you describe the commander's disturbance?"

"Without an extensive analysis I could not describe it accurately."

"You have no idea of what it is?"

"Of course the surface picture is clear. Commander Queeg subconsciously feels that he is disliked because he is wicked, stupid, and personally insignificant. This guilt and hostility trace back to infancy."

"How has he compensated?"

"In two ways, mainly. The paranoid pattern, which is useless and not desirable, and his naval career, which is extremely useful and desirable."

"You say his military career is a result of his disturbance?"

"Most military careers are."

Greenwald glanced up surreptitiously at Blakely. "Would you explain that, Doctor?"

"I simply mean that it represents an escape, a chance to return to the womb and be reborn with a synthetic blameless self."

Challee stood. "How far is this totally irrelevant technical discussion going to be pushed?"

"Are you objecting to the question?" Blakely said, scowling.

"I am requesting the court to set limits to time-wasting by the defense in confusing irrelevancies."

"Request noted. Proceed with cross-examination."

Greenwald resumed, "Doctor, did you note any peculiar habit Commander Queeg had? Something he did with his hands?"

"Do you mean rolling the marbles?"

"Yes, did he do that in your presence?"

"Not for the first week or so. Then he told me about it and I recommended that he resume the habit if it made him more comfortable. And he did so."

"Describe the habit, please."

"Well, it's an incessant rolling or rattling of two marbles in his hand—either hand."

"Did he say why he did it?"

"His hands tremble. He does it to steady his hands and conceal the trembling."

"Why do his hands tremble?"

"The inner tension. It's one of the surface symptoms."

"Does the rolling of balls have significance in the Freudian analysis?"

Bird glanced at the court uneasily. "Well, you go into technical jargon there."

"Please make it as non-technical as possible."

"Well, without analysis of the person you can only guess at the symbolism. It might be suppressed masturbation. It might be fondling poisonous pellets of feces. It all depends on——"

"Feces?"

"In the infantile world excrement is a deadly poison and therefore an instrument of vengeance. It would then be an expression of rage and hostility against the world." The court members were exchanging half-amused, half-horrified side glances. Challee protested again about the waste of court time, and Blakely again overruled him. The president was squinting at the Freudian doctor as though he were some unbelievable freak.

"Doctor," Greenwald went on, "you have testified that the commander is a disturbed, not an adjusted, person."

"Yes."

"In laymen's terms, then, he's sick."

Bird smiled. "I remember agreeing to the rough resemblance of the terms *disturbed* and *sick*. But by those terms an awful lot of people are sick——"

"But this trial only has Commander Queeg's sickness at issue. If he's sick, how could your board have given him a clean bill of health?"

"You're playing on words, I'm afraid. We found no disability."

"Could his sickness, greatly intensified, disable him?"

"Very greatly intensified, yes."

Greenwald said with sudden sharpness, "Isn't there another possibility, Doctor?"

"What do you mean?"

"Suppose the requirements of command were many times as severe as you believe them to be—wouldn't even this mild sickness disable Queeg?"

"That's absurdly hypothetical, because——"

"Is it? Have you ever had sea duty, Doctor?"

"No."

"Have you ever *been* to sea?"

"No." Bird was losing his self-possessed look.

"How long have you been in the Navy?"

"Five months—no, six, I guess, now——"

"Have you had any dealings with ships' captains before this case?"

"No."

"On what do you base your estimate of the stresses of command?"

"Well, my general knowledge——"

"Do you think command requires a highly gifted, exceptional person?"

"Well, no——"

"It doesn't?"

"Not highly gifted, no. Adequate responses, fairly good intelligence, and sufficient training and experience, but——"

"Is that enough equipment for, say, a skilled psychiatrist?"

"Well, not exactly—that is, it's a different field——"

"In other words, it takes more ability to be a psychiatrist than the captain of a naval vessel?" The lawyer looked toward Blakely.

"It takes—that is, different abilities are required. You're making the invidious comparison, not I."

"Doctor, you have admitted Commander Queeg is sick, which is more than Dr. Lundeen did. The only remaining question is, *how* sick. You don't think he's sick enough to be disabled for command. I suggest that since evidently you don't know much about the requirements of command you may be wrong in your conclusion."

"I repudiate your suggestion." Bird looked like an insulted boy. His voiced quivered. "You've deliberately substituted the word *sick,* which is a loose, a polarized word, for the correct——"

"Pardon me, what kind of word?"

"Polarized—loaded, invidious—I never said sick. My grasp of the requirements of command is adequate or I would have disqualified myself from serving on the board——"

"Maybe you should have."

Challee shouted, "The witness is being badgered."

"I withdraw my last statement. No more questions." Greenwald strode to his seat.

For ten minutes Challee tried to get Bird to withdraw the word "sick." The young doctor was upset. He became querulous and dogmatic, and threw up clouds of terminology. He refused to abandon the word. Challee finally excused the balky, hostile psychiatrist. He introduced as evidence the medical board's report, the Ulithi doctor's report, several of Queeg's fitness reports, and sundry logs and records of the *Caine*. His presentation was finished.

"It's three o'clock," said Blakely. "Is the defense ready to present its case?"

"I only have two witnesses, sir," said the pilot. "The first is the accused."

"Does the accused request that he be permitted to testify?"

At a nod from his lawyer, Maryk stood. "I do so request, sir."

"Stenographer will affirmatively record that the statutory request was made. . . . Defense proceed to present its case."

Maryk told the story of the morning of December 18. It was a repetition of Willie Keith's version. Greenwald said, "Was the ship in the last extremity when you relieved the captain?"

"It was."

"On what facts do you base that judgment?"

Maryk ran his tongue over his lips. "Well, several things, like—well, we were unable to hold course. We broached to three times in an hour. We were rolling too steeply for the inclinometer to record. We were shipping solid water in the wheelhouse. The generators were cutting out. The lights and the gyro cut off and on. The ship wasn't answering to emergency rudder and engine settings. The radar was jammed out by sea return. We were lost and out of control."

"Did you point these things out to the captain?"

"Repeatedly for an hour. I begged him to ballast and head into the wind."

"What was his response?"

"Well, mostly a glazed look and no answer, or a repetition of his own desires."

"Which were what?"

"I guess to hold fleet course until we went down."

"When did you start keeping your medical log on the captain?"

"Shortly after the Kwajalein invasion."

"Why did you start it?"

"Well, I began to think the captain might be mentally ill."

"Why?"

"His dropping of the yellow dye marker off Kwajalein, and then cutting off the water, and Stilwell's court-martial."

"Describe these three events in detail."

Blakely interrupted the executive officer's account of the Kwajalein incident to question him closely about bearings and distances, and the gap between the *Caine* and the landing boats. He made notes of the answers. "After these three episodes," said Greenwald, "why didn't you go directly to higher authority?"

"I wasn't sure of my ground. That's why I started the log. I figured if I ever saw I was wrong I'd burn the log. If I was right it would be necessary information."

"When did you show it to Lieutenant Keefer?"

"After the strawberry business, months later."

"Describe the strawberry business."

Maryk told the story baldly.

"Now, Lieutenant. After the typhoon was over, did Captain Queeg make any effort to regain command?"

"Yes, on the morning of the nineteenth. We'd just sighted the fleet and were joining up to return to Ulithi."

"Describe what happened."

"Well, I was in the charthouse writing up a dispatch to report the relief to the OTC. The captain came in and looked over my shoulder. He said 'Do you mind coming to my cabin and having a talk before you send that?' I said I didn't mind. I went below and we talked. It was the same thing again at first, about how I'd be tried for mutiny. He said 'You've applied for transfer to the regular Navy. You know this means the end of all that, don't you?' Then he went into a long thing about how he loved the Navy and had no other interest in life, and even if he was cleared this would ruin his record. I said I felt sorry for him, and I really did. And he pointed out that he was bound to get relieved in a few weeks anyway, so I wasn't accomplishing anything. Finally he came out with his proposal. He said he'd forget the whole thing and never report me. He would resume command, and the whole matter would be forgotten and written off—just an incident of bad nerves during the typhoon."

"What did you say to the proposal?"

"Well, I was amazed. I said, 'Captain, the whole ship knows about it. It's written up in the quartermaster's log and the OOD's log. I've already signed the OOD log as commanding officer.' Well, he hemmed and hawed, and finally said those were penciled rough logs and it all probably just amounted to a few lines, and it wouldn't be the first time rough logs had been corrected and fixed up after the fact."

"Did you remind him of the rule against erasures?"

"Yes, and he kind of laughed and said there were rules and rules, including the rule of self-preservation. He said it was either that or a court-martial for mutiny for me, and a black mark on his record which he didn't deserve, and he didn't see that a few scribbled pencil lines were worth all that."

"Did you persist in your refusal?"

"Yes."

"What followed?"

"He began to plead and beg. It went on for quite some time, and was very unpleasant."

"Did he act irrationally?"

"No. He—he cried at one point. But he was rational. But in the end he became terrifically angry and told me to go ahead and hang myself, and ordered me out of his cabin. So I sent the dispatch."

"Why didn't you accept the captain's offer?"

"I didn't see how I could."

"But the danger from the typhoon was over. Didn't you think he could conn the ship back to Ulithi?"

"I'd already committed an official act and I didn't believe making erasures in the logs would change it. Also I still believed he was mentally ill."

"But you say he was rational."

"Captain Queeg was usually okay except under great pressure, when he tended to become mentally disabled."

"Then you had the chance, twenty-four hours later, of expunging the whole event from the official record with the captain's knowledge and approval?"

"Yes."

"Lieutenant Maryk, were you panicky at any time during the typhoon?"

"I was not."

"How can you substantiate your statement?"

"Well, I—well, by what happened. After relieving the captain I rescued five survivors from the *George Black* at the height of the typhoon. I don't think a panicky officer could have effected the rescue under those conditions."

"Did you relieve Captain Queeg willfully?"

"Yes, I knew what I was doing."

"Did you relieve without authority?"

"No. My authority was Articles 184, 185, 186."

"Did you relieve without justifiable cause?"

"No. My justifiable cause was the captain's mental breakdown at a time when the ship was in danger."

"No further questions."

Challee came toward Maryk, saying in a tone of open hostility, "Just to start with, Mr. Maryk, wasn't the captain on the bridge all the time you were *effecting* that rescue?"

"He was."

"Didn't he order you to come about and look for survivors?"

"After I'd already come about, he said he was ordering me to do it."

"Didn't he direct you in the whole rescue operation?"

"Well, he kept commenting on my orders."

"Could you possibly have effected that rescue without his orders, or comments, as you call them?"

"Well, I tried to be polite. He was still senior officer present. But I was too busy to pay attention to his comments and I don't remember them."

"Didn't he even have to remind you to do an elementary thing like putting the cargo net over the side?"

"I was holding off on the cargo net till the last minute. I didn't want it to be carried away by the seas. He reminded me, but he didn't have to."

"Mr. Maryk, what kind of rating would you give yourself for loyalty to your captain?"

"That's hard to answer."

"I'll bet it is. Four-oh? Two-five? Zero?"

"I think I was a loyal officer."

"Did you issue a seventy-two-hour pass to Stilwell in December '43 against the captain's express instructions?"

"I did."

"Do you call that a loyal act?"

"No. It was a disloyal act."

Challee was caught off balance. He stared at Maryk. "You admit to a disloyal act in your first days as executive officer?"

"Yes."

"Very interesting. Why did you commit a disloyal act?"

"I have no excuse. I didn't do that kind of thing again."

"But you admit starting your term as exec as you finished it, with disloyalty?"

"I don't admit to finishing disloyally."

"Did you hear sarcastic and insulting remarks passed by the other officers about your captain?"

"I did."

"How did you punish them?"

"I didn't punish them. I repeatedly warned them against the practice and I didn't allow it in my presence."

"But you didn't punish this outright insubordination? Why didn't you?"

"There are limits to what you can do in a situation."

Challee clawed over Maryk's story of the typhoon, catching him in minor inconsistencies and memory lapses. But the exec, with dull stolidness, admitted to mistakes and inconsistencies, and stuck to his story. Then the judge advocate switched to Maryk's background, and brought out that his grades had been lower than average in high school and college, and that he had had no training in psychiatry or any other science.

"Then where did you get all of these highfalutin ideas about paranoia?"

"Out of books."

"What books? Name the titles."

"Medical-type books about mental illness."

"Was that your intellectual hobby—reading about psychiatry?"

"No. I borrowed the books off of ships' doctors here and there, after I began to think the captain was sick."

"And you, with your background—did you imagine you understood these highly technical, abstruse scientific works?"

"Well, I got something out of them."

"Have you ever heard the expression, 'A little knowledge is a dangerous thing?' "

"Yes."

"You got a headful of terms you didn't understand, and on that basis you had the temerity to depose a commanding officer on the grounds of mental illness. Is that correct?"

"I didn't relieve him because of what the books said. The ship was in danger——"

"Never mind the ship. We're discussing your grasp of psychiatry, Lieutenant." Challee belabored him with dozens of psychiatric terms, asking him for definitions and explanations. He reduced the exec to glum monosyllables and frequent repetitions of "I don't know."

"In fact, you don't know what you're talking about when you discuss mental illness, is that right?"

"I didn't say I knew much about it."

"And yet you thought you knew enough to commit an act that might be outright mutiny, justifying yourself by your grasp of psychiatric diagnosis?"

"I wanted to save the ship."

"What right had you to usurp the captain's responsibility for the ship's safety—setting aside your psychiatric insight?"

"Well, I——" Maryk stared dumbly.

"Answer the question, please! Either your act was justified by your psychiatric diagnosis of Queeg—or else it was the most serious breach of naval discipline of which you were capable. Isn't that right?"

"If he wasn't sick it would have been a mutinous act. But he was sick."

"Have you heard the diagnosis of the qualified psychiatrists who have testified?"

"Yes."

"What was their diagnosis—was he sick or wasn't he on 18 December?"

"They say he wasn't."

"Lieutenant Maryk, did you think your ship-handling judgment was better than the captain's?"

"In normal circumstances the captain could handle the ship. Under pressure he became erratic."

"Isn't the reverse possible—that under pressure *you* became erratic, and couldn't understand the captain's sound decisions? Is that possible?"

"It's possible, but——"

"As between a captain and an executive officer, who is presumed by the Navy to have the better judgment in ship handling?"

"The captain."

"Now, Lieutenant, your so-called justification consists in two assertions, doesn't it—one, that the captain was mentally ill, and two, that the ship was in a dangerous situation—correct?"

"Yes."

"The doctors have found that he wasn't mentally ill, haven't they?"

"That's their opinion, yes——"

"Then this court must presume that the captain's estimate of the ship's situation was right and yours was wrong, isn't that so?"

Maryk said, "Yes, except—just don't forget the doctors could be wrong. They weren't there."

"Then your entire defense, Lieutenant Maryk, boils down to this. Your on-the-spot snap psychiatric diagnosis—despite your confessed ignorance of psychiatry—is superior to the judgment of three psychiatrists after three weeks of exhaustive professional examination. That is your defense, isn't it?"

Maryk took a long pause, then said shakily, "All I can say is, they didn't see him when the ship was in trouble."

Challee turned and grinned openly at the court. He went on, "Who was the third ranking officer on your ship?"

"Lieutenant Keefer."

"Was he a good officer?"

"Yes."

"What's his civilian background?"

"He's an author."

"Do you consider his mind as good as yours? Or perhaps better?"

"Perhaps better."

"Did you show him this medical log of yours?"

"Yes."

"Was he convinced by it that the captain was mentally ill?"

"No."

"Did he dissuade you from trying to have the captain relieved, two weeks before the typhoon?"

"Yes."

"And yet two weeks later—despite the whole weight of naval discipline—despite the arguments of the next officer in rank to you, a superior intellect by your own admission, arguments that had previously convinced you your diagnosis was wrong—you went ahead and seized command of your ship?"

"I relieved him because he definitely seemed sick during the typhoon."

"Don't you think it's illogical, or fantastically conceited, to insist on your ignorant diagnosis now against the opinion of three psychiatrists?"

Maryk looked around unhappily at Greenwald, who was staring at the desk. The exec's forehead was covered with wrinkles. He swung his head back and forth, like an annoyed bull. "Well, maybe it sounds that way. I don't know."

"Very well. Now then. This amazing interview in which the captain offered to falsify official records. Were there any witnesses to it?"

"No, we were alone in the captain's cabin."

"Were any erasures made? Is there the slightest thread of tangible evidence to support your story?"

"The captain knows it happened."

"You rely for confirmation of this insulting libel upon the very officer you are libeling?"

"I don't know what he'll say."

"Are you predicting that Commander Queeg will perjure himself on the stand?"

"I'm not predicting anything."

"Is there a possibility that you imagined this story, which can't be confirmed or refuted except by the other interested party, to bolster your magnificent defense that you know more psychiatry than psychiatrists?"

"I didn't imagine it."

"But you *still* imagine your diagnosis of Captain Queeg is superior to the doctors?' "

"Only—only about Queeg on the morning of the typhoon," Maryk stammered. There was sweat on his brown forehead.

"No more questions," Challee said sarcastically.

Maryk looked to his counsel. Greenwald shook his head slightly, and said, "No re-examination." The exec came off the stand with a stunned expression. Blakely adjourned the court after Greenwald told him that the last defense witness, Captain Queeg, would appear in the morning.

QUEEG VS. GREENWALD

The defense counsel introduced as evidence photostatic copies of Maryk's fitness reports, and then called Queeg. The ex-captain of the

Caine, taking the stand, was as debonair and assured as he had been on the first day. The exec marveled again at the change wrought by sunshine, and rest, and a new blue uniform. Queeg was like a poster picture of a commanding officer of the Navy.

Greenwald lost no time in getting to the attack. "Commander, on the morning of December 19, did you have an interview in your room with Lieutenant Maryk?"

"Let's see. That's the day after the typhoon. Yes, I did."

"Was it at your request?"

"Yes."

"What was the substance of that interview?"

"Well, as I say, I felt sorry for him. I hated to see him ruining his life with one panicky mistake. Particularly as I knew his ambition was to make the Navy his career. I tried as hard as I could to show him what a mistake he had made. I recommended that he relinquish command to me, and I offered to be as lenient as I could in reporting what had happened."

"What was his response?"

"Well, as you know, he persisted in the course that led to this court-martial."

"You say you felt sorry for him. Weren't you worried about the effect of the episode on your own career?"

"Well, after all, I knew the verdict of the doctors would turn out as it did. I can't say I was very worried."

"Did you offer not to report the incident at all?"

"Of course not. I offered to report the incident in the most extenuating way I could."

"How could you have extenuated it?"

"Well, I thought there were extenuating circumstances. A rough situation where a junior officer might well lose his head. And there was the rescue, which he brought off well under my direction. I was assuming mainly that by restoring command to me he'd acknowledge the error. It was the only course at that point that might have saved him."

"You never offered not to report the incident?"

"How could I? It was already recorded in the logs."

"Were the logs in pencil, or typed, or what?"

"That would make no difference."

"Were they in pencil, Commander?"

"Well, let's see. Probably they were—QM log and OOD rough log always are. I doubt the yeoman would have gotten around to typing smooth logs in all the excitement."

"Did you offer to erase the incident from the penciled logs and make no report at all?"

"I did not. Erasures aren't permitted in penciled logs."

"Lieutenant Maryk has testified under oath, Commander, that you made such an offer. Not only that, but you begged and pleaded and even wept to get him to agree to erase those few pencil lines, in return for which you promised to hush up the incident completely and make no report."

"That isn't true." Queeg spoke calmly and pleasantly.

"There isn't any truth in it at all?"

"Well, it's a distortion of what I told you. My version is the exact truth."

"You deny the proposal to erase the logs and hush up the story?"

"I deny it completely. That's the part he made up. And the weeping and the pleading. That's fantastic."

"You are accusing Mr. Maryk of perjury?"

"I'm not accusing him. He's accused of enough as it stands. You're likely to hear a lot of strange things from Mr. Maryk about me, that's all."

"Isn't one of you obviously not telling the truth about that interview?"

"It appears so."

"Can you prove it isn't you?"

"Only by citing a clean record of over eight years as a naval officer, against the word of a man on trial for a mutinous act."

"It's his word against yours, then, in this matter?"

"Unfortunately there wasn't anyone else in my cabin at the time."

"Commander, did you recommend to the commodore at Ulithi that Maryk be allowed to take the *Caine* to Lingayen Gulf?"

"I thought that would come up. I did, yes."

"Despite the fact that, according to your story, you had seen him make a panicky mistake in a tight situation—a mistake of the most disastrous kind?"

"Well, I wasn't recommending him for command. The commodore put it to me that the Navy desperately needed minesweepers. He asked me to put aside personal considerations. I did put aside personal considerations. Maryk vindicated the training I had given him. And if as a result of that he gets acquitted and I carry a black mark for the rest of my naval career I'll still say I did the right thing."

"How could you be sure he wouldn't make another panicky mistake which would cost all the lives on the *Caine?*"

"Well, he didn't, did he? I took a calculated risk, and he didn't."

"Commander, the *Caine* took a Kamikaze hit at Lingayen, and yet Maryk brought the ship back safely. Was that likely in a man given to panicky mistakes?"

"Well, I understand it was a glancing hit, practically a miss. Anyway, for all I know, Keefer took charge in the pinch. Keefer is an outstanding officer, best on the ship. I relied more on him than on Maryk."

"Commander Queeg, did you ever receive a hundred ten dollars from Lieutenant Junior Grade Keith?"

"I may have. I don't recall offhand that I did."

"He testified that you did."

"I did? On what occasion?"

"On the occasion of a loss of a crate of yours in San Francisco Bay. He assumed responsibility and paid for the loss."

"Yes. I remember now. It was over a year ago. December or thereabouts. He was responsible for the loss, and insisted on paying, and so he did."

"What was in the crate that cost a hundred and ten dollars?"

"Personal belongings. I don't recall. Probably uniforms, books, navigating instruments—the usual."

"You remember the figure of a hundred and ten dollars?"

"Something like that, I don't recall exactly."

"How was Keith responsible for the loss?"

"Well, he was boat officer and in charge of the unloading. He issued foolish and contradictory orders. The men got rattled and the crate fell into the water and sank."

"A wooden crate full of clothes sank?"

"There were other things in it, I guess. I had some souvenir coral rocks."

"Commander, wasn't the crate entirely full of bottles of intoxicating liquor?"

After a barely perceptible pause—the skip of a heartbeat, no more— Queeg answered, "Certainly not."

"Keith has testified you charged him for thirty-one bottles of liquor."

"You'll hear plenty of strange distortions about me from Keith and Maryk. They're the two culprits here and they're apt to make all kinds of strange statements."

"Did you make this crate yourself?"

"No. My carpenter's mate did."

"What was his name?"

"I don't recall. It'll be on the personnel records. He's been gone from the ship a long time."

"Where is this carpenter's mate now, Commander?"

"I don't know. I transferred him to the beach at Funafuti at the request of the commodore for a carpenter. This was back in May."

"You don't recall his name?"

"No."

"Was it Carpenter's Mate Second Class Otis F. Langhorne?"

"Lang, Langhorne. Sounds right."

"Commander, there is a Carpenter's Mate First Class Otis F. Langhorne at present in damage-control school at Treasure Island, right here in the bay. Defense has arranged to subpoena him if necessary."

Queeg was obviously brought up short. His head sank between his shoulders. He shot a look at Challee. "You're sure it's the same one?"

"His service record shows twenty-one months aboard the U.S.S. *Caine.* Your signature is in it. Would it be useful to have him subpoenaed, sir?"

Challee said, "Objection to this entire interminable irrelevancy about the crate, and request it be stricken from the record."

Greenwald said, "The credibility of the witness is being established. I submit to the court that nothing could be more relevant to this trial."

Challee was overruled. The question was repeated. Queeg said, "Well, it's a question which crate Langhorne nailed up. I had two crates, as I recall now."

"Oh?" Greenwald paused for a long time. "Well! This is a new angle not mentioned by Keith. Did Langhorn make both crates, sir?"

"Well, I don't recall whether I had both crates on that occasion or two crates on two different occasions. It's all very trivial and happened a long time ago and I've had a year of combat steaming in between and a typhoon and all this hospital business and I'm not too clear. As I recall now on two different occasions there were two crates."

"What was the other occasion?"

"I don't recall. It might even have been back in peacetime, for all I know."

"Did you lose both crates in San Francisco Bay?"

"As I say, I'm not clear on all this, I don't recall."

"Commander, there are many points in this trial which turn on the issue of credibility between yourself and other officers. If you wish I will request a five-minute recess while you clear your mind as well as you can on the matter of these crates."

"That won't be necessary. Just let me think for a moment, please." In the silence Blakely's pencil made a thin rattling noise as he rolled it under his palm on the bench. Queeg sat staring from under his eyebrows. "Kay. I have it straight now. I made a misstatement. I lost a crate in San Diego Harbor back in '38 or '39 I think it was, under similar circumstances. That was the one containing clothes. The crate Keith lost did contain liquor."

"Thirty-one bottles?"

"Something like that."

"How did you obtain thirty-one bottles of——"

Challee said, "May it please the court, *Courts and Boards* requires evidence to be developed briefly, materially, and relevantly. It is useless for me to stall this trial indefinitely with objections. I question defense's entire tactic of expanding on irrelevancies which confuse the issue."

Blakely said, "Court is aware of requirements of evidence and thanks the judge advocate for emphasizing them. Defense will proceed."

"How did you obtain thirty-one bottles of whisky, Commander, in wartime?" said Greenwald.

"Bought up the rations of my officers at the wine mess in Pearl."

"You transported this liquor from Pearl to the States in your ship? Do you know the regulations——"

Queeg broke in, "I'm aware of regulations. The crate was sealed prior to getting under way. I gave it the same locked stowage I gave the medicinal brandy. Liquor wasn't obtainable in the States, and was at Pearl. I'd had three years of steady combat duty. I gave myself this leeway as captain of the *Caine* and it was a common practice and I believe rank has its privileges, as they say. I had no intention of concealing it from the court and I'm not ashamed of it. I simply mixed up the two crates in my mind."

"Keith testified, Commander, that you gave all the orders to the boat crew which caused the loss of the crate."

"That's a lie."

"Also that you refused to sign his leave papers until he paid for the loss."

"That's another lie."

"It seems to be the issue of credibility again, sir—this time your word against Keith's. Correct?"

"You'll hear nothing but lies about me from Keith. He has an insane hatred for me."

"Do you know why, sir?"

"I can't say, unless it's his resentment against fancied injuries to his crony, this sailor Stilwell. Those two were mighty affectionate."

"Affectionate, sir?"

"Well, it seems to me every time Keith thought I looked cross-eyed at Stilwell there was all kinds of screeching and hollering from Keith as though I were picking on his wife or something. I don't know how else to explain the two of them ganging up so fast to back Maryk when he relieved me unless they were pretty sweet on each other and had a sort of understanding."

"Commander, are you suggesting there were abnormal relations between Lieutenant Keith and the sailor Stilwell?"

"I'm not suggesting a thing," Queeg said with a sly grin. "I'm stating plain facts that everybody knew who had eyes to see."

Greenwald looked around at Blakely. "Does the court desire to caution the witness about the gravity of this insinuated charge?"

"I'm not insinuating a thing, sir!" Queeg said nasally. "I don't know of anything improper between those two men and I deny insinuating anything. I said Keith was always taking Stilwell's part and it's the easiest thing in the world to prove and that's all I said or meant. I resent the twisting of my words."

Blakely, his face all wrinkled, said to Greenwald, "Are you going to pursue this topic?"

"No, sir."

"Very well. Go ahead."

"Commander Queeg, during the period when the *Caine* was towing targets at Pearl Harbor did you ever steam over your own towline and cut it?"

"Objection!" Challee was on his feet again. Blakely gave him a frankly irritated look and ordered the court cleared, motioning to the two lawyers to remain behind.

The skin of Challee's face was leaden gray. "I beg the court's indulgence. I must object. This towline business is the last straw. The tactics of the defense counsel are an outrage on the dignity of these proceedings. He's systematically turning this trial into a court-martial of Commander Queeg. He's not bringing out any evidence bearing on the issue. He's trying to smear and defame Queeg and nothing else."

Greenwald said, "Sir, the judge advocate has made it perfectly clear that he thinks he has a prima facie case in the report of the three psychiatrists. Maybe he wants the defense to switch to a guilty plea. But I say it's still up to the court, not to shore-bound doctors, however brilliant, to judge whether the captain of the *Caine* was mentally well enough to retain his self-control and his post during a typhoon. This is a direct argument to the issue. I have no way to conduct it except to review the witness's performance of duty in critical situations prior to the typhoon."

"Counsel will step outside," said Blakely.

"I must respectfully state," said the judge advocate, "that in my opinion, if my objection is overruled, and the reviewing authority disapproves the court's ruling, it will be a fatal error invalidating the entire proceedings, and a miscarriage of justice will result."

"Very well, clear the court."

There was a fifteen-minute wait. Blakely and the other court members looked grim when the parties returned. "The objection is overruled. The witness will answer the question." Challee appeared stunned, sitting down slowly. The stenographer read the question about the towline from the record.

Queeg answered promptly, "Well, here's the story on the particular slander. I saw some AA bursts close aboard to starboard. I was gravely concerned that my ship might be within range of somebody's firing. We were in a gunnery area. I was watching the burst. This same sailor Stilwell, a very dreamy and unreliable man, was at the helm. He failed to warn me that we were coming around the full 360 degrees. I saw what was happening, finally, and instantly reversed course, and I avoided passing over the towline, to my best knowledge. However, the line parted during the turn. There was a lot of vicious gossip, circulated mainly by Stilwell and Keith, to the effect that I'd cut the towline. I ascribed the mishap to a defective line in my written report to ComServPac. And he was cognizant of all this vicious gossip. And he knew all the circumstances. And he still accepted my report. It's on file. So I say it's conceivable that this vicious gossip was correct, but I consider it much more likely that the judgment of ComServPac in the matter can be relied on."

Greenwald nodded. "You were distracted, you say, by AA bursts. Did anything else distract you?"

"Not that I recall."

"Were you engaged in reprimanding a signalman named Urban at length for having his shirttail out, while your ship was turning 360 degrees?"

"Who says that—Keith again?"

"Will you answer the question, Commander?"

"It's a malicious lie, of course."

"Was Urban on the bridge at the time?"

"Yes."

"Was his shirttail out?"

"Yes, and I reprimanded him. That took me about two seconds. I'm not in the habit of dwelling on those things. Then there were these AA bursts, and that was what distracted me."

"Did you point out these AA bursts to the OOD or the exec?"

"I may have. I don't recall. I didn't run weeping to my OOD on every occasion. I may very well have kept my own counsel. And since this shirttail thing has been brought up—and it's a very typical Keith distortion, the whole business—I'd like to say that Ensign Keith as morale officer was in charge of enforcing uniform regulations and completely soldiered on the job. When I took over the ship it was like the Chinese Navy. And I bore down on Keith to watch those shirttails and he kept funking it and for all I know that's another reason he hated me and circulated all this about my cutting the towline."

"Ensign Keith did not testify on this point, Commander. Can you name any officer who will testify that he saw those AA bursts?"

"Maybe all of them did and then again maybe none of them did. It was fifteen months ago and we've been fighting a war and we've had much more on our mind than a few AA bursts off Pearl."

"Did you drop a yellow dye marker off Jacob Island on the first morning of the invasion of Kwajalein?"

"I may have. I don't recall."

"Did your orders include dropping the marker?"

"I don't recall. There have been several other invasions since."

"Do you recall what your first mission was during the invasion?"

"Yes. To lead a group of attack boats to the line of departure for Jacob Island."

"Did you fulfill that mission?"

"Yes."

"Why did you drop the dye marker?"

"I don't know for sure that I did drop one."

"Commander, the orders of the *Caine* on that morning are a matter of record, and there's no mention of dropping a dye marker. This court has heard repeated testimony to the effect that you did drop one. Do you deny that testimony?"

"Well, it sounds as though I may have dropped it to mark the line of departure plainly, if I did it, but it's all dim in my mind."

"How far was the line of departure from the beach?"

"As I recall, a thousand yards."

"Did you stay close to the attack boats, leading them in?"

"Well, naturally, not wanting to swamp them with my bow wave, I was a bit ahead."

"How far ahead?"

"This all happened a year ago——"

"Fifty yards? Twenty thousand yards?"

"Well, I don't know. A couple of hundred yards, maybe."

"Commander, did you run a mile ahead of the attack boats, drop your marker, and retire at high speed, leaving the boats to grope to the line of departure as best they could?"

Challee leaped to his feet. "The question is abusive and flagrantly leading."

"I am willing to withdraw the question," said Greenwald wearily, "in view of the commander's dim memory, and proceed to more recent events."

"Court desires to question the witness," said Blakely. Greenwald retreated to his desk, watching the president's face. "Commander Queeg," Blakely said, "in view of the implications in this line of testimony, I urge you to search your memory for correct answers."

"I am certainly trying to do that, sir, but as I say these are very small points and I've been through several campaigns since Kwajalein and the typhoon and now all this business——"

"I appreciate that. If necessary the court can call a recess for several days to obtain depositions from officers and men of that attack group.

It will facilitate justice if you can remember enough to give a few definite answers on points of fact. First of all, can you recall whether your orders contained instructions to drop a dye marker?"

"Well, to the best of my recollection they didn't. That can be checked against the record. But I believe I can say definitely that they didn't, as I recall now."

"Very well. Will you please repeat your explanation of why you dropped it?"

"Well, I guess to mark the line of departure plainly."

"Were those boats on the line of departure when you turned away from the beach?"

"As near as I could calculate, yes. This was all a matter of tangent bearings and radar ranges of course, but I brought them as close to the line as was humanly possible."

"In that case, Commander, if they were already on the line, what purpose did the dye marker serve?"

Queeg hesitated. "Well, you might say a safety factor. Just another added mark. Maybe I erred in being overcautious and making sure they knew where they were but then again I've always believed you can't err on the side of safety."

"From the time you made rendezvous with the boats, Commander, until the time you dropped the marker, what was the widest gap between you and the boats?"

"Well, distances are deceptive over water, particularly with those low-lying boats."

"Did you stay within hailing distance of them?" Blakely said with a slight acrid impatient note.

"Hailing distance? No. We communicated by semaphore. I might have swamped them if I'd stayed within hailing distance."

Blakely pointed at the redheaded officer at the far left of the bench. "Lieutenant Murphy informs the court that he was a boat officer in similar situations in three invasions. He says the common practice was to stay within hailing distance, never more than a hundred or a hundred fifty yards apart."

Queeg, slumped in his seat, looked out from under his eyebrows at the lieutenant. "Well, that may be. It was a windy day and the bow wave made a lot of wash. It was simpler to semaphore than to go screaming through megaphones."

"Did you have the conn?"

Queeg paused. "As I recall now Lieutenant Maryk did, and I now recall I had to caution him for opening the gap too wide."

"How wide?"

"I can't say, but at one point there was definitely too much open water and I called him aside and admonished him not to run away from the boats."

"Why did your executive officer have the conn?"

"Well, he was navigator and for split-second precision instead of repeating a lot of orders back and forth—— And it's all coming back to me now. As I recall I dropped the marker because Maryk had opened the gap so wide and I wanted to be sure the boats knew exactly where the line of departure was."

"Didn't you direct him to slow down when you saw the gap widening?"

"Well, but it was all happening very fast and I may have been watching the beach for a few seconds and then I saw we were running away. And so that's why I dropped the marker, to compensate for Maryk's running away from the boats."

"These are your factual recollections, Commander?" Blakely's face was grave.

"Those are the facts, sir."

Blakely said to Greenwald, "You may resume your examination."

The lawyer, leaning against his desk, said at once, "Commander Queeg, did you make it a practice, during invasions, to station yourself on the side of the bridge that was sheltered from the beach?"

Queeg said angrily, "That's an insulting question, and the answer is no, I had to be on all sides of the bridge at once, constantly running from one side to the other because Maryk was navigator and Keith was my OOD at general quarters and both of them were invariably scurrying to the safe side of the bridge so I was captain and navigator and OOD all rolled in one and that's why I had to move constantly from one side of the bridge to the other. And that's the truth, whatever lies may have been said about me in this court."

Greenwald, slack-mouthed, his face expressionless, kept his eyes on the court members, who stirred in their chairs. "Commander," he said, as soon as Queeg subsided, "do you recall an incident during the Saipan invasion when the U.S.S. *Stanfield* was fired on by a shore battery?"

"I most certainly do." The ex-captain glowered at Greenwald, breathing heavily. "I don't know what lies have been sworn to in this court about that little matter, but I'll be glad to set the record straight on that, too. This same Mr. Keith we're talking about went hollering and screaming all over the bridge making a big grandstand play about wanting to fire on the shore battery when the *Stanfield* was in my line of fire and it was absolutely impossible to fire. And so I returned to my patrol station because that was my assigned duty, patrolling, not interdicting fire on shore batteries, and the plane was sunk without a trace and as for the *Stanfield* it was taking mighty good care of itself."

"What is the turning circle of the *Caine,* sir?"

"A thousand yards, but——"

"Sir, in swinging a thousand yards didn't the *Stanfield* move out of your line of fire to give you a clear shot at the shore battery?"

"For all I know the *Stanfield* paralleled my course. I never had a clear shot, that's all I know."

"Court desires to question the witness," said Blakely.

Challee stood. "Sir, the witness is obviously and understandably agitated by this ordeal, and I request a recess to give him a breathing space——"

"I am not in the least agitated," exclaimed Queeg, "and I'm glad to answer any and all questions here and in fact I demand a chance to set the record straight on anything derogatory to me in the testimony that's gone before. I did not make a single mistake in fifteen months aboard the *Caine* and I can prove it and my record has been spotless until now and I don't want it smirched by a whole lot of lies and distortions by disloyal officers."

"Commander, would you like a recess?" said Blakely.

"Definitely not, sir. I request there be no recess if it's up to me."

"Very well. Was the *Stanfield* hit during this incident?"

"No it was not, sir."

"Was it straddled?"

"It was straddled, yes, sir."

"And there was no way you could maneuver to lend it fire support? Did you try?"

"As I say, sir, it was in my line of fire and my estimate of the situation was that in the circumstances my duty was to get back on anti-sub station and not run around trying to make a grandstand play with pot shots at the beach and that was my command decision and I will stand on it as being in accordance with every existing doctrine, sir. It's a question of mission. My mission was patrol."

"Commander, wouldn't you consider returning enemy fire, directed at yourself or at a nearby unit, an overriding mission?"

"Definitely, sir, if the range was clear. The *Stanfield* was in my line of fire, however."

Blakely glanced around at the other court members, his eyebrows puckered, and then nodded shortly to Greenwald. The lawyer said, "Commander, on the morning of 18 December, at the moment you were relieved, was the *Caine* in the last extremity?"

"It certainly was not!"

"Was it in grave danger at that moment?"

"Absolutely not. I had that ship under complete control."

"Did you tell the other officers that you had intended to come north, as Maryk did, at ten o'clock—that is, about fifteen minutes after the relief took place?"

Queeg plunged his hand into his coat pocket and brought out two glistening steel balls. "Yes, I did make that statement, and such had been my intention."

"Why did you intend to abandon fleet course, Commander, if the ship wasn't in danger?"

There was a long silence. Then Queeg said, "Well, I don't see any inconsistency there. I've repeatedly stated in my testimony that my rule is safety first. As I say the ship wasn't in danger but a typhoon is still a typhoon and I'd just about decided that we'd do as well riding it out head to sea. I might have executed my intention at ten o'clock and then again I might not have. I was still weighing all the factors but as I say I had that ship under control and even after Maryk relieved me I saw to it that it remained under control. I never abandoned my post."

"Then Maryk's decision to come north was not a panicky, irrational blunder?"

"His panicky blunder was relieving me. I kept him from making any disastrous mistakes thereafter. I didn't intend to vindicate myself at the cost of all the lives on the *Caine*."

"Commander Queeg, have you read Lieutenant Maryk's medical log?"

"I have read that interesting document, yes sir, I have. It is the biggest conglomeration of lies and distortions and half-truths I've ever seen and I'm extremely glad you asked me because I want to get my side of it all on the record."

"Please state your version, or any factual comments on the episodes in the log, sir."

"Well, now, starting right with that strawberry business the real truth is that I was betrayed and thrown and double-crossed by my executive officer and this precious gentleman Mr. Keith who between them corrupted my wardroom so that I was one man against a whole ship without any support from my officers—— Now, you take that strawberry business—why, if that wasn't a case of outright conspiracy to protect a malefactor from justice—Maryk carefully leaves out the little fact that I had conclusively proved by a process of elimination that someone had a key to the icebox. He says it was the steward's mates who ate the strawberries but if I wanted to take the trouble I could prove to this court geometrically that they couldn't have. It's the water business all over again, like when the crew was taking baths seven times a day and our evaps were definitely on the fritz half the time and I was trying to inculcate the simplest principles of water conservation, but no, Mr. Maryk the hero of the crew wanted to go right on mollycoddling them and—or you take the coffee business—no, well, the strawberry thing first—it all hinged on a thorough search for the key and that was where Mr. Maryk as usual with the help of Mr. Keith fudged it. Just went through a lot of phony motions that proved nothing and—like thinking the incessant burning out of Silexes which were government property was a joke, which was the attitude of everybody from Maryk down, no sense of responsibility though I emphasized over and over that the war wouldn't last forever, that all these things would have to be accounted for. It was a constant battle, always the same thing, Maryk and Keith undermining my authority, always arguments, though I personally liked Keith and kept trying to train him up only to get stabbed in the back when—— I think I've covered the strawberry business and— oh, yes, Stilwell's court-martial. That was a disgraceful business, quite typical——"

Commander Queeg passed to a review of the court-martial, which was also, he said, a conspiracy of Keith and Maryk to discredit him. Then he discussed the failures of the laundry, the sloppiness of the mess statements and ship's service inventories, and went on from subject to subject in this way, cataloguing his grievances against his officers, mainly Maryk and Keith. He hardly paused for breath. He seemed unable to pause. His narrative became less distinct as he talked, his jumps in time and place more sudden and harder to follow. He talked on and on, rolling the balls, his face glowing with satisfaction as he scored all these successive points in his vindication. Greenwald strolled to his desk and leaned against it, listening respectfully. The court members stared at the witness. Challee slouched, biting his nails. The sentences became longer and more meandering. Blakely began to glance at the clock.

Queeg went on for eight or nine minutes in this way, and ended up, "Well, naturally, I can only cover these things roughly from memory but if I've left anything out why you just ask me specific questions and I'll tackle them one by one, but I believe I've hit the main points."

"It was a very thorough and complete answer, thank you," Greenwald said. He drew two glossy black photostats from a folder on his desk. "Commander, I show you authenticated copies of two fitness reports you wrote on Lieutenant Maryk. Do you recognize them as such?"

Queeg took the papers and said grumpily, glancing at them, "Yes, I do."

"Please read to the court your comment on Maryk of January 1944."

"I've already stated," Queeg said, "that at first he put on the act of a red-hot but cooled off in time——"

"We have that testimony, Commander. Please read the comment."

Queeg read in a choked voice a highly laudatory description of Maryk.

"Thank you, Commander. That was January. Now by July, six months later, had the *Caine* already been through the Kwajalein and Saipan invasions?"

"Yes."

"Had the following incidents already occurred: the water shortage, the coffee investigation, the Stilwell court-martial, and the suspension of movies, among others?"

Queeg hesitated. "Well, by then, yes, I think."

"Please read your comment of 1 July on Lieutenant Maryk."

Queeg stared at the photostat for a long time, hunched over, and began mumbling, " 'This officer has if anything improved in his performance of duty since the last fitness report. He is consistently loyal, unflagging, thorough, courageous, and efficient. He is considered at present fully qualified for command of a 1200-ton DMS. His professional zeal and integrity set him apart as an outstanding example for

other officers, reserve and regular alike. He cannot be too highly commended. He is recommended for transfer to the regular Navy.' "

"Thank you, Commander. No further questions."

Greenwald walked to his desk and sat. The witness looked toward
the judge advocate appealingly. Challee stood slowly, like an old man
with rheumatism. He approached the witness stand, and seemed about
to speak. Then he turned to Blakely. "No cross-examination."

"You are excused, Commander," Blakely said. Queeg went out of
the courtroom in the same way that Maryk had seen him pass through
the wheelhouse a thousand times—shoulders hunched, head down, feet
scurrying, the balls rolling in his fingers.

Greenwald said, "Defense has finished its presentation."

"Recess until one o'clock," said Blakely.

THE VERDICT

Challee had the face of a man sailing into a fist fight when he rose for
his opening argument.

"If it please the court, I am almost at a loss to discuss the case the defense has presented. I have nothing to refute. It's no case at all. It has
nothing to do with the charge or the specification. It has nothing whatever to do with the accused, or the acts for which he is undergoing a general court-martial.

"The defense counsel's very first question in this trial was, 'Commander, have you ever heard the expression "Old Yellowstain"?' I objected then, I object now to the entire strategy and tactics of the defense
counsel before this court. His one idea has been to twist the proceedings
around so that the accused would become not Maryk but Commander
Queeg. To a certain extent he has succeeded. He has dragged out every possible vicious and malicious criticism of the commander from the
other witnesses, and forced Queeg to defend himself against them in
open court, on the spur of the moment, without preparation, without
advice of counsel, without any of the normal privileges and safeguards
of an accused man under naval law.

"All right. What has defense counsel proved in this orgy of mudslinging, insults, trick questions, and defamation? Let's assume that
everything he tried to prove against Commander Queeg is true—
which I don't for a moment concede—even so, what has he proved, I

say, except that Queeg was not a good officer? What has he tried to bring out except that the commander's term aboard the *Caine* was an unhappy mess of bad judgment and poor administration? Did that give Lieutenant Maryk the right of summary relief of command? Can this court possibly endorse the precedent that a captain who seems to be making mistakes can be deposed by underlings? And that his only recourse after that is to be placed on the witness stand at a general court-martial to answer every petty gripe and justify all his command decisions to a hostile lawyer taking the part of his insubordinate inferiors? Such a precedent is nothing but a blank check for mutiny. It is the absolute destruction of the chain of command.

"The one issue in this trial was the insanity of Commander Queeg—the insanity, not the mistakes or misdeeds or poor judgment. The language of Articles 184, 185, and 186 excludes every possibility except the complete, utter, and unmistakable madness of the captain. The defense made no effort to establish such a justification for the simple reason that it never existed. Captain Queeg always was and still is as sane as any of us, whatever his errors may have been, and defense counsel knows it.

"Has any officer of this court ever sailed with a captain who committed no errors of judgment? Has any officer who has been in the Navy more than a few years failed to find himself under a captain with marked personal and emotional eccentricities? Naval command is the greatest strain that can be brought to bear on a person. The captain is a god—in theory. Some lapse more, some less, from that ideal. But the procurement policies of the Navy are rigid. That is why the presumption is always overwhelmingly on the side of the commanding officer in any dispute. He's a man who has been tried in the fire. Whatever his weaknesses—and they may even be grave weaknesses—he's a man who can command a combatant ship.

"In proof of this I need only cite the recorded fact that this case is the first in thirty years impugning the captain of a Navy ship under those articles. And even in this case the scientific findings of psychiatrists are forcibly and unanimously on the side of the Navy's system of command appointments. The doctors say that the Navy *did* know what it was doing in giving the *Caine* to Commander Queeg.

"With the leeway the court gave him, defense counsel brought out every single mistake, every single lapse of judgment that the captain of the *Caine* made or that some underling thought he made. The court knows that it all adds up to puling complaints against strictness and meticulousness—all but one point. That point is the imputation that this officer of the Navy was a coward under fire. I shall not discuss that point. I leave it to this court to determine whether a coward could rise to command of a combatant ship and remain undetected by his superiors through fifteen months of battle service. I count on the court to see the difference between bad judgment and poltroonery. I leave it to the court to reject this smear on the Navy.

"Let's look at the facts. Commander Queeg was given command of an obsolete, decaying, run-down ship. He brought it through fifteen months of combat unscathed, and carried out a multitude of assignments to the satisfaction of his superiors. There's no complaint against him on the record by his superiors—only by his underlings. He achieved this record of satisfactory battle service despite the hostility and disloyalty of his officers. He achieved it despite personal inner tensions, which the doctors have described—and which the defense viciously hammered at in a vain attempt to exaggerate them into insanity. Commander Queeg's achievement in the face of his own emotional difficulties and the disloyalty of his wardroom adds up, not to a bad record, but to a fine one, to an impressive one. He emerges as a loyal, hard-working, terribly conscientious officer who has been unjustly forced through a harrowing ordeal.

"The accused emerges without any justification. The defense counsel brought no psychiatrists to refute the findings of the medical board. He didn't because he couldn't have found any. Once the cloud of mudslinging settles down, the facts remain as they were at the outset. A commanding officer of a United States Navy ship was relieved of his command willfully and without authority. The claimed authority of Articles 184, 185, and 186 was voided by the medical board. No justifiable cause, either mental illness or any other, has been brought forward by the defense. It has been proved by expert testimony that Commander Queeg's ship-handling decisions in the typhoon up to the moment he was relieved were not only sensible and sound, but the best possible in the circumstances.

"The accused stands convicted by the facts. In his defense not one mitigating fact has been established. The court will reject, I am certain, the cynical, insulting attempt of the defense counsel to sway its emotions. The court will find the specification proved by the facts."

*

The contrast between Challee's manner and Greenwald's could not have been sharper. The pilot was soft, apologetic, hesitant after the judge advocate's passionate shouting. He kept looking from Blakely to Challee. He started by mentioning that he had undertaken Maryk's defense reluctantly at the judge advocate's request. "I was reluctant," he said, "because I knew that the only possible defense of the accused was to show in court the mental incompetence of an officer of the Navy. It has been the most unpleasant duty I've ever had to perform. Let me make one thing clear. It is not and never has been the contention of the defense that Commander Queeg is a coward. The entire case of the defense rests on the opposite assumption: that no man who rises to command of a United States naval ship can possibly be a coward. And that therefore if he commits questionable acts under fire the explanation must lie elsewhere."

Proceeding in the same calm, diffident tone, Greenwald reviewed all the damaging evidence against Queeg, laying especial stress on the points that had seemed to impress Blakely. He emphasized that both psychiatrists had admitted, in one form of words or another, that Queeg was sick. And he repeated over and over that it was up to the court, who knew the sea, to decide whether or not the sickness of Queeg was bad enough to incapacitate him. He referred briefly and apologetically to Queeg's behavior in court—his evasiveness, incoherence, changing stories, and inability to stop speaking—as further unfortunate evidence of his mental illness. He said very little about Maryk. It was all Queeg, Queeg, Queeg.

The court debated for an hour and ten minutes. Maryk was acquitted.

LAWYERS, JUDGES, JURORS AND A WITNESS

A. A. Milne

.

THE BARRISTER

The New Bailey was crowded with a gay and fashionable throng. It was a remarkable case of shoplifting. Aurora Delaine, nineteen, was charged with feloniously stealing and conveying certain articles, the property of the Universal Stores, to wit thirty-five yards of book-muslin, ten pairs of gloves, a sponge, two gimlets, five jars of cold cream, a copy of the Clergy List, three hat-guards, a mariner's compass, a box of drawing-pins, an egg-breaker, six blouses, and a cabman's whistle. The theft had been proved by Albert Jobson, a shopwalker, who gave evidence to the effect that he followed her through the different departments and saw her take the things mentioned in the indictment.

"Just a moment," interrupted the Judge. "Who is defending the prisoner?"

There was an unexpected silence. Rupert Carleton, who had dropped idly into court, looked round in sudden excitement. The poor girl had no counsel! What if he—yes, he would seize the chance! He stood up boldly. "I am, my lord," he said.

Rupert Carleton was still in the twenties, but he had been a briefless barrister for some years. Yet, though briefs would not come, he had been very far from idle. He had stood for Parliament in both the Conservative and Liberal interests (not to mention his own). He had written half a dozen unproduced plays, and he was engaged to be married. But success in his own profession had been delayed. Now at last was his opportunity.

He pulled his wig down firmly over his ears, took out a pair of pince-nez and rose to cross-examine. It was the cross-examination which is now given as a model in every legal textbook.

"Mr. Jobson," he began suavely, "you say that you saw the accused steal these various articles, and that they were afterwards found upon her?"

"Yes."

"I put it to you," said Rupert, and waited intently for the answer, "that that is a pure invention on your part?"

"No."

With a superhuman effort Rupert hid his disappointment. Unexpected as the answer was, he preserved his impassivity.

"I suggest," he tried again, "that you followed her about and concealed this collection of things in her cloak with a view to advertising your winter sale?"

"No. I saw her steal them."

Rupert frowned; the man seemed impervious to the simplest suggestion. With masterly decision he tapped his pince-nez and fell back upon his third line of defense. "You saw her steal them? What you mean is that you saw her take them from the different counters and put them in her bag?"

"Yes."

"With the intention of paying for them in the ordinary way?"

"No."

"Please be very careful. You said in your evidence that the prisoner, when told she would be charged, cried, 'To think that I should have come to this! Will no one save me?' I suggest that she went up to you with her collection of purchases, pulled out her purse, and said, 'What does all this come to? I can't get anyone to serve me.' "

"No."

The obstinacy of some people! Rupert put back his pince-nez in his pocket and brought out another pair. The historic cross-examination continued.

"We will let that pass for the moment," he said. He consulted a sheet of paper and then looked sternly at Mr. Jobson. "Mr. Jobson, how many times have you been married?"

"Once."

"Quite so." He hesitated and then decided to risk it. "I suggest that your wife left you?"

"Yes."

It was a long shot, but once again the bold course had paid. Rupert heaved a sigh of relief.

"Will you tell the gentlemen of the jury," he said, with deadly politeness, *"why* she left you?"

"She died."

A lesser man might have been embarrassed, but Rupert's iron nerve did not fail him.

"Exactly!" he said. "And was that or was that not on the night when you were turned out of the Hampstead Parliament for intoxication?"

"I never was."

"Indeed? Will you cast your mind back to the night of 24 April, 1897? What were you doing on that night?"

"I have no idea," said Jobson, after casting his mind back and waiting in vain for some result.

"In that case you cannot swear that you were not being turned out of the Hampstead Parliament——"

"But I never belonged to it."

Rupert leaped at the damaging admission.

"What? You told the Court that you lived at Hampstead, and yet you say that you never belonged to the Hampstead Parliament? Is *that* your idea of patriotism?"

"I said I lived at Hackney."

"To the Hackney Parliament, I should say. I am suggesting that you were turned out of the Hackney Parliament for——"

"I don't belong to that either."

"Exactly!" said Rupert triumphantly. "Having been turned out for intoxication?"

"And never did belong."

"Indeed? May I take it, then, that you prefer to spend your evenings in the public-house?"

"If you want to know," said Jobson angrily, "I belong to the Hackney Chess Circle, and that takes up most of my evenings."

Rupert gave a sigh of satisfaction and turned to the jury.

"At *last,* gentlemen, we have got it. I thought we should arrive at the truth in the end, in spite of Mr. Jobson's prevarications." He turned to the witness. "Now, sir," he said sternly, "you have already told the Court that you have no idea what you were doing on the night of 24 April, 1897. I put it to you once more that this blankness of memory is due to the fact that you were in a state of intoxication on the premises of the Hackney Chess Circle. Can you swear on your oath that this is not so?"

A murmur of admiration for the relentless way in which the truth had been tracked down ran through the court. Rupert drew himself up and put on both pairs of pince-nez at once.

"Come, sir!" he said. "The jury is waiting."

But it was not Albert Jobson who answered. It was the counsel for the prosecution. "My lord," he said, getting up slowly, "this has come as a complete surprise to me. In the circumstances I must advise my clients to withdraw from the case."

"A very proper decision," said his lordship. "The prisoner is discharged without a stain on her character."

Briefs poured in upon Rupert next day, and he was engaged for all the big Chancery cases. Within a week his six plays were accepted, and within a fortnight he had entered Parliament as the miners' Member for Coalville. His marriage took place at the end of a month. The wedding presents were even more numerous and costly than usual, and included thirty-five yards of book-muslin, ten pairs of gloves, a sponge, two gimlets, five jars of cold cream, a copy of the Clergy List, three hat-guards, a mariner's compass, a box of drawing-pins, an egg-breaker, six blouses, and a cabman's whistle. They were marked quite simply, "From a Grateful Friend."

William Faulkner

:

TOMORROW

Uncle Gavin had not always been county attorney. But the time when he had not been was more than twenty years ago and it had lasted for such a short period that only the old men remembered it, and even some of them did not. Because in that time he had had but one case.

He was a young man then, twenty-eight, only a year out of the state university law school where, at grandfather's instigation, he had gone after his return from Harvard and Heidelberg; and he had taken the case voluntarily, persuaded grandfather to let him handle it alone, which grandfather did, because everyone believed the trial would be a mere formality.

So he tried the case. Years afterward he still said it was the only case, either as a private defender or a public prosecutor, in which he was convinced that right and justice were on his side, that he ever lost. Actually he did not lose it—a mistrial in the fall court term, an acquittal in the following spring term—the defendant a solid, well-to-do farmer, husband and father, too, named Bookwright, from a section called Frenchman's Bend in the remote southeastern corner of the county; the victim a swaggering bravo calling himself Buck Thorpe and called Bucksnort by the other young men whom he had subjugated with his fists during the three years he had been in Frenchman's Bend; kinless, who had appeared overnight from nowhere, a brawler, a gambler, known to be a distiller of illicit whiskey and caught once on the road to Memphis with a small drove of stolen cattle, which the owner promptly identified. He had a bill of sale for them, but none in the country knew the name signed to it.

And the story itself was old and unoriginal enough: The country girl of seventeen, her imagination fired by the swagger and the prowess and the daring and the glib tongue; the father who tried to reason with her and got exactly as far as parents usually do in such cases; then the interdiction, the forbidden door, the inevitable elopement at midnight; and at four o'clock the next morning Bookwright waked Will Varner, the justice of the peace and the chief officer of the district, and handed Varner his pistol and said, "I have come to surrender. I killed Thorpe two hours ago." And a neighbor named Quick, who was first on the scene, found the half-drawn pistol in Thorpe's hand; and a week after the brief account was printed in the Memphis papers, a woman appeared in Frenchman's Bend who claimed to be Thorpe's wife, and with a wedding license to prove it, trying to claim what money or property he might have left.

I can remember the surprise that the grand jury even found a true bill; when the clerk read the indictment, the betting was twenty to one that the jury would not be out ten minutes. The district attorney even conducted the case through an assistant, and it did not take an hour to submit all the evidence. Then Uncle Gavin rose, and I remember how he looked at the jury—the eleven farmers and storekeepers and the twelfth man, who was to ruin his case—a farmer, too, a thin man, small, with thin gray hair and that appearance of hill farmers—at once frail and work-worn, yet curiously imperishable—who seem to become old men at fifty and then become invincible to time. Uncle Gavin's voice was quiet, almost monotonous, not ranting as criminal-court trials had taught us to expect; only the words were a little different from the ones he would use in later years. But even then, although he had been talking to them for only a year, he could already talk so that all the people in our country—the Negroes, the hill people, the rich flatland plantation owners—understood what he said.

"All of us in this country, the South, have been taught from birth a few things which we hold to above all else. One of the first of these— not the best; just one of the first—is that only a life can pay for the life it takes; that the one death is only half complete. If that is so, then we could have saved both these lives by stopping this defendant before he left his house that night; we could have saved at least one of them, even if we had had to take this defendant's life from him in order to stop him. Only we didn't know in time. And that's what I am talking about —not about the dead man and his character and the morality of the act he was engaged in; not about self-defense, whether or not this defendant was justified in forcing the issue to the point of taking life, but about us who are not dead and what we don't know—about all of us, human beings who at bottom want to do right, want not to harm others; human beings with all the complexity of human passions and feelings and beliefs, in the accepting or rejecting of which we had no choice, trying to do the best we can with them or despite them—this defendant, another human being with that same complexity of passions and instincts and beliefs, faced by a problem—the inevitable misery of his child who, with the headstrong folly of youth—again that same old complexity which she, too, did not ask to inherit—was incapable of her own preservation—and solved that problem to the best of his ability and beliefs, asking help of no one, and then abode by his decision and his act."

He sat down. The district attorney's assistant merely rose and bowed to the court and sat down again. The jury went out and we didn't even leave the room. Even the judge didn't retire. And I remember the long breath, something, which went through the room when the clock hand above the bench passed the ten-minute mark and then passed the half-hour mark, and the judge beckoned a bailiff and whispered to him, and the bailiff went out and returned and whispered to the judge, and the judge rose and banged his gavel and recessed the court.

I hurried home and ate my dinner and hurried back to town. The office was empty. Even grandfather, who took his nap after dinner, regardless of who hung and who didn't, returned first; after three o'clock then, and the whole town knew now that Uncle Gavin's jury was hung by one man, eleven to one for acquittal; then Uncle Gavin came in fast, and grandfather said, "Well, Gavin, at least you stopped talking in time to hang just your jury and not your client."

"That's right, sir," Uncle Gavin said. Because he was looking at me with his bright eyes, his thin, quick face, his wild hair already beginning to turn white. "Come here, Chick," he said. "I need you for a minute."

"Ask Judge Frazier to allow you to retract your oration, then let Charley sum up for you," grandfather said. But we were outside then, on the stairs, Uncle Gavin stopping halfway down, so that we stood exactly halfway from anywhere, his hand on my shoulder, his eyes brighter and intenter than ever.

"This is not cricket," he said. "But justice is accomplished lots of times by methods that won't bear looking at. They have moved the jury to the back room in Mrs. Rouncewell's boardinghouse. The room right opposite that mulberry tree. If you could get into the back yard without anybody seeing you, and be careful when you climb the tree——"

Nobody saw me. But I could look through the windy mulberry leaves into the room, and see and hear, both—the nine angry and disgusted men sprawled in chairs at the far end of the room; Mr. Holland, the foreman, and another man standing in front of the chair in which the little, worn, dried-out hill man sat. His name was Fentry. I remembered all their names, because Uncle Gavin said that to be a successful lawyer and politician in our country you did not need a silver tongue nor even an intelligence; you needed only an infallible memory for names. But I would have remembered his name anyway, because it was Stonewall Jackson—Stonewall Jackson Fentry.

"Don't you admit that he was running off with Bookwright's seventeen-year-old daughter?" Mr. Holland said. "Don't you admit that he had a pistol in his hand when they found him? Don't you admit that he wasn't hardly buried before that woman turned up and proved she was already his wife? Don't you admit that he was not only no-good but dangerous, and that if it hadn't been Bookwright, sooner or later somebody else would have had to, and that Bookwright was just unlucky?"

"Yes," Fentry said.

"Then what do you want?" Mr. Holland said. "What do you want?"

"I can't help it," Fentry said. "I ain't going to vote Mr. Bookwright free."

And he didn't. And that afternoon Judge Frazier discharged the jury and set the case for retrial in the next term of court; and the next morning Uncle Gavin came for me before I had finished breakfast.

"Tell your mother we might be gone overnight," he said. "Tell her I promise not to let you get either shot, snake-bit or surfeited with soda pop. . . . Because I've got to know," he said. We were driving fast now, out the northeast road, and his eyes were bright, not baffled, just intent and eager. "He was born and raised and lived all his life out here at the very other end of the county, thirty miles from Frenchman's Bend. He said under oath that he had never even seen Bookwright before, and you can look at him and see that he never had enough time off from hard work to learn how to lie in. I doubt if he ever even heard Bookwright's name before."

We drove until almost noon. We were in the hills now, out of the rich flat land, among the pine and bracken, the poor soil, the little tilted and barren patches of gaunt corn and cotton which somehow endured, as the people they clothed and fed somehow endured; the roads we followed less than lanes, winding and narrow, rutted and dust choked, the car in second gear half the time. Then we saw the mailbox, the crude lettering: G. A. Fentry; beyond it, the two-room log house with an open hall, and even I, a boy of twelve, could see that no woman's hand had touched it in a lot of years. We entered the gate.

Then a voice said, "Stop! Stop where you are!" And we hadn't even seen him—an old man, barefoot, with a fierce white bristle of mustache, in patched denim faded almost to the color of skim milk, smaller, thinner even than the son, standing at the edge of the worn gallery, holding a shotgun across his middle and shaking with fury or perhaps with the palsy of age.

"Mr. Fentry——" Uncle Gavin said.

"You've badgered and harried him enough!" the old man said. It was fury; the voice seemed to rise suddenly with a fiercer, an uncontrollable blaze of it: "Get out of here! Get off my land! Go!"

"Come," Uncle Gavin said quietly. And still his eyes were only bright, eager, intent and grave. We did not drive fast now. The next mailbox was within the mile, and this time the house was even painted, with beds of petunias beside the steps, and the land about it was better, and this time the man rose from the gallery and came down to the gate.

"Howdy, Mr. Stevens," he said. "So Jackson Fentry hung your jury for you."

"Howdy, Mr. Pruitt," Uncle Gavin said. "It looks like he did. Tell me."

And Pruitt told him, even though at that time Uncle Gavin would forget now and then and his language would slip back to Harvard and even to Heidelberg. It was as if people looked at his face and knew that what he asked was not just for his own curiosity or his own selfish using.

"Only ma knows more about it than I do," Pruitt said. "Come up to the gallery."

We followed him to the gallery, where a plump, white-haired old lady in a clean gingham sunbonnet and dress and a clean white apron sat in a low rocking chair, shelling field peas into a wooden bowl. "This is Lawyer Stevens," Pruitt said. "Captain Stevens' son, from town. He wants to know about Jackson Fentry."

So we sat, too, while they told it, the son and the mother talking in rotation.

"That place of theirs," Pruitt said. "You seen some of it from the road. And what you didn't see don't look no better. But his pa and his grandpa worked it, made a living for themselves and raised families and paid their taxes and owed no man. I don't know how they done it, but they did. And Jackson was helping from the time he got big enough to reach up to the plow handles. He never got much bigger than that neither. None of them ever did. I reckon that was why. And Jackson worked it, too, in his time, until he was about twenty-five and already looking forty, asking no odds of nobody, not married and not nothing, him and his pa living alone and doing their own washing and cooking, because how can a man afford to marry when him and his pa have just one pair of shoes between them. If it had been worth while getting a wife a-tall, since that place had already killed his ma and his grandma both before they were forty years old. Until one night——"

"Nonsense," Mrs. Pruitt said. "When your pa and me married, we didn't even own a roof over our heads. We moved into a rented house, on rented land——"

"All right," Pruitt said. "Until one night he come to me and said how he had got him a sawmilling job down at Frenchman's Bend."

"Frenchman's Bend?" Uncle Gavin said, and now his eyes were much brighter and quicker than just intent. "Yes," he said.

"A day-wage job," Pruitt said. "Not to get rich; just to earn a little extra money maybe, risking a year or two to earn a little extra money, against the life his grandpa led until he died between the plow handles one day, and that his pa would lead until he died in a corn furrow, and then it would be his turn, and not even no son to come and pick him up out of the dirt. And that he had traded with a nigger to help his pa work their place while he was gone, and would I kind of go up there now and then and see that his pa was all right."

"Which you did," Mrs. Pruitt said.

"I went close enough," Pruitt said. "I would get close enough to the field to hear him cussing at the nigger for not moving fast enough and to watch the nigger trying to keep up with him, and to think what a good thing it was Jackson hadn't got two niggers to work the place while he was gone, because if that old man—and he was close to sixty then—

had had to spend one full day sitting in a chair in the shade with nothing in his hands to chop or hoe with, he would have died before sundown. So Jackson left. He walked. They didn't have but one mule. They ain't never had but one mule. But it ain't but about thirty miles. He was gone about two and a half years. Then one day——"

"He come home that first Christmas," Mrs. Pruitt said.

"That's right," Pruitt said. "He walked them thirty miles home and spent Christmas Day, and walked them other thirty miles back to the sawmill."

"Whose sawmill?" Uncle Gavin said.

"Quick's," Pruitt said. "Old Man Ben Quick's. It was the second Christmas he never come home. Then, about the beginning of March, about when the river bottom at Frenchman's Bend would be starting to dry out to where you could skid logs through it and you would have thought he would be settled down good to his third year of sawmilling, he come home to stay. He didn't walk this time. He come in a hired buggy. Because he had the goat and the baby."

"Wait," Uncle Gavin said.

"We never knew how he got home," Mrs. Pruitt said. "Because he had been home over a week before we even found out he had the baby."

"Wait," Uncle Gavin said.

They waited, looking at him, Pruitt sitting on the gallery railing and Mrs. Pruitt's fingers still shelling the peas out of the long brittle hulls, looking at Uncle Gavin. His eyes were not exultant now any more than they had been baffled or even very speculative before; they had just got brighter, as if whatever it was behind them had flared up, steady and fiercer, yet still quiet, as if it were going faster than the telling was going.

"Yes," he said. "Tell me."

"And when I finally heard about it and went up there," Mrs. Pruitt said, "that baby wasn't two weeks old. And how he had kept it alive, and just on goat's milk——"

"I don't know if you know it," Pruitt said. "A goat ain't like a cow. You milk a goat every two hours or so. That means all night too."

"Yes," Mrs. Pruitt said. "He didn't even have diaper cloths. He had some split floursacks the midwife had showed him how to put on. So I made some cloths and I would go up there; he had kept the nigger on to help his pa in the field and he was doing the cooking and washing and nursing that baby, milking the goat to feed it; and I would say, 'Let me take it. At least until he can be weaned. You come stay at my house, too, if you want,' and him just looking at me—little, thin, already wore-out, that never in his whole life had ever set down to a table and et all he could hold—saying, 'I thank you, ma'am. I can make out.' "

"Which was correct," Pruitt said. "I don't know how he was at sawmilling, and he never had no farm to find out what kind of a farmer he was. But he raised that boy."

"Yes," Mrs. Pruitt said. "And I kept on after him: 'We hadn't even heard you was married,' I said. 'Yessum,' he said. 'We was married last year. When the baby come, she died.' 'Who was she?' I said. 'Was she a Frenchman Bend girl?' 'No'm,' he said. 'She come from downstate.' 'What was her name?' I said. 'Miss Smith,' he said."

"He hadn't even had enough time off from hard work to learn how to lie either," Pruitt said. "But he raised that boy. After their crops were in in the fall, he let the nigger go, and next spring him and the old man done the work like they use to. He had made a kind of satchel, like they say Indians does, to carry the boy in. I would go up there now and then while the ground was still cold and see Jackson and his pa plowing and chopping brush, and that satchel hanging on a fence post and that boy asleep bolt upright in it like it was a feather bed. He learned to walk that spring, and I would stand there at the fence and watch that durn little critter out there in the middle of the furrow, trying his best to keep up with Jackson, until Jackson would stop the plow at the turn row and go back and get him and set him straddle of his neck and take up the plow and go on. In the late summer he could walk pretty good. Jackson made him a little hoe out of a stick and a scrap of shingle, and you could see Jackson chopping in the middle-thigh cotton, but you couldn't see the boy at all; you could just see the cotton shaking where he was."

"Jackson made his clothes," Mrs. Pruitt said. "Stitched them himself, by hand. I made a few garments and took them up there. I never done it but once though. He took them and he thanked me. But you could see it. It was like he even begrudged the earth itself for what that child had to eat to keep alive. And I tried to persuade Jackson to take him to church, have him baptized. 'He's already named,' he said. 'His name is Jackson and Longstreet Fentry. Pa fit under both of them.' "

"He never went nowhere," Pruitt said. "Because where you saw Jackson, you saw that boy. If he had had to steal that boy down there at Frenchman's Bend, he couldn't 'a' hid no closer. It was even the old man that would ride over to Haven Hill store to buy their supplies, and the only time Jackson and that boy was separated as much as one full breath was once a year when Jackson would ride in to Jefferson to pay their taxes, and when I first seen the boy I thought of a setter puppy, until one day I knowed Jackson had gone to pay their taxes and I went up there and the boy was under the bed, not making any fuss, just backed up into the corner, looking out at me. He didn't blink once. He was exactly like a fox or a wolf cub somebody had caught just last night."

We watched him take from his pocket a tin of snuff and tilt a measure of it into the lid and then into his lower lip, tapping the final grain from the lid with delicate deliberation.

"All right," Uncle Gavin said. "Then what?"

"That's all," Pruitt said. "In the next summer him and the boy disappeared."

"Disappeared?" Uncle Gavin said.

"That's right. They were just gone one morning. I didn't know when. And one day I couldn't stand it no longer, I went up there and the house was empty, and I went on to the field where the old man was plowing, and at first I thought the spreader between his plow handles had broke and he had tied a sapling across the handles, until he seen me and snatched the sapling off, and it was that shotgun, and I reckon what he said to me was about what he said to you this morning when you stopped there. Next year he had the nigger helping him again. Then, about five years later, Jackson come back. I don't know when. He was just there one morning. And the nigger was gone again, and him and his pa worked the place like they use to. And one day I couldn't stand it no longer, I went up there and I stood at the fence where he was plowing, until after a while the land he was breaking brought him up to the fence, and still he hadn't never looked at me; he plowed right by me, not ten feet away, still without looking at me, and he turned and come back, and I said, 'Did he die, Jackson?' and then he looked at me. 'The boy,' I said. And he said. 'What boy?' "

They invited us to stay for dinner.

Uncle Gavin thanked them. "We brought a snack with us," he said. "And it's thirty miles to Varner's store, and twenty-two from there to Jefferson. And our roads ain't quite used to automobiles yet."

So it was just sundown when we drove up to Varner's store in Frenchman's Bend Village; again a man rose from the deserted gallery and came down the steps to the car.

It was Isham Quick, the witness who had first reached Thorpe's body—a tall, gangling man in the middle forties, with a dreamy kind of face and near-sighted eyes, until you saw there was something shrewd behind them, even a little quizzical.

"I been waiting for you," he said. "Looks like you made a water haul." He blinked at Uncle Gavin. "That Fentry."

"Yes," Uncle Gavin said. "Why didn't you tell me?"

"I didn't recognize it myself," Quick said. "It wasn't until I heard your jury was hung, and by one man, that I associated them names."

"Names?" Uncle Gavin said. "What na—— Never mind. Just tell it."

So we sat on the gallery of the locked and deserted store while the cicadas shrilled and rattled in the trees and the lightning bugs blinked and drifted above the dusty road, and Quick told it, sprawled on the bench beyond Uncle Gavin, loose-jointed, like he would come all to pieces the first time he moved, talking in a lazy sardonic voice, like he had all night to tell it in and it would take all night to tell it. But it wasn't that long. It wasn't long enough for what was in it. But Uncle Gavin says it don't take many words to tell the sum of any human experience; that somebody has already done it in eight: He was born, he suffered and he died.

"It was pap that hired him. But when I found out where he had come from, I knowed he would work, because folks in that country hadn't never had time to learn nothing but hard work. And I knowed he would be honest for the same reason: that there wasn't nothing in his country a man could want bad enough to learn how to steal it. What I seem to have underestimated was his capacity for love. I reckon I figured that, coming from where he come from, he never had none a-tall, and for that same previous reason—that even the comprehension of love had done been lost out of him back down the generations where the first one of them had had to take his final choice between the pursuit of love and the pursuit of keeping on breathing.

"So he come to work, doing the same work and drawing the same pay as the niggers done. Until in the late fall, when the bottom got wet and we got ready to shut down for the winter, I found out he had made a trade with pap to stay on until spring as watchman and caretaker, with three days out to go home Christmas. And he did, and the next year when we started up, he had done learned so much about it and he stuck to it so, that by the middle of summer he was running the whole mill hisself, and by the end of summer pap never went out there no more a-tall and I just went when I felt like it, maybe once a week or so; and by fall pap was even talking about building him a shack to live in in place of that shuck mattress and a old broke-down cookstove in the boiler shed. And he stayed through that winter too. When he went home that Christmas we never even knowed it, when he went or when he come back, because even I hadn't been out there since fall.

"Then one afternoon in February—there had been a mild spell and I reckon I was restless—I rode out there. The first thing I seen was her, and it was the first time I had ever done that—a woman, young, and maybe when she was in her normal health she might have been pretty, too; I don't know. Because she wasn't just thin, she was gaunted. She was sick, more than just starved-looking, even if she was still on her feet, and it wasn't just because she was going to have that baby in a considerable less than another month. And I says, 'Who is that?' and he looked at me and says, 'That's my wife,' and I says, 'Since when? You never had no wife last fall. And that child ain't a month off.' And he says, 'Do you want us to leave?' and I says, 'What do I want you to leave for?' I'm going to tell this from what I know now, what I found out after them two brothers showed up here three years later with their court paper, not from what he ever told me, because he never told nobody nothing."

"All right," Uncle Gavin said. "Tell."

"I don't know where he found her. I don't know if he found her somewhere, or if she just walked into the mill one day or one night and he looked up and seen her, and it was like the fellow says—nobody knows where or when love or lightning either is going to strike, except that it ain't going to strike there twice, because it don't have to. And I don't believe she was hunting for the husband that had deserted her— likely he cut and run soon as she told him about the baby—and I don't believe she was scared or ashamed to go back home just because her brother and father had tried to keep her from marrying the husband, in the first place. I believe it was just some more of that same kind of black-complected and not extra-intelligent and pretty durn ruthless blood pride that them brothers themselves was waving around here for about a hour that day.

"Anyway, there she was, and I reckon she knowed her time was going to be short, and him saying to her, 'Let's get married,' and her saying, 'I can't marry you. I've already got a husband.' And her time come and she was down then, on that shuck mattress, and him feeding her with a spoon, likely, and I reckon she knowed she wouldn't get up from it, and he got the midwife, and the baby was born, and likely her and the midwife both knowed by then she would never get up from that mattress and maybe they even convinced him at last, or maybe she knowed it wouldn't make no difference nohow and said yes, and he taken the mule pap let him keep at the mill and rid seven miles to Preacher Whitfield's and brung Whitfield back about daylight, and Whitfield married them and she died, and him and Whitfield buried her. And that night he come to the house and told pap he was quitting, and left the mule, and I went out to the mill a few days later and he was gone—just the shuck mattress and the stove, and the dishes and skillet mammy let him have, all washed and clean and set on the shelf. And in the third summer from then, them two brothers, them Thorpes———"

"Thorpes," Uncle Gavin said. It wasn't loud. It was getting dark fast now, as it does in our country, and I couldn't see his face at all any more. "Tell," he said.

"Black-complected like she was—the youngest one looked a heap like her—coming up in the surrey, with the deputy or bailiff or whatever he was, and the paper all wrote out and stamped and sealed all regular, and I says, 'You can't do this. She come here of her own accord, sick and with nothing, and he taken her in and fed her and nursed her and got help to born that child and a preacher to bury her; they was even married before she died. The preacher and the midwife both will prove it.' And the oldest brother says, 'He couldn't marry her. She already had a husband. We done already attended to him.' And I says, 'All right. He taken that boy when nobody come to claim him. He has raised that boy and clothed and fed him for two years and better.' And the oldest one drawed a money purse outen his pocket and let it drop back again. 'We aim to do right about that, too—when we have seen the boy,' he says. 'He is our kin. We want him and we aim to have him.' And that wasn't the first time it ever occurred to me that this world ain't run like it ought to be run a heap of more times than what it is, and I says, 'It's thirty miles up there. I reckon you all will want to lay over here tonight and rest your horses.' And the oldest one looked at me and says, 'The team ain't tired. We won't stop.' 'Then I'm going with you,' I says. 'You are welcome to come,' he says.

"We drove until midnight. So I thought I would have a chance then, even if I never had nothing to ride. But when we unhitched and laid down on the ground, the oldest brother never laid down. 'I ain't sleepy,' he says. 'I'll set up a while.' So it wasn't no use, and I went to sleep and then the sun was up and it was too late then, and about middle morning we come to that mailbox with the name on it you couldn't miss, and the empty house with nobody in sight or hearing neither, until we heard the ax and went around to the back, and he looked up from the woodpile and seen what I reckon he had been expecting to see every time the sun rose for going on three years now. Because he never even stopped. He said to the little boy, 'Run. Run to the field to grandpap. Run,' and come straight at the oldest brother with the ax already raised and the down-stroke already started, until I managed to catch it by the haft just as the oldest brother grabbed him and we lifted him clean off the ground, holding him, or trying to. 'Stop it, Jackson!' I says. 'Stop it! They got the law!'

"Then a puny something was kicking and clawing me about the legs; it was the little boy, not making a sound, just swarming around me and the brother both, hitting at us as high as he could reach with a piece of wood Fentry had been chopping. 'Catch him and take him on to the surrey,' the oldest one says. So the youngest one caught him; he was almost as hard to hold as Fentry, kicking and plunging even after the youngest one had picked him up, and still not making a sound, and Fentry jerking and lunging like two men until the youngest one and the boy was out of sight. Then he collapsed. It was like all his bones had turned to water, so that me and the oldest brother lowered him down to the chopping block like he never had no bones a-tall, laying back against the wood he had cut, panting, with a little froth of spit at each corner of his mouth. 'It's the law, Jackson,' I says. 'Her husband is still alive.'

" 'I know it,' he says. It wasn't much more than whispering. 'I been expecting it. I reckon that's why it taken me so by surprise. I'm all right now.'

" 'I'm sorry for it,' the brother says. 'We never found out about none of it until last week. But he is our kin. We want him home. You done well by him. We thank you. His mother thanks you. Here,' he says. He taken the money purse outen his pocket and puts it into Fentry's hand. Then he turned and went away. After a while I heard the carriage turn and go back down the hill. Then I couldn't hear it any more. I don't know whether Fentry ever heard it or not.

" 'It's the law, Jackson,' I says. 'But there's two sides to the law.

We'll go to town and talk to Captain Stevens. I'll go with you.'

"Then he set up on the chopping block, setting up slow and stiff. He wasn't panting so hard now and he looked better now, except for his eyes, and they was mostly just dazed looking. Then he raised the hand that had the money purse in it and started to mop his face with the money purse, like it was a handkerchief; I don't believe he even knowed there was anything in his hand until then, because he taken his hand down and looked at the money purse for maybe five seconds, and then he tossed it—he didn't fling it; he just tossed it like you would a handful of dirt you had been examining to see what it would make— over behind the chopping block and got up and walked across the yard toward the woods, walking straight and not fast, and not looking much bigger than that little boy, and into the woods. 'Jackson,' I says. But he never looked back.

"And I stayed that night at Rufus Pruitt's and borrowed a mule from him; I said I was just looking around, because I didn't feel much like talking to nobody, and the next morning I hitched the mule at that gate and started up the path, and I didn't see old man Fentry on the gallery a-tall at first.

"When I did see him he was moving so fast I didn't even know what he had in his hands until it went 'boom!' and I heard the shot rattling in the leaves overhead and Rufus Pruitt's mule trying his durn best either to break the hitch rein or hang hisself from the gatepost.

"And one day about six months after he had located here to do the balance of his drinking and fighting and sleight-of-hand with other folks' cattle, Bucksnort was on the gallery here, drunk still and running his mouth, and about a half dozen of the ones he had beat unconscious from time to time by foul means and even by fair on occasion, as such emergencies arose, laughing every time he stopped to draw a fresh breath. And I happened to look up, and Fentry was setting on his mule out there in the road.

"He was just setting there, with the dust of them thirty miles caking into the mule's sweat, looking at Thorpe. I don't know how long he had been there, not saying nothing, just setting there and looking at Thorpe; then he turned the mule and rid back up the road toward them hills he hadn't ought to never have left. Except maybe it's like the fellow says, and there ain't nowhere you can hide from either lightning or love. And I didn't know why then. I hadn't associated them names. I knowed that Thorpe was familiar to me, but that other business had been twenty years ago and I had forgotten it until I heard about that hung jury of yourn. Of course he wasn't going to vote Bookwright free. . . . It's dark. Let's go to supper."

But it was only twenty-two miles to town now, and we were on the highway now, the gravel; we would be home in an hour and a half, because sometimes we could make thirty and thirty-five miles an hour, and Uncle Gavin said that someday all the main roads in Mississippi would be paved like the streets in Memphis and every family in America would own a car. We were going fast now.

"Of course he wasn't," Uncle Gavin said. "The lowly and invincible of the earth—to endure and endure and then endure, tomorrow and tomorrow and tomorrow. Of course he wasn't going to vote Bookwright free."

"I would have," I said. "I would have freed him. Because Buck Thorpe was bad. He——"

"No, you wouldn't," Uncle Gavin said. He gripped my knee with one hand even though we were going fast, the yellow light beam level on the yellow road, the bugs swirling down into the light beam and ballooning away. "It wasn't Buck Thorpe, the adult, the man. He would have shot that man as quick as Bookwright did, if he had been in Bookwright's place. It was because somewhere in the debased and brutalized flesh which Bookwright slew there still remained, not the spirit maybe, but at least the memory, of that little boy, that Jackson and Longstreet Fentry, even though the man the boy had become didn't know it, and only Fentry did. And you wouldn't have freed him either. Don't ever forget that. Never."

Honoré de Balzac

:

HOW THE PRETTY MAID OF PORTILLON
CONVINCED HER JUDGE

The maid of Portillon, who became, as everyone knows, La Tascher-
ette, was, before she became a dyer, a laundress at the said place of
Portillon, from which she took her name. If any there be who do not
know Tours, it may be well to state that Portillon is down the Loire, on
the same side as St. Cyr, about as far from the bridge which leads to the
cathedral of Tours as the said bridge is distant from Marmoutier, since
the bridge is in the center of the embankment between Portillon and
Marmoutier. Do you thoroughly understand?

Yes? Good! Now the maid had there her washhouse, from which she
ran to the Loire with her washing in a second, and took the ferry-boat
to get to St. Martin, which was on the other side of the river, for she had
to deliver the greater part of her work in Chateauneuf and other
places. About Midsummer day, seven years before marrying old Taschereau, she had just reached the right age to be loved. As she was a
merry girl she allowed herself to be loved, without making a choice
from any of the lads who pursued her with their intentions. Although
there used to come to the bench under her window the son of Rabelais,
who had seven boats on the Loire, Jehan's eldest, Marchandeau the
tailor, and Peccard the ecclesiastical goldsmith, she made fun of them
all, because she wished to be taken to church before burthening herself
with a man, which proves that she was an honest woman until she was
wheedled out of her virtue. She was one of those girls who take great
care not to be contaminated, but who, if by chance they get deceived,
let things take their course, thinking that for one stain or for fifty a good

434

polishing up is necessary. These characters demand our indulgence.

A young noble of the court perceived her one day when she was crossing the water in the glare of the noonday sun, which lit up her ample charms, and seeing her, asked who she was. An old man, who was working on the banks, told him she was called the Pretty Maid of Portillon, a laundress, celebrated for her merry ways and her virtue. This young lord, besides ruffles to starch, had many precious linen draperies and things; he resolved to give the custom of his house to this girl, whom he stopped on the road. He was thanked by her and heartily, because he was the Sire du Fou, the king's chamberlain. This encounter made her so joyful that her mouth was full of his name. She talked about it a great deal to the people of St. Martin, and when she got back to her washhouse was still full of it, and on the morrow at her work her tongue went nineteen to the dozen, and all on the same subject, so that as much was said concerning my Lord du Fou in Portillon as of God in a sermon; that is, a great deal too much.

"If she works like that in cold water, what will she do in warm?" said an old washerwoman. "She wants du Fou; he'll give her du Fou!"

The first time this giddy wench, with her head full of Monsieur du Fou, had to deliver the linen at his hotel, the chamberlain wished to see her, and was very profuse in praises and compliments concerning her charms, and wound up by telling her that she was not at all silly to be beautiful, and therefore he would give her more than she expected. The deed followed the word, for the moment his people were out of the room, he began to caress the maid, who thinking he was about to take out the money from his purse, dared not look at the purse, but said, like a girl ashamed to take her wages, "It will be for the first time."

"It will be soon," said he.

Some people say that he had great difficulty in forcing her to accept what he offered her, and hardly forced her at all; others that he forced her badly, because she came out, like an army flagging on the route, crying and groaning, and came to the judge. It happened that the judge was out. La Portillone awaited his return in his room, weeping and saying to the servant that she had been robbed, because Monseigneur du Fou had given her nothing but his mischief; whilst a canon of the chapter used to give her large sums for that which M. du Fou wanted for nothing. If she loved a man she would think it wise to do things for him for nothing, because it would be a pleasure to her; but the chamberlain had treated her roughly, and not kindly and gently, as he should have done, and that therefore he owed her the thousand crowns of the canon. The judge came in, saw the wench, and wished to kiss her, but she put herself on guard, and said she had come to make a complaint. The judge replied that certainly she could have the offender hanged if she liked, because he was most anxious to serve her. The injured maiden replied that she did not wish the death of her man, but that he should pay her a thousand gold crowns, because she had been robbed against her will.

"Ha! ha!" said the judge, "what he took was worth more than that."

"For the thousand crowns I'll cry quits, because I shall be able to live without washing."

"He who has robbed you, is he well off?"

"Oh, yes."

"Then he shall pay dearly for it. Who is it?"

"Monseigneur du Fou."

"Oh, that alters the case," said the judge.

"But justice?" said she.

"I said the case, not the justice of it," replied the judge. "I must know how the affair occurred."

Then the girl related naïvely how she was arranging the young lord's ruffles in his wardrobe, when he began to play with her skirts, and she turned round, saying—

"Go on with you!"

"You have no case," said the judge, "for by that speech he thought that you gave him leave to go on. Ha! ha!"

Then she declared that she had defended herself, weeping and crying out, and that that constitutes an assault.

"A wench's antics to incite him," said the judge.

Finally, La Portillone declared that against her will she had been taken around the waist and thrown, although she had kicked and cried and struggled, but that seeing no help at hand, she had lost courage.

"Good! Good!" said the judge. "Did you take pleasure in the affair?"

"No," said she. "My anguish can only be paid for with a thousand crowns."

"My dear," said the judge, "I cannot receive your complaint, because I believe no girl can be thus treated against her will."

"Hi! hi! hi! Ask your servant," said the little laundress, sobbing, "and hear what she'll tell you."

The servant affirmed that there were pleasant assaults and unpleasant ones; that if La Portillone had received neither amusement nor money, either one or the other was due her. This wise counsel threw the judge into a state of great perplexity.

"Jacqueline," said he, "before I sup I'll get to the bottom of this. Now go and fetch my needle and the red thread that I sew the legal paper bags with."

Jacqueline came back with a big needle, pierced with a pretty little hole, and a big red thread, such as the judges use. Then she remained standing to see the question decided, very much disturbed, as was also the complainant at these mysterious preparations.

"My dear," said the judge, "I am going to hold the bodkin, of which the eye is sufficiently large, to put this thread into it without trouble. If you do put it in, I will take up your case, and will make Monseigneur offer you a compromise."

"What's that?" said she. "I will not allow it."

"It is a word used in justice to signify an agreement."

"A compromise is then agreeable with justice?" said La Portillone.

"My dear, this violence has also opened your mind. Are you ready?"

"Yes," said she.

The waggish judge gave the poor nymph fair play, holding the eye steady for her; but when she wished to slip in the thread that she had twisted to make straight, he moved a little, and the thread went on the other side. She suspected the judge's argument, wetted the thread, stretched it, and came back again. The judge moved, twisted about, and wriggled like a bashful maiden; still the cursed thread would not enter. The girl kept trying at the eye, and the judge kept fidgeting. The marriage of the thread could not be consummated, the bodkin remained virgin, and the servant began to laugh, saying to La Portillone that she knew better how to endure than to perform. Then the roguish judge laughed too, and the fair Portillone cried for her golden crowns.

"If you don't keep still," cried she, losing patience; "if you keep moving about I shall never be able to put the thread in."

"Then, my dear, if you had done the same, Monseigneur would have been unsuccessful too. Think, too, how easy is the one affair, and how difficult the other."

The pretty wench, who declared she had been forced, remained thoughtful, and sought to find a means to convince the judge by showing how she had been compelled to yield, since the honor of all poor girls liable to violence was at stake.

"Monseigneur, in order that the bet may be fair, I must do exactly as the young lord did. If I had only had to move I should be moving still, but he went through other performances."

"Let us hear them," replied the judge.

Then La Portillone straightens the thread; and rubs it in the wax of the candle, to make it firm and straight; then she looks towards the eye of the bodkin, held by the judge, slipping always to the right or to the left. Then she began making endearing little speeches, such as, "Ah, the pretty little bodkin! What a pretty mark to aim at! Never did I see such a little jewel! What a pretty little eye! Let me put this little thread into it! Ah! You will hurt my poor thread, my nice little thread! Keep still! Come, my love of a judge, judge of my love! Won't the thread go nicely into this iron gate, which makes good use of the thread, for it comes out very much out of order?" Then she burst out laughing, for she was better up in this game than the judge, who laughed too, so saucy and comical and arch was she, pushing the thread backwards and forwards. She kept the poor judge with the case in his hand until seven o'clock, keeping on fidgeting and moving about like a schoolboy let loose; but as La Portillone kept on trying to put the thread in, he could not help it. As, however, his joint was burning, and his wrist was tired, he was obliged to rest himself for a minute on the side of the table; then very dexterously the fair maid of Portillon slipped the thread in, saying—

"That's how the thing occurred."

"But my joint was burning."

"So was mine," said she.

The judge, convinced, told La Portillone that he would speak to Monseigneur du Fou, and would himself carry the affair through, since it was certain the young lord had embraced her against her will, but that for valid reasons he would keep the affair dark. On the morrow the judge went to the Court and saw the Monseigneur du Fou, to whom he recounted the young woman's complaint, and how she had set forth her case. This complaint lodged in Court, tickled the king immensely. Young du Fou having said that there was some truth in it, the king asked if he had much difficulty, and as he replied, innocently, "No," the king declared the girl was quite worth a hundred gold crowns, and the chamberlain gave them to the judge, in order not to be taxed with stinginess, and said that starch would be a good income to La Portillone. The judge came back to La Portillone, and said, smiling, that he had raised a hundred gold crowns for her. But if she desired the balance of the thousand, there were at that moment in the king's apartments certain lords who, knowing the case, had offered to make up the sum for her with her consent. The little hussy did not refuse this offer, saying, that in order to do no more washing in the future she did not mind doing a little hard work now. She gratefully acknowledged the trouble the good judge had taken, and gained her thousand crowns in a month. From this came the falsehoods and jokes concerning her because out of these ten lords jealousy made a hundred, whilst, differently from young men, La Portillone settled down to a virtuous life directly she had her thousand crowns. Even a duke, who would have counted out five hundred crowns, would have found this girl rebellious, which proves she was niggardly with her property. It is true that the king caused her to be sent for to his retreat of Rue Quinquangrogne, on the mall of Chardonneret, found her extremely pretty, exceedingly affectionate, enjoyed her society, and forbade the sergeants to interfere with her in any way whatever. Seeing she was so beautiful, Nicole Beaupertuis, the king's mistress, gave her a hundred gold crowns to go to Orlèans, in order to see if the color of the Loire was the same there as at Portillon. She went there, and the more willingly because she did not care very much for the king. When the good man came who confessed the king in his last hour, and was afterwards canonized, La Portillone went to him to polish up her conscience, did penance, and founded a bed in the leper-house of St. Lazare-les-Tours. Many ladies whom you know have been assaulted by more than two lords, and have founded no other beds than those of their own houses. It is well to relate this fact in order to cleanse the reputation of this honest girl, who herself once washed dirty things, and who afterwards became famous for her clever tricks and her wit. She gave a proof of her merit in marrying Taschereau, whom she cuckolded right merrily, as has been related in the story of *The Reproach*. This proves to us most satisfactorily that with strength and patience justice itself can be violated.

Honoré de Balzac

:

THE JUDGE ILL-JUDGED

from *A Commission in Lunacy*

In his capacity as magistrate, Monsieur Popinot was always clothed in black; a peculiarity which contributed to make him ridiculous in the eyes of persons who are in the habit of judging all things superficially. Men who seek to maintain their dignity by such clothing ought, undoubtedly, to subject themselves to minute and continual care of it; but this dear Monsieur Popinot was absolutely incapable of producing upon himself the puritanical neatness which the wearing of black demands. His trousers, always shabby, seemed of the stuff called *voile,* of which barristers' gowns are made; and long usage had produced such innumerable creases that in certain places white or red or shiny stripes appeared, revealing either sordid avarice or abject poverty. His coarse woolen socks grinned from the sides of his misshapen shoes. His linen had that rusty look caused by long lying-by in drawers and wardrobes, —proving that the late Madame Popinot was afflicted with the linen mania; true, no doubt, to Flemish customs, the family washing was probably done but twice a year. The coat and waistcoat of the excellent magistrate were in keeping with his trousers, shoes, stockings, and linen. He had the luck of his slovenliness; for whenever it came to pass that he bought a new coat he conformed it to the rest of his apparel by getting it spotted with inexplicable promptitude. The good man waited for his cook to tell him of the shabbiness of his hat before he got another. His cravat was always awry, and never did he straighten his crumpled shirt-collar when his judge's bands had set it askew. He took

440

no care of his grizzled hair, and seldom shaved more than twice a week. He never wore gloves, but rammed his hands habitually into his pockets, the openings to which, always dirty and nearly always torn, added one feature more to the general neglect of his person.

Whoso has frequented the Palais de Justice in Paris, a place where all varieties of black garments may be observed, can readily picture to his mind's eye the appearance of Monsieur Popinot. The habit of being seated all day long affects the body to a great degree, just as the tedium of listening to interminable pleadings affects the physiognomy of magistrates. Shut up in ridiculously narrow rooms, without dignity of architecture, where the air is soon vitiated, the Parisian judge is forced to acquire a frowning visage, puckered by listening and saddened by ennui; his skin gets sickly and takes on a greenish or an earthy tint, according to the temperament of the individual. In fact, the most blooming young man would become, within a given time, a pale machine, a mechanism applying the Code to all sorts of cases with the phlegm of a clock's mainspring.

If, therefore, Nature had not endowed Monsieur Popinot with an agreeable exterior, the magistracy had certainly not embellished it. His bony frame presented knotty joints. His big knees, his large feet, his large hands contrasted oddly with a sacerdotal face, vaguely resembling a calf's head, gentle to insipidity, poorly lighted by whitish green eyes, drained of its blood, divided in two by a long flat nose, surmounted by a forehead without intellectual protuberance, and flanked by a pair of enormous ears which flopped gracelessly.

One sole feature made this face acceptable to a physiognomist. The lips of the man's mouth expressed a kindness that was well-nigh divine. They were thick red lips with countless creases; they were mobile, they curved, and on them Nature had imprinted the noblest sentiments. They were lips that spoke to the heart and revealed in this old man clearness of mind, the gift of second-sight, and an angelic spirit; therefore you would ill have judged him had you done so only by his retreating forehead, his eyes without warmth, and his pitiable appearance. His life corresponded to his countenance; it was worn by incessant toil, and it covered the virtues of a saint.

His great legal acquirements had made him so well known that when Napoleon reorganized the whole system of law in 1806 and 1811, Popinot was, on the advice of Cambacérès, among the first to be appointed judge of the Imperial court of Paris. Popinot was no intriguer. At each new crisis, each new demand for office, the ministry set Popinot aside in favor of more exacting claims; for the good man never set foot in the houses of the arch-chancellor or the chief-justice. He was gradually shoved aside on all lists for promotion by the more active and pushing men; until, finally, he was made a substitute judge. Then a general out-cry arose at the Palais: "Popinot a substitute judge!" The injustice of the act struck the whole legal world, barristers, solicitors, clerks, every-body, except Popinot himself, who made no complaint of it. The first clamor over, everyone came to think that, on the whole, it was for the best in this best of all possible worlds—which, certainly, must be the legal world.

Popinot continued to be a substitute judge until the day came when a distinguished Keeper of the Seals, during the Restoration, avenged the wrong done to the modest, silent man by the great officers of the Em-pire. After being a substitute judge for a dozen years, Monsieur Popi-not was, no doubt, fated to die in the subordinate position of an exam-ining judge in one of the Lower courts of the Seine.

To explain the obscure fate of one of the most superior men the bench has ever known, it is necessary to enter into certain considera-tions which will serve to explain his life and character, and will also re-veal something of the running-gear of that great machine called the Law. Monsieur Popinot was rated by three successive presidents of the Seine courts in a category of *judgery,* the only word that expresses the idea we desire to convey. He did not obtain from any of them the reputation for capacity which his work had already deserved. Just as a painter is relegated into a certain category—that of landscape, por-trait, historical, marine, or genre painting—by the public of artists, connoisseurs, and ninnies, who, out of envy or critical omnipotence or prejudice, barricade him in his own intellect, so Popinot was given his limits, and was hemmed in to them.

Judges, barristers, and lawyers, generally, all those who pasture on judicial territory, recognize two elements to every cause: legality and equity. Equity derives from facts alone, legality is the application of principles to facts. A man may be right in equity, and wrong legally, without blame to the judge for his decision. Between the man's con-sciousness and his act, there is a mass of determining reasons unknown to the judge, but which, in fact, condemn or legitimatize an act. A judge is not God: his duty is to adapt facts to principles; to judge them in infinite variety by the application of one test. If the judge had the power of reading consciences and discerning motives so as to render absolutely just judgments, he would be the greatest of men. France employs about six thousand judges; no generation has six thousand great men at her service.

Popinot, in the center of Parisian civilization, was a very able cadi, who, by the constitution of his mind, and by dint of rubbing the letter of the law into the spirit of the facts, had come to see the great defect of arbitrary applications. Aided by his strong judicial second-sight, he pierced through the double layer of falsehood with which a legal advocate hides the real kernel of a case. A judge in the same sense that the great Desplein was a surgeon, he could penetrate a conscience as Desplein saw into a body. His life and his morals had led him to an exact appreciation of the most secret thoughts through his scrutiny of acts. He burrowed into a case as Cuvier burrowed into the soil of the globe. Like that great thinker, he went from deduction to deduction before he drew conclusions, and reproduced the past of a conscience as Cuvier reconstructed an anoplotherium. Apropos of a decision, he would often wake up in the night, roused suddenly by some ray of truth which darted vividly into his mind. Struck with the deep injustice which frequently ends a legal struggle, in which so much is to the scoundrel's profit, and so little serves an honest man, he often gave a judgment in favor of equity rather than legality in cases where the question admitted of intuition. Consequently his colleagues regarded him as unpractical; besides, his reasons, stated at great length, prolonged their deliberations. When Popinot discovered their unwillingness to listen to him he took pains to give his opinion more briefly. He was said to be a bad judge of all affairs into which equity could enter, but as his genius of appreciation was very striking, his judgment lucid, his penetration deep, he was considered to possess a special aptitude for the laborious duties of an examining judge. Thus it was that he remained during the greater part of his judicial career in that capacity.

Although his qualifications made him eminently fitted for that arduous office, yet the kindness of his heart kept him ever on the rack; he was constantly held as in a vise between his conscience and his pity. The functions of an examining judge, though better paid than those of a civil judge, tempt no one, for they are too confining. Popinot, modest, virtuous, without ambition and indefatigable, never complained; he made the sacrifice of his own tastes, his own tenderheartedness to the public good, and allowed himself to be kept down to the slavery of criminal law, where, indeed, he contrived to be both just and beneficent. Sometimes his usher would secretly give a prisoner the money to buy tobacco or get a warm garment for winter, as he led the man back from the judge's office to the Souricière—the strong room at the Palais, where the prisoners waited until the judges were ready to examine them.

Popinot knew the secret of being an inflexible judge and a merciful man. Consequently, no one was able to obtain confessions as easily as he, without having recourse to the judicial wiles of an examining judge. He had, besides, the shrewdness of an observer. This man, almost silly in countenance, simple and absent-minded, was able to detect the wiliest schemes of the Crispins of the galleys; he could foil the most astute of wantons, and melt the heart of the veriest scoundrel. Circumstances that are quite uncommon had sharpened his natural perspicacity; but in order to state them, it is necessary to glance into his private life, for his character as a judge was exercised solely on the social and outward side of him; within was another man, grander, and little known.

Twelve years before this present history begins, in 1816, during the terrible famine which coincided fatally with the stay of the so-called Allies in France, Popinot was appointed president of a special committee instituted to distribute relief to the starving people of his quarter, at the very moment when he was planning to leave the rue du Fouarre, a place of residence as displeasing to himself as to his wife. The great lawyer, the expert criminal judge, whose very superiority seemed to his colleagues weakness, had, for the last five years, observed the results of judicial action without studying their causes. But now, as he climbed to garrets and came face to face with poverty, as he studied the hard necessities which gradually brought the poor and suffering to wrong actions, and took the measure of their bitter griefs, he was seized with compassion. The upright judge became, henceforth, the Saint Vincent de Paul of those grown children, those suffering workmen.

His transformation did not at once attain to wisdom. Benevolence has its moments of rashly yielding to temptation like vice. Charity can empty the purse of a saint, as roulette absorbs the property of a gambler. Popinot went from one misfortune to another, bestowing alms on the right hand and on the left; then, after raising the rags which cover like a compress the fevered wound of that great public wretchedness, he became, at the end of a year, the providence of his quarter of the city. He was president, as we have said, of the committee of benevolence and the bureau of charity. Wherever gratuitous work was needed, there he toiled without pretension, like the "Man with the short cloak," who spent his life carrying soup to hungry families.

Popinot had the happiness, however, of acting in a higher sphere. He foresaw everything; he prevented crime; he provided work for those who were out of it; he placed the helpless where they were cared for; he distributed all succor with discernment; he made himself the adviser of the widow, the guardian of the fatherless, and the secret partner of many a little trade. No one at the Palais or in Paris knew of this hidden life. There are virtues so dazzling that they are comfortable only in obscurity; those who practice them hasten to put their light under a bushel. As for the people whom he succored, they all, working by day and weary at night, made no talk of his kindness; ungrateful as children, who can never pay their debt of gratitude because they owe so much. There is such a thing as forced ingratitude. But what true heart ever sowed beneficence for the purpose of reaping gratitude, and of thinking its own deeds great?

After the second year of this secret apostleship, Popinot converted the ground-floor of his house into one large receiving-room, which was lighted by three windows with iron bars, opening on the street. The walls and ceiling of this large room were whitewashed, and the furniture consisted of wooden benches like those in schools, a common closet, a walnut desk and an armchair. In the closet were the registers in which he kept the record of his cases, the blanks for his "bread tickets," and his day-book. He kept his books in a business manner, that he might not be the dupe of his own heart. All the poverty of the quarter was carefully registered, each case having its own account, like that of a customer on the books of a merchant. When he felt in doubt about a family, or an individual who applied for help, he had recourse to the police of the district. His servant, Lavienne, a man made for such a master, was his aide-de-camp. Lavienne released or renewed all articles in pawn; he visited the most poverty-stricken places and families while Popinot was busy at the Palais.

From four to seven o'clock in the morning in summer, and from six to nine in winter, the huge room on the ground-floor was crowded with women, children, and indigent persons, to whom Popinot gave audience. There was no need of a stove in winter, for the swarm of bodies created a stifling atmosphere. Lavienne, however, took the precaution to cover the damp floor with straw. By dint of constant usage the benches were as polished as varnished mahogany, and the walls, to a man's height, had received a coating of some unspeakable tint from the rags and dilapidated garments of these poor people. The unfortunate creatures were so attached to Popinot that when in the early morning they clustered about the door before it opened (the women trying to keep warm with their hands under their rags, the men by beating their arms), not a voice was raised above a whisper lest it might trouble his sleep.

The rag-pickers, that race of nocturnal beings, knew the house well, and often looked up to see the judge's window lighted at untimely hours. Thieves passing along the street would say to each other, "That's his house," and they respected it. The judge's day was divided as follows: the mornings belonged to the poor; the middle of the day to criminals; the evenings to judicial toil.

The genius of observation which characterized Popinot was therefore twofold in its application; he divined the virtues of poverty—good feelings crushed, noble actions in embryo, self-devotions invisible— just as he saw in the depths of consciences the faintest outlines of crime, the finest threads of delinquency.

Popinot's patrimony amounted to three thousand francs a year. His wife, sister to Horace Bianchon's father, a doctor at Sancerre, had brought him about twice as much. She had now been dead five years and had left all her property to her husband. As the salary of a substitute judge was not considerable, and Popinot had only become an examining judge within the last four years, it is easy to guess the cause of his parsimony in clothes and in all that concerned himself and own life, when we reflect on the smallness of his income and the greatness of his beneficence. Besides, taking another view of it, indifference in the matter of clothes is a distinctive mark of the higher knowledge, of art madly worshipped, of thought perpetually active. To complete this portrait it suffices to add that Popinot was one of the few judges of the courts of the Seine on whom the Legion of Honor was not bestowed.

Such was the man whom the chief-justice of the Second Court, to which Popinot belonged, had appointed to make an examination into the condition of the Marquis d'Espard on a petition presented by the wife for a commission in lunacy.

The rue du Fouarre, where so many miserable creatures swarmed in the early mornings, became deserted after nine o'clock, resuming at that hour its usual gloomy and forlorn aspect. Bianchon therefore pressed his horse, wishing to come upon his uncle in the midst of his audience. He thought, not without a smile, of the singular contrast the judge would present to the salons of Madame d'Espard; and he resolved to persuade him into wearing clothes that should not seem absolutely ridiculous.

"I wonder if he has such a thing as a new coat," thought Bianchon, as he entered the rue du Fouarre, where the windows of the lower room were faintly lighted. "I think I had better consult Lavienne about it."

At the unwonted sound of wheels a dozen poor wretches came out on the steps, and pulled off their hats on seeing the doctor; for Bianchon, who treated his uncle's clients gratuitously, was almost as well known among them as the judge himself.

Bianchon now beheld his uncle in the middle of the room, the benches all around him swarming with paupers in the most grotesque singularities of costume; the sight of which would have filled the least artistic individual with delight and wonder. Certainly a Rembrandt, did any exist in our day, might have conceived from the sight of the silent misery artlessly posing there the noblest of compositions. Here the rugged face of a stern old man with a white beard and apostolic skull, presented a Saint Peter made to hand. His breast, partly uncovered, showed prominent muscles, indications of an iron constitution which had enabled him to bear so far an epic of sorrow. There a young woman suckling her last child to keep it from crying, was holding another, a boy about five years old, between her knees. Her breast, the whiteness of which was shining through her rags, the child with transparent skin, the brother whose attitude betrayed a future *gamin,* touched the soul of an onlooker by the sort of graceful contrast it offered to the long file of dreary faces reddened by the cold which surrounded this poor family. Farther on, an old woman, pale and hard, presented that repulsive type of pauperism in revolt, ready to avenge itself in one day's riot for all its past misery. There, too, was the workman, young, debilitated, and out of work; whose intelligent eye showed faculties repressed by wants fought with hopelessly; silent about his sufferings, yet dying from lack of opportunity to break his way through the bars of that cage of misery where so many needs were swarming. Women were in the majority; the husbands, who had gone to their workshops, left their wives to plead the cause of their poor homes with that wit which characterizes the women of the people, who are nearly always queens in their hovel. On all those heads were seen torn foulards, on all those bodies mud-bedraggled skirts, frayed kerchiefs, dirty short-gowns, and eyes that shone like so many live flames. Horrible combination! the first sight of which inspired disgust, but presently caused a sort of terror, when it was seen that the humble resignation of these souls struggling against every want of life, was simply assumed as a means of speculation on benevolence. Two candles which lighted the vast room flickered in the sort of fog caused by the fetid atmosphere of this ill-ventilated place.

The judge was by no means the least picturesque person in this assemblage. On his head was a rusty cotton night-cap. As he wore no cravat, his neck, red with cold, and much wrinkled, rose sharply above the ragged collar of his old dressing-gown. His tired face bore the half-stupid expression of great preoccupation of mind. His mouth, in common with that of most hard workers, was drawn together like a purse with its strings tied. His forehead, contracted by close attention, seemed to bear the weight of the confidences that were being made to him; he felt, analyzed, and judged them all. Attentive as a moneylender by "the little week," his eyes left the pages of his register to pierce to the inner being of the applicant, whom he examined with that rapidity of vision by which misers quiet their suspicions.

Standing behind his master, and ready to execute his orders, Lavienne was keeping order, receiving the newcomers and encouraging their timidity. When the doctor entered, a movement seemed to take place along the benches. Lavienne turned his head and was much surprised to see Bianchon.

"Ah! There you are, my boy," said Popinot, stretching out his hand. "What brings you here at this time of day?"

"I was afraid you might make a certain judicial visit about which I have come to talk, before I had a chance to see you."

"Well," resumed the judge, addressing himself to a stout little woman who was standing by, "if you don't tell me what the trouble is I can't guess it, my girl."

"Make haste," said Lavienne; "don't take other folks' time."

"Monsieur," said the woman at last, coloring high, and dropping her voice so that none but the judge and Lavienne should hear her. "I peddle fruit, and I owed for the board of my last baby, and so I was laying by my poor earnings—"

"Well, and your husband took them," said Popinot, divining the end of the confession.

"Yes, monsieur."

"What is your name?"

"La Pomponne."

"And your husband's?"

"Toupinet."

"Rue du Petit-Banquier?" continued Popinot, referring to the pages of his register. "He is in prison," he added, reading a remark written on the margin of a report of the case.

"For debt only, my dear monsieur."

Popinot nodded.

"But, monsieur, I haven't money enough to buy fruit for my barrow; and the landlord he came yesterday and forced me to pay him, or else be turned out into the street."

Lavienne stooped to his master and said a few words in his ear.

"Well, how much do you want to buy your fruit in the market?"

"Ah! My dear monsieur, I should want, to carry on my business— yes, I should want—at least ten francs."

The judge made a sign to Lavienne, who took the ten francs from a large bag and gave them to the woman, while the judge entered the loan upon one of his books. Seeing the thrill of joy that passed over the woman's whole body, Bianchon divined the anxiety with which the poor creature had doubtless come to the judge's house.

"Your turn," said Lavienne to the old man with the white beard.

Bianchon took the servant aside and asked how long these interviews were likely to last.

"Monsieur has seen a hundred persons already, and there are fifty more *to do*," said Lavienne. "Monsieur will have time to pay his first visits and return."

"My boy," said the judge, turning round and seizing Horace by the arms, "see; here are two addresses, not far from here—one rue de Seine, the other rue de l'Arbalète. Just run round there, will you? Rue de Seine there's a young girl who has tried to smother herself; and you'll find, rue de l'Arbalète, a man who ought to go to your hospital. I'll wait breakfast for you."

Bianchon returned in about an hour. The rue du Fouarre was by that time deserted; day was dawning; his uncle was ready to go upstairs, for the last poor wretch whose misery he had lessened was just departing, and Lavienne's bag was empty.

"Well," said the judge, as they went upstairs, "how are they?"

"The man is dead," replied Bianchon; "the girl will pull through."

Mark Twain

:

ACT OF GOD IN NEVADA

The mountains are very high and steep about Carson, Eagle and
Washoe Valleys—very high and steep, and so when the snow gets to
melting off fast in the Spring and the warm surface-earth begins to
moisten and soften, the disastrous landslides commence. The reader
cannot know what a landslide is, unless he has lived in that country
and seen the whole side of a mountain taken off some fine morning
and deposited down in the valley, leaving a vast, treeless, unsightly
scar upon the mountain's front to keep the circumstances fresh in his
memory all the years that he may go on living within seventy miles of
that place.

General Buncombe was shipped out to Nevada in the invoice of Territorial offices, to be United States Attorney. He considered himself a
lawyer of parts, and he very much wanted an opportunity to manifest
it—partly for the pure gratification of it and partly because his salary
was Territorially meager (which is a strong expression). Now the older
citizens of a new territory look down upon the rest of the world with a
calm, benevolent compassion, as long as it keeps out of the way—
when it gets in the way they snub it. Sometimes this latter takes the
shape of a practical joke.

One morning Dick Hyde rode furiously up to General Buncombe's
door in Carson City and rushed into his presence without stopping to
tie his horse. He seemed much excited. He told the General that he
wanted him to conduct a suit for him and would pay him five hundred

451

dollars if he achieved a victory. And then, with violent gestures and a world of profanity, he poured out his griefs. He said it was pretty well known that for some years he had been farming (or ranching as the more customary term is) in Washoe District, and making a successful thing of it, and furthermore it was known that his ranch was situated just in the edge of the valley, and that Tom Morgan owned a ranch immediately above it on the mountain side. And now the trouble was, that one of those hated and dreaded landslides had come and slid Morgan's ranch, fences, cabins, cattle, barns and everything down on top of *his* ranch and exactly covered up every single vestige of his property, to a depth of about thirty-eight feet. Morgan was in possession and refused to vacate the premises—said he was occupying his own cabin and not interfering with anybody else's—and said the cabin was standing on the same dirt and same ranch it had always stood on, and he would like to see anybody make him vacate.

"And when I reminded him," said Hyde, weeping, "that it was on top of my ranch and that he was trespassing, he had the infernal meanness to ask me why didn't I *stay* on my ranch and hold possession when I see him a-coming. Why didn't I *stay* on it, the blathering lunatic—by George, when I heard that racket and looked up the hill it was just like the whole world was a-ripping and a-tearing down that mountain side—splinters, and cordwood, thunder and lightning, hail and snow, odds and ends of haystacks, and awful clouds of dust!—trees going end over end in the air, rocks as big as a house jumping 'bout a thousand feet high and busting into ten million pieces, cattle turned inside out and a-coming head on with their tails hanging out between their teeth! —and in the midst of all that wrack and destruction sot that cussed Morgan on his gatepost, a-wondering why I didn't *stay and hold possession!* Laws bless me, I just took one glimpse, General, and lit out'n the county in three jumps exactly.

"But what grinds me is that Morgan hangs on there and won't move off'n that ranch—says it's his'n and he's going to keep it—likes it better'n he did when it was higher up the hill. Mad! Well, I've been so mad for two days I couldn't find my way to town—been wandering around in the brush in a starving condition—got anything here to drink, General? But I'm here *now,* and I'm a-going to law. You hear me!"

Never in all the world, perhaps, were a man's feelings so outraged as were the General's. He said he had never heard of such high-handed conduct in all his life as this Morgan's. And he said there was no use in going to law—Morgan had no shadow of right to remain where he was—nobody in the wide world would uphold him in it, and no lawyer would take his case and no judge listen to it. Hyde said that right there was where he was mistaken—everybody in town sustained Morgan; Hal Brayton, a very smart lawyer, had taken his case; the courts being in vacation, it was to be tried before a referee, and ex-Governor Roop had already been appointed to that office and would open his court in a large public hall near the hotel at two that afternoon.

The General was amazed. He said he had suspected before that the people of that Territory were fools, and now he knew it. But he said rest easy, rest easy and collect the witnesses, for the victory was just as certain as if the conflict were already over. Hyde wiped away his tears and left.

At two in the afternoon referee Roop's Court opened, and Roop appeared throned among his sheriffs, the witnesses and spectators, and wearing upon his face a solemnity so awe-inspiring that some of his fellow-conspirators had misgivings that maybe he had not comprehended, after all, that this was merely a joke. An unearthly stillness prevailed, for at the slightest noise the judge uttered sternly the command:

"Order in the Court!"

And the sheriffs promptly echoed it. Presently the General elbowed his way through the crowd of spectators, with his arms full of lawbooks, and on his ears fell an order from the judge which was the first respectful recognition of his high official dignity that had ever saluted them, and it trickled pleasantly through his whole system:

"Way for the United States Attorney!"

The witnesses were called—legislators, high government officers, ranchmen, miners, Indians, Chinamen, Negroes. Three fourths of them were called by the defendant Morgan, but no matter, the testimony invariably went in favor of the plaintiff Hyde. Each new witness only added new testimony to the absurdity of a man's claiming to own another man's property because his farm had slid down on top of it. Then the Morgan lawyers made their speeches, and seemed to make singularly weak ones—they did really nothing to help the Morgan cause. And now the General, with exultation in his face, got up and made an impassioned effort; he pounded the table, he banged the lawbooks, he shouted, and roared, and howled, he quoted from everything and everybody, poetry, sarcasm, statistics, history, pathos, bathos, blasphemy, and wound up with a grand war-whoop for free speech, freedom of the press, free schools, the Glorious Bird of America and the principles of eternal justice! [Applause.]

When the General sat down, he did it with the conviction that if there was anything in good strong testimony, a great speech and believing and admiring countenances all around, Mr. Morgan's case was killed. Ex-Governor Roop leaned his head upon his hand for some minutes, thinking, and the still audience waited for his decision. Then he got up and stood erect, with bended head, and thought again. Then he walked the floor with long, deliberate strides, his chin in his hand, and still the audience waited. At last he returned to his throne, seated himself, and began, impressively:

"Gentlemen, I feel the great responsibility that rests upon me this day. This is no ordinary case. On the contrary it is plain that it is the most solemn and awful that ever man was called upon to decide. Gentlemen, I have listened attentively to the evidence, and have perceived that the weight of it, the overwhelming weight of it, is in favor of the plaintiff Hyde. I have listened also to the remarks of counsel, with high interest—and especially will I commend the masterly and irrefutable logic of the distinguished gentleman who represents the plaintiff. But, gentlemen, let us beware how we allow mere human testimony, human ingenuity in argument and human ideas of equity, to influence us at a moment so solemn as this. Gentlemen, it ill becomes us worms as we are, to meddle with the decrees of Heaven. It is plain to me that Heaven, in its inscrutable wisdom, has seen fit to move this defendant's ranch for a purpose. We are but creatures, and we must submit. If Heaven has chosen to favor the defendant Morgan in this marked and wonderful manner; and if Heaven, dissatisfied with the position of the Morgan ranch upon the mountain side, has chosen to remove it to a position more eligible and more advantageous for its owner, it ill becomes us, insects as we are, to question the legality of the act or inquire into the reasons that prompted it. No—Heaven created the ranches and it is Heaven's prerogative to rearrange them, to experiment with them, to shift them around at its pleasure. It is for us to submit, without repining. I warn you that this thing which has happened is a thing with which the sacrilegious hands and brains and tongues of men must not meddle. Gentlemen, it is the verdict of this court that the plaintiff, Richard Hyde, has been deprived of his ranch by the visitation of God! And from this decision there is no appeal."

Buncombe seized his cargo of lawbooks and plunged out of the courtroom frantic with indignation. He pronounced Roop to be a miraculous fool, an inspired idiot. In all good faith he returned at night and remonstrated with Roop upon his extravagant decision, and implored him to walk the floor and think for half an hour, and see if he could not figure out some sort of modification of the verdict. Roop yielded at last and got up to walk. He walked two hours and a half, and at last his face lit up happily and he told Buncombe it had occurred to him that the ranch underneath the new Morgan ranch still belonged to Hyde, that his title to the ground was just as good as it had ever been, and therefore he was of opinion that Hyde had a right to dig it out from under there and—

The General never waited to hear the end of it. He was always an impatient and irascible man, that way. At the end of two months the fact that he had been played upon with a joke had managed to bore itself, like another Hoosac Tunnel, through the solid adamant of his understanding.

Sir Walter Scott

:

ALAN FAIRFORD'S FIRST CAUSE
from *Redgauntlet*

LETTER XIII

ALAN FAIRFORD TO DARSIE LATIMER

I write on the instant, as you direct; and in a tragicomic humor, for I
have a tear in my eye, and a smile on my cheek. Dearest Darsie, sure
never a being but yourself could be so generous—sure never a being but
yourself could be so absurd! I remember when you were a boy you wished
to make your fine new whip a present to old aunt Peggy, merely because
she admired it; and now, with like unreflecting and inappropriate liber-
ality, you would resign your beloved to a smoke-dried young sophister,
who cares not one of the hairs which it is his occupation to split, for all
the daughters of Eve. *I* in love with your Lilias—your Greenmantle—
your unknown enchantress!—why I scarce saw her for five minutes,
and even then only the tip of her chin was distinctly visible. She was
well made, and the tip of her chin was of a most promising cast for the
rest of the face; but Heaven save you! She came upon business! And for
a lawyer to fall in love with a pretty client on a single consultation,
would be as wise as if he became enamored of a particularly bright sun-
beam which chanced for a moment to gild his bar-wig. I give you my
word I am heart-whole; and moreover, I assure you, that before I suf-

fer a woman to sit near my heart's core, I must see her full face, without mask or mantle, ay, and know a good deal of her mind into the bargain. So never fret yourself on my account, my kind and generous Darsie; but, for your own sake, have a care, and let not an idle attachment, so lightly taken up, lead you into serious danger.

On this subject I feel so apprehensive, that now when I am decorated with the honors of the gown, I should have abandoned my career at the very starting to come to you, but for my father having contrived to clog my heels with fetters of a professional nature. I will tell you the matter at length, for it is comical enough; and why should not you list to my juridical adventures, as well as I to those of your fiddling knight-errantry?

It was after dinner, and I was considering how I might best introduce to my father the private resolution I had formed to set off for Dumfries-shire, or whether I had not better run away at once, and plead my excuse by letter, when, assuming the peculiar look with which he communicates any of his intentions respecting me, that he suspects may not be altogether acceptable, "Alan," he said, "ye now wear a gown— ye have opened shop, as we would say of a more mechanical profession; and, doubtless, ye think the floor of the courts is strewed with guineas, and that ye have only to stoop down to gather them?"

"I hope I am sensible, sir," I replied, "that I have some knowledge and practice to acquire, and must stoop for that in the first place."

"It is well said," answered my father; and, always afraid to give too much encouragement, added, "Very well said, if it be well acted up to—Stoop to get knowledge and practice is the very word. Ye know very well, Alan, that in the other faculty who study the *Ars medendi,* before the young doctor gets to the bedsides of palaces, he must, as they call it, walk the hospitals; and cure Lazarus of his sores, before he be admitted to prescribe for Dives, when he has gout or indigestion———"

"I am aware, sir, that———"

"Whisht—do not interrupt the court—Well—also the chirurgeons have a useful practice, by which they put their apprentices and *tyrones* to work upon senseless dead bodies, to which, as they can do no good, so they certainly can do as little harm; while at the same time the *tyro,* or apprentice, gains experience, and becomes fit to whip off a leg or arm from a living subject, as cleanly as ye would slice an onion."

"I believe I guess your meaning, sir," answered I; "and were it not for a very particular engagement———"

"Do not speak to me of engagements; but whisht—there is a good lad—and do not interrupt the court."

My father, you know, is apt—be it said with all filial duty—to be a little prolix in his harangues. I had nothing for it but to lean back and listen.

"Maybe you think, Alan, because I have, doubtless, the management of some actions in dependence, whilk my worthy clients have entrusted me with, that I may think of airting them your way *instanter;* and so setting you up in practice, so far as my small business or influence may go; and doubtless, Alan, that is a day whilk I hope may come round. But, then, before I give, as the proverb hath it, 'My own fish-guts to my own sea-maws,' I must, for the sake of my own character, be very sure that my sea-maw can pick them to some purpose. What say ye?"

"I am so far," answered I, "from wishing to get early into practice, sir, that I would willingly bestow a few days——"

"In farther study, ye would say, Alan. But that is not the way either —ye must walk the hospitals—ye must cure Lazarus—ye must cut and carve on a departed subject, to show your skill."

"I am sure," I replied, "I will undertake the cause of any poor man with pleasure, and bestow as much pains upon it as if it were a Duke's; but for the next two or three days——"

"They must be devoted to close study, Alan—very close study indeed; for ye must stand primed for a hearing *in presentia Dominorum,* upon Tuesday next."

"I, sir?" I replied in astonishment—"I have not opened my mouth in the Outer-House yet!"

"Never mind the Court of the Gentiles, man," said my father; "we will have you into the Sanctuary at once—over shoes, over boots."

"But, sir, I should really spoil any cause thrust on me so hastily."

"Ye cannot spoil it, Alan," said my father, rubbing his hands with much complacency; "that is the very cream of the business, man—it is just, as I said before, a subject upon whilk all the *tyrones* have been trying their whittles for fifteen years; and as there have been about ten or a dozen agents concerned, and each took his own way, the case is come to that pass that Stair or Arniston could not mend it; and I do not think even you, Alan, can do it much harm—ye may get credit by it, but ye can lose none."

"And pray what is the name of my happy client, sir?" said I, ungraciously enough, I believe.

"It is a well-known name in the Parliament-House," replied my father. "To say the truth, I expect him every moment; it is Peter Peebles." *

"Peter Peebles!" exclaimed I, in astonishment; he is an insane beggar—as poor as Job, and as mad as a March hare!"

"He has been pleaing in the court for fifteen years," said my father, in a tone of commiseration, which seemed to acknowledge that this fact was enough to account for the poor man's condition both in mind and circumstances.

"Besides, sir," I added, "he is on the Poor's Roll; and you know there are advocates regularly appointed to manage those cases; and for me to presume to interfere——"

"Whisht, Alan!—Never interrupt the court—All *that* is managed for ye like a tee'd ball"; (my father sometimes draws his similes from his once favorite game of golf);—"you must know, Alan, that Peter's cause was to have been opened by young Dumtoustie—ye may ken the lad, a son of Dumtoustie of that ilk, member of Parliament for the county of ——, and a nephew of Laird's younger brother, worthy Lord Bladderskate, whilk ye are aware sounds as like being akin to a peatship† and a sheriffdom, as a sieve is sib to a riddle. Now, Saunders Drudgeit, my lord's clerk, came to me this morning in the House, like ane bereft of his wits; for it seems that young Dumtoustie is ane of the Poor's Lawyers, and Peter Peebles's process had been remitted to him of course. But so soon as the harebrained goose saw the pokes,‡ (as indeed, Alan, they are none of the least), he took fright, called for his nag, lap on, and away to the country is he gone; and so, said Saunders, my lord is at his wit's end wi' vexation and shame, to see his nevoy break off the course at the very starting. 'I'll tell you, Saunders,' said I, 'were I my lord, and a friend or kinsman of mine should leave the town while the court was sitting, that kinsman, or be he what he liked, should never darken my door again.' And then, Alan, I thought to turn

* This unfortunate litigant (for a person named Peter Peebles actually flourished) frequented the courts of justice in Scotland about the year 1792, and the sketch of his appearance is given from recollection. The author is of opinion, that he himself had at one time the honor to be counsel for Peter Peebles, whose voluminous course of litigation served as a sort of assay-pieces to most young men who were called to the bar. The scene of the consultation is entirely imaginary.
† Formerly a lawyer, supposed to be under the peculiar patronage of any particular judge, was invidiously termed his *peat* or *pet*.
‡ Process-bags.

the ball our own way; and I said that you were a gey sharp birkie, just off the irons, and if it would oblige my lord, and so forth, you would open Peter's cause on Tuesday, and make some handsome apology for the necessary absence of your learned friend, and the loss which your client and the court had sustained, and so forth. Saunders lap at the proposition like a cock at a grossart; for, he said, the only chance was to get a new hand, that did not ken the charge he was taking upon him; for there was not a lad of two Sessions' standing that was not dead-sick of Peter Peebles and his cause; and he advised me to break the matter gently to you at the first; but I told him you were a good bairn, Alan, and had no will and pleasure in these matters but mine."

What could I say, Darsie, in answer to this arrangement, so very well meant—so very vexatious at the same time?—To imitate the defection and flight of young Dumtoustie, was at once to destroy my father's hopes of me for ever; nay, such is the keenness with which he regards all connected with his profession, it might have been a step to breaking his heart. I was obliged, therefore, to bow in sad acquiescence, when my father called to James Wilkinson to bring the two bits of pokes he would find on his table.

Exit James, and presently re-enters, bending under the load of two huge leathern bags, full of papers to the brim, and labelled on the greasy backs with the magic impress of the clerks of court, and the title, *Peebles against Plainstanes.* This huge mass was deposited on the table, and my father, with no ordinary glee in his countenance, began to draw out the various bundles of papers, secured by none of your red tape or whipcord, but stout, substantial casts of tarred rope, such as might have held small craft at their moorings.

I made a last and desperate effort to get rid of the impending job. "I am really afraid, sir, that this case seems so much complicated, and there is so little time to prepare, that we had better move the Court to supersede it till next Session."

"How, sir?—How, Alan?" said my father—"Would you approbate and reprobate, sir?—You have accepted the poor man's cause, and if you have not his fee in your pocket, it is because he has none to give you; and now would you approbate and reprobate in the same breath of your mouth?—Think of your oath of office, Alan, and your duty to your father, my dear boy."

Once more, what could I say?—I saw from my father's hurried and alarmed manner, that nothing could vex him so much as failing in the point he had determined to carry, and once more intimated my readiness to do my best under every disadvantage.

"Well, well, my boy," said my father, "the Lord will make your days long in the land, for the honor you have given to your father's gray hairs. You may find wiser advisers, Alan, but none that can wish you better."

My father, you know, does not usually give way to expressions of affection, and they are interesting in proportion to their rarity. My eyes began to fill at seeing his glisten; and my delight at having given him such sensible gratification would have been unmixed but for the thoughts of you. These out of the question, I could have grappled with the bags, had they been as large as corn-sacks. But, to turn what was grave into farce, the door opened, and Wilkinson ushered in Peter Peebles.

You must have seen this original, Darsie, who, like others in the same predicament, continues to haunt the courts of justice, where he has made shipwreck of time, means, and understanding. Such insane paupers have sometimes seemed to me to resemble wrecks lying upon the shoals on the Goodwin Sands, or in Yarmouth Roads, warning other vessels to keep aloof from the banks on which they have been lost; or rather, such ruined clients are like scarecrows and potato-bogles, distributed through the courts to scare away fools from the scene of litigation.

The identical Peter wears a huge great-coat, threadbare and patched itself, yet carefully so disposed and secured by what buttons remain, and many supplementary pins, as to conceal the still more infirm state of his under garments. The shoes and stockings of a ploughman were, however, seen to meet at his knees with a pair of brownish, blackish breeches; a rusty-colored handkerchief, that has been black in its day, surrounded his throat, and was an apology for linen. His hair, half gray, half black, escaped in elf-locks around a huge wig, made of tow, as it seemed to me, and so much shrunk, that it stood up on the very top of his head; above which he plants, when covered, an immense cocked hat, which, like the chieftain's banner in an ancient battle, may be seen any sederunt day betwixt nine and ten, high towering above all the fluctuating and changeful scene in the Outer-House, where his eccentricities often make him the center of a group of petulant and teasing boys, who exercise upon him every art of ingenious torture. His countenance, originally that of a portly, comely burgess, is now emaciated with poverty and anxiety, and rendered wild by an insane lightness about the eyes; a withered and blighted skin and complexion; features begrimed with snuff, charged with the self-importance peculiar to insanity; and a habit of perpetually speaking to himself. Such was my unfortunate client; and I must allow, Darsie, that my profession had need to do a great deal of good, if, as is much to be feared, it brings many individuals to such a pass.

After we had been, with a good deal of form, presented to each other, at which time I easily saw by my father's manner that he was desirous of supporting Peter's character in my eyes, as much as circumstances would permit, "Alan," he said, "this is the gentleman who has agreed to accept of you as his counsel, in place of young Dumtoustie."

"Entirely out of favor to my old acquaintance your father," said Peter, with a benign and patronizing countenance, "out of respect to your father, and my old intimacy with Lord Bladderskate. Otherwise, by the *Regiam Majestatem!* I would have presented a petition and complaint against Daniel Dumtoustie, Advocate, by name and surname—I would, by all the practiques!—I know the forms of process; and I am not to be trifled with."

My father here interrupted my client, and reminded him that there was a good deal of business to do, as he proposed to give the young counsel an outline of the state of the conjoined process, with a view to letting him into the merits of the cause, disencumbered from the points of form. "I have made a short abbreviate, Mr. Peebles," said he; "having sat up late last night, and employed much of this morning in wading through these papers, to save Alan some trouble, and I am now about to state the result."

"I will state it myself," said Peter, breaking in without reverence upon his solicitor.

"No, by no means," said my father; "I am your agent for the time."

"Mine eleventh in number," said Peter; "I have a new one every year; I wish I could get a new coat as regularly."

"Your agent for the time," resumed my father; "and you, who are acquainted with the forms, know that the client states the cause to the agent—the agent to the counsel——"

"The counsel to the Lord Ordinary," continued Peter, once set-a-going, like the peal of an alarm clock, "the Ordinary to the Inner-House, the President to the Bench. It is just like the rope to the man, the man to the ox, the ox to the water, the water to the fire——"

"Hush, for Heaven's sake, Mr. Peebles," said my father, cutting his recitation short; "time wears on—we must get to business—you must not interrupt the court, you know—hem, hem! From this abbreviate it appears——"

"Before you begin," said Peter Peebles, "I'll thank you to order me a morsel of bread and cheese, or some cauld meat, or broth, or the like alimentary provision; I was so anxious to see your son, that I could not eat a mouthful of dinner."

Heartily glad, I believe, to have so good a chance of stopping his client's mouth, effectually, my father ordered some cold meat; to which James Wilkinson, for the honor of the house, was about to add the brandy bottle, which remained on the sideboard, but, at a wink from my father, supplied its place with small beer. Peter charged the provisions with the rapacity of a famished lion; and so well did the diversion engage him, that though, while my father stated the case, he looked at him repeatedly, as if he meant to interrupt his statement, yet he always found more agreeable employment for his mouth, and returned to the cold beef with an avidity which convinced me he had not had such an opportunity for many a day of satiating his appetite. Omitting much formal phraseology, and many legal details, I will endeavor to give you, in exchange for your fiddler's tale, the history of a litigant, or rather, the history of his lawsuit.

"Peter Peebles and Paul Plainstanes," said my father, "entered into partnership, in the year——, as mercers and linendrapers, in the Luckenbooths, and carried on a great line of business to mutual advantage. But the learned counsel needeth not to be told, *societas est mater discordiarum,* partnership oft makes pleaship. The company being dissolved by mutual consent, in the year——, the affairs had to be wound up, and after certain attempts to settle the matter extra-judicially, it was at last brought into the Court, and has branched out into several distinct processes, most of whilk have been conjoined by the Ordinary. It is to the state of these processes that counsel's attention is particularly directed. There is the original action of Peebles *v.* Plainstanes, convening him for payment of £3,000, less or more, as alleged balance due by Plainstanes. 2dly, There is a counter action, in which Plainstanes is pursuer and Peebles defender, for £2,500, less or more, being balance alleged *per contra,* to be due by Peebles. 3dly, Mr. Peebles's seventh agent advised an action of Compt and Reckoning at his instance, wherein what balance should prove due on either side might be fairly struck and ascertained. 4thly, To meet the hypothetical case, that

Peebles might be found liable in a balance to Plainstanes, Mr. Wild-goose, Mr. Peebles's eighth agent, recommended a Multiplepoinding to bring all parties concerned into the field."

My brain was like to turn at this account of lawsuit within lawsuit, like a nest of chip-boxes, with all of which I was expected to make myself acquainted.

"I understand," I said, "that Mr. Peebles claims a sum of money from Plainstanes—how then can he be his debtor? And if not his debtor, how can he bring a Multiplepoinding, the very summons of which sets forth, that the pursuer does owe certain monies, which he is desirous to pay by warrant of a judge?" *

"Ye know little of the matter, I doubt, friend," said Mr. Peebles; "a Multiplepoinding is the safest *remedium juris* in the whole form of process. I have known it conjoined with a declarator of marriage— Your beef is excellent," he said to my father, who in vain endeavored to resume his legal disquisition; "but something highly powdered—and the twopenny is undeniable; but it is small swipes—small swipes more of hop than malt—with your leave, I'll try your black bottle."

My father started to help him with his own hand, and in due measure; but, infinitely to my amusement, Peter got possession of the bottle by the neck, and my father's ideas of hospitality were far too scrupulous to permit his attempting, by any direct means, to redeem it; so that Peter returned to the table triumphant, with his prey in his clutch.

"Better have a wine-glass, Mr. Peebles," said my father, in an admonitory tone, "you will find it pretty strong."

"If the kirk is ower muckle, we can sing mass in the quire," said Peter, helping himself in the goblet out of which he had been drinking the small beer. "What is it, usquebaugh?—BRANDY, as I am an honest man! I had almost forgotten the name and taste of brandy. —Mr. Fairford elder, your good health" (a mouthful of brandy)— "Mr. Alan Fairford, wishing you well through your arduous undertaking" (another go-down of the comfortable liquor). "And now, though you have given a tolerable breviate of this great lawsuit, of whilk everybody has heard something that has walked the boards in the Outer-House (here's to ye again, by way of interim decreet), yet ye have omitted to speak a word of the arrestments."

"I was just coming to that point, Mr. Peebles."

* Multiplepoinding is, I believe, equivalent to what is called in England a case of Double Distress.

"Or of the action of suspension of the charge on the bill."

"I was just coming to that."

"Or the advocation of the Sheriff-Court process."

"I was just coming to it."

"As Tweed comes to Melrose, I think," said the litigant; and then filling his goblet about a quarter full of brandy, as if in absence of mind, "Oh, Mr. Alan Fairford, ye are a lucky man to buckle to such a cause as mine at the very outset! It is like a specimen on all causes, man. By the Regiam, there is not a *remedium juris* in the practiques but ye'll find a spice o't. Here's to your getting weel through with it—Pshut—I am drinking naked spirits, I think. But if the heathen be ower strong, we'll christen him with the brewer" (here he added a little small beer to his beverage, paused, rolled his eyes, winked, and proceeded)— "Mr. Fairford—the action of assault and battery, Mr. Fairford, when I compelled the villain Plainstanes to pull my nose within two steps of King Charles's statue in the Parliament Close—there I had him in a hose-net. Never man could tell me how to shape that process—no counsel that ever selled wind could condescend and say whether it were best to proceed by way of petition and complaint, *ad vindictam publican,* with consent of his Majesty's advocate, or by action on the statute for battery *pendente lite,* whilk would be the winning my plea at once, and so getting a back-door out of Court—By the Regiam, that beef and brandy is uncohet at my heart—I maun try the ale again" (sipped a little beer); "and the ale's but cauld, I maun e'en put in the rest of the brandy."

He was as good as his word, and proceeded in so loud and animated a style of elocution, thumping the table, drinking and snuffing alternately, that my father, abandoning all attempts to interrupt him, sat silent and ashamed, suffering, and anxious for the conclusion of the scene.

"And then to come back to my pet process of all—my battery and assault process, when I had the good luck to provoke him to pull my nose at the very threshold of the Court, whilk was the very thing I wanted—Mr. Pest, ye ken him, Daddie Fairford? Old Pest was for making it out *hamesucken,* for he said the Court might be said—said —ugh!—to be my dwelling-place. I dwell mair there than ony gate else, and the essence of hamesucken is to strike a man in his dwelling-place—mind that, young advocate—and so there's hope Plainstanes may be hanged, as many has for a less matter; for, my Lords—will Pest say to the Justiciary bodies—my Lords, the Parliament House is

Peebles's place of dwelling, says he—being *commune forum,* and *commune forum est commune domicilium*—Lass, fetch another glass of whisky, and score it—time to gae hame—by the practiques, I cannot find the jug—yet there's twa of them, I think. By the Regiam, Fairford—Daddie Fairford—lend us twal pennies to buy sneeshing, mine is done—Macer, call another cause."

The box fell from his hands, and his body would at the same time have fallen from the chair, had not I supported him.

"This is intolerable," said my father—"Call a chairman, James Wilkinson, to carry this degraded, worthless, drunken beast home."

When Peter Peebles was removed from this memorable consultation, under the care of an able-bodied Celt, my father hastily bundled up the papers, as a showman, whose exhibition has miscarried, hastes to remove his booth. "Here are my memoranda, Alan," he said, in a hurried way; "look them carefully over—compare them with the processes, and turn it in your head before Tuesday. Many a good speech has been made for a beast of a client; and hark ye, lad, hark ye—I never intended to cheat you of your fee when all was done, though I would have liked to have heard the speech first; but there is nothing like corning the horse before the journey. Here are five good guineas in a silk purse—of your poor mother's netting, Alan—she would have been a blithe woman to have seen her young son with a gown on his back—but no more of that—be a good boy, and to the work like a tiger."

I did set to work, Darsie; for who could resist such motives? With my father's assistance, I have mastered the details, confused as they are; and on Tuesday, I shall plead as well for Peter Peebles, as I could for a duke. Indeed, I feel my head so clear on the subject, as to be able to write this long letter to you; into which, however, Peter and his lawsuit have insinuated themselves so far, as to show you how much they at present occupy my thoughts. Once more, be careful of yourself, and mindful of me, who am ever thine, while

ALAN FAIRFORD

Anatole France

:

MONSIEUR THOMAS

I once knew an austere judge. His name was Thomas de Maulan. He was a country gentleman. During the seven years ministry of Marshal MacMahon he had become a magistrate in the hope that one day he would administer justice in the king's name. He had principles which he believed to be unalterable, having never attempted to examine them. As soon as one examines a principle one discovers something beneath it and perceives that it was not a principle at all. Both his religious and his social principles Thomas de Maulan kept outside the range of his curiosity.

He was judge in the court of first instance in the little town of X——, where I was then living. His appearance inspired esteem and even a certain sympathy. His figure was tall, thin, and bony, his face was sallow. His extreme simplicity gave him a somewhat distinguished air. He liked to be called Monsieur Thomas, not that he despised his social position, but because he considered himself too poor to support it. I knew enough of him to recognize that his appearance was not deceptive and that though weak in character and narrow in intelligence he had a noble soul. I discovered that he possessed high moral qualities. But, having had occasion to observe him in the fulfilment of his functions as examining magistrate and judge, I perceived that his very uprightness and his conception of duty rendered him cruel and sometimes completely deprived him of insight. His extreme piety caused him to be unconsciously obsessed by the ideas of sin and expiation, of crime and

467

punishment; and it was obvious that in punishing criminals he experienced the agreeable sensation of purifying them. Human justice he regarded as a faint yet beautiful reflection of divine justice. In childhood he had been taught that suffering is good, that it is a merit in itself, a virtue, an expiation. This he believed firmly; and he held that suffering is the due of whomsoever has sinned. He loved to chastise. His punishments were the outcome of the kindness of his heart. Accustomed to give thanks to the God who, for his eternal salvation, afflicted him with toothache and colic as a punishment for Adam's sin, he sentenced vagrants and vagabonds to imprisonment and reparation as one who bestows benefits. His legal philosophy was founded upon his catechism; his pitilessness proceeded from his directness and simplicity of mind. One could not call him cruel. But not being sensual neither was he sensitive. He had no precise physical idea of human suffering. His conception of it was purely moral and dogmatic. There was something mystic in his preference for the system of solitary confinement, and it was not without a certain joyfulness of heart and eye that one day he showed me over a fine prison which had recently been built in his district: a white thing, clean, silent, terrible; cells arranged in a circle, and the warder in the center in an observation chamber. It looked like a laboratory constructed by lunatics for the manufacture of lunatics. And malevolent lunatics indeed are those inventors of the solitary system who in order to convert a wrongdoer into a moral being subject him to a regime which turns him into an imbecile or a savage. That was not the opinion of Monsieur Thomas. He gazed with silent satisfaction on those atrocious cells. At the back of his mind was the idea that the prisoner is never alone since God is with him. And his calm, self-satisfied glance seemed to say: "Here I have brought five or six persons face to face with their Creator and Sovereign Judge. There is no more enviable fate in the world."

It fell to this magistrate's lot to conduct the inquiry in several cases, among others in that of a teacher. Lay and clerical education were then at open war. The republicans having denounced the ignorance and brutality of the priests, the clerical newspaper of the district accused a lay teacher of having made a child sit on a red-hot stove. Among the country aristocracy this accusation found credence. Revolting details were related and the common gossip aroused the attention of justice. Monsieur Thomas, who was an honest man, would never have listened to his passions, had he known them to be passions. But he regarded them as duties because they were religious. He believed it to be his duty to consider complaints urged against a godless school, and he failed to perceive his extreme eagerness to consider them. I must not omit to say that he conducted the inquiry with meticulous care and infinite trouble. He conducted it according to the ordinary methods of justice, and he obtained wonderful results. Thirty school children, persistently interrogated, replied at first badly, afterwards better, and finally very well. After a month's examination, they replied so well that they all gave the same answer. The thirty depositions agreed, they were identical, literally identical, and these children who on the first day said they had seen nothing, now declared with one unfaltering voice, employing exactly the same words, that their little schoolfellow had been seated bareskinned, on a red-hot stove. Monsieur le Juge Thomas was congratulating himself on so satisfactory a result, when the teacher proved irrefutably that there had never been a stove in the school. Then Monsieur Thomas began to suspect that the children were lying. But what he never perceived was that he himself had unwittingly dictated their evidence and taught it to them by heart.

The prosecution was nonsuited. The teacher was dismissed the court after having been severely reprimanded by the judge, who strongly urged him in the future to restrain his brutal instincts. Outside his deserted school the priest's scholars made a hullaballoo. And when he went out he was greeted with cries of "Ha! ha! *Grille-Cul* (Roastback)"; and stones were thrown at him. The Inspector of Primary Schools being informed of the state of affairs, drew up a report stating that this teacher had no authority over his pupils and concluding that his immediate transference to another school would be advisable. He was sent to a village where a dialect was spoken which he did not understand. Even there he was called *Grille-Cul*. It was the only French term that was known there.

During my intercourse with Monsieur Thomas I learnt how all evidence given before an examining magistrate comes to be uniform in style. He received me in his room whilst with the assistance of his clerk he was examining a witness. I was about to withdraw, but he begged me to remain, saying that my presence would in no way interfere with a proper administration of justice.

I sat down in a corner and listened to the questions and answers:

"Duval, did you see the accused at six o'clock in the evening?"

"That is to say, Monsieur le Juge, my wife was at the window. Then she said to me: 'There's Socquardot going by!' "

"His presence under your window must have struck her as remarkable since she took the trouble to mention it to you particularly. And did the gait of the accused arouse your suspicion?"

"I will tell you how it was, Monsieur le Juge. My wife said to me: 'There's Socquardot going by!' Then I looked and said: 'Why yes, it's Socquardot!' "

"Precisely! Clerk, write down: At six o'clock in the evening, the couple Duval saw the accused loafing round the house and walking with a suspicious gait."

Monsieur Thomas put a few more questions to the witness, who was a day laborer by occupation: he received replies and dictated to his clerk their translation into judge's jargon. Then the witness listened to the reading of his evidence, signed it, bowed and withdrew.

"Why," I asked, "do you not record the evidence as it is given you instead of translating it into words never used by the witness?"

Monsieur Thomas gazed at me with astonishment and replied calmly:

"I do not understand your meaning. I record the evidence as faithfully as possible. Every magistrate does. And in all the law reports there is not a single instance of evidence having been altered or distorted by a judge. If, in conformity with the invariable custom of my colleagues, I modify the exact terms used by the witnesses, it is because such witnesses as this Duval, whom you have just heard, express themselves badly, and it would be derogatory to the dignity of justice to record incorrect, low and frequently gross expressions when there is no point in doing so. But, my dear sir, I think you fail to realize the conditions of a judicial examination. You must bear in mind the object of the magistrate in recording and classifying evidence. It is not for his own enlightenment alone but for that of the tribunal. It is not enough for him to see the case clearly, it must be equally clear to the minds of the judges. He has therefore to bring into prominence those charges which are sometimes concealed beneath the incoherent or diffuse story of a witness or confused by the ambiguous replies of the accused. If it were to be registered without order or method the most convicting evidence would lose its point and the majority of criminals would escape punishment."

"But surely," I asked, "a proceeding which consists in fixing the wandering thoughts of witnesses must be very dangerous."

"It would be if magistrates were not conscientious. But I never yet met a magistrate who was not deeply conscious of his duty. And yet I have sat on the Bench with Protestants, Deists and Jews. But they were magistrates."

"At least you must admit, Monsieur Thomas, that your method possesses one disadvantage: when you read the written account of his evidence to the witness, he can hardly understand it, since you have introduced into it terms he is not accustomed to employ and the sense of which escapes him. What does your expression 'suspicious gait' convey to the mind of this laborer?"

He replied eagerly:

"I have thought of that, and against this danger I have taken the greatest precautions. I will give you an example. A short time ago a witness of a somewhat limited intelligence and of whose morals I was ignorant, appeared not to attend to the clerk's reading of the witness's evidence. I had it read a second time, having urged the deponent to give it his sustained attention. By what I could see he did nothing of the kind. Then in order to bring home to him a more correct appreciation of his duty and his responsibility I made use of a stratagem. I dictated to the clerk one final phrase which contradicted everything that had gone before. I asked the witness to sign. Then, just as he was putting pen to paper, I seized his arm. 'Wretch!' I cried, 'you are about to sign a declaration contrary to the one you have made and by so doing to commit a crime.' "

"Well! and what did he say to you?"

"He replied piteously: 'Monsieur le Juge, you are cleverer than I, you must know best what I ought to write.'

"You see," added Monsieur Thomas, "that a judge anxious to fulfil his function well can guard himself against any danger of making a mistake. Believe me, my dear sir, judicial error is a myth."

Anonymous (*Fifteenth Century*)

:

THE FARCE OF THE WORTHY MASTER, PIERRE PATELIN, THE LAWYER

CHARACTERS

THE JUDGE, *whom no man dare judge.*

PATELIN, *the lawyer, a counselor indeed, possessing all those virtues which a good counselor should possess.*

GUILLEMETTE, *his wife, a fit wife for a lawyer.*

GUILLAUME JOCEAULME, *the draper, a successful merchant who has been cheating his customers from the day he began selling.*

TIBALD LAMBKIN, *a shepherd, a fellow, who, if his lot in life had been better, might have become a lawyer like* PATELIN, *or a merchant like* JOCEAULME.

This happened in a little town in France in the Year of Our Lord, 1400.

SCENE I

On either side of the stage is a street scene. In back, a curtain is partly drawn to each side showing the interior of PATELIN'S *house.* PATELIN *sits in bed reading a large folio; on a chair next to the bed* GUILLEMETTE *sits mending an old dress. On a bench a little to the side are kitchen utensils: a frying pan, a broom, etc. On the bed lies a nightgown and a cap.*

GUILLEMETTE: You have nothing to say now, I suppose, have you? . . . While I needs must mend rags a beggar would be ashamed to wear— and you, a member of the learned profession! . . . a lawyer . . .

PATELIN (*In bed*): There was a time when my door was crowded with clients . . . when I had plenty of work . . . and fine clothes to wear too.

GUILLEMETTE: Of what good is that to-day?—eh?

PATELIN: Wife, I was too shrewd for them. Men don't like people wiser than themselves.

GUILLEMETTE: Aye, you could always beat them at law. . . . But that was long ago.

PATELIN: It hurts me truly to see you mending rags . . . and wives of men who are thick skulled asses wearing golden threaded cloth and fine wool. There is that draper's wife across the way . . .

GUILLEMETTE: Cease the cackling. (*Silently working for a while*) I'd give something rare and costly for a new gown on St. Mary's day. Heaven knows I need it.

PATELIN: So you do and so do I as well. It is not fit to see one of the learned profession walking about like a beggar on the highway. Ah! If I could only get some clients! I know my law well enough yet. There is not many a one can beat me at the finer points.

GUILLEMETTE: A fig for it all! Of what good is it? We are all but starved . . . and as for clothes—look. (*Holds up the dress she is mending.*)

PATELIN: Silence, good wife! Could I but have some business and put my head with seriousness to it . . . Who knows but the days of plenty would soon enough return!

GUILLEMETTE: There is not a soul in town but a fool would trust himself to you. They know too well your way of handling cases. They say you are a master . . . at cheating. (PATELIN *rises indignant.*)

PATELIN: They mean at law . . . at law, good wife. Ha, I should like to see a lawyer beat me at it . . . and . . . (*Suddenly stops, thinks for a moment, then his whole face lights up*) I am going to market. I have just thought of a little business I have there. (*Gets out of bed.*)

GUILLEMETTE: Going to market? What for? You have no money.

PATELIN: I am going to market . . . on business . . . to the long-nosed donkey, our neighbor . . . the Draper.

GUILLEMETTE: What for?

PATELIN: To buy some cloth. . . .

GUILLEMETTE: Holy Saints! You know well he is more close-fisted than any other merchant in town. He'll never trust you.

PATELIN: Ah, that's just why I am going. The more miserly, the easier to gull; and . . . I have thought of something fine, . . . that will get us enough cloth . . . both for you and me.

GUILLEMETTE: You must be mad.

PATELIN (*Not heeding her*): Let me see . . . (*Measuring her with his arm's length*) Two and one-half for you . . . (*Measuring himself in the same way*) three for me . . . and . . . What color would you want? Green or red?

GUILLEMETTE: I'll be pleased with any kind. Beggars can't be choosers. But don't think I believe what you say. I am not a fool. You'll never get any from Master Joceaulme. He'll never trust you, I am certain.

PATELIN: Who knows? Who knows? He might . . . and then really get paid . . . on Doom's-day. . . . Ho, ho, . . .

GUILLEMETTE: Don't you think you had better make haste, lest all the cloth be sold?

PATELIN (*Offended, walking off*): Wife, I forgive you. You are only a woman. I'll teach you a fine lesson now. If I don't bring home a fine piece of cloth—dark green or blue, such as wives of great lords wear, then never believe another word I say.

GUILLEMETTE: But how will you do it? You haven't a copper in your pocket.

PATELIN: Ah! That's a secret. Just wait and see. So . . . (*To himself as he walks slowly away*) two and one-half for her and three for me. . . . Look well to the house while I am away, wife. (*Exit.*)

GUILLEMETTE: What fool of a merchant'll trust him! . . . unless he is blind and deaf! (*The back curtains are closed and now only the Street Scene is visible.*)

SCENE II

PATELIN comes from his door and walks slowly across to THE DRAPER'S *table.* THE DRAPER *is just coming out with a pack of cloth and wools which he throws on the table. He busies himself arranging his goods.* PATELIN *looks on for a while, then goes right up to him.*

PATELIN: Ho, there, worthy Master William Joceaulme, permit me the pleasure of shaking your hand. How do you feel?

THE DRAPER: Very fine, the Saints be thanked.

PATELIN: I am truly happy to hear that. And business?

THE DRAPER: You know how . . . one day one way, the other, altogether different. You can never tell when ill luck may blow your way.

PATELIN: May the Saints keep it from your doors! It's the very phrase I often heard your father use. God rest his soul among the Martyrs! What a man he was! Wise! There was not an event in Church, State, or market he did not foretell. No other was more esteemed. And you —they say that you are more and more like him each day.

THE DRAPER: Do seat yourself, good Master Patelin!

PATELIN: Oh, I can well stand.

THE DRAPER: Oh, but you must. (*Forcing him to sit on the bench.*)

PATELIN: Ah! I knew him well, your father. You resemble him as one drop of milk another. Lord, what a man he was! Wise! We, among the learned, called him the weather-cock. Well-nigh every piece of clothing I wore came from his shop.

THE DRAPER: He was an honest man, and people liked to buy from him.

PATELIN: A more honest soul there never was. And I have often heard said the apple has fallen nigh the tree.

THE DRAPER: Of a truth, good Master . . .

PATELIN: It's not flattery either. (*Looking intently at him*) Lord, but you do resemble him! No child was ever so like his father. Each marked like the other. This is just his nose, his ears, nay, the very dimple on his chin.

THE DRAPER: Yes, they do say I look much like him.

PATELIN: Like one drop of water another. . . . And kind-hearted! He was ever ready to trust and help, no matter who came along. The Lord knows he was ever the gainer by it. Even the worst scoundrels thought twice before cheating him.

THE DRAPER: A merchant must always take heed, good Master Patelin. You can never know whether a man is honest or not.

PATELIN: Aye, that's true. But he had a way of guessing whether it was an honest man he was dealing with that was a marvel to behold. Many a funny tale he told of it—when we sat over a bottle of wine. (*Feeling the cloth on the table*) What a fine piece of cloth! Did you make it from your own wool? Your father always used to weave his cloths from the wool of his own sheep.

THE DRAPER: So do I, Sir. From the wool of my own sheep.

PATELIN: You don't say so! This is business in a manner I like to see it done. The father all over again.

THE DRAPER (*Seeing the possibility of a sale*): Ah, worthy Master Patelin, it is a great hardship indeed, to which I put myself because of this. And the loss and cost! Here a shepherd kills your sheep, I have a case against one of those scoundrels right now. The weavers ask pay like goldsmiths. But to me this is all of little account. . . . I'd attend to the making of each piece myself were it to cost ten times as much as I get in return. . . . So long as I please those who buy.

PATELIN: I can see this. It would make a fine gown.

THE DRAPER: You could not get a finer piece even in the city of Paris.

PATELIN: I am sorry I am not out to do any buying just now, though I am tempted to.

THE DRAPER: Business bad? Money scarce?

PATELIN: No, indeed not. I have a nice little sum of gold crowns even now, but I am about to invest them in something profitable. . . . It's as strong as iron this cloth here. (*Examining it.*)

THE DRAPER: You may take my word for it, Master, there is not a finer or stronger in town. What's more, it can be bought cheap just now. It's a fine investment. Wool is certain to go up.

PATELIN: Aye, it's a fine piece of cloth, Master Joceaulme. . . . But then I shouldn't . . . yet . . .

THE DRAPER: Come, Master Patelin, come. You need the cloth and have the money to buy. Then you'll invest a few crowns less. A man should always have a gown tucked away in the coffer. What would you say if some fine day, comes along the town crier shouting: There has been a new judge appointed and it is Master Pa . . .

PATELIN: You must have your little joke, worthy Sir. Just like your father. I would pass his shop, a friendly chat . . . and then my purse was much the lighter for it. But I never regretted it, never.

THE DRAPER: You wouldn't now, either. It's well worth buying.

PATELIN: It tempts me. . . . It would look well on my good wife, and I could use it well for myself.

THE DRAPER: It needs but your saying. Come, what's the word, Master?

PATELIN: Well. . . .

THE DRAPER: It's yours even though you hadn't a copper.

PATELIN (*Somewhat absent minded*): Oh, I know that.

THE DRAPER: What?

PATELIN: I'll take it.

THE DRAPER: That's talking. How much do you want?

PATELIN: How much is it per yard?

THE DRAPER: Which do you like best? The blue?

PATELIN: Yes, that is the one.

THE DRAPER: You want a rock bottom price, no haggling. This is the finest piece in my shop. . . . For you I'll make it twenty-one sous per yard.

PATELIN: Holy Saints! Master! What do you take me for? A fool? It isn't the first time I am buying cloth.

THE DRAPER: It's the price it cost me myself; by all the Saints in Heaven.

PATELIN: That's too much,—entirely too much.

THE DRAPER: Wool costs like holy oil now, and these shepherds are forever robbing me.

PATELIN: Well, there is truth in what you say. I'll take it at the price. I like to see every man make his honest penny. Measure it.

THE DRAPER: How much do you want?

PATELIN: Let me see. Two and a half for her, three for me, that makes five and a half.

THE DRAPER: Take hold there, Master, here they are: (*Measuring out*) one . . . two . . . three . . . four . . . five. I'll make it six. You'll not mind the few coppers more.

PATELIN: Not when I get something fine in return. Then I need a cap too.

THE DRAPER: Would you like me to measure it backwards?

PATELIN: Oh, no, I trust your honesty. How much is it?

THE DRAPER: Six yards at twenty-one sous the yard—that's exactly nine francs.

PATELIN: Nine francs . . . (*Under his breath*) Here it goes. Nine francs.

THE DRAPER: Yes and a good bargain you got.

PATELIN (*Searching his pockets*): No . . . I have but little with me, and I must buy some small things. You'll get your money to-morrow.

THE DRAPER: What!!! . . . No . . . No . . .

PATELIN: Well, good Master Joceaulme, you don't think I carry gold coin with me, do you? You'd have me give thieves a good chance to steal it? Your father trusted me many a time. And you, Master William, should take after your father.

THE DRAPER: I like my money cash.

PATELIN: It's there waiting for you, good Master Draper. You can come for it, I hope.

THE DRAPER: It's bad custom to sell on credit.

PATELIN: Did I ask you for credit: for a month, a week, a day? Come to my house at noon, and you will find your money ready. Does that satisfy you?

THE DRAPER: I prefer my money cash, right on the purchase. . . .

PATELIN: And then, Master William, you have not been to my house for I don't know how long. Your father was there many a time—but you don't seem to care for poor folk like myself.

THE DRAPER: It's we merchants who are poor. We have no bags of gold lying idle for investments.

PATELIN: They are there, Master, waiting for you. And my good wife put a fine goose on the spit just when I left. You can have a tender wing. Your father always liked it.

THE DRAPER: Perhaps. . . . It's true. I haven't been to your house for a long time. I'll come at noon, Master Patelin, and bring the cloth with me.

PATELIN (*Snatching the cloth from him*): Oh, I would never trouble you. I can carry it.

THE DRAPER: But . . .

PATELIN: No, good Sir, not for the wealth of the East. I would not think of asking *you* to carry it for *me*.

THE DRAPER: I'd rather . . . well . . . I'll soon be there, Master. I'll come before the noon meal. Don't forget the nine francs.

PATELIN: Aye I'll not. And there'll be a bottle of red wine . . . and a fine fat goose. Be certain to come. (*Exit* PATELIN.)

THE DRAPER: That I will right soon. Ho, ho, ho—ha, ha, ha—the fool! A good bargain he got! Twenty-one sous the yard. It isn't worth one-half that. And on top of it a fine dinner . . . Burgundy wine and a roasted goose! For a customer like that every day! Now I'll take in my cloth. I'll soon to his house. (*Takes up the cloth and leaves.*)

SCENE III

The back curtains are drawn aside showing PATELIN'S *chamber.*

PATELIN (*Running in*): Wife, wife . . . (GUILLEMETTE *enters, the old gown in her hand*) Well, Madam . . . now . . . I've got it, . . . right here I have it. What did I tell you?

GUILLEMETTE: What have you?

PATELIN: Something you desire greatly. But what are you doing with this old rag? I think it will do well for a bed for your cat. I did promise you a new gown and get you one I did.

GUILLEMETTE: What's gotten into your head? Did you drink anything on the way?

PATELIN: And it's paid for, Madam. It's paid for, I tell you.

GUILLEMETTE: Are you making sport of me? What are you plappering!

PATELIN: I have it right here.

GUILLEMETTE: What have you?

PATELIN: Cloth fit for the Queen of Sheba. (*Displaying the cloth*) Here it is!

GUILLEMETTE: Holy Virgin! Where did you steal it! Who'll pay for it? What kind of a scrape have you gotten into now?

PATELIN: You need not worry, good Dame. It's paid for . . . and a good price at that.

GUILLEMETTE: Why, how much did it cost? You did not have a copper when you left.

PATELIN: It cost nine francs, fair Lady . . . a bottle of red wine . . . and the wing of a roasted goose.

GUILLEMETTE: Are you crazy? You had no money, no goose!!!

PATELIN: Aye, aye, that I did. I paid for it as it behooves one of the learned profession of law: in promissory statements. And the merchant who took them is no fool either, oh, no; not a fool at all; but a very wise man and a shrewd. . . .

GUILLEMETTE: Who was he? How . . .

PATELIN: He is the king of asses, the pope of idiots, the chancellor of baboons . . . our worthy neighbor, the long-nosed Draper, Master Joceaulme.

GUILLEMETTE: Will you cease this jabbering and tell me how it happened? How did he come to trust you? There is no worse skinflint in town than he.

PATELIN: Ah, wife! My head! My knowledge of the law! I turned him into a noble and fine lord. I told him what a jewel his father was; I laid on him all the nine virtues thick as wax, and, . . . in the end he trusted me most willingly with six yards of his fine cloth.

GUILLEMETTE: Ho, ho, ho, you are a marvel! And when does he expect to get paid?

PATELIN: By noon.

GUILLEMETTE: Holy Lord, what will we do when he comes for the money?

PATELIN: He'll be here for it and soon to boot. He must be dreaming even now of his nine francs, and his wine, and the goose. Oh, we'll give him a goose! Now you get the bed ready and I'll get in.

GUILLEMETTE: What for?

PATELIN: As soon as he comes and asks for me, swear by all the Saints that I've been in bed here for the last two months. Tell it in a sad voice and with tears in your eyes. And if he says anything, shout at him to speak lower. If he cries: "My cloth, my money," tell him he is crazy, that I haven't been from bed for weeks. And if he doesn't go with that, I'll dance him a little tune that'll make him wonder whether he is on earth or in hell. (PATELIN *puts on his night-gown and cap.* GUILLEMETTE *goes to the door and returns quickly.*)

GUILLEMETTE: He is coming, he is coming; what if he arrests you?

PATELIN: Don't worry; just do what I tell you. Quick, hide the cloth under the bed clothes. Don't forget. I've been sick for two months.

GUILLEMETTE: Quick, quick, here he is. (PATELIN *gets into bed and draws the curtains.* GUILLEMETTE *sits down and begins to mend the old dress.* THE DRAPER *enters.*)

THE DRAPER: Good day, fair Dame.

GUILLEMETTE: Sh . . . for the Saint's sake. Speak lower.

THE DRAPER: Why? What's the matter?

GUILLEMETTE: You don't know!

THE DRAPER: Where is he?

GUILLEMETTE: Alas! Nearer to paradise than to earth. (*Begins to cry.*)

THE DRAPER: Who?

GUILLEMETTE: How can you be so heartless and ask me that, when you know he has been in bed for the last eleven weeks.

THE DRAPER: Who?

GUILLEMETTE: My husband.

THE DRAPER: Who?

GUILLEMETTE: My husband—Master Pierre, once a lawyer, . . . and now a sick man . . . on his death-bed.

THE DRAPER: What!!!!!

GUILLEMETTE (*Crying*): You have not heard of it? Alas! And . . .

THE DRAPER: And who was it just took six yards of cloth from my shop?

GUILLEMETTE: Alas! How am I to know? It was surely not he.

THE DRAPER: You must be dreaming, good woman. Are you his wife? The wife of Pierre Patelin, the lawyer?

GUILLEMETTE: That I am, good Sir.

THE DRAPER: Then it was your husband, who was such a good friend of my father, who came to my shop a quarter of an hour ago and bought six yards of cloth for nine francs. And now I am here for my money. Where is he?

GUILLEMETTE: This is no time for jesting, good Sir.

THE DRAPER: Are you crazy? I want my money, that's all.

GUILLEMETTE: Don't scream. It's little sleep he gets as it is, and here you come squealing like a dying pig. He has been in bed for nigh twelve weeks and hardly slept three nights.

THE DRAPER: Who? What are you talking about?

GUILLEMETTE: Who! My poor sick husband. (*Weeps.*)

THE DRAPER: Come! What's this? Stop that fooling. I want my money, my nine francs.

GUILLEMETTE (*Screaming*): Don't scream so loud. He is dying.

THE DRAPER: But that's a black lie. He was at my shop, but a quarter of an hour ago.

PATELIN (*Groaning from behind the curtain*): Au, au, au . . .

GUILLEMETTE: Ah, there he is on his death-bed. He has been there for thirteen weeks yesterday without eating as much as a fly.

THE DRAPER: What are you talking about? He was at my shop just now and bought six yards of cloth . . . blue cloth.

GUILLEMETTE: How can you make sport of me. Good Master William, don't you see how he is! Do speak lower. Noise puts him in agony.

THE DRAPER: The devil speak lower! It's you who are howling. Give me my money, and I'll not speak at all.

GUILLEMETTE (*Screaming*): He is deadly sick. This is no time for fooling. Stop screaming. What is it you want?

THE DRAPER: I want my money, or the cloth . . . the cloth he bought from me only a little while ago.

GUILLEMETTE: What are you talking about, my good man? There is something strange in your voice.

THE DRAPER: You see, good lady, your husband, Pierre Patelin, the learned counselor, who was such a good friend of my father, came to my shop but a quarter of an hour ago and chose six yards of blue cloth . . . and then told me to come to his house to get the money and . . .

GUILLEMETTE: Ha, ha, ha, what a fine joke. You seem to be in good humor to-day, Master Draper! To-day! . . . When he has been in bed for fourteen weeks . . . on the point of death! (*She screams louder and louder all the time*) To-day, hey! Why do you come to make sport of me? Get out, get out!

THE DRAPER: I will. Give me my money first . . . or give me my cloth. Where is he with it?

GUILLEMETTE: Ah me! He is very sick and refuses to eat a bite.

THE DRAPER: I am speaking about my cloth. If he does not want it, or hasn't the money, I'll gladly take it back. He took it this morning. I'll swear to it. Ask him yourself. I saw him and spoke to him. A piece of blue cloth.

GUILLEMETTE: Are you cracked or have you been drinking?

THE DRAPER (*Becoming frantic*): He took six yards of cloth, blue cloth!

GUILLEMETTE: What do I care whether it is green or blue? My husband has not left the house for the last fifteen weeks.

THE DRAPER: May the Lord bless me! But I am sure I saw him. It was he, I am sure.

GUILLEMETTE: Have you no heart? You have had enough of your fooling.

THE DRAPER: Damn it all! If you think I am a fool . . .

PATELIN (*Behind the curtain*): Au, au, au, come and raise my pillow.

Stop the braying of that ass! Everything is black and yellow! Drive
these black beasts away! Marmara, carimari, carimara!

THE DRAPER: It's he!

GUILLEMETTE: Yes, it is; alas!

THE DRAPER: Good Master Patelin, I've come for my nine francs, . . .
which you promised me . . .

PATELIN (*Sitting up and sticks his head out between the curtains*): Ha,
you dog . . . come here. Shut the door. Rub the soles of my feet
. . . tickle my toes. . . . Drive these devils away. It's a monk; there,
up he goes . . .

THE DRAPER: What's this? Are you crazy?

PATELIN (*Getting out of bed*): Ha . . . do you see him? A black monk
flying in the air with the Draper hanging on his nose. Catch him . . .
quick. (*Speaking right in* THE DRAPER's *face, who retreats*) The cat!
The monk! Up he flies, and there are ten little devils tweaking your
long nose! Heigh, ho! (*Goes back to bed, falling on it seemingly exhausted.*)

GUILLEMETTE (*In loud lamentations*): Now see what you have done.

THE DRAPER: But what does this mean? . . . I don't understand it.

GUILLEMETTE: Don't you see, don't you see!

THE DRAPER: It serves me right; why did I ever sell on credit. But I sold
it, I am certain of that, and I would swear 'twas to him this morning.
Did he become sick since he returned?

GUILLEMETTE: Are you beginning that joke all over again?

THE DRAPER: I am sure I sold it to him. Ah, but this may be just a
cooked up story. By God! . . . tell me, have you a goose on the spit?

GUILLEMETTE: A goose on the spit! No-o-o-o, not on the spit! You are
the nearest . . . But I've had enough of this. Get out and leave me
in peace.

THE DRAPER: Maybe you are right. I am commencing to doubt it all.
Don't cry. I must think this over for a while. But . . . the devil. I
am sure I had six yards of cloth . . . and he chose the blue. I gave
it to him with my own hands. Yet . . . here he is in bed sick . . .
fifteen weeks. But he was at my shop a little while ago. "Come to my
house and eat some goose," he said. Never, never, holy Lord, will I
trust anyone again.

GUILLEMETTE: Perhaps your memory is getting wobbly with age. I think
you had better go and look before you talk. Maybe the cloth is still
there. (*Exit* THE DRAPER, *across the front stage and into his shop.*)

PATELIN (*Getting up cautiously and speaking low*): Is he gone?

GUILLEMETTE: Take care, he may come back.

PATELIN: I can't stand this any longer. (*Jumps out*) We put it to him heavy, didn't we, my pretty one, eh? Ho, ho, ho. (*Laughs uproariously.*)

THE DRAPER (*Coming from his shop, looking under the table*): The thief, the liar, the damned liar, he did buy . . . steal it? It isn't there. This was all sham. Ha, I'll get it, though. (*Runs toward* PATELIN'S *house*) What's this I hear . . . laughing! . . . The robbers (*Rushes in*) You thieves . . . I want my cloth. . . .

(PATELIN *finding no time to get back into bed, gets hold of the broom, puts the frying pan on his head and begins to jump around straddling the broom stick.* GUILLEMETTE *can't stop laughing.*)

THE DRAPER: Laughing in my very nose, eh! Ah, my money, pay . . .

GUILLEMETTE: I am laughing for unhappiness. Look, how the poor man is, it is you who have done this, with your bellowing.

PATELIN: Ha. . . . Where is the Guitar. . . . The lady Guitar I married. . . . She gave birth to twenty little Guitars yesterday. Ho, ho. Come my children. . . . Light the lanterns. Ho, ho, ha . . . (*Stops, looking intently into the air.*)

THE DRAPER: Damn your jabbering. My money! Please, my money . . . for the cloth. . . .

GUILLEMETTE: Again. . . . Didn't you have enough before? But . . . Oh . . . (*Looking intently at him*) Now I understand!!! Why, I am sure of it. You are mad . . . else you wouldn't talk this way.

THE DRAPER: Oh, holy Lord . . . perhaps I am.

PATELIN (*Begins to jump around as if possessed, playing a thousand and one crazy antics*): Mère de dieu, la coronade . . . que de l'argent il ne me sonne. Hast understood me, gentle Sir?

THE DRAPER: What's this? I want my money . . .

GUILLEMETTE: He is speaking in delirium; he once had an uncle in Limoges and it's the language of that country. (PATELIN *gives* THE DRAPER *a kick and falls down as if exhausted.*)

THE DRAPER: Oh! Oh! Where am I? This is the strangest sickness I ever saw.

GUILLEMETTE (*Who has run to her husband*): Do you see what you have done?

PATELIN (*Jumps up and acts still wilder*): Ha! The devil . . . the green cat . . . with the Draper. I am happy . . . (*Chases* THE DRAPER *and his wife around the room.* GUILLEMETTE *seeks protection, clinging to* THE DRAPER.)

GUILLEMETTE: Oh, I am afraid, I am afraid. Help me, kind Sir, he may do me some harm.

THE DRAPER (*Running around the room with* GUILLEMETTE *clinging to him*): Holy Ghost, what's this? He is bewitching me.

PATELIN (*Trying to explain signs to* THE DRAPER, *who retreats.* PATELIN *follows him whacking the floor and furniture and occasionally getting in one on* THE DRAPER. *Finally* THE DRAPER *gets on one side of the bed, and* PATELIN *on the other. In that position he addresses him in a preachy, serious voice*): Et bona dies sit vobis, magister amantissime, pater reverendissime, quomodo brulis? (*Falls on the floor near the bed as if dead.*)

GUILLEMETTE: Oh, kind Sir. Help me. He is dead. Help me put him to bed . . . (*They both drag him into bed.*)

THE DRAPER: It were well for me to go, I think. He might die and I might be blamed for it. It must have been some imp or some devil who took my cloth . . . and I came here for the money, led by an evil spirit. It's passing strange . . . but I think I had better go. (*Exit.*)

(THE DRAPER *goes to his shop.* GUILLEMETTE *watches, turning every moment to* PATELIN *who has sat up in bed, warning him not to get out. When* THE DRAPER *disappears, she turns around and bursts out laughing.*)

PATELIN (*Jumping out*): Now, wife, what do you think of me, eh? (*Takes the cloth*) Oh! Didn't we play a clever game? By Saint Peter, I did not think I could do it so well. He got a hot goose, didn't he? (*Spreading the cloth*) This'll do for both and there'll be a goodly piece left.

GUILLEMETTE: You are an angel. Oh, ho! And now let us go and begin to cut it up. (*Both exeunt.*)

SCENE IV
The Street Scene

JOCEAULME *comes from the shop with a piece of cloth under
his arm. He is much upset. Looks once more under the table
for the cloth which* PATELIN *took.*

THE DRAPER: The devil! These hounds. . . . I'll get them yet. Here a
fine piece of cloth! Only the fiend himself knows who took it—and
then that shepherd. To think of it . . . robbing me for years. But him
I'll get surely. I'll see him hanged, yet. By the holy Lord I will.
(TIBALD LAMBKIN *appears from the other side*) Ah, here he
comes. . . .

THE SHEPHERD (*Stutters, thick voice; a typical yokel*): God give you a
good day, sweet Sir. I greet you, good Sir. . . . I was not sure it was
you, good Sir. . . .

THE DRAPER: You were not, eh? You knave; but you will soon know for
certain . . . when your head is on the gallows . . . high up . . .

THE SHEPHERD: Yes, good Sir . . . no . . . I saw the constable . . .
and he spoke to me that you want to see me . . .

THE DRAPER: Oh, no! Not I, my fine thief . . . but the judge.

THE SHEPHERD: Oh, Lord! Why did you summon me. I don't know why.
I never killed your sheep.

THE DRAPER: Oh, no, you are a saint. It's you, you mangy dog . . . all
the while you were robbing me of my sheep. But now you'll pay for it
with your head. I'll see you hanged.

THE SHEPHERD: Hanged by the neck! Oh, Lord! Good Master, have pity.

THE DRAPER: Pity, eh? And you had pity when you were robbing me of
my cloth . . . I mean my sheep. Thief, scoundrel, you robber . . .
where is my cloth . . . my sheep?

THE SHEPHERD: They died of sickness, Sir . . .

THE DRAPER: You lie, you caitiff, you stole them and now . . .

THE SHEPHERD: It is not so, good Master. I swear. On my soul . . .

THE DRAPER: You have no soul, you thief. By all the Saints, I'll see you
dangling this Saturday . . .

THE SHEPHERD: Good and sweet Master, won't you please make a settlement . . . and not bring me to court.

THE DRAPER: Away, you thief. I'll make you pay for those six yards . . .
I mean those sheep. You just wait. (*Walks off in a fury.*)

THE SHEPHERD: Oh, Lord! I must quickly find a lawyer . . . I've heard of Master Patelin . . . they say no man is better at gulling. It's here he lives. (PATELIN *comes just then from his house. When he sees* LAMBKIN *he tries to get back, fearing it may the* THE DRAPER, *but on hearing his voice he stops*): Ho, there, Master! Is it you who are Master Patelin the lawyer?

PATELIN: What is you want of him?

THE SHEPHERD: I have a little business for him.

PATELIN: Oh! is it that! Well, I am Master Patelin. Good man, tell me the nature of your business. Is it anything pertaining to the law?

THE SHEPHERD: I'll pay well. . . . I am a shepherd, good Master. A poor man, but I can pay well. I need a lawyer for a little case I have.

PATELIN: Come this way, where we can talk lower. Someone might overhear us . . . I mean disturb us. Now good man, what may your business be?

THE SHEPHERD: Good Master Lawyer, teach me what to say to the judge.

PATELIN: What is it you have done, or has someone done you an injustice?

THE SHEPHERD: Must I tell you everything . . . exactly as it happened?

PATELIN: You can tell me the truth, I am your lawyer. . . . But good friend, counsel is costly.

THE SHEPHERD: I'll pay all right. It's my Master whose sheep I stole who summoned me to the Judge. He is going to have me hanged because I stole his sheep. You see . . . He paid like a miser . . . Must I tell you the truth!

PATELIN: I have told you once. You must tell me how everything really happened.

THE SHEPHERD: Well . . . he paid like a miser . . . so I told him some sheep had the hoof sickness and died from it . . . and I buried them far . . . far . . . away, so that the others shouldn't get it. But I really killed them and ate the meat and used the wool for myself—and he caught me right so that I cannot deny it. Now I beseech you . . . I can pay well—though he has the law on his side . . . whether you cannot beat him. If you can, I'll pay you in fine, gold crowns, sweet Master.

PATELIN: Gold crowns!!! H'm, what's your name?

THE SHEPHERD: Tibald Lambkin, a poor shepherd, but I have a few crowns put aside. You just . . .

PATELIN: What do you intend to pay for this case?

THE SHEPHERD: Will five . . . four crowns be enough, sweet Sir?

PATELIN (*Hardly able to contain himself for excitement*): Ah! . . . H'm . . . well . . . that will be plenty seeing that you are a poor man. But I get much greater sums, friend, I do. . . . Did you say . . . five?

THE SHEPHERD: Yes, sweet Sir.

PATELIN: You'll have to make it six. I may tell you though, that your case is a good one, and I am sure to win it. But now tell me, are there any witnesses the plaintiff can produce? Those who saw you killing the sheep?

THE SHEPHERD: Not one. . . .

PATELIN: That's fine.

THE SHEPHERD: . . . But more'n a dozen.

PATELIN: That's bad. H'm, let me see now . . . no . . . (*He seems to hold a deep and learned debate with himself*) No . . . but . . . The book says otherwise. (*Suddenly his face lights up*) By all the Saints, and the nine hundred and ninety-nine Virgins! I've got it . . . aye, what a wonderful idea! Two ideas in one day! You can understand a sly trick, can't you, fellow?

THE SHEPHERD: Can I? Ho, ho, ho, ho . . .

PATELIN: But you'll pay as you promised.

THE SHEPHERD: Hang me if I don't. But I can't pay if I hang, ho, ho, ho . . .

PATELIN (*Gleefully*): Now, first, you have never seen me; nor heard of me . . .

THE SHEPHERD: Oh, no, not that . . .

PATELIN: Silent until I have finished. Second, you mustn't talk a single word but "Ba" . . . (*Imitating the bleating of a sheep*) Only bleat like your sheep. No matter what they talk to you. Just say Ba. . . . Even if they call you an ass, or an idiot, or villain, or fool, don't answer anything but Ba. . . . Just as if you were a sheep.

THE SHEPHERD: Oh, I can do that.

PATELIN: Even if I talk to you, say nothing but Ba. . . . And if they split roaring at you, just say Ba . . . The rest you leave to me. I'll get you out for certain.

THE SHEPHERD: I'll surely not say another word. And I will do it right proper.

PATELIN: Your case is as good as won. But don't forget the seven gold crowns.

THE SHEPHERD: I'll sure not, wise and sweet Master Patelin.

CRIER (*Is heard from afar*): "The court, make room" . . .

PATELIN: Ah, here they come. Don't forget Ba. . . . I'll be there to help you. And . . . the money . . . don't forget that.

> (*Attendants, constables, town clerks and villagers enter. Two clerks carry a seat for* THE JUDGE *which is placed in the center of the stage.* THE JUDGE, *fat and grouchy, comes to the front, looks about for a moment, then goes to his seat and sits down.*)

THE JUDGE: If there is any business to be done, come to it; the court wants to adjourn.

PATELIN: May heaven bless you and grant you all you desire.

THE JUDGE: Welcome, Sir. May the Saints give you plenty of clients.

> (THE DRAPER *now comes running in.* PATELIN *suddenly realizes that it is against him that* THE SHEPHERD *must be defended and expresses uneasiness. He hides himself behind the crowd.*)

THE DRAPER: My lawyer is soon coming, your Worship. He has a little business elsewhere which is detaining him.

THE JUDGE: You must think I have nothing to do but to wait for your lawyer. You are the plaintiff, aren't you? Bring your complaint. Where is the defendant?

THE DRAPER: Right there, your worship; that lummox shepherd, who has been hiding behind that good citizen there as if he couldn't say ba. . . . But your Honor, it's in fear of justice.

THE JUDGE: Both being present, I will examine you. (*To* THE DRAPER) Tell me all the facts of your case. Was he in your hire?

THE DRAPER: Yes, your Lordship. He killed my sheep and after I treated him like a father . . .

THE JUDGE: Did you pay him a good wage?

PATELIN (*Edging up sideways, and covering his face with his hand*) Your Lordship, I have heard it said that he never paid him a copper for his work.

THE DRAPER (*Recognizing* PATELIN): By all that's holy . . . You . . . !!!!??? 'Tis he and no other.

THE JUDGE: Why do you cover your face, Master Patelin?

PATELIN: Oh, your Lordship, I have a terrible toothache.

THE JUDGE: I am sorry for you, for I had one myself the other day. I'll tell you a fine cure, Master. Hold your feet in cold water wherein are three hoofs of a red cow from Gascogne. This'll draw the ache into the nails of your toes and you can then rid yourself of it with great ease by cutting them. 'Tis a sovereign remedy. Try it and see, Master. But let us go on. Come Master Draper, I am in a hurry.

THE DRAPER (*Not heeding* THE JUDGE *but still staring at* PATELIN): It's you, isn't it? It's to you I sold six yards of cloth. Where is my money?

THE JUDGE: What is that you are talking about?

PATELIN: His mind is clouded, your Lordship. He is not accustomed to speaking clearly. Perhaps the defendant will enlighten us. You . . .

THE DRAPER: I am not speaking clearly!! You thief . . . liar . . .

PATELIN: Your Worship, I think I understand him now. It's strange how incoherently those who have no legal training speak. I think he means he could have made six yards of cloth from the sheep the shepherd is supposed to have stolen or killed.

THE JUDGE: Aye, so it would seem. Come, Master William, finish your tale.

PATELIN: Get to the facts as the judge directs you.

THE DRAPER: And you dare talk to me like that!

THE JUDGE: Master William, come to your sheep.

(*During the rest of the court scene* PATELIN *works always so as to attract the attention of* THE DRAPER *every time he tries to talk of his sheep, and so diverts his attention from that and leads him to talk of the cloth. Whenever* THE DRAPER *talks of his case,* PATELIN *either sticks his face up to him or places himself in such a position that* THE DRAPER *must see him.*)

THE DRAPER: You see, your Lordship . . . he took my six yards of cloth this morning . . . the thief . . .

THE JUDGE: Do you think I am a fool or an ass? Either you come to the point or I'll dismiss the case.

PATELIN: Your Worship, let us call the defendant. He, I am sure, will speak clearer than this Draper.

THE JUDGE: Yes, that will be wise. Step forward, Shepherd.

THE SHEPHERD: Ba . . . a . . .

THE JUDGE: What's this, am I a goat?

THE SHEPHERD: Ba . . . a . . .

PATELIN: Your Lordship, it seems this man is half-witted and thinks himself among his sheep.

THE DRAPER: Damn you! He can talk, and he is not half-witted either . . . but a thief like you. It was you who took my cloth!

THE JUDGE: Cloth! What are you talking about, anyhow? Now, you either get back to your sheep or I'll dismiss the case.

THE DRAPER: I will, your Lordship, though the other lies as near to my heart, but I'll leave it for another time. That shepherd there . . . he took six yards of cloth . . . I mean, sheep. Your Honor must forgive me. This thief . . . my shepherd, he told me I would get my money . . . for the cloth as soon . . . I mean this shepherd was to watch over my flocks and he played sick when I came to his house. Ah, Master Pierre. . . . He killed my sheep and told me they died from hoof-sickness . . . and I saw him take the cloth . . . I mean he swore he never killed them. And his wife swore he was sick and said he never took the cloth . . . No, that shepherd there. . . . He took the sheep and made out he was crazy. . . . Oh, my Lord! I don't know what . . .

THE JUDGE (*Leaping up*): Keep quiet, you don't know what you are talking about. You are crazy. I have listened to your idiotic talk about sheep, and cloth, and wool, and money. What is it you want here? Either you answer sensibly, or . . . this is your last chance!

PATELIN: There is surely something strange about this poor man's talk, and I would advise that a physician be consulted. At times though, it seems as if he were talking about some money he owes this poor shepherd.

THE DRAPER: You thief! You robber! You might at least keep quiet. Where is my cloth? You have it. . . . You are not sick.

THE JUDGE: What has he? Who isn't sick? Are you going to talk of your business or not?

THE DRAPER: He has it as certain as there is a God in heaven. But I'll speak of this later. Now, I'll attend to this thief, this shepherd.

PATELIN: This shepherd cannot answer the charges himself, your Lordship. I will gladly give my services to defend him.

THE JUDGE: You won't get much for your pains.

PATELIN: Ah, but the knowledge that I am doing a kind and honest deed, and then I may be able to stop this haggling which annoys your Lordship so much.

THE JUDGE: I'd be greatly thankful.

THE DRAPER: You'll defend him . . . you thief . . . you . . .

THE JUDGE: Now, Master William, you keep quiet or I'll have you put in the stocks. I have listened long enough to your idiotic gab. Proceed, Master Patelin.

PATELIN: I thank your Lordship. Now, come on, my good fellow. It's for your own good I am working as you heard me say. Just because

I would do you a kind deed. Answer everything well and direct.

THE SHEPHERD: Ba . . . a . . .

PATELIN: Come, I am your lawyer, not a lamb.

THE SHEPHERD: Ba . . .

PATELIN: What's Ba . . . ? Are you crazy? Tell me, did this man pay you money for your work?

THE SHEPHERD: Ba . . .

PATELIN (*Seemingly losing his temper*): You idiot, answer, it's I, your lawyer who is talking to you. Answer.

THE SHEPHERD: Ba . . .

THE DRAPER (*Who has listened open-mouthed and bewildered*): But, your Lordship, he can talk when he wants to. He spoke to me this morning.

PATELIN (*Severely*): Everything happened to you this morning, Master Joceaulme. Now it seems to me, it would be far wiser for you to send this shepherd back to his sheep, he is used to their company far more than to that of men. It does not look as if this fool had sense enough to kill a fly, let alone a sheep.

THE DRAPER: You . . . you . . . robber . . . liar!!!

THE JUDGE: I honestly think they are both crazy.

PATELIN: It seems as if your Lordship is right.

THE DRAPER: I am crazy! You scoundrel! You robber! Where is my cloth? They are both thieves . . .

THE JUDGE: Keep quiet, I say.

THE DRAPER: But, your Lordship!

THE JUDGE: All you get is vexation, in dealing with dolts and idiots, be they male or female, so says the law. To finish this wrangling the court is adjourned.

THE DRAPER: And my cloth . . . my money . . . I mean my sheep! Is there no justice? Will you not listen to me?

THE JUDGE: Eh, listen to you, you miser? You dare scoff at justice? You hire half crazy people; and then you don't pay them, then you bellow something about cloth which has nothing to do with the case and expect me to listen to you?

THE DRAPER: But he took my cloth . . . and he killed my sheep. I swear to you. There he stands, the thief. (*Pointing to* PATELIN.)

THE JUDGE: Stop your bellowing. I discharge this half-witted shepherd. Get home and don't ever come in my sight again no matter how many bailiffs summon you.

PATELIN (*To* THE SHEPHERD): Say thanks to his Lordship.

THE SHEPHERD: Ba . . .

THE JUDGE: By all the Saints, never have I come upon such a nest of idiots!

THE DRAPER: My cloth gone . . . my sheep . . .

THE JUDGE: Huh! You . . . Well, I have business elsewhere. May I never see your like again. The court is adjourned. Good day, Master Patelin.

PATELIN: A joyous day to you.

(*All leave except* PATELIN, THE DRAPER, *and* THE SHEPHERD.)

THE DRAPER: You thieves . . . you scoundrels! You . . . You . . .

PATELIN: Don't shout yourself hoarse, good Master Joceaulme.

THE DRAPER: You stole my cloth and played crazy . . . and now it was because of you, that I lost my sheep . . .

PATELIN: A fine tale! Do you think anyone will believe you?

THE DRAPER: I am not blind. Didn't I see you dancing this morning. I saw you . . .

PATELIN: Are you so certain. Good Sir, it may have been Jean de Noyon. He resembles me very much.

THE DRAPER: But I know you when I see you. You screamed and acted mad, shouting a tale of dogs and . . .

PATELIN: Perhaps you imagined it all. Go back to my house and see if I am not *still* there.

THE DRAPER (*Looks much puzzled*): May the Lord . . . Perhaps . . . But I'll go to your house and if I don't find you there, I'll go to the Judge and see to it that he listens to my story. I'll get a lawyer from Paris. (*To* THE SHEPHERD *who has been standing at a safe distance*) You thief! I'll get you yet. I'll go to your house now. (*To* PATELIN.)

PATELIN: That's a wise action. (*Exit* THE DRAPER.)

PATELIN: Now Tibald, my fellow. What do you think of me? Didn't we do a fine piece of work?

THE SHEPHERD: Ba . . .

PATELIN: Yes. Ho, ho—wasn't it great?

THE SHEPHERD: Ba . . .

PATELIN: No one is near now; your Master is gone. It was a great idea, wasn't it? This legal stroke. You may speak now without fear.

THE SHEPHERD: Ba . . .

PATELIN: I said you could speak without fear, no one is near. Where is the money?

THE SHEPHERD: Ba . . .

PATELIN: I can't stay with you all day. What is this game?

THE SHEPHERD: Ba . . .

PATELIN: How now? Come I have business elsewhere.

THE SHEPHERD: Ba . . .

PATELIN: What do you mean. You are not going to pay?

THE SHEPHERD (*With a grin*): Ba . . .

PATELIN: Yes, you played your rôle well, good Lambkin. But now it's over. Next time you may count on me again. Now my money; the six crowns.

THE SHEPHERD: Ba . . .

PATELIN (*Sees the game now, stops. In a somewhat pathetic voice*): Is that all I am going to get for my work?

THE SHEPHERD: Ba . . .

PATELIN (*Getting furious*): By the holy Lord, I'll have a bailiff after you, you thief . . . you scoundrel . . . you robber . . .

THE SHEPHERD: Ho, ho, ho . . . Ba . . . ! The Judge said I need never come back. And—ho, ho, ho, I never knew you . . . Ba . . . a . . . a! (*Runs out.*)

PATELIN (*Silent for a time, then grinning pathetically*): Alas! 'Tis only paying me in my own coin. . . . Nevertheless 'twas a fine idea. . . . (*Exit.*)

CURTAIN

James Reid Parker

.

WELCOME TO AUNT KITTY'S

"Good morning, Mr. Devore," the voice at the other end of the wire said. "This is Catherine Buckley. I understand I'm supposed to call you about a consultation."

"Oh?" Mr. Devore said in bewilderment. Then he remembered. "Oh, yes. How do you do?" A few days before, Chester Hibben—Chester L. Hibben of the Wolverine Commercial Car Corporation—had come up to him in the Harvard Club and remarked casually, "By the way, I've told a friend of mine to make an appointment with you for a consultation. Remarkably interesting woman by the name of Buckley. She's going to get in touch with you in a day or two."

Miss Buckley went on to say that she hoped Mr. Devore would be able to help her solve a little problem that was troubling her.

"I hope so, too," he said gallantly. "I need hardly say that Forbes, Hathaway, Bryan & Devore will always be very glad to be of service to a friend of Chester Hibben. Perhaps you can give me some idea of your difficulty?"

"To put it in plain English," she said cheerfully, "I've got a beautiful mess on my hands. It all has to do with a mean buck nigger down in Guadeloupe. He's Mattie's husband—Mattie's one of my maids—and if what she says is true, he'd just as soon run a knife through your heart as eat a piece of candy."

"What?" said Mr. Devore, sitting bolt upright. None of his clients, not even Thomas Grier of Annesley Bolt & Screw had ever spoken quite so vividly.

"Oh, I don't mean *your* heart," Miss Buckley said, rippling with laughter. "I mean anybody's heart—Mattie's, probably. And I don't want to lose Mattie on account of anything worse than old age if I can help it. She's valuable to me. What I want is to have this man kept out of the country. He's all set to come here. I want the immigration men to watch out for him and see that he doesn't get in. That's easy enough, isn't it?"

"Well—" Mr. Devore hesitated.

"Look," Miss Buckley said impatiently, "just notify them, that's all, or whatever it is you do officially. He's dangerous and he means business. Mattie's worth a lot to me, a whole lot. I don't care *how* much money it costs to fix this."

"It all sounds most unusual." Mr. Devore's tone was doubtful. He had been wholly sincere in saying that he was glad to be of service to a friend of Chester Hibben. Indeed, only a desire not to offend the Wolverine Commercial Car Corporation deterred him now from saying firmly that he could not possibly assist her and hanging up the receiver.

"Of course it's unusual! That's why I'm calling you about it. I think you and Mattie'd better have a little talk. If you're free this afternoon around five or so, why not come up here? I'll give you a drink. I'd send Mattie down to your office except that she'd probably get rattled and waste your time. Up here she'll feel at home. How about it? Five o'clock be all right?"

"Really, Miss Buckley, my calendar is so crowded that—"

"Oh, of course, if you have another engagement, come right out and say so. You won't be hurting Aunt Kitty's feelings."

Mr. Devore realized that one must meet briskness with—well, if not with equal briskness, at least with a definite answer. "Thank you," he said, a trifle austerely. "I shall try my best to arrange it." Miss Buckley was something new to him. Her voice had authority. Unaccustomed to being told what to do, Mr. Devore obeyed.

"It's settled, then," she said. "I'll see you at my place of business around five o'clock."

"Place of business?" he asked with interest.

"That's right," said Miss Buckley, and she gave him the address. "You know, it's a funny thing, the last lawyer I had talked just the way you do. Well, I'm getting off the subject. Good-bye now."

So she had had another lawyer. Who? And why had she given him up? If he had died, why hadn't she retained another member of the same firm? Mr. Devore disliked not being able to examine and dispose of these interesting points.

Toward the end of the afternoon he took a taxi to East Fifty-sixth Street. He could afford to inconvenience himself just this once, as far as Miss Buckley's affairs were concerned, out of courtesy to Chester Hibben, but after this visit he would, of course, turn the matter over to one of the clerks. His destination, he found, was an expensive-looking apartment house. He was received by a stately doorman in mulberry livery. In the lobby, Mr. Devore met another attendant, equally splendid, who became something less than cordial when the lawyer said, "Miss Catherine Buckley?"

"Who shall I say is calling?" The man's attitude seemed to be one of suspicion.

"Mr. Devore. Mr. Henry Devore."

"Oh, yes," the attendant said in a much friendlier tone. "Step right in the elevator, Mr. Devore. You're expected. What sorta threw me off was the way you gave the name. Most people just come in and say 'Kitty's.' Matter of fact, she usually don't get nobody at all till about ten." He winked, leaving Mr. Devore a trifle dazed, and made no further comment until they arrived and he threw open the elevator door. "Okey doke," he said, grinning fraternally. "Penthouse." Mr. Devore found himself in a tiny foyer. Another door opened and a Negro maid said, "Yes, *sir.*" Behind her a plump, middle-aged woman in a chartreuse velvet house coat lifted her arm in a cordial salute. She brushed a mop of fuzzy hair back from her forehead and gripped Mr. Devore's hand.

"Welcome to Aunt Kitty's!" she boomed at him. "Zipporah, go tell Mattie the gentleman's here and that I want to see her in the bar. Tell her to bring the snapshots."

"You the gentleman's gonna help Mattie?" the maid inquired sociably.

"He certainly is!" Miss Buckley said with vigor. "None other! Come along, Mr. Devore. What's your first name—Henry, isn't it? Let's go up to the bar. Harry for short, I suppose? We go up these stairs right here. I've got the bar in a special little penthouse of its own. I had a room built on top of all this on account of the noise. I think it was a damn clever thing to do, personally. And the floor below this one belongs to Laddie Selden, who owns the building, so there's no trouble as far as that goes." She was wheezing a little when they reached the floor above, a room handsomely decorated in blue leather, cork, and aluminum, with a professional-looking bar, a blond-finish automatic gramophone, and, in the center of the floor, a small parquet for dancing. "You never saw the Seventieth Street house, did you? It had the worst possible layout. I never had a comfortable minute the whole three years I was there. But here I'm relaxing. It costs me plenty, but why worry? Everybody seems to like it. Daiquiri?"

Mr. Devore sat gingerly on the edge of a banquette and held his breath. What had he let himself in for, he wondered in horror, and how would he ever be able to explain Miss Buckley to his partners? He realized that allowing a clerk to handle her problem was out of the question. It would have to be a junior partner, and someone completely trustworthy. Preferably a young man who would view the situation with the utmost seriousness and feel nothing more than pity for this unfortunate woman. But *was* there such a young man on the staff of Forbes, Hathaway, Bryan & Devore? He had an uncomfortable suspicion that there was not. Miss Buckley, who had gone behind the bar, was mixing a drink with the same precision and sixth sense for measurements that he always admired when he watched the bartender at the Lawyers Club.

"The girls don't get here until seven-thirty or eight or thereabouts," she said. "They make up and dress here. Lovely clothes, Harry. You ought to pay us a visit sometime. My girls are darling. Maybe a little too well developed for chorus work, but that's all. I take most of my girls from show business for sentiment's sake, and I treat 'em right. After all"—she sighed—"I can't ever forget the way *I* looked in my Alfred Cheney Johnston pictures. I've got a lovely one I'll show you sometime. I'm in a black lace shawl. You know how long it's been since they had my picture in the New Amsterdam lobby? Twenty years!" she chuckled richly. "I got out before the 'two big features for fifteen cents' got in. You *did* say a Daiquiri, didn't you? Because it looks as if I've gone right ahead and made one. . . . Oh, hello, Mattie, this is Mr. Devore. Harry, this is Mattie."

An affable Negress who looked as if she might be in her thirties had come into the room. Like Zipporah, she was trimly dressed in a gray-and-white uniform. "Go ahead and sit down, Mattie," Miss Buckley said. "In the first place, he's your lawyer, and in the second place, we're all living in one great big democracy. So they tell me. Have a Daiquiri, Mattie? I don't get someone like Mr. Devore up here for you every day. Incidentally, did Grace's white lamé come back from Plotnick?"

"Thanks, Miss Kitty," Mattie said, accepting a glass. "Yes, Ma'am, it's back. He fixed the sloe-gin spot. It come out fine."

Mr. Devore found himself thinking that although he had been a carefree young man at Harvard, he had never had any preparation for anything quite like this. The conflict in his mind as to which junior partner he should delegate to take Mattie's case had grown more and more disturbing. It should be someone as like himself as possible. Regretfully, he decided that young Mr. Latimer, whom he liked, was perhaps too worldly, too debonair, besides having the grave fault of enjoying any experience that made a good story. Mr. Devore, aware that he himself might figure prominently in any Latimer anecdote about Miss Buckley, gave an involuntary shudder. He wondered about Mr. Thomas Keoghan, who had the advantage of wearing horn-rimmed glasses and living with an unmarried sister in New Rochelle. But of course one could never really be certain about quiet young men. Still waters.

"She's got three snapshots of what's-his-name," Miss Buckley said. "Give them to him, Mattie. He'll want to use them sooner or later." The maid handed some photographs to Mr. Devore. Her husband, whom she identified as one Théophile Descamps, was an unprepossessing animal. Mr. Devore regarded Exhibit A without relish.

"And what do you propose that I do with these, Miss Buckley?"

She raised her glass. "To absent friends," she murmured, and sipped the mixture with satisfaction. "Why ask me? You ought to know better than I do. Have negatives made, then some more prints, and send them to the immigration people. New York, Miami, Tampa, Galveston, Baltimore, Philly, Boston—you know, all around. He might use a phony name, but I guess when they see that kisser, they'll really put their hearts into their work."

"He'd most likely come right here to New York," Mattie said helpfully.

"Might as well be thorough about it," Miss Buckley said with a shrug. "That's my motto. Go on, Harry, drink your drink. And how about asking Mattie some questions?"

"Eventually one of our junior partners will have to talk to—ah—to Mrs. Descamps in order to decide what can be done about her case, but meanwhile I shall be glad to listen to whatever details you think necessary," Mr. Devore said with careful formality. Prompted by Miss

Buckley, he learned colorful particulars about the private life of the Descamps. When the necessary background had been covered, Miss Buckley suddenly named a substantial sum and asked him whether it would cover everything. He said uncertainly that he believed it would, but when she offered to go downstairs and write a check ("I like to get things finished and out of the way"), he said in haste that this was not necessary and that in due course Forbes, Hathaway, Bryan & Devore would notify her regarding costs.

"When I think of the money I've said good-bye to in this sucker world, I get the creeps!" Miss Buckley sighed. "But I've hired my last shyster. One thing I've learned—it doesn't pay to monkey around with cheap lawyers. Mattie, you're certainly getting to be a luxury. If Mr. Devore's finished with you, you'd better run along."

The maid thanked them and departed.

"We'll have another little drink for friendship's sake," said Miss Buckley, returning to the bar. "Harry, how is it you've never been up to see us? I mean when business is going on. I kind of expected to see you and Chester Hibben drop in together some evening."

"Why—ah—thank you," he said nervously. "I'm not at all sure, however, that I *can*—or, rather, that my *time* can be adjusted in such a way as to—"

She was studying him with amused curiosity. "All right, all right," she said. "You're the boss." They had another drink and, much to his relief, Mr. Devore succeeded in maintaining a diplomatic aloofness. He maintained it even after they had gone downstairs, even after Zipporah had given him his hat and helped him with his coat and Mattie had repeated her thanks.

"Zipporah's mad as hell," Mattie said with a low chuckle. "She was all set to make Théophile."

"Nuts!" Zipporah said companionably. "All cats look alike inna dahk."

"Nice language!" Miss Buckley commented, but without any real indignation. "Zipporah, you keep your mouth shut." She turned to Mr. Devore. "And maybe you'll decide to drop in and see us some evening, Harry. Might do you a lot of good to take off the stuffed shirt." She gave him a genial little poke.

As Mr. Devore went down to the street he told himself that he really had good cause to be annoyed at Chester Hibben and Wolverine. While Cavalier Tobacco, Annesley Bolt & Screw, and the Bethesda Refining

Corporation no doubt were equally guilty of occasional peccadilloes, at least they had never burdened him with a Catherine Buckley. He rehearsed what he was going to say to Mr. Keoghan: "My partners and I have always entertained the greatest admiration for your tact, Mr. Keoghan, and naturally we think of you before anyone else when we are confronted with an extremely delicate situation."

"Wouldn't you know it!" the doorman said gloomily. "Raining again."

"In that case I shall require a cab," said Mr. Devore, thankful that there was no humiliating twinkle in the doorman's eye. "We've been quite at the mercy of the weather these days, haven't we?"

James Reid Parker

:

THE ARCHIMANDRITE'S NIECE

Mr. Devore stood in front of one of the windows of his office and gazed out at the heavy fog which encompassed the towers of Pine Street. He would have denied at any time, but particularly on this dreary morning, that his professional life was informed with color, and would have insisted that this was not a matter for regret. The beauty of the law, Mr. Devore had often remarked to Miss Deevey, as well as to many lesser employees, was the beauty of its codified orderliness.

Now the fog was blurring the lights across the street and turning them into sulphur-yellow splotches in the gray waste. Mr. Devore's office, while as orderly as even he could wish, was hardly more cheerful than the haze beyond. As Miss Fannie Devore must have decided when she was choosing the fabric for her bachelor brother's window draperies, anything that bordered on the frivolous would be out of keeping with the austerity that prevailed throughout the temple of Forbes, Hathaway, Bryan & Devore, within which the lawyers carefully prepared Delphic advice for the nervous corporations which approached them for counsel. Mr. Devore was awaiting a Mme. Liapchev, the protégée of an important client.

The day before, Mrs. Herbert Kraft had talked to him eagerly and incoherently on the telephone for twenty-three minutes about the difficulties that beset a woman she knew. A charming person, she said, and one whom Mr. Devore was sure to admire and pity. Mrs. Kraft had

502

gone on in this vein for some time, until Mr. Devore had begun to wonder just what minor infraction of the law the friend could have committed. He had heard similar preambles before.

"You say she is in a serious predicament and is having trouble with the authorities?"

"With the State Department. Didn't I mention that? And it isn't Mme. Liapchev herself who is having trouble. At least, she is, but only indirectly. It's a member of her family. I haven't been able to grasp the situation very clearly myself, but she'll explain everything to you. I'd like to send her down to your office tomorrow. She's visiting us for a while. Tomorrow *will* be all right, won't it? And please try to do something for her, for my sake."

"Of course!" Mr. Devore had said warmly. The Herbert Krafts could, and did, set him whatever tasks they chose, and for an excellent reason. Forbes, Hathaway, Bryan & Devore enjoyed a substantial annual retainer for representing Mr. Kraft's various enterprises.

The morning was well under way when Miss Deevey announced, with something of a sniff, that Mme. Liapchev was calling. Mr. Devore, astutely comprehending that the sniff meant something like "I hope you're not going to fritter away the whole morning," said in a warning tone that the visitor was a friend of Mrs. Herbert Kraft and that he would see her at once.

A distinctly handsome woman came into the room. She wore black, and her manner was impressive. She was a frowningly majestic brunette, in the forties, perhaps, and not unlike Sir Joshua Reynolds' portrait of Mrs. Siddons. Mr. Devore rose and bowed courteously.

"I am Helena Nicolaevna Liapchev," she said, and they shook hands.

"How do you do?" said Mr. Devore. "I am always very happy to be of service to a friend of Mrs. Kraft's."

"God will comfort you," she said. "God will wash and refresh your soul!"

Mr. Devore was startled. His relationship with God, while correctly Episcopalian, had never been intimate. He felt toward God much as he felt toward his friends the H. Chauncey Folgers. He made a point of paying a formal call on God once or twice a year, just as he made a point of paying one or two formal calls on the Folgers. It was inconceivable that either Chauncey Folger or God would ever try to wash and refresh his soul.

"I can tell," he said, recovering as quickly as he could from his discomfiture, "I can tell from your very charming accent that you are Russian."

"You are mistaken. I am Bulgar. My husband was Bulgar, and I am obliged to have his nationality."

"Er—yes, I see," Mr. Devore said politely. "Then—ah—what *are* you? I mean, what are you by *birth?*"

"I am Slavonian," she said with pride. "Or perhaps you are accustomed to say Slovenian?" Mr. Devore responded with a vague smile. "I was born a Prebičević, in the town of Koprivinica in Croatia-Slavonia," Mme. Liapchev went on. Then her expression darkened for a moment. "My mother was Hercegovinian. I did not love my mother."

Mr. Devore tried to picture in his mind a detailed map of the Balkans, but became confused.

"My father's family was devoted to the Church," Mme. Liapchev said suddenly. "It gave many brilliant men to the Church. That is why my uncle is in such trouble. He never should have joined the Church. He should have become a political leader, but his father commanded him to turn to a spiritual life. His problem might have been even worse, of course. He might have risen in the hierarchy instead of in a brotherhood. Imagine how terrible if he had become a metropolitan or even a patriarch and then permitted his political enthusiasms to appear! He would have drawn much more attention to himself than he does as an archimandrite. But you must not misunderstand me"— Mr. Devore was trying harder than ever not to—"he should never have gone so far as to become what he is now. He certainly should not have become an archimandrite. A hegumenos, perhaps, but no more. He should have asked to be allowed to remain the Hegumenos of Enos. It is quite a small monastery, but so nice, so charmingly situated, and the gardens are very attractive. The altitude is high, and the water agrees with him. The water at St. Methodius does not agree with my uncle. It gives him—what is the word for it? I am not sure what the word for it is. It gives him—"

"Yes, yes," Mr. Devore said hastily. "I know. I quite understand. I once had a similar affliction myself in—ah—Pittsburgh."

"It is unthinkable that the Archimandrite of St. Methodius should undertake political activities in Slavonia. The Hegumenos of Enos, yes. That would have excited comparatively little comment, but the Archimandrite of St. Methodius, no!"

"No?" Mr. Devore said, looking at her in wonder.

"When I was a young girl in Koprivinica, it would have been preposterous even to imagine such a thing," Mme. Liapchev said. "And now he has disappeared! I have written to the brotherhood, and the brotherhood has sent me a beautiful and touching reply. It is as ignorant of my uncle's whereabouts as I am. It is supposed that he is in Croatia-Slavonia. He had been contemplating such a visit. I should explain that he habitually carried papers which permitted him to enter Yugoslavia from St. Methodius. St. Methodius is in the Florina province, which is to say northwestern Greece, perhaps forty kilometers east of Albania."

"Ah, yes, northwestern Greece," said Mr. Devore, dazed by the variety of regions that had to be taken into account. "Forty kilometers east of Albania." He began to scribble on a memorandum pad. "This *was* what you wanted to see me about, wasn't it—the disappearance of this gentleman?"

"Certainly."

"Who, as I understand it, went *from* Greece *to* Yugoslavia?"

"To Croatia-Slavonia," Mme. Liapchev corrected him. "It is the only part of Yugoslavia to which one would care to go. In Serbia there are merely swine. I would go so far as to say that my uncle did not even go to Croatia. You can depend upon it—he went to Slavonia."

"You have not yet told me your uncle's name," Mr. Devore said, holding his pencil over the pad.

"His name is Cyril. The family name, as I believe I said, is Prebičević, but my uncle is now known simply as the Archimandrite of St. Methodius."

Mr. Devore could not help feeling that Cyril was a deceptively mild name for so troublesome an uncle, but he was glad to record at last a piece of information that was easy to spell. He had doubts about his rendition of a number of the words in his visitor's deposition. When he looked up, he noted with regret that Mme. Liapchev seemed about to grow fervent again. There was a return of the inspired expression which he had seen when she had commended him to God.

"Who knows what may have happened to him by now?" she said with a musical quaver. "The Drave Banovina should be searched!"

"I presume you are speaking of a river?" Mr. Devore said, feeling strangely divided between irritation and sympathy.

"Certainly not!" She dropped the inspired expression and manifested a certain impatience. "I am speaking of the district that comprises what we know as Old Slavonia. Forgive me"—she became gentle once more, and there was an alarmingly intimate quality in her voice when she was gentle—"I make the mistake of supposing that you are acquainted with my country, do I not? There are nine *banovinas.*"

"Nine?" said Mr. Devore, going into a kind of trance.

"I feel sure that he is going around the countryside of the Drave Banovina, criticizing all the politicians who are not to his taste and telling the people to do dangerous things. My uncle has a habit of speaking so recklessly! On certain occasions he has been mistaken for a madman."

Mr. Devore pulled himself together. "I infer that your uncle is a highly imprudent person," he said. "We have men like that in this country, thanks to the extraordinary liberties which prevail here. Your uncle evidently uses the Church as a cloak for radicalism."

Mme. Liapchev was shocked. *"Radicalism?* He is a *conservative!* He was the first to demand vengeance after the Skupština tragedy!"

Mr. Devore felt that it was time for him to assert himself. "I'm afraid I don't know anything about the—ah—the Skupština tragedy," he said firmly.

"You don't remember it? You don't remember Puniša Račić? He fired on the Croat deputies in the Skupština. Račić was a Montenegrin radical. Oh, it was too shocking! I shall never forget it. No one in Slavonia will ever forget it, in spite of the fact that the Croats are unbelievably inferior to the people of the Drave Banovina. At least, the deputies were not Serbs! It would have been so much better if they *had* been!"

"Quite so. And now to return to the matter we were discussing." He had no intention of enduring any more of these complications, not even for Mrs. Herbert Kraft's sake. "Perhaps he has some close friends to whom you could write."

"Friends?" Mme. Liapchev seemed to consider this a novel idea. She pondered the suggestion for a few moments and then said, "I believe there is a Dr. Hrdla in Moravia. Unless my uncle has quarreled with him. My uncle quarrels with everyone. But Moravia—can one send letters to Moravia these days? I do not think so. No, there is no close friend to whom I could write."

"Perhaps our own State Department could help you," Mr. Devore said. Then he remembered it was with the State Department that she was supposed to be having trouble. He gave her a puzzled look.

"The State Department!" she said with scorn. "They are stupid there. They told me I was not to bother them any more. They told me I must not come back!"

Mr. Devore understood perfectly. "When your uncle goes into"—he hesitated, but decided to be independent of geographical niceties—"into Yugoslavia, does he visit anyone in particular?"

"I have never heard him speak of anyone," she said with a shrug. "He has never mentioned anyone in his letters. His chief reason for going is to annoy the Muslim faction."

"Indeed?" Mr. Devore said with cold exasperation. He had made up his mind. "Our friend Mrs. Kraft," he continued, "is a kindhearted woman. She is always generous, but I fear impulsively so. Like so many kindhearted women"—even with his self-assurance restored, he felt it expedient to stress the tribute—"she is not always aware when obstacles *can* be surmounted and when obstacles *cannot* be surmounted. I must confess that there is absolutely nothing I can do for you. Frankly, it seems to me that the information you wish can be secured only through consular channels, with which you are probably more familiar than I am. I must ask you to tell Mrs. Kraft how sorry I am that I, in my very limited sphere, am helpless to bring such an affair as this to a successful end."

He waited uncomfortably for a display of histrionics, but none materialized. Mme. Liapchev showed no sign of anger or even of acute disappointment. She looked at him dreamily and smoothed her gloves with exquisite grace.

"You are so sympathetic," she said, either with rapt admiration or an excellent imitation of it. "So sympathetic and so *good!*"

"I—ah—I regret that I can be of no assistance to you, but surely you can understand that I am powerless."

"Yes," she said softly. "I regret it so much."

When Mme. Liapchev had departed, Mr. Devore found that he was able to relax a little. But he was afraid Mrs. Kraft's reaction would be one of chagrin and perhaps something even stronger.

He happened not to meet Mrs. Kraft until almost a month later, when they encountered each other in the lobby of Carnegie Hall. Mrs. Kraft said "Henry Devore!" in a reproachful tone. What led Mr. Devore to take heart, however, was the fact that at the same time she sounded playfully arch.

"I'm always picking out the perfect wife for you, Henry," she said, "and you never give them the least little bit of encouragement!"

Anton Chekhov

:

STRONG IMPRESSIONS

It happened not so long ago in the Moscow circuit court. The jurymen, left in the court for the night, before lying down to sleep fell into conversation about strong impressions. They were led to this discussion by recalling a witness who, by his own account, had begun to stammer and had gone gray owing to a terrible moment. The jurymen decided that before going to sleep, each one of them should ransack among his memories and tell something that had happened to him. Man's life is brief, but yet there is no man who cannot boast that there have been terrible moments in his past.

One juryman told the story of how he was nearly drowned; another described how, in a place where there were neither doctors nor chemists, he had one night poisoned his own son through giving him zinc vitriol by mistake for soda. The child did not die, but the father nearly went out of his mind. A third, a man not old but in bad health, told how he had twice attempted to commit suicide: the first time by shooting himself and the second time by throwing himself before a train.

The fourth, a foppishly dressed, fat little man, told us the following story:

"I was not more than twenty-two or twenty-three when I fell head over ears in love with my present wife and made her an offer. Now I could with pleasure thrash myself for my early marriage, but at the time, I don't know what would have become of me if Natasha had refused me. My love was absolutely the real thing, just as it is described

508

in novels—frantic, passionate, and so on. My happiness overwhelmed me and I did not know how to get away from it, and I bored my father and my friends and the servants, continually talking about the fervor of my passion. Happy people are the most sickening bores. I was a fearful bore; I feel ashamed of it even now. . . .

"Among my friends there was in those days a young man who was beginning his career as a lawyer. Now he is a lawyer known all over Russia; in those days he was only just beginning to gain recognition and was not rich and famous enough to be entitled to cut an old friend when he met him. I used to go and see him once or twice a week. We used to loll on sofas and begin discussing philosophy.

"One day I was lying on his sofa, arguing that there was no more ungrateful profession than that of a lawyer. I tried to prove that as soon as the examination of witnesses is over the court can easily dispense with both the counsels for the prosecution and for the defense, because they are neither of them necessary and are only in the way. If a grown-up juryman, morally and mentally sane, is convinced that the ceiling is white, or that Ivanov is guilty, to struggle with that conviction and to vanquish it is beyond the power of any Demosthenes. Who can convince me that I have a red mustache when I know that it is black? As I listen to an orator I may perhaps grow sentimental and weep, but my fundamental conviction, based for the most part on unmistakable evidence and fact, is not changed in the least. My lawyer maintained that I was young and foolish and that I was talking childish nonsense. In his opinion, for one thing, an obvious fact becomes still more obvious through light being thrown upon it by conscientious, well-informed people; for another, talent is an elemental force, a hurricane capable of turning even stones to dust, let alone such trifles as the convictions of artisans and merchants of the second guild. It is as hard for human weakness to struggle against talent as to look at the sun without winking, or to stop the wind. One simple mortal by the power of the word turns thousands of convinced savages to Christianity; Odysseus was a man of the firmest convictions, but he succumbed to the Syrens, and so on. All history consists of similar examples, and in life they are met with at every turn; and so it is bound to be, or the intelligent and talented man would have no superiority over the stupid and incompetent.

"I stuck to my point, and went on maintaining that convictions are stronger than any talent, though, frankly speaking, I could not have defined exactly what I meant by conviction or what I meant by talent. Most likely I simply talked for the sake of talking.

" 'Take you, for example,' said the lawyer. 'You are convinced at this moment that your fiancée is an angel and that there is not a man in the whole town happier than you. But I tell you: ten or twenty minutes would be enough for me to make you sit down to this table and write to your fiancée, breaking off your engagement.'

"I laughed.

" 'Don't laugh, I am speaking seriously,' said my friend. 'If I choose, in twenty minutes you will be happy at the thought that you need not get married. Goodness knows what talent I have, but you are not one of the strong sort.'

" 'Well, try it on!' said I.

" 'No, what for? I am only telling you this. You are a good boy and it would be cruel to subject you to such an experiment. And besides I am not in good form to-day.'

"We sat down to supper. The wine and the thought of Natasha, my beloved, flooded my whole being with youth and happiness. My happiness was so boundless that the lawyer sitting opposite to me with his green eyes seemed to me an unhappy man, so small, so gray. . . .

" 'Do try!' I persisted. 'Come, I entreat you!'

"The lawyer shook his head and frowned. Evidently I was beginning to bore him.

" 'I know,' he said, 'after my experiment you will say, thank you, and will call me your savior; but you see I must think of your fiancée too. She loves you; your jilting her would make her suffer. And what a charming creature she is! I envy you.'

"The lawyer sighed, sipped his wine, and began talking of how charming my Natasha was. He had an extraordinary gift of description. He could knock you off a regular string of words about a woman's eyelashes or her little finger. I listened to him with relish.

" 'I have seen a great many women in my day,' he said, 'but I give you my word of honor, I speak as a friend, your Natasha Andreyevna is a pearl, a rare girl. Of course she has her defects—many of them, in fact, if you like—but still she is fascinating.'

"And the lawyer began talking of my fiancée's defects. Now I understand very well that he was talking of women in general, of their weak points in general, but at the time it seemed to me that he was talking only of Natasha. He went into ecstasies over her turn-up nose, her shrieks, her shrill laugh, her airs and graces, precisely all the things I so disliked in her. All that was, to his thinking, infinitely sweet, graceful, and feminine.

"Without my noticing it, he quickly passed from his enthusiastic tone to one of fatherly admonition, and then to a light and derisive one. . . . There was no presiding judge and no one to check the diffusiveness of the lawyer. I had not time to open my mouth, besides, what could I say? What my friend said was not new, it was what everyone has known for ages, and the whole venom lay not in what he said, but in the damnable form he put it in. It really was beyond anything!

"As I listened to him then I learned that the same word has thousands of shades of meaning according to the tone in which it is pronounced, and the form which is given to the sentence. Of course I cannot reproduce the tone or the form; I can only say that as I listened to my friend and walked up and down the room, I was moved to resentment, indignation, and contempt together with him. I even believed him when with tears in his eyes he informed me that I was a great man, that I was worthy of a better fate, that I was destined to achieve something in the future which marriage would hinder!

" 'My friend!' he exclaimed, pressing my hand. 'I beseech you, I adjure you: stop before it is too late. Stop! May Heaven preserve you from this strange, cruel mistake! My friend, do not ruin your youth!'

"Believe me or not, as you choose, but the long and the short of it was that I sat down to the table and wrote to my fiancée, breaking off the engagement. As I wrote I felt relieved that it was not yet too late to rectify my mistake. Sealing the letter, I hastened out into the street to post it. The lawyer himself came with me.

" 'Excellent! Capital!' he applauded me as my letter to Natasha disappeared into the darkness of the box. 'I congratulate you with all my heart. I am glad for you.'

"After walking a dozen paces with me the lawyer went on:

" 'Of course, marriage has its good points. I, for instance, belong to the class of people to whom marriage and home life is everything.'

"And he proceeded to describe his life, and lay before me all the hideousness of a solitary bachelor existence.

"He spoke with enthusiasm of his future wife, of the sweets of ordinary family life, and was so eloquent, so sincere in his ecstasies that by the time we had reached his door, I was in despair.

" 'What are you doing to me, you horrible man?' I said, gasping.

'You have ruined me! Why did you make me write that cursed letter? I love her, I love her!'

"And I protested my love. I was horrified at my conduct which now seemed to me wild and senseless. It is impossible, gentlemen, to imagine a more violent emotion than I experienced at that moment. Oh, what I went through, what I suffered! If some kind person had thrust a revolver into my hand at that moment, I should have put a bullet through my brains with pleasure.

" 'Come, come . . .' said the lawyer, slapping me on the shoulder, and he laughed. 'Give over crying. The letter won't reach your fiancée. It was not you who wrote the address but I, and I muddled it so they won't be able to make it out at the postoffice. It will be a lesson to you not to argue about what you don't understand.'

"Now, gentlemen, I leave it to the next to speak."

The fifth juryman settled himself more comfortably, and had just opened his mouth to begin his story when we heard the clock strike on Spassky Tower.

"Twelve . . ." one of the jurymen counted. "And into which class, gentlemen, would you put the emotions that are being experienced now by the man we are trying? He, that murderer, is spending the night in a convict cell here in the court, sitting or lying down and of course not sleeping, and throughout the whole sleepless night listening to that chime. What is he thinking of? What visions are haunting him?"

And the jurymen all suddenly forgot about strong impressions; what their companion who had once written a letter to his Natasha had suffered seemed unimportant, even not amusing; and no one said anything more; they began quietly and in silence lying down to sleep.

Théobald Mathew

:

THE BLUSHING BEGINNER AND
THE BEARDED JURYMAN

A Solicitor Briefed a Blushing Beginner to Defend a Prisoner at the Assizes. He Assured the Blushing Beginner that there was no Cause for Anxiety as the Prisoner hadn't an Earthly. When the Jury Acquitted the Prisoner the Blushing Beginner could Hardly Believe his Ears. He felt that he had indeed been Wise to Devote so much Time to the Study of the Works of Quintilian on Oratory and the Great Speeches of Such Masters as Cicero and Demosthenes. That his Address to the Jury had Done the Trick he had Little Doubt. For he had Observed that a Juryman with a Black Beard in the Front Row had Paid Close Attention to his Best Points. Which Particular Portion of his Speech had been Most Effective the Blushing Beginner could not be Sure. He Inclined to think it was the Peroration. For when he had Come to the Bit about the Dawn Breaking and the Sun Gilding the Distant Hills the Bearded Juryman had Shewn Considerable Emotion. Thus Meditating, the Blushing Beginner Proceeded from the Court to his Lodgings in High Spirits. On his Way he Observed the Bearded Juryman just Ahead of him. Hurrying Forward, the Blushing Beginner Wished the Bearded Juryman a Good Evening and Engaged him in Conversation. "Could you tell me," he said, "without Divulging any Secret of the Jury-box, what it was that Convinced you of the Prisoner's Innocence? Was it my Cross-examination of the Prosecutor? Or the Failure of the Crown to Call Robinson? Or was it, perchance, the Argument which I Put Forward in my Final Speech?" The Bearded

513

Juryman Replied, with Some Warmth, that he didn't Know or Care what the other Mugs Thought, but for his Part he (the Bearded Juryman) didn't See why his Sister's Son should be Sent to Quod even if the Boy *had* Stole a Tenner from the Blinking Blighter who had Done him (the Bearded Juryman) over a Deal Two Years ago. The Bearded Juryman then Expectorated Fiercely and Turned into the "Blue Pig" for Further Refreshment. The Blushing Beginner Gathered from these Remarks that there were Collateral Reasons for the Opinion of the Bearded Juryman which were not Strictly Relevant to the Main Issues in the Case. But he Decided to Treat the Bearded Juryman's Disclosures as Confidential.

Moral.—*Study Quintilian on Oratory.*

Théobald Mathew

:

THE WITTY JUDGE AND THE
˙BRONCHIAL USHER

A witty Judge, while Perusing the Depositions for the Forthcoming Sessions at the Old Bailey, Saw the Chance of a Lifetime. A Prisoner Bearing the Name of William Shakespeare was Charged with Obtaining Money by False Pretences. It seemed that his Habit had been to Simulate Epileptic Fits in Order to Arouse the Sympathy of Bystanders. His Stock-in-Trade was a Piece of Yellow Soap, which, Diligently Chewed, Produced the Effect of Foaming at the Mouth. This Symptom, together with Gnashing of the Teeth and Rolling of the Eyes, had Convinced Large Numbers of Spectators of the Genuineness of his Attacks. William Shakespeare had Consequently Enjoyed an Income which was Amply Sufficient for his Daily Requirements.

The Witty Judge Felt that if, at the Appropriate Moment, he were to Observe that this Seemed to be a Case of *Poeta Gnashitur Non Fit,* his Reputation as a Jester of the First Order would be Made for Ever.

The case of *R. v. Shakespeare* Came On. Unhappily (as it Proved) the Usher of the Court was a Bronchial Subject. On the Day in Question he was Afflicted with a Severe Catarrh and a Rich and Resounding Cough. Half Way through the Opening of the Case for the Prosecution, which was Conducted by a Counsel of No Importance, the Witty Judge Felt that the Psychological Moment had Arrived. By Way of Preparing the Ground he Asked in an Innocent Manner Whether there was not Once a Poet named William Shakespeare. Counsel Replied in the Affirmative. The Witty Judge was in the Very Act of Loosing Off his Epoch-

515

making Jest when the Bronchial Usher was Seized with a Paroxysm of Coughing which was Audible in Newgate Street. Then an Appalling Calamity Occurred. The Counsel of No Importance, Resuming his Interrupted Address, Said that his Lordship's Question Prompted the Remark that this Seemed to be a Case of *Poeta Gnashitur Non Fit*. He had Made the Witty Judge's Joke! The Court Rocked with Laughter, in which the Prisoner (who was Something of a Scholar) Joined Heartily, and the Reporters Signaled to their Messengers in Order that the Stop-Press Editions might Give to the World the Joke of the Century.

The Witty Judge was Equal to the Occasion. With Austere Dignity he Rebuked the Counsel of No Importance for his Unseemly Levity, and Begged the Press, in the Interests of Decency, not to Allude to an Incident which had Distressed him Greatly.

When the Court Rose the Witty Judge Told the Bronchial Usher Exactly what he Thought of him. He also Took Immediate Steps to have him Transferred from the Old Bailey to the Commercial Court.

Moral.—*Preparation is the Soul of Wit.*

W. Somerset Maugham

:

THE HAPPY COUPLE

I don't know that I very much liked Landon. He was a member of a club I belonged to, and I had often sat next to him at lunch. He was a judge at Old Bailey, and it was through him I was able to get a privileged seat in court when there was an interesting trial that I wanted to attend. He was an imposing figure on the bench in his great full-bottomed wig, his red robes and his ermine tippet; and with his long, white face, thin lips and pale blue eyes, a somewhat terrifying one. He was just, but harsh; and sometimes it made me uncomfortable to hear the bitter scolding he gave a convicted prisoner whom he was about to sentence to a long term of imprisonment. But his acid humor at the lunch-table and his willingness to discuss the cases he had tried made him sufficiently good company for me to disregard the slight ma- laise I felt in his presence. I asked him once whether he did not feel a certain uneasiness of mind after he had sent a man to the gallows. He smiled as he sipped his glass of port.

"Not at all. The man's had a fair trial; I've summed up as fairly as I could, and the jury has found him guilty. When I condemn him to death, I sentence him to a punishment he richly deserves; and when the court rises, I put the case out of my head. Nobody but a sentimen- tal fool would do anything else."

I knew he liked to talk to me, but I never thought he looked upon me as anything but a club acquaintance, so I was not a little surprised when one day I received a telegram from him saying that he was

517

spending his vacation on the Riviera, and would like to stay with me for two or three days on his way to Italy. I wired that I should be glad to see him. But it was with a certain trepidation that I met him at the station.

On the day of his arrival, to help me out, I asked Miss Gray, a neighbor and an old friend of mine, to dinner. She was of mature age, but charming, and she had a flow of lively conversation which I knew nothing could discourage. I gave them a very good dinner, and though I had no port to offer the judge, I was able to provide him with a good bottle of Montrachet and an even better bottle of Mouton Rothschild. He enjoyed them both; and I was glad of that, because when I had offered him a cocktail, he had refused with indignation.

"I have never understood," he said, "how people presumably civilized can indulge in a habit that is not only barbarous but disgusting."

I may state that this did not deter Miss Gray and me from having a couple of dry Martinis, though it was with impatience and distaste that he watched us drink them.

But the dinner was a success. The good wine and Miss Gray's sprightly chatter combined to give Landon a geniality I had never before seen in him. It was plain to me that notwithstanding his austere appearance he liked feminine society; and Miss Gray in a becoming dress, with her neat head only just touched with gray and her delicate features, her sparkling eyes, was still alluring. After dinner the judge, with some old brandy still further to mellow him, let himself go, and for a couple of hours held us entranced while he told us of celebrated trials in which he had been concerned. I was not surprised therefore that when Miss Gray asked us to lunch with her next day, Landon, even before I could answer, accepted with alacrity.

"A very nice woman," he said when she had left us. "And a head on her shoulders. She must have been very pretty as a girl. She's not bad now. Why isn't she married?"

"She always says nobody asked her."

"Stuff and nonsense! Women ought to marry. Too many of these women about who want their independence. I have no patience with them."

Miss Gray lived in a little house facing the sea at St. Jean, which is a couple of miles from my own house at Cap Ferrat. We drove down next day at one and were shown into her sitting-room.

"I have a surprise for you," she said to me, as we shook hands. "The Craigs are coming."

"You've got to know them at last."

"Well, I thought it was too absurd that we should live next door to one another, and bathe from the same beach every day and not speak. So I forced myself on them, and they've promised to come to lunch today. I wanted you to meet them, to see what you make of them." She turned to Landon. "I hope you don't mind."

But he was on his best behavior.

"I'm sure I shall be delighted to meet any friends of yours, Miss Gray," he said.

"But they're not friends of mine. I've seen a lot of them, but I never spoke to them till yesterday. It'll be a treat for them to meet an author and a celebrated judge."

I had heard a good deal of the Craigs from Miss Gray during the previous three weeks. They had taken the cottage next to hers, and, first she feared they would be a nuisance. She liked her own company and did not want to be bothered with the trivialities of social intercourse. But she very quickly discovered that the Craigs were as plainly disinclined to strike up an acquaintance with her as she with them. Though in that little place they could not but meet two or three times a day, the Craigs never by so much a glance gave an indication that they had ever seen her before. Miss Gray told me she thought it very tactful of them to make no attempt to intrude upon her privacy, but I had an idea that she was not affronted, a little puzzled rather, that they apparently wanted to know her as little as she wanted to know them. I had guessed some time before that she would not be able to resist making the first advance. On one occasion, while we were walking, we passed them, and I was able to have a good look at them. Craig was a handsome man, with a red, honest face, a gray mustache and thick strong gray hair. He held himself well, and there was a bluff heartiness of manner about him that suggested a broker who had retired on a handsome fortune. His wife was a woman hard of visage, tall and of masculine appearance, with dull, fair hair too elaborately dressed, a large nose, a large mouth and a weather-beaten skin. She was not only plain but grim. Her clothes, pretty, flimsy and graceful, sat oddly upon her, for they would better have suited a girl of eighteen, and Mrs. Craig was certainly forty. Miss Gray told me they were well cut and expensive.

I thought he looked commonplace and she looked disagreeable, and I told Miss Gray she was lucky that they were obviously disposed to keep themselves to themselves.

"There's something rather sweet about them," she answered.

"What?"

"They love one another. And they adore the baby."

For they had a child that was not more than a year old; and from this Miss Gray had concluded that they had not long been married. She liked to watch them with their baby. A nurse took it out every morning in a pram, but before this, father and mother spent an ecstatic quarter of an hour teaching it to walk. They stood a few yards apart and urged the child to flounder from one to the other; and each time it tumbled into the parental arms, it was lifted up and rapturously embraced. And when finally it was tucked up in the smart pram, they hung over it with charming baby talk and watched it out of sight as though they couldn't bear to let it go.

Miss Gray used often to see them walking up and down the lawn of their garden arm in arm; they did not talk, as though they were so happy to be together that conversation was unnecessary; and it warmed her heart to observe the affection which that dour, unsympathetic woman so obviously felt for her tall, handsome husband. It was a pretty sight to see Mrs. Craig brush an invisible speck of dust off his coat, and Miss Gray was convinced that she purposely made holes in his socks in order to have the pleasure of darning them. And it looked as though he loved her as much as she loved him. Every now and then he would give her a glance, and she would look up at him and smile, and he gave her cheek a little pat. Because they were no longer young, their mutual devotion was peculiarly touching.

I never knew why Miss Gray had never married; I felt as certain as the judge that she had had plenty of chances; and I asked myself, when she talked to me about the Craigs, whether the sight of this matrimonial felicity didn't give her a slight pang. I suppose complete happiness is very rare in this world, but these two people seemed to enjoy it, and it may be that Miss Gray was so strangely interested in them only because she could not quite suppress the feeling in her heart that by remaining single she had missed something.

Because she didn't know what their first names were, she called them Edwin and Angelina. She made up a story about them. She told it to me one day; and when I ridiculed it, she was quite short with me. This, as far as I can remember, is how it went: They had fallen in love with one another years before—perhaps twenty years—when Angelina, a young girl then, had the fresh grace of her teens and Edwin was a brave youth setting out joyously on the journey of life. And since the gods, who are said to look upon young love with kindliness, nevertheless do not bother their heads with practical matters, neither Edwin nor Angelina had a penny. It was impossible for them to marry, but they had courage, hope and confidence. Edwin made up his mind to go out to South America or Malaya or where you like, make his fortune and return to marry the girl who had patiently waited for him. It couldn't take more than two or three years, five at the utmost; and what is that, when you're twenty and the whole of life is before you? Meanwhile of course Angelina would live with her widowed mother.

But things didn't pan out according to schedule. Edwin found it more difficult than he had expected to make a fortune; in fact, he found it hard to earn enough money to keep body and soul together, and only Angelina's love and her tender letters gave him the heart to continue the struggle. At the end of five years he was not much better off than when he started. Angelina would willingly have joined him and shared his poverty, but it was impossible for her to leave her mother, bedridden as she was, poor thing, and there was nothing for them to do but have patience. And so the years passed slowly, and Edwin's hair grew gray, and Angelina became grim and haggard. Hers was the harder lot, for she could do nothing but wait. The cruel glass showed such charms as she had possessed slipping away from her one by one; and at last she discovered that youth, with a mocking laugh and a pirouette, had left her for good. Her sweetness turned sour from long tending of a querulous invalid; her mind was narrowed by the society of the small town in which she lived. Her friends married and had children, but she remained a prisoner to duty.

She wondered if Edwin still loved her. She wondered if he would ever come back. She often despaired. Ten years went by, and fifteen, and twenty. Then Edwin wrote to say that his affairs were settled, he had made enough money for them to live upon in comfort, and if she were still willing to marry him, he would return at once. By a merciful interposition of providence, Angelina's mother chose that very moment to abandon a world in which she had made herself a thorough nuisance. But when after so long a separation they met, Angelina saw with dismay that Edwin was as young as ever. It's true his hair was gray, but it infinitely became him. He had always been good-looking, but now he was a very handsome man in the flower of his age. She felt as old as the hills. She was conscious of her narrowness, her terrible provincialism, compared with the breadth he had acquired by his long sojourn in foreign countries. He was gay and breezy as of old, but her spirit was crushed. The bitterness of life had warped her soul. It seemed monstrous to bind that alert and active man to her by a promise twenty years old, and she offered him his release. He went deathly pale.

"Don't you care for me any more?" he cried brokenly.

And she realized on a sudden—oh, the rapture, oh, the relief!—that to him too she was just the same as she had ever been. He had thought of her always as she was; her portrait had been, as it were, stamped on his heart, so that now, when the real woman stood before him, she was, to him, still eighteen.

So they were married.

"I don't believe a word of it," I said when Miss Gray had brought her story to its happy ending.

"I insist on your believing it," she said. "I'm convinced it's true, and I haven't the smallest doubt that they'll live happily together to a ripe old age." Then she made a remark that I thought rather shrewd. "Their love is founded on an illusion, perhaps; but since it has to them all the appearance of reality, what does it matter?"

While I have told you this idyllic story of Miss Gray's invention, the three of us, our hostess, Landon and myself, waited for the Craigs to come.

"Have you ever noticed that if people live next door to you, they're invariably late?" Miss Gray asked the judge.

"No, I haven't," he answered acidly. "I'm always punctual myself, and I expect other people to be punctual."

"I suppose it's no good offering you a cocktail?"

"None whatever, madam."

"But I have some sherry that they tell me isn't bad."

The judge took the bottle out of her hands and looked at the label. A faint smile broke on his thin lips.

"This is a civilized drink, Miss Gray. With your permission I will help myself. I never knew a woman yet who knew how to pour out a glass of wine. One should hold a woman by the waist, but a bottle by the neck."

While he was sipping the old sherry with every sign of satisfaction, Miss Gray glanced out of the window.

"Oh, that's why the Craigs are late. They were waiting for the baby to come back."

I followed her eyes and saw that the nurse had just pushed the pram past Miss Gray's house on her way home. Craig took the baby out of the pram and lifted it high in the air. The baby, trying to tug at his mustache, crowed gleefully. Mrs. Craig stood by watching, and the smile on her face made her harsh features almost pleasant. The window was open, and we heard her speak.

"Come along, darling," she said, "we're late."

He put the baby back in the pram, and they came up to the door of Miss Gray's house and rang the bell. The maid showed them in. They shook hands with Miss Gray, and because I was standing near, she introduced me to them. Then she turned to the judge.

"And this is Sir Edward Landon—Mr. and Mrs. Craig."

One would have expected the judge to move forward with an out-stretched hand, but he remained stock-still. He put his eyeglass up to his eye, that eyeglass that I had on more than one occasion seen him use with devastating effect in court, and stared at the newcomers.

"Gosh, what a dirty customer," I said to myself.

He let the glass drop from his eye.

"How do you do," he said. "Am I mistaken in thinking that we've met before?"

The question turned my eyes to the Criags. They stood side by side close to one another, as though they had drawn together for mutual protection. They did not speak. Mrs. Craig looked terrified. Craig's red face was darkened by a purple flush, and his eyes appeared almost to start out of his head. But that only lasted a second.

"I don't think so," he said in a rich, deep voice. "Of course I've heard of you, Sir Edward."

"More people know Tom Fool than Tom Fool knows," said he.

Miss Gray meanwhile had been giving the cocktail-shaker a shake, and now she handed cocktails to her two guests. She had noticed nothing. I didn't know what it all meant; in fact, I wasn't sure it meant anything. The incident, if incident there was, passed so quickly that I was half inclined to think that I had read into the strangers' momentary embarrassment on being introduced to a celebrated man something for which there was no foundation. I set about making myself pleasant. I asked them how they liked the Riviera and if they were comfortable in their house. Miss Gray joined in, and we chatted, as one does with strangers, of commonplace things. They talked easily and pleasantly. Mrs. Craig said how much they enjoyed the bathing and complained of the difficulty of getting fish at the seaside. I was aware that the judge did not join in the conversation, but looked down at his feet as though he were unconscious of the company.

Lunch was announced. We went into the dining-room. We were only five, and it was a small round table, so the conversation could not be anything but general. I must confess that it was carried on chiefly by Miss Gray and myself. The judge was silent, but he often was, for he was a moody creature, and I paid no attention. I noticed that he ate the omelette with good appetite, and when it was passed round again took a second helping. The Craigs struck me as a little shy, but that didn't surprise me, and as the second course was produced they began to talk more freely. It didn't strike me that they were very amusing people; they didn't seem interested in very much besides their baby, the vagaries of the two Italian maids they had, and an occasional flutter at Monte Carlo; and I couldn't help thinking that Miss Gray had erred in making their acquaintance. Then suddenly something happened: Craig rose abruptly from his chair and fell headlong to the floor. We jumped up. Mrs. Craig threw herself down, over her husband, and took his head in her hands.

"It's all right, George," she cried in an agonized tone. "It's all right!"

"Put his head down," I said. "He's only fainted."

I felt his pulse and could feel nothing. I said he had fainted, but I wasn't sure it wasn't a stroke. He was the sort of heavy, plethoric man who might easily have one. Miss Gray dipped her napkin into water and dabbed his forehead. Mrs. Craig seemed distraught. Then I noticed that Landon had remained quietly sitting in his chair.

"If he's fainted, you're not helping him to recover by crowding round him," he said acidly.

Mrs. Craig turned her head and gave him a look of bitter hatred.

"I'll ring up the doctor," said Miss Gray.

"No, I don't think that's necessary," I said. "He's coming to."

I could feel his pulse growing stronger, and in a minute or two he opened his eyes. He gasped when he realized what had happened, and tried to struggle to his feet.

"Don't move," I said. "Lie still a little longer."

I got him to drink a glass of brandy, and the color came back to his face.

"I feel all right now," he said.

"We'll get you into the next room, and you can lie on the sofa for a bit."

"No, I'd sooner go home. It's only a step."

He got up from the floor.

"Yes, let's go back," said Mrs. Craig. She turned to Miss Gray. "I'm so sorry; he's never done anything like this before."

They were determined to go, and I thought myself it was the best thing for them to do.

"Put him to bed and keep him there, and he'll be as right as rain tomorrow."

Mrs. Craig took one of his arms and I took the other; Miss Gray opened the door, and though still a bit shaky, he was able to walk. When we arrived at the Craigs' home, I offered to go in and help undress him; but they would neither of them hear of it. I went back to Miss Gray's and found them at dessert.

"I wonder why he fainted," Miss Gray was saying. "All the windows are open, and it's not particularly hot today."

"I wonder," said the judge.

I noticed that his thin pale face bore an expression of some complacency. We had our coffee; and then, since the judge and I were going to play golf, we got into the car and drove up the hill to my house.

"How did Miss Gray get to know those people?" Landon asked me. "They struck me as rather second-rate. I shouldn't have thought they were very much her mark."

"You know women. She likes her privacy, and when they settled in next door, she was quite decided that she wouldn't have anything to do with them; but when she discovered that they didn't want to have anything to do with her, she couldn't rest till she'd made their acquaintance."

I told him the story she had invented about her neighbors. He listened with an expressionless face.

"I'm afraid your friend Miss Gray is a sentimental donkey, my dear fellow," he said when I had come to an end. "I tell you, women ought to marry. She'd soon have had all that nonsense knocked out of her if she'd had half a dozen brats."

"What do you know about the Craigs?" I asked.

He gave me a frigid glance.

"I? Why should I know anything about them? I thought they were very ordinary people."

I wish I knew how to describe the strong impression he gave me, both by the glacial austerity of his look and by the rasping finality of his tone, that he was not prepared to say anything more. We finished the drive in silence.

Landon was well on in his sixties, and he was the kind of golfer who never hits a long ball but is never off the straight, and he was a deadly putter, so, though he gave me strokes, he beat me handsomely. After dinner I took him in to Monte Carlo, where he finished the evening by winning a couple of thousand francs at the roulette table. These successive events put him into a remarkably good humor.

"A very pleasant day," he said when we parted for the night. "I've thoroughly enjoyed it."

I spent the next morning at work, and we did not meet till lunch. We were just finishing when I was called to the telephone.

When I came back, my guest was drinking a second cup of coffee.

"That was Miss Gray," I said.

"Oh? What had she to say?"

"The Craigs have done a bolt. They disappeared last night. The maids live in the village; and when they came this morning, they found the house empty. They'd skipped—the Craigs, the nurse and the baby—and taken their luggage with them. They left money on the table for the maids' wages, the rent to the end of their tenancy and the tradesmen's bills."

The judge said nothing. He took a cigar from the box, examined it carefully and then lit it with deliberation.

"What have you got to say about that?" I asked.

"My dear fellow, are you obliged to use these American phrases? Isn't English good enough for you?"

"Is that an American phrase? It expresses exactly what I mean. You can't imagine I'm such a fool as not to have noticed that you and the Craigs had met before; and if they've vanished into thin air like figments of the imagination, it's a fairly reasonable conclusion that the circumstances under which you met were not altogether pleasant."

The judge gave a little chuckle, and there was a twinkle in his cold blue eyes.

"That was a very good brandy you gave me last night," he said.

"It's against my principles to drink liqueurs after lunch, but it's a very dull man who allows his principles to enslave him, and for once I think I should enjoy one."

I sent for the brandy and watched the judge while he poured himself out a generous measure. He took a sip with obvious satisfaction.

"Do you remember the Wingford murder?" he asked me.

"No."

"Perhaps you weren't in England at the time. Pity—you might have come to the trial. You'd have enjoyed it. It caused a lot of excitement; the papers were full of it.

"Miss Wingford was a rich spinster of mature age who lived in the country with a companion. She was a healthy woman for her age; and when she died rather suddenly, her friends were surprised. Her physician, a fellow called Brandon, signed the certificate and she was duly buried. The will was read, and it appeared that she had left everything she had, something between sixty and seventy thousand pounds, to her companion. The relations were very sore, but there was nothing they could do about it. The will had been drawn up by her lawyer and witnessed by his clerk and Dr. Brandon.

"But Miss Wingford had a maid who had been with her for thirty years and had always understood that she would be remembered in the will; she claimed that Miss Wingford had promised to leave her well provided for, and when she found that she wasn't even mentioned, she flew into a passion. She told the nephew and the two nieces who had come down for the funeral that she was sure Miss Wingford had been poisoned, and she said that if they didn't go to the police, she'd go herself. Well, they didn't do that, but they went to see Dr. Brandon. He laughed. He said that Miss Wingford had had a weak heart and he'd been treating her for years. She died just as he had always expected her to die, peacefully in her sleep; and he advised them not to pay any attention to what the maid said. She had always hated the companion, a Miss Starling, and been jealous of her. Dr. Brandon was highly respected; he had been Miss Wingford's doctor for a long time, and the two nieces, who'd stayed with her often, knew him well. He was not profiting by the will, and there seemed no reason to doubt his word, so the family thought there was nothing to do but make the best of a bad job and went back to London.

"But the maid went on talking; she talked so much that at last the police, much against their will, I must admit, were obliged to take notice, and an order to exhume the body was made. There was an inquest, and it was found that Miss Wingford had died from an overdose of veronal. The coroner's jury found that it had been administered by Miss Starling, and she was arrested. A detective was sent down from Scotland Yard, and he got together some unexpected evidence. It appeared that there'd been a good deal of gossip about Miss Starling and Dr. Brandon. They'd been seen a lot together in places in which there was no reason for them to be except that they wanted to be together, and the general impression in the village was that they were only waiting for Miss Wingford to die to get married. That put a very different complexion on the case. To make a long story short, the police got enough evidence in their opinion to justify them in arresting the doctor and charging him and Miss Starling with the murder of the old lady."

The judge took another sip of brandy.

"The case came up for trial before me. The case for the prosecution was that the accused were madly in love with one another and had done the poor old lady to death so that they could marry on the fortune Miss Starling had wheedled her employer into leaving her. Miss Wingford always had a cup of cocoa when she went to bed, which Miss Starling prepared for her; and the counsel for the prosecution claimed that it was in this that Miss Starling had dissolved the tablets that caused Miss Wingford's death. The accused elected to give evidence on their own behalf, and they made a miserable showing in the witness-box. They lied their heads off. Though witnesses testified they had seen them walking together at night with their arms round one another's waists, though Brandon's maid testified she had seen them kissing one another in the doctor's house, they swore they were no more than friends. And oddly enough, medical evidence proved that Miss Starling was *virgo intacta.*

"Brandon admitted that he had given Miss Wingford a bottle of veronal tablets because she complained of sleeplessness, but declared he had warned her never to take more than one, and then only when absolutely necessary. The defense sought to prove that she had taken the tablets either by accident or because she wanted to commit suicide. That didn't hold water for a moment. Miss Wingford was a jolly, normal old lady who thoroughly enjoyed life; and her death occurred two days before the expected arrival of an old friend for a week's visit. She hadn't complained to the maid of sleeping badly—in fact, her maid had always thought her a very good sleeper. It was impossible to believe that she had accidentally taken a sufficient number of tablets to kill herself. Personally, I had no doubt that it was a put-up job between the doctor and the companion. The motive was obvious and sufficient. I summed up and I hope summed up fairly; but it was my duty to put the facts before the jury, and to my mind the facts were damning. The jury filed out. I don't suppose you know that when you are sitting on the bench, you somehow get the feeling of the court. You have to be on your guard against it, to be sure it doesn't influence you. I never had it more strongly than on that day that there wasn't a soul in court who wasn't convinced that those two people had committed the crime with which they were charged. I hadn't the shadow of a doubt that the jury would bring in a verdict of guilty. Juries are incalculable. They were out for three hours, and when they came back I knew at once that I was mistaken. In a murder case, when a jury is going to bring in a verdict of guilty they won't look at the prisoner; they look away. I noticed that three or four of the jurymen glanced at the two prisoners in the dock. They brought in a verdict of not guilty. The real names of Mr. and Mrs. Craig are Dr. and Mrs. Brandon. I'm just as certain as I am that I'm sitting here that they committed between them a cruel and heartless murder and richly deserved to be hanged."

"What do you think made the jury find them not guilty?"

"I've asked myself that; and do you know the only explanation I can give? The fact that it was conclusively proved that they had never been lovers. And if you come to think of it, that's one of the most curious features of the whole case. That woman was prepared to commit murder to get the man she loved, but she wasn't prepared to have an illicit love-affair with him."

"Human nature is very odd, isn't it?"

"Very," said Landon, helping himself to another glass of brandy.

O. Henry

:

THE HYPOTHESES OF FAILURE

Lawyer Gooch bestowed his undivided attention upon the engrossing arts of his profession. But one flight of fancy did he allow his mind to entertain. He was fond of likening his suite of office rooms to the bottom of a ship. The rooms were three in number, with a door opening from one to another. These doors could also be closed.

"Ships," Lawyer Gooch would say, "are constructed for safety, with separate, water-tight compartments in their bottoms. If one compartment springs a leak it fills with water; but the good ship goes on unhurt. Were it not for the separating bulkheads one leak would sink the vessel. Now it often happens that while I am occupied with clients, other clients with conflicting interests call. With the assistance of Archibald—an office boy with a future—I cause the dangerous influx to be diverted into separate compartments, while I sound with my legal plummet the depth of each. If necessary, they may be baled into the hallway and permitted to escape by way of the stairs, which we may term the lee scuppers. Thus the good ship of business is kept afloat; whereas if the element that supports her were allowed to mingle freely in her hold we might be swamped—ha, ha, ha!"

The law is dry. Good jokes are few. Surely it might be permitted Lawyer Gooch to mitigate the bore of briefs, the tedium of torts and the prosiness of processes with even so light a levy upon the good property of humor.

Lawyer Gooch's practice leaned largely to the settlement of marital infelicities. Did matrimony languish through complications, he mediated, soothed and arbitrated. Did it suffer from implications, he re-adjusted, defended and championed. Did it arrive at the extremity of duplications, he always got light sentences for his clients.

But not always was Lawyer Gooch the keen, armed, wily belligerent, ready with his two-edged sword to lop off the shackles of Hymen. He had been known to build up instead of demolishing, to reunite instead of severing, to lead erring and foolish ones back into the fold instead of scattering the flock. Often had he by his eloquent and moving appeals sent husband and wife, weeping, back into each other's arms. Frequently he had coached childhood so successfully that, at the psychological moment (and at a given signal) the plaintive pipe of "Papa, won't you tum home adain to me and muvver?" had won the day and upheld the pillars of a tottering home.

Unprejudiced persons admitted that Lawyer Gooch received as big fees from these reyoked clients as would have been paid him had the cases been contested in court. Prejudiced ones intimated that his fees were doubled, because the penitent couples always came back later for the divorce, anyhow.

There came a season in June when the legal ship of Lawyer Gooch (to borrow his own figure) was nearly becalmed. The divorce mill grinds slowly in June. It is the month of Cupid and Hymen.

Lawyer Gooch, then, sat idle in the middle room of his clientless suite. A small anteroom connected—or rather separated—this apartment from the hallway. Here was stationed Archibald, who wrested from visitors their cards or oral nomenclature which he bore to his master while they waited.

Suddenly, on this day, there came a great knocking at the outermost door.

Archibald, opening it, was thrust aside as superfluous by the visitor, who without due reverence at once penetrated to the office of Lawyer Gooch and threw himself with good-natured insolence into a comfortable chair facing that gentleman.

"You are Phineas C. Gooch, attorney-at-law?" said the visitor, his tone of voice and inflection making his words at once a question, an assertion and an accusation.

Before committing himself by a reply, the lawyer estimated his possible client in one of his brief but shrewd and calculating glances.

The man was of the emphatic type—large-sized, active, bold and debonair in demeanor, vain beyond a doubt, slightly swaggering, ready and at ease. He was well-clothed, but with a shade too much ornateness. He was seeking a lawyer; but if that fact would seem to saddle him with troubles they were not patent in his beaming eye and courageous air.

"My name is Gooch," at length the lawyer admitted. Upon pressure he would also have confessed to the Phineas C. But he did not consider it good practice to volunteer information. "I did not receive your card," he continued, by way of rebuke, "so I——"

"I know you didn't," remarked the visitor, coolly; "and you won't just yet. Light up?" He threw a leg over an arm of his chair, and tossed a handful of rich-hued cigars upon the table. Lawyer Gooch knew the brand. He thawed just enough to accept the invitation to smoke.

"You are a divorce lawyer," said the cardless visitor. This time there was no interrogation in his voice. Nor did his words constitute a simple assertion. They formed a charge—a denunciation—as one would say to a dog: "You are a dog." Lawyer Gooch was silent under the imputation.

"You handle," continued the visitor, "all the various ramifications of busted-up connubiality. You are a surgeon, we might say, who extracts Cupid's darts when he shoots 'em into the wrong parties. You furnish patent, incandescant lights for premises where the torch of Hymen has burned so low you can't light a cigar at it. Am I right, Mr. Gooch?"

"I have undertaken cases," said the lawyer, guardedly, "in the line to which your figurative speech seems to refer. Do you wish to consult me professionally, Mr.——" The lawyer paused, with significance.

"Not yet," said the other, with an arch wave of his cigar, "not just yet. Let us approach the subject with the caution that should have been used in the original act that makes this pow-wow necessary. There exists a matrimonial jumble to be straightened out. But before I give you names I want your honest—well, anyhow, your professional opinion on the merits of the mix-up. I want you to size up the catastrophe—abstractedly—you understand? I'm Mr. Nobody; and I've got a story to tell you. Then you say what's what. Do you get my wireless?"

"You want to state a hypothetical case?" suggested Lawyer Gooch.

"That's the word I was after. 'Apothecary' was the best shot I could make at it in my mind. The hypothetical goes. I'll state the case. Suppose there's a woman—a deuced fine-looking woman—who has run away from her husband and home? She's badly mashed on another man who went to her town to work up some real estate business. Now, we may as well call this woman's husband Thomas R. Billings, for that's his name. I'm giving you straight tips on the cognomens. The Lothario chap is Henry K. Jessup. The Billingses lived in a little town called Susanville—a good many miles from here. Now, Jessup leaves Susanville two weeks ago. The next day Mrs. Billings follows him. She's dead gone on this man Jessup; you can bet your law library on that."

Lawyer Gooch's client said this with such unctuous satisfaction that even the callous lawyer experienced a slight ripple of repulsion. He now saw clearly in his fatuous visitor the conceit of the lady-killer, the egoistic complacency of the successful trifler.

"Now," continued the visitor, "suppose this Mrs. Billings wasn't happy at home? We'll say she and her husband didn't gee worth a cent. They've got incompatibility to burn. The things she likes, Billings wouldn't have as a gift with trading-stamps. It's Tabby and Rover with them all the time. She's an educated woman in science and culture, and she reads things out loud at meetings. Billings is not on. He don't appreciate progress and obelisks and ethics, and things of that sort. Old Billings is simply a blink when it comes to such things. The lady is out and out above his class. Now, lawyer, don't it look like a fair equalization of rights and wrongs that a woman like that should be allowed to throw down Billings and take the man that can appreciate her?"

"Incompatibility," said Lawyer Gooch, "is undoubtedly the source of much marital discord and unhappiness. Where it is positively proved, divorce would seem to be the equitable remedy. Are you—excuse me —is this man Jessup one to whom the lady may safely trust her future?"

"Oh, you can bet on Jessup," said the client, with a confident wag of his head. "Jessup's all right. He'll do the square thing. Why, he left Susanville just to keep people from talking about Mrs. Billings. But she followed him up, and now, of course, he'll stick to her. When she gets a divorce, all legal and proper, Jessup will do the proper thing."

"And now," said Lawyer Gooch, "continuing the hypothesis, if you prefer, and supposing that my services should be desired in the case, what——"

The client rose impulsively to his feet.

"Oh, dang the hypothetical business," he exclaimed, impatiently. "Let's let her drop, and get down to straight talk. You ought to know who I am by this time. I want that woman to have her divorce. I'll pay for it. The day you set Mrs. Billings free I'll pay you five hundred dollars."

Lawyer Gooch's client banged his fist upon the table to punctuate his generosity.

"If that is the case——" began the lawyer.

"Lady to see you, sir," bawled Archibald, bouncing in from his anteroom. He had orders to always announce immediately any client that might come. There was no sense in turning business away.

Lawyer Gooch took client number one by the arm and led him suavely into one of the adjoining rooms. "Favor me by remaining here a few minutes, sir," said he. "I will return and resume our consultation with the least possible delay. I am rather expecting a visit from a very wealthy old lady in connection with a will. I will not keep you waiting long."

The breezy gentleman seated himself with obliging acquiescence, and took up a magazine. The lawyer returned to the middle office, carefully closing behind him the connecting door.

"Show the lady in, Archibald," he said to the office boy, who was awaiting the order.

A tall lady, of commanding presence and sternly handsome, entered the room. She wore robes—robes; not clothes—ample and fluent. In her eye could be perceived the lambent flame of genius and soul. In her hand was a green bag of the capacity of a bushel, and an umbrella that also seemed to wear a robe, ample and fluent. She accepted a chair.

"Are you Mr. Phineas C. Gooch, the lawyer?" she asked, in formal and unconciliatory tones.

"I am," answered Lawyer Gooch, without circumlocution. He never circumlocuted when dealing with a woman. Women circumlocute. Time is wasted when both sides in a debate employ the same tactics.

"As a lawyer, sir," began the lady, "you may have acquired some knowledge of the human heart. Do you believe that the pusillanimous and petty conventions of our artificial social life should stand as an obstacle in the way of a noble and affectionate heart when it finds its true mate among the miserable and worthless wretches in the world that are called men?"

"Madam," said Lawyer Gooch, in the tone that he used in curbing his female clients, "this is an office for conducting the practice of law. I am a lawyer, not a philosopher nor the editor of an 'Answers to the Lovelorn' column of a newspaper. I have other clients waiting. I will ask you kindly to come to the point."

"Well, you needn't get so stiff around the gills about it," said the lady, with a snap of her luminous eyes and a startling gyration of her umbrella. "Business is what I've come for. I want your opinion in the matter of a suit for divorce, as the vulgar would call it, but which is really only the readjustment of the false and ignoble conditions that the short-sighted laws of man have interposed between a loving——"

"I beg your pardon, madam," interrupted Lawyer Gooch, with some impatience, "for reminding you again that this is a law office. Perhaps Mrs. Wilcox——"

"Mrs. Wilcox is all right," cut in the lady, with a hint of asperity. "And so are Tolstoi, and Mrs. Gertrude Atherton, and Omar Khayyam, and Mr. Edward Bok. I've read 'em all. I would like to discuss with you the divine right of the soul as opposed to the freedom-destroying restrictions of a bigoted and narrow-minded society. But I will proceed to business. I would prefer to lay the matter before you in an impersonal way until you pass upon its merits. That is to describe it as a supposable instance, without——"

"You wish to state a hypothetical case?" said Lawyer Gooch.

"I was going to say that," said the lady, sharply. "Now, suppose there is a woman who is all soul and heart and aspirations for a complete existence. This woman has a husband who is far below her in intellect, in taste—in everything. Bah! he is a brute. He despises literature. He sneers at the lofty thoughts of the world's great thinkers. He thinks only of real estate and such sordid things. He is no mate for a woman with soul. We will say that this unfortunate wife one day meets with her ideal—a man with brain and heart and force. She loves him. Although this man feels the thrill of a new-found affinity he is too noble, too honorable to declare himself. He flies from the presence of his beloved. She flies after him, trampling, with superb indifference, upon the fetters with which an unenlightened social system would bind her. Now, what will a divorce cost? Eliza Ann Timmins, the poetess of Sycamore Gap, got one for three hundred and forty dollars. Can I —I mean can this lady I speak of get one that cheap?"

"Madam," said Lawyer Gooch, "your last two or three sentences delight me with their intelligence and clearness. Can we not now abandon the hypothetical and come down to names and business?"

"I should say so," exclaimed the lady, adopting the practical with admirable readiness. "Thomas R. Billings is the name of the low brute who stands between the happiness of his legal—his legal, but not his spiritual—wife and Henry K. Jessup, the noble man whom nature intended for her mate. I," concluded the client, with an air of dramatic revelation, "am Mrs. Billings!"

"Gentleman to see you, sir," shouted Archibald, invading the room almost at a handspring. Lawyer Gooch arose from his chair.

"Mrs. Billings," he said courteously, "allow me to conduct you into the adjoining office apartment for a few minutes. I am expecting a very wealthy old gentleman on business connected with a will. In a very short while I will join you, and continue our consultation."

With his accustomed chivalrous manner, Lawyer Gooch ushered his soulful client into the remaining unoccupied room, and came out, closing the door with circumspection.

The next visitor introduced by Archibald was a thin, nervous, irritable-looking man of middle age, with a worried and apprehensive expression of countenance. He carried in one hand a small satchel, which he set down upon the floor beside the chair which the lawyer placed for him. His clothing was of good quality, but it was worn without regard to neatness or style, and appeared to be covered with the dust of travel.

"You make a specialty of divorce cases," he said, in an agitated but business-like tone.

"I may say," began Lawyer Gooch, "that my practice has not altogether avoided——"

"I know you do," interrupted client number three. "You needn't tell me. I've heard all about you. I have a case to lay before you without necessarily disclosing any connection that I might have with it—that is——"

"You wish," said Lawyer Gooch, "to state a hypothetical case."

"You may call it that. I am a plain man of business. I will be as brief as possible. We will first take up the hypothetical woman. We will say she is married uncongenially. In many ways she is a superior woman. Physically she is considered to be handsome. She is devoted to what she calls literature—poetry and prose, and such stuff. Her husband is a plain man in the business walks of life. Their home has not been happy, although the husband has tried to make it so. Some time ago a man—a stranger—came to the peaceful town in which they lived and engaged in some real estate operations. This woman met him, and became unaccountably infatuated with him. Her attentions became so open that the man felt the community to be no safe place for him, so he left it. She abandoned husband and home, and followed him. She forsook her home, where she was provided with every comfort, to follow this man who had inspired her with such a strange affection. Is there anything more to be deplored," concluded the client, in a trembling voice, "than the wrecking of a home by a woman's uncalculating folly?"

Lawyer Gooch delivered the cautious opinion that there was not.

"This man she has gone to join," resumed the visitor, "is not the man to make her happy. It is a wild and foolish self-deception that makes her think he will. Her husband, in spite of their many disagreements, is the only one capable of dealing with her sensitive and peculiar nature. But this she does not realize now."

"Would you consider a divorce the logical cure in the case you present?" asked Lawyer Gooch, who felt that the conversation was wandering too far from the field of business.

"A divorce!" exclaimed the client, feelingly—almost tearfully. "No, no—not that. I have read, Mr. Gooch, of many instances where your sympathy and kindly interest led you to act as a mediator between estranged husband and wife, and brought them together again. Let us drop the hypothetical case—I need conceal no longer that it is I who am the sufferer in this sad affair—the names you shall have— Thomas R. Billings and wife—and Henry K. Jessup, the man with whom she is infatuated."

Client number three laid his hand upon Mr. Gooch's arm. Deep emotion was written upon his careworn face. "For Heaven's sake," he said fervently, "help me in this hour of trouble. Seek out Mrs. Billings, and persuade her to abandon this distressing pursuit of her lamentable folly. Tell her, Mr. Gooch, that her husband is willing to receive her back to his heart and home—promise her anything that will induce her to return. I have heard of your success in these matters. Mrs. Billings cannot be very far away. I am worn out with travel and weariness. Twice during the pursuit I saw her, but various circumstances prevented our having an interview. Will you undertake this mission for me, Mr. Gooch, and earn my everlasting gratitude?"

"It is true," said Lawyer Gooch, frowning slightly at the other's last words, but immediately calling up an expression of virtuous benevolence, "that on a number of occasions I have been successful in persuading couples who sought the severing of their matrimonial bonds to think better of their rash intentions and return to their homes reconciled. But I assure you that the work is often exceedingly difficult. The amount of argument, perseverance, and, if I may be allowed to say it, eloquence that it requires would astonish you. But this is a case in which my sympathies would be wholly enlisted. I feel deeply for you sir, and I would be most happy to see husband and wife reunited. But my time," concluded the lawyer, looking at his watch as if suddenly reminded of the fact, "is valuable."

"I am aware of that," said the client, "and if you will take the case and persuade Mrs. Billings to return home and leave the man alone that she is following—on that day I will pay you the sum of one thousand dollars. I have made a little money in real estate during the recent boom in Susanville, and I will not begrudge that amount."

"Retain your seat for a few moments, please," said Lawyer Gooch, arising, and again consulting his watch. "I have another client waiting in an adjoining room whom I had very nearly forgotten. I will return in the briefest possible space."

The situation was now one that fully satisfied Lawyer Gooch's love of intricacy and complication. He revelled in cases that presented such subtle problems and possibilities. It pleased him to think that he was master of the happiness and fate of the three individuals who sat, unconscious of one another's presence, within his reach. His old figure of the ship glided into his mind. But now the figure failed, for to have filled every compartment of an actual vessel would have been to endanger her safety; while here, with his compartments full, his ship of affairs could but sail on to the advantageous port of a fine, fat fee. The thing for him to do, of course, was to wring the best bargain he could from some one of his anxious cargo.

First he called to the office boy: "Lock the outer door, Archibald, and admit no one." Then he moved, with long, silent strides into the room in which client number one waited. That gentleman sat, patiently scanning the pictures in a magazine, with a cigar in his mouth and his feet upon a table.

"Well," he remarked, cheerfully, as the lawyer entered, "have you made up your mind? Does five hundred dollars go for getting the fair lady a divorce?"

"You mean that as a retainer?" asked Lawyer Gooch, softly interrogative.

"Hey? No; for the whole job. It's enough, ain't it?"

"My fee," said Lawyer Gooch, "would be one thousand five hundred dollars. Five hundred dollars down, and the remainder upon issuance of the divorce."

A loud whistle came from client number one. His feet descended to the floor.

"Guess we can't close the deal," he said, arising. "I cleaned up five hundred dollars in a little real estate dicker down in Susanville. I'd do anything I could to free the lady, but it out-sizes my pile."

"Could you stand one thousand two hundred dollars?" asked the lawyer, insinuatingly.

"Five hundred is my limit, I tell you. Guess I'll have to hunt up a cheaper lawyer." The client put on his hat.

"Out this way, please," said Lawyer Gooch, opening the door that led into the hallway.

As the gentleman flowed out of the compartment and down the stairs, Lawyer Gooch smiled to himself. "Exit Mr. Jessup," he murmured, as he fingered the Henry Clay tuft of hair at his ear. "And now for the forsaken husband." He returned to the middle office, and assumed a businesslike manner.

"I understand," he said to client number three, "that you agree to pay one thousand dollars if I bring about, or am instrumental in bringing about, the return of Mrs. Billings to her home, and her abandonment of her infatuated pursuit of the man for whom she has conceived such a violent fancy. Also that the case is now unreservedly in my hands on that basis. Is that correct?"

"Entirely," said the other, eagerly. "And I can produce the cash any time at two hours' notice."

Lawyer Gooch stood up at his full height. His thin figure seemed to expand. His thumbs sought the armholes of his vest. Upon his face was a look of sympathetic benignity that he always wore during such undertakings.

"Then, sir," he said, in kindly tones, "I think I can promise you an early relief from your troubles. I have that much confidence in my powers of argument and persuasion, in the natural impulses of the human heart toward good, and in the strong influence of a husband's unfaltering love. Mrs. Billings, sir, is here—in that room——" the lawyer's long arm pointed to the door. "I will call her in at once; and our united pleadings——"

Lawyer Gooch paused, for client number three had leaped from his chair as if propelled by steel springs, and clutched his satchel.

"What the devil," he exclaimed, harshly, "do you mean? That woman in there! I thought I shook her off forty miles back."

He ran to the open window, looked out below, and threw one leg over the sill.

"Stop!" cried Lawyer Gooch, in amazement. "What would you do? Come, Mr. Billings, and face your erring but innocent wife. Our combined entreaties cannot fail to——"

"Billings!" shouted the now thoroughly moved client; "I'll Billings you, you old idiot!"

Turning, he hurled his satchel with fury at the lawyer's head. It struck that astounded peacemaker between the eyes, causing him to stagger backward a pace or two. When Lawyer Gooch recovered his wits he saw that his client had disappeared. Rushing to the window, he leaned out, and saw the recreant gathering himself up from the top of a shed upon which he had dropped from the second-story window. Without stopping to collect his hat he then plunged downward the remaining ten feet to the alley, up which he flew with prodigious celerity until the surrounding building swallowed him up from view.

Lawyer Gooch passed his hand tremblingly across his brow. It was an habitual act with him, serving to clear his thoughts. Perhaps also it now seemed to soothe the spot where a very hard alligator-hide satchel had struck.

The satchel lay upon the floor, wide open, with its contents spilled about. Mechanically Lawyer Gooch stooped to gather up the articles. The first was a collar; and the omniscient eye of the man of law perceived, wonderingly, the initials H.K.J. marked upon it. Then came a comb, a brush, a folded map and a piece of soap. Lastly, a handful of old business letters, addressed—every one of them—to "Henry K. Jessup, Esq."

Lawyer Gooch closed the satchel, and set it upon the table. He hesitated for a moment, and then put on his hat and walked into the office boy's anteroom.

"Archibald," he said mildly, as he opened the hall door, "I am going around to the Supreme Court rooms. In five minutes you may step into the inner office, and inform the lady who is waiting there that"—here Lawyer Gooch made use of the vernacular—"that there's nothing doing."

Louis Auchincloss

:

THE LEGENDS OF HENRY EVERETT

When I first went to work as a clerk for the law firm of Everett & Coates, Henry Fellows Everett was already more of a legend than a man. He was in his early eighties and one of the last of that great generation of lawyers, the generation of Paul D. Cravath and Francis Lynde Stetson, which had forged the modern corporate law firm, that bright and gleaming sword, out of the rusty materials lying about the old-fashioned city lawyer's office of seventy years ago. The members of these firms today, and indeed for the past thirty years, have unlike their predecessors conformed to a certain pattern: they have become genial, available, democratic with their clerks and sympathetic with their clients, ready with a generality for every emergency and a funny story for every banquet. Eccentricity, the prerogative of the older generation, has gone out of fashion, though the middle-aged lawyer still remembers it lovingly and tells nostalgic tales of his early clerkship when he was shouted at and abused by a ferocious but magnificent taskmaster. This nostalgia, of course, is not so much a nostalgia for the days of his own subordination as for the era of the lawyer's greater glory, that halcyon time when clients as well as clerks could be shouted at, even shown the door, when fees were paid in the stock of expanding companies, when a Joseph H. Choate could persuade the Supreme Court that an income tax was unconstitutional and a William Nelson Cromwell could negotiate the Panama Canal.

Mr. Everett, younger than any of these individuals and correspondingly less of an individualist, was nonetheless a true member of the great generation. His paneled office in Everett & Coates, twice as large as any other, was hung with photographs of statesmen and peace conferences and framed illuminated manuscripts expressing tribute and conferring degrees. Rarely if ever did a clerk penetrate its interior; Mr. Everett dealt almost exclusively with his partners, who addressed him as "Chief" with a little smile that only heightened one's sense of their veneration. He was a small thin man with stooping shoulders and long, thin, brown sunken cheeks. He had gray hair, parted in the middle, which always sat so neatly on the top of his head that I think it must have been a toupee. He had large clear eyes that were almost expressionless and a sharp, rasping voice except when he spoke in public, when it had the emotional mellifluousness that comes with self-confidence or even self-admiration. He was direct, nervous and highly irritable; he was always, so to speak, stripped for action, and his single-mindedness made one feel disorganized and inefficient. It was not till I saw him one day wearing a golf cap, a bow tie and a pair of knickers that it struck me of a sudden that his air of intensity and preoccupation was that of a small boy.

The first time that I worked for Mr. Everett directly was when I went up to his house on Madison Avenue to take him and Mrs. Everett their wills. They were leaving for Europe that night and the will signing, as was always the case with his personal affairs, had been put off by the old man to the last moment, when there was no one but myself in the department to handle it. The other clerk, whom I had brought to act as a witness, and I were ushered into the library to wait. Law reports lined the high shelves; the portrait of Mr. Everett over the mantel, in the robes of a Harvard doctor of laws, stared through open mahogany doors at the brooding marble figure of Justice in the hall. The atmosphere was dank, institutional, more like a bar association than a private house.

When Mr. Everett appeared he was, as usual, nervous and impatient. He barely nodded to us.

"Have you got it there?" he snapped, taking the will from me. "Lot of damn foolishness this doing a will over every year." He sat down and turned the pages quickly, muttering to himself as he did so. "Trying to take advantage of every last wrinkle in the new tax laws. Trying too hard, that's what I tell them."

Mrs. Everett came in and shook hands with us, very nicely. She was a plain, dumpy woman with a round face and dyed red hair. She was bigger than her husband and seemed to be trying to contract herself to a more suitable size. I had heard that she behaved more like a trained nurse to her husband than a wife, giving in to him in everything except his health, but supervising that to an alarming degree, calling up his office and canceling his appointments without warning, hiding his briefcase, changing travel accommodations, and bearing the angry storm of his resentment with the glittering little smile of the dedicated. She settled down at a table with her will, putting on her pince-nez.

"I won't understand a word of it, you know," she complained timidly to me. "I never do. Do I really have to read it?"

"I'm afraid you should."

"Mrs. Everett read the copy you sent her," her husband snapped at me impatiently. "She and I went over it together and approved it. This is the same thing, isn't it?"

"Yes, sir. But how can she be sure unless she reads the original?"

"Oh, bother, Westcott," the old man retorted, "she knows what she wants done, and this does it. You can't expect her to follow the jargon. I've been over it myself, clause by clause, with Kingman."

I swallowed hard. Mr. Kingman, my boss, had specifically instructed me to be sure that they both read the originals.

"Let me put it this way, sir," I said. "Suppose there were ever a question and I had to testify? Wouldn't I have to say under oath that Mrs. Everett not only wouldn't read her will, but that she hadn't understood it?"

For a moment he glared at me and then grunted and looked away.

"All right, all right," he said. "If we must go through the rigmarole, I suppose we must. I'll run over it again with her."

He leaned over Mrs. Everett's shoulder and started explaining the will to her, summarizing the provisions hastily and inaccurately and turning the pages with an impatient hand while she sat beneath him, quiet and uncomprehending. I said nothing. I had exhausted my courage.

"All right," he said at last, handing the wills back to me. "What next? Can we actually sign them? Or do you have some other hocus-pocus?"

He made an even worse fuss when I insisted on asking him the proper questions: whether or not he had read his will, whether it had been prepared in accordance with his instructions, whether we were to act as witnesses, and so forth. He finally raised both his hands above his head in a mock gesture of oath-taking and snapped: "Yes, yes, yes, I swear, so help me, amen, whatever you want, but let's get on with it, for heaven's sake," and taking the document from my hand he signed his name on the last page with a great sprawling flourish. It was only when I picked it up to read the attestation clause that I saw that he had signed Mrs. Everett's will. I looked around at the other witness, who was peering over my shoulder. His eyes were round with dismay.

"Mr. Everett," I said falteringly.

"Yes, yes, what is it?"

"You've signed your wife's will."

"What's that? Give it here." He snatched if from me again and stared at it soberly. "Well, my God! Why in the name of thunder don't they send somebody who knows enough to give me the right will?" He turned on me, his eyes bright. "Or would that be asking too much? I suppose it would. I suppose, in this day and age, it really would!"

"I didn't give it to you, sir," I said sullenly. "You took it from me. And if I may say so, this whole thing has been too hurried from the start."

He stared at me for a moment, and then back at the inappropriate signature.

"Mrs. Everett can scratch it out," he said in a milder tone, "and then sign her own name under it. The presence of my signature is, after all, legally speaking, an irrelevance."

"That may be true, sir," I said, feeling bolder as he seemed to back down. "But it would be foolish, in my opinion, to take any chances. I'll have the will retyped and bring it back tonight."

"But I'm sailing for Europe tonight!"

"Then I'll bring it to the boat."

He gave me a sharp look.

"Are you working on the theory," he demanded, "that I'm one of those old fools who likes to be barked back at? Because I warn you, I find that theory a most offensive one. For years now impertinent young men from the office have invaded the privacy of my home to holler at me. It has not got them ahead, I assure you."

"I'm not hollering, Mr. Everett," I pointed out. "I'm only telling you the things that I'm supposed to tell you."

After the pause that followed this, he simply nodded.

"I'll see you at the boat," he said.

Apparently however, he did not mind occasional firm treatment, for when I went that night with my other witness to his cabin on the *Queen Mary* he signed his will as docilely as an office stenographer getting her legal work free.

He then made us stay while he and Mrs. Everett entertained the partners and their wives who had come to see them off. He proved a surprisingly genial host, moving jerkily around the stateroom to see that everyone had enough champagne, laughing loudly if rather mirthlessly at their jokes and telling legal anecdotes and even fishing stories. I had a curious feeling, however, that he was playing a role and enjoying it, as he must have enjoyed playing the old tartar that afternoon.

I didn't work for him again until some weeks after his return from Europe when I was delegated, in Mr. Kingman's absence, to accompany him to the Appellate Division where he was to argue a will contest on appeal. It was really not a case of sufficient importance to warrant his time, but the decedent had been a friend of his, and he had insisted on handling it personally. I was glad of the chance to see the great man at work. He spoke easily and smoothly before five judges, all of whom knew and respected him and none of whom, I imagined, would have pressed him too closely with tight questions. It was more like a legal discussion over an after-dinner brandy than an argument in court, and I felt rather sorry for the plaintiff's lawyer, to whom Mr. Everett showed the good manners of a clubman to a fellow member's guest who is misbehaving himself.

I congratulated him afterward, as we got into the back of his car, and he chuckled, obviously pleased.

"Experience still counts for something, Westcott," he said, leaning back in his seat. "Not much, I grant, but something. Oh, yes, still something."

He was in a good mood and insisted on taking me uptown to his club for a drink. I murmured something about going back to the office, which he dismissed with a single impatient gesture of his hand. Obviously, he wanted to talk.

"They say we don't have the judges we used to have," he told me gruffly as we sat at a table in the dark, empty bar, each with a dry martini. "Don't believe a word of it. Take those fellows this afternoon. Good men, every one of them. Of course, everything in the past seems better when you're middle-aged. But when you're old the way I am, it all seems part of the same thing. And the past doesn't impress you any more than the present, or the future, for that matter. The sacred Holmes, for example. They worship him today. I always thought he was a bit of a charlatan myself, with his endless chatter about manhood and war. Did you ever read a speech of his called 'The Soldier's Faith'? 'I thank God for our polo players,' he says. And why? Because they risk life and limb." He snorted contemptuously. "That's Holmes to the life. Afraid we'd go soft unless we might get killed."

"You mean he was like Hemingway?" I asked. "A muscular philosopher?"

He fixed me with his blank stare, a reminder, perhaps, that I was there to listen, not to comment.

"I haven't read your Mr. Hemingway," he retorted. "I haven't read his fiction, that is. But then I don't read fiction. I read poetry, philosophy and history, and I counsel you to do the same. Oh, I've read his *Death in the Afternoon,* yes." He nodded several times at this. "But that, after all, is different. That deals with my favorite subject."

I stared.

"Do you mean bullfighting, sir?"

He laughed. It was a harsh, jarring laugh.

"I mean death, young man," he said emphatically. Then he looked at me for a moment with a gaze that seemed to be taking in things behind me. "Oh, you're uncomfortable now, of course," he continued in a remote, sarcastic tone. "The old, I know, should never mention death. It's so far from you and so near to us. But what do you think we *think* about, we old?"

I lowered my eyes in embarrassment.

"We think about all the things you hope you won't be thinking about when *you're* old," he went on bitterly. "We think about when we're going to die, and what happens to us then. And don't let anybody fool you, young man, we think about it all the time!"

"You don't believe in an after-life, sir?"

My question rang out, hollow and fatuous, and I waited for him to jump down my throat. But he only shrugged his shoulders.

"Oh, I used to," he said, suddenly tired. "When I was young. I had faith in a scared, self-deluding sort of way. But my older brother was an atheist. It used to make him angry that I would never *know* that he was right and I was wrong. He said there ought to be a moment after death when the truth was made known. Just a single, clear, all-knowing moment before eternal blackness. And in that moment, he used to say, I would hear him laughing. Like Alberich in the darkness."

"How horrible!"

My exclamation broke into his mood and seemed to change it.

"It was horrible, wasn't it?" he said in a milder tone, smiling again. "Well, who knows? Perhaps I shall hear him. Perhaps not. But you need another drink. And, by the way, I should like you to dine with Mrs. Everett and myself tonight. It will be dull for you, but it will be a change for us. And the old should have some prerogatives."

I assured him that it would not be dull for me, but he only shrugged his shoulders again. It was obviously a matter of indifference to him whether or not it was. We had another drink and motored up to his house.

We were five at dinner, as the Edward Everetts as well as myself had been invited. Edward was Mr. Everett's only son, about fifty, thin and bald and tired-looking. A partner in Everett & Coates, a position which he owed quite as much to his own ability as to his father's, he was a dry, harmless man of superficial friendliness who laughed pleasantly enough at other people's jokes and rarely told any of his own. It was his own way, perhaps, of indicating his belief that no subject other than law could really be taken seriously. His wife was a tense, rather gasping woman who kept her sharp black eyes riveted on her father-in-law during dinner, exclaiming over each truculent monosyllable that he dropped.

"I wish I'd heard you in court today, Papa," she cried. "I bet you were simply scrumptious! Wasn't he scrumptious, Mr. Westcott?"

"I suppose you might call it that, Mrs. Everett."

"Suppose? Aren't you *sure?*"

"Perhaps, Helen, Mr. Westcott would have used another word to describe me. He has sharp eyes, and youth, you know, can be cruel."

"Not to you, darling. *Never!*"

The old man turned away from her.

"Did you get a chance to read my brief, Edward? Do you think they'll reverse?"

"Of course, I don't know, Father, if the Appellate Division decides cases on the basis of scrumptiousness—"

"Edward, you're making fun of me? Before your father, too!"

"Not at all, my dear. But to answer your question, Father, I would think, in the light of Bryan versus Fox——"

"Oh, Edward, of course, your father will win! Arguing the case himself and all that! Won't he, Mother Everett?"

"He's not going to win anything at all if he keeps up this pace. Henry, you're to go to bed at nine o'clock tonight. Remember you promised me?"

I sat in growing indignation during the rest of the meal as Mrs. Edward cooed at the old man, patted his hand, shrieked hysterically if he said anything that could be construed as funny, keeping him amused, for all the world as if he had come down for the weekend from a sanatorium, while his wife, silent, thinking only of the meal, not listening to the conversation, frowned at the butler and wagged a warning finger to indicate "no more fruit for Mr. Everett" or no more wine for his already empty glass.

It was, I could immediately see, the other side of the coin, the domestic version of the downtown legend. If in the office Mr. Everett was renowned as a tartar, a disciplinarian, a man who made other men jump, in the home this picture was to be softened by the touch of the old "sweetie-pie," the husband who meekly puts on his rubbers when his wife directs, the family man, to be loved, bullied, cajoled and passionately defended against all who might "misunderstand" him.

He seemed to have a sense of this himself, for after dinner he took me down to the library alone, leaving the others in the living room.

"There's something I want to discuss with you, Westcott," he said, sitting by the fire and stretching out his feet on the footstool. "I have a speech to make to the bar association on the sixtieth anniversary of my admission to the bar. It occurred to me that you might be of some assistance. Ordinarily I work these things out with somebody at the office with more experience than you have, but I think you and I might find our points of view congenial." I told him I would be flattered.

"What will your speech be about, sir?"

"What do you think?" he demanded, turning suddenly and fixing me with a stare of mock indignation. "What do you ever hear on such occasions? There's a recognized pattern, isn't there? I shall begin with the customary recollections of the great departed professors of law at Harvard. I will then proceed to a series of heart-warming anecdotes about my early practice. One of these will deal with a rusty old judge, some famous, lovable character of the period. It will, also, of course, serve to illustrate the intensity of my early industry in contrast to the relaxed standards of today. After this it will be almost time for me to spread my wings and flap off into the blue skies of legal philosophy, quoting Plato, Cardozo and Holmes, reasserting my faith in mankind and the bar despite the threat of communism and the atom bomb. And I shall conclude, needless to say, with a ringing note of hope for the future." Here he jumped to his feet and stretched out his arms like a dramatic orator. " 'And as the curtain descends for the last time upon my life, as surely as it appears, but only appears, to descend upon our free world today, I can yet see, in the glimmer of lights along the bay—' " He broke off with a snort. "You finish it. Any way you want. With Arnold or Marshall or Gray. Or even with your favorite Mr. Hemingway, if you choose. For you see what I see, young man. You see it doesn't amount to a hill of beans."

There was a knock at the door, but it opened before Mr. Everett could even grunt, and the round shining eyes and long thin nose of his daughter-in-law poked in at us.

"Are you working, Papa? Are you letting him, Mr. Westcott? Oh, for shame! When we all know he's been in court today and needs his rest. Oh, no. Come upstairs, Papa, and trounce me at backgammon. You know, he can, too, Mr. Westcott. You never saw such a fiend at any game."

"I'll be up when I'm ready, Helen," he said sharply. "I'm busy now."

Her face grew very long at this, with a kind of mock humility, and she winked at me as if to show me how to respond to his changes of mood, how to shift to the role of the hurt and sulking child.

"All right, if that's the way you're going to treat me," she said, with a little pout. "Just you see if I'll stay here another minute. I'll go up and tell Mother Everett on you."

When she had closed the door again, Mr. Everett turned to me with quiet acidity.

"You will excuse my daughter-in-law," he said. "Her apologists tell me that she means well and that she thinks I enjoy being treated like an un-house-trained puppy. Dear me. I remember, some years ago, when I had the good fortune to have Morris Cohen here for dinner. The poor gentleman was obliged for some minutes to carry on a conversation with Helen. I shall never forget his response to one of her questions. 'My dear young lady,' he said, 'how can I answer you? Your remark is without thought content.' Perfect, wasn't it? Without thought content. And such simplicity, too. Classic."

I felt my first, perhaps rather belated chill at this. Helen was a fool, of course, but even I could see that her apologists, whoever they were, might be right. Undoubtedly she did mean well. There had been a coldness in his manner of repeating Mr. Cohen's remark, an absence of family feeling that seemed suddenly to twitch off the poor woman's covering and to expose her, stripped and shivering. It was not a pleasant picture. I wanted to admire Mr. Everett; I was excited and flattered by his notice of me, but when I really admired I hated reservations, and there was a touch of cruelty in his air of satisfaction that I could not ignore. Walking home later that night I decided that if he saw things clearly, heartlessly, even destructively, it was only to a chosen few whose discretion he trusted that he imparted his vision. For the rest he fulfilled his family duties. He submitted for the most part unprotestingly to the loving if misguided ministrations of his relatives. He discussed fishing and even baseball with his partners. He was benign when the situation required. To such a man a lack of charity could occasionally be forgiven. Certainly by his intimates, if one had the honor to be of that small and privileged group. Already, although I did not know it, I was doing what the others had done. I was constructing my own legend of Henry Everett.

When I was again summoned to Mr. Everett's, a week later, I found him alone in the library. He seemed quite pleased about something.

"I know just how we'll do it, Westcott," he exclaimed as I came in, "I see it all. The speech will be in the mood of Tennyson's 'Ulysses,' filled with the note of what may yet be done. 'Tho' much is taken, much abides,' that idea. What do you think?"

I hesitated.

"You think it's corny?"

"I'm afraid I do, sir."

"But they'll love it, you know they will!"

"Yes, sir. I'm afraid they will."

He chuckled and turned back to the book of poetry in his hand.

"I like this bit about Telemachus. It's Edward to the life." He read aloud to me:

> *Most blameless is he, centered in the sphere*
> *Of common duties, decent not to fail*

In offices of tenderness, and pay
Meet adoration to my household gods,
When I am gone.

He nodded his head several times, in agreement with the bard. "And Ulysses has no use for him, that's the point." He put the book down and stared silently into the fire. I could feel his good humor slipping away from him already as it had at his club when we had discussed death. "Which means, of course," he continued with a sigh, "that I have no use for Edward. He's so middle-aged, you see, and we old have no use for middle age. Now he and Helen have a son—you don't know him, he's still in law school—who has that precious glow of youth in his eyes. It will all be gone at twenty-five, I know, and maybe it's just as well. Then he can get on with the serious business of living, and I predict that he will be more fatuous than his mother. But nonetheless, when he turns his wide eyes on me and asks, as if he were the first person in the whole world to have thought of it, 'Grandpa, do you think a lawyer should represent a man whom he knows to be guilty?' I care more than when Edward tells me about the last case he's argued before the Supreme Court. And make no mistake, Edward is a first-class lawyer, which that boy will never be. That's the thing about Edward. He's good."

I watched him silently, knowing by now that he did not pause for my comments.

"And who am I to sneer at Edward?" he went on in sudden anger, getting up and coming toward me menacingly. "An old fool who likes to think he's Ulysses so he can look down at Telemachus! Strutting about and puffing and pretending that at eighty-two he's going 'to sail beyond the sunset, and the baths of all the western stars' until he dies!" He stretched both his arms out in bitter parody of his own self-dramatization. "I'm an ass, Westcott! Remember that, an ass! Yet even as I say it, I'm secretly hoping that you'll still find me magnificent. I'm acting for you as much as I shall be acting for the bar association when I make that speech!"

He collapsed once again into his chair and his head slumped forward on his chest. The room was suddenly full of his stertorous breathing.

I got up in a panic, wondering if he had had a heart attack.

"Mr. Everett!" I cried. "Mr. Everett," I repeated, "are you all right?"

"Go away, young man," he muttered. "Go away."

I hurried upstairs to find Mrs. Everett, who was in the sitting room.

She followed me swiftly, without a word, but when we got to the library the heavy breathing had stopped. He was asleep. She examined him sharply for a moment and then nodded, in relief.

"You may as well go now, Mr. Westcott," she whispered. "We'll let you know when he needs you again."

They never did, however, nor was I surprised. It would have been perfectly natural for the family to assume that my effect on the old man was disturbing. This could even, I suppose, have been true, although it seemed unlikely to me. Any other young and respectful person could have served him as well for an audience. A few days later Edward Everett came into my office with the uneasy cordiality of the partner making a personal visit. There was a shy, semiconspiratorial air about him, as though he were trying to let me know that he knew what I had seen and heard and was begging me, timidly enough but nicely enough, to be quiet about it.

"The old man appreciates what you've done, Peter," he said, "and you'll be glad to know that he's got the speech licked. It's just a question of a few finishing touches. He told me to tell you that he thinks he can do the rest alone. I can give him a hand myself if he needs it."

As a matter of fact, I was relieved. I had not been looking forward to my next session with Mr. Everett. It was one thing to play with the idea that I had become, in some curious fashion, the spiritual intimate of the old man's final chapter, that I might, if the relationship continued, find myself at some future date an indispensable witness to his biographers. It was quite another to be the lonely companion of his melancholia. I may have been sufficiently a dissenter to have enjoyed hearing the old and revered idol belch in the solitude of his temple and to have laughed at his sneers at the officious priests who busied themselves about the folds of his garments. But that was enough. When he grasped the pillars of the temple like the blind Samson and threatened to bring down the whole structure on top of all the priests, including even the doubters like myself, it was time to get out. I had to live in this world, and presumably for a longer time in the future than Mr. Everett.

I did not see him again until the bar association dinner was given in the banquet hall of a large hotel and attended by several hundred people, including all the partners and associates of Everett & Coates. The old man, looking very well, sat, of course, at the head table between the president of the association and the chief judge of the Court of Appeals. He listened to the long speeches of praise rendered in his honor with the air of one practiced in that delicate art. He sat with his head hanging down, very still, occasionally shaking it sharply to indicate his failure to merit some particular fulsome tribute. When he laughed at a joke, he laughed heartily, shaking both shoulders. The applause when he finally rose to speak was tumultuous.

"It is commonly said that the wisest man is he who knows that he knows nothing," he began. Then he paused and reached down for his napkin with which he lightly touched his lips.

His voice, as always when he spoke in public, was rich and strong. "I wonder how many of us ever really stop to consider what it means to know nothing. Nothing at all." He paused again for emphasis. "Not even to know, for example, what Descartes assumed: that man is a thinking creature. Not even to know, as an obvious consequence, that he exists at all. Oh, I can assure you, ladies and gentlemen, that when a man really and truly *knows* that he knows nothing, he does not purr about it from behind a white waistcoat to the eminent members of his profession." There was a ripple of appreciative laughter. Mr. Everett however, kept his eyes dramatically and abstractedly fixed on the wall opposite him. "He locks himself up, rather," he continued grimly, "in the silence of his chamber and has the good grace not to inflict his discovery on young people whose eyes are filled with the warm charm of their own illusion. If he knows anything—that is, if he knows that he has learned nothing—he knows that this illusion is worth all the clairvoyance that ignorant people admire in himself."

I stirred self-consciously in my chair, wondering if these words could possibly be meant for me, if this was his handsome if rather dramatic apology for any bewilderment he might have caused me. I glanced about at my neighbors to see if they noted anything unusual in the speech. Their faces, however, were bland and composed. Most of them, of course, were only half listening, lulled by the roll of after-dinner sentences, expecting what they were used to, nobility of expression, high dignity of thought, a double scotch and soda, and an early evening. Surely, however, some would listen and understand and shudder at the bleak wind of his doubts, surely some would see the consequences of his destructive premise. But I was going, as usual, too far. They would assume, would they not, that he was dealing in paradoxes, that the right arm of the accomplished speaker would gather in all that the left had scattered wide?

And they assumed correctly, for in a minute he went on.

"But it is one thing to know or even suspect that one knows nothing and quite another to *believe* in nothing—"

So there it was, the stratagem, and I could breathe in relief, as he rolled easily on from the terrors of conscious ignorance to the compensations of faith, from Nietzsche and Spengler and nihilism and the ultimate horror of Hitler and Stalin to the principles of Jefferson and the early fathers and their validity today. He gave himself a field day; he was more exuberant, more emotional, more convincing than I would have believed possible, and when he ended with the words of Holmes on his ninetieth birthday, the entire room rose and the applause lasted for ten uninterrupted minutes. If he was acting, as he had told me, I could only conclude that, at least for the moment, he had convinced himself. The tears in his eyes were real. Turning, when it was all over, to take my place in the long, slow line of men before the coat closet, I saw Mrs. Edward give her husband a timid little smile of congratulation across the table where we had been sitting.

Bret Harte

:

COLONEL STARBOTTLE FOR THE PLAINTIFF

It had been a day of triumph for Colonel Starbottle. First, for his personality, as it would have been difficult to separate the Colonel's achievements from his individuality; second, for his oratorical abilities as a sympathetic pleader; and third, for his functions as the leading legal counsel for the Eureka Ditch Company *versus* the State of California. On his strictly legal performances in this issue I prefer not to speak; there were those who denied them, although the jury had accepted them in the face of the ruling of the half-amused, half-cynical Judge himself. For an hour they had laughed with the Colonel, wept with him, been stirred to personal indignation or patriotic exaltation by his passionate and lofty periods—what else could they do than give him their verdict? If it was alleged by some that the American eagle, Thomas Jefferson, and the Resolutions of '98 had nothing whatever to do with the contest of a ditch company over a doubtfully worded legislative document; that wholesale abuse of the State Attorney and his political motives had not the slightest connection with the legal question raised—it was, nevertheless, generally accepted that the losing party would have been only too glad to have the Colonel on their side. And Colonel Starbottle knew this, as, perspiring, florid, and panting, he rebuttoned the lower buttons of his blue frock-coat, which had become loosed in an oratorical spasm, and readjusted his old-fashioned, spotless shirt frill above it as he strutted from the court-room amidst the handshakings and acclamations of his friends.

And here an unprecedented thing occurred. The Colonel absolutely

555

declined spirituous refreshment at the neighboring Palmetto Saloon, and declared his intention of proceeding directly to his office in the adjoining square. Nevertheless, the Colonel quitted the building alone, and apparently unarmed, except for his faithful gold-headed stick, which hung as usual from his forearm. The crowd gazed after him with undisguised admiration of this new evidence of his pluck. It was remembered also that a mysterious note had been handed to him at the conclusion of his speech—evidently a challenge from the State Attorney. It was quite plain that the Colonel—a practiced duelist—was hastening home to answer it.

But herein they were wrong. The note was in a female hand, and simply requested the Colonel to accord an interview with the writer at the Colonel's office as soon as he left the court. But it was an engagement that the Colonel—as devoted to the fair sex as he was to the "code"—was no less prompt in accepting. He flicked away the dust from his spotless white trousers and varnished boots with his handkerchief, and settled his black cravat under his Byron collar as he neared his office. He was surprised, however, on opening the door of his private office, to find his visitor already there; he was still more startled to find her somewhat past middle age and plainly attired. But the Colonel was brought up in a school of Southern politeness, already antique in the republic, and his bow of courtesy belonged to the epoch of his shirt frill and strapped trousers. No one could have detected his disappointment in his manner, albeit his sentences were short and incomplete. But the Colonel's colloquial speech was apt to be fragmentary incoherencies of his larger oratorical utterances.

"A thousand pardons—for—er—having kept a lady waiting—er! But—er—congratulations of friends—and—er—courtesy due to them —er—interfered with—though perhaps only heightened—by procrastination—the pleasure of—ha!" And the Colonel completed his sentence with a gallant wave of his fat but white and well-kept hand.

"Yes! I came to see you along o' that speech of yours. I was in court. When I heard you gettin' it off on that jury, I says to myself, 'That's the kind o' lawyer *I* want. A man that's flowery and convincin'! Just the man to take up our case.' "

"Ah! It's a matter of business, I see," said the Colonel, inwardly relieved, but externally careless. "And—er—may I ask the nature of the case?"

"Well! it's a breach-o'-promise suit," said the visitor calmly.

If the Colonel had been surprised before, he was now really startled, and with an added horror that required all his politeness to conceal. Breach-of-promise cases were his peculiar aversion. He had always held them to be a kind of litigation which could have been obviated by the prompt killing of the masculine offender—in which case he would have gladly defended the killer. But a suit for damages—*damages!*—with the reading of love-letters before a hilarious jury and court, was against all his instincts. His chivalry was outraged; his sense of humor was small, and in the course of his career he had lost one or two important cases through an unexpected development of this quality in a jury.

The woman had evidently noticed his hesitation, but mistook its cause. "It ain't me—but my darter."

The Colonel recovered his politeness. "Ah! I am relieved, my dear madam! I could hardly conceive a man ignorant enough to—er—er—throw away such evident good fortune—or base enough to deceive the trustfulness of womanhood—matured and experienced only in the chivalry of our sex, ha!"

The woman smiled grimly. "Yes!—it's my darter, Zaidee Hooker—so ye might spare some of them pretty speeches for *her*—before the jury."

The Colonel winced slightly before this doubtful prospect, but smiled. "Ha! Yes!—certainly—the jury. But—er—my dear lady, need we go as far as that? Cannot this affair be settled—er—out of court? Could not this—er—individual—be admonished—told that he must give satisfaction—personal satisfaction—for his dastardly conduct—to—er—near relative—or even valued personal friend? The—er—arrangements necessary for that purpose I myself would undertake."

He was quite sincere; indeed, his small black eyes shone with that fire which a pretty woman or an "affair of honor" could alone kindle. The visitor stared vacantly at him, and said slowly, "And what good is that goin' to do *us?*"

"Compel him to—er—perform his promise," said the Colonel, leaning back in his chair.

"Ketch him doin' it!" she exclaimed scornfully. "No—that ain't wot we're after. We must make him *pay!* Damages—and nothin' short o' *that*."

The Colonel bit his lip. "I suppose," he said gloomily, "you have documentary evidence—written promises and protestations—er—er—love-letters, in fact?"

"No—nary a letter! Ye see, that's jest it—and that's where *you* come in. You've got to convince that jury yourself. You've got to show what it is—tell the whole story your own way. Lord! to a man like you that's nothin'."

Startling as this admission might have been to any other lawyer, Starbottle was absolutely relieved by it. The absence of any mirth-provoking correspondence, and the appeal solely to his own powers of persuasion, actually struck his fancy. He lightly put aside the compliment with a wave of his white hand.

"Of course," he said confidently, "there is strongly presumptive and corroborative evidence? Perhaps you can give me—er—a brief outline of the affair?"

"Zaidee kin do that straight enough, I reckon," said the woman; "what I want to know first is, kin you take the case?"

The Colonel did not hesitate; his curiosity was piqued. "I certainly can. I have no doubt your daughter will put me in possession of sufficient facts and details—to constitute what we call—er—a brief."

"She kin be brief enough—or long enough—for the matter of that," said the woman, rising. The Colonel accepted this implied witticism with a smile.

"And when may I have the pleasure of seeing her?" he asked politely.

"Well, I reckon as soon as I can trot out and call her. She's just outside, meanderin' in the road—kinder shy, ye know, at first."

She walked to the door. The astounded Colonel nevertheless gallantly accompanied her as she stepped out into the street and called shrilly, "You Zaidee!"

A young girl here apparently detached herself from a tree and the ostentatious perusal of an old election poster, and sauntered down towards the office door. Like her mother, she was plainly dressed; unlike her, she had a pale, rather refined face, with a demure mouth and downcast eyes. This was all the Colonel saw as he bowed profoundly and led the way into his office, for she accepted his salutations without lifting her head. He helped her gallantly to a chair, on which she seated herself sideways, somewhat ceremoniously, with her eyes following the point of her parasol as she traced a pattern on the carpet. A second chair offered to the mother, that lady, however, declined. "I reckon to leave you and Zaidee together to talk it out," she said; turning to her daughter, she added, "Jest you tell him all, Zaidee," and before the Colonel could rise again, disappeared from the room. In spite of his professional experience, Starbottle was for a moment embarrassed. The young girl, however, broke the silence without looking up.

"Adoniram K. Hotchkiss," she began, in a monotonous voice, as if it were a recitation addressed to the public, "first began to take notice of me a year ago. Arter that—off and on"—

"One moment," interrupted the astounded Colonel; "do you mean Hotchkiss the President of the Ditch Company?" He had recognized the name of a prominent citizen—a rigid, ascetic, taciturn, middle-aged man—a deacon—and more than that, the head of the company he had just defended. It seemed inconceivable.

"That's him," she continued, with eyes still fixed on the parasol and without changing her monotonous tone—"off and on ever since. Most of the time at the Free-Will Baptist Church—at morning service, prayer-meetings, and such. And at home—outside—er—in the road."

"Is it this gentleman—Mr. Adoniram K. Hotchkiss—who—er—promised marriage?" stammered the Colonel.

"Yes."

The Colonel shifted uneasily in his chair. "Most extraordinary! for—you see—my dear young lady—this becomes—a—er—most delicate affair."

"That's what maw said," returned the young woman simply, yet with the faintest smile playing around her demure lips and downcast cheek.

"I mean," said the Colonel, with a pained yet courteous smile, "that this—er—gentleman—is in fact—er—one of my clients."

"That's what maw said too, and of course your knowing him will make it all the easier for you."

A slight flush crossed the Colonel's cheek as he returned quickly and a little stiffly, "On the contrary—er—it may make it impossible for me to—er—act in this matter."

The girl lifted her eyes. The Colonel held his breath as the long lashes were raised to his level. Even to an ordinary observer that sudden revelation of her eyes seemed to transform her face with subtle witchery. They were large, brown, and soft, yet filled with an extraordinary penetration and prescience. They were the eyes of an experienced woman of thirty fixed in the face of a child. What else the Colonel saw there Heaven only knows! He felt his inmost secrets plucked from him—his whole soul laid bare—his vanity, belligerency, gallantry —even his mediaeval chivalry, penetrated, and yet illuminated, in that single glance. And when the eyelids fell again, he felt that a greater part of himself had been swallowed up in them.

"I beg your pardon," he said hurriedly. "I mean—this matter may be arranged—er—amicably. My interest with—and as you wisely say —my—er—knowledge of my client—er—Mr. Hotchkiss—may effect —a compromise."

"And *damages,*" said the young girl, readdressing her parasol, as if she had never looked up.

The Colonel winced. "And—er—undoubtedly *compensation*—if you do not press a fulfillment of the promise. Unless," he said, with an attempted return to his former easy gallantry, which, however, the recollection of her eyes made difficult, "it is a question of—er—the affections."

"Which?" asked his fair client softly.

"If you still love him?" explained the Colonel, actually blushing.

Zaidee again looked up; again taking the Colonel's breath away with eyes that expressed not only the fullest perception of what he had *said,* but of what he thought and had not said, and with an added subtle suggestion of what he might have thought. "That's tellin'," she said, dropping her long lashes again.

The Colonel laughed vacantly. Then feeling himself growing imbecile, he forced an equally weak gravity. "Pardon me—I understand there are no letters; may I know the way in which he formulated his declaration and promises?"

"Hymn-books."

"I beg your pardon," said the mystified lawyer.

"Hymn-books—marked words in them with pencil—and passed 'em on to me," repeated Zaidee. "Like 'love,' 'dear,' 'precious,' 'sweet,' and 'blessed,'" she added, accenting each word with a push of her parasol on the carpet. "Sometimes a whole line outer Tate and Brady—and Solomon's Song, you know, and sich."

"I believe," said the Colonel loftily, "that the—er—phrases of sacred psalmody lend themselves to the language of the affections. But in regard to the distinct promise of marriage—was there—er—no *other* expression?"

"Marriage Service in the prayer-book—lines and words outer that—all marked," Zaidee replied.

The Colonel nodded naturally and approvingly. "Very good. Were others cognizant of this? Were there any witnesses?"

"Of course not," said the girl. "Only me and him. It was generally at church-time—or prayer-meeting. Once, in passing the plate, he slipped one o' them peppermint lozenges with the letters stamped on it 'I love you' for me to take."

The Colonel coughed slightly. "And you have the lozenge?"

"I ate it."

"Ah," said the Colonel. After a pause he added delicately, "But were these attentions—er—confined to—er—sacred precincts? Did he meet you elsewhere?"

"Useter pass our house on the road," returned the girl, dropping into her monotonous recital, "and useter signal."

"Ah, signal?" repeated the Colonel approvingly.

"Yes! He'd say 'Keerow,' and I'd say 'Keeree.' Suthing like a bird, you know."

Indeed, as she lifted her voice in imitation of the call, the Colonel thought it certainly very sweet and birdlike. At least as *she* gave it. With his remembrance of the grim deacon he had doubts as to the melodiousness of *his* utterance. He gravely made her repeat it.

"And after that signal?" he added suggestively.

"He'd pass on."

The Colonel again coughed slightly, and tapped his desk with his penholder.

"Were there any endearments—er—caresses—er—such as taking your hand—er—clasping your waist?" he suggested, with a gallant yet respectful sweep of his white hand and bowing of his head; "er—slight pressure of your fingers in the changes of a dance—I mean," he corrected himself, with an apologetic cough—"in the passing of the plate?"

"No; he was not what you'd call 'fond,' " returned the girl.

"Ah! Adoniram K. Hotchkiss was not 'fond' in the ordinary acceptance of the word," noted the Colonel, with professional gravity.

She lifted her disturbing eyes, and again absorbed his in her own. She also said "Yes," although her eyes in their mysterious prescience of all he was thinking disclaimed the necessity of any answer at all. He smiled vacantly. There was a long pause; on which she slowly disengaged her parasol from the carpet pattern, and stood up.

"I reckon that's about all," she said.

"Er—yes—but one moment," began the Colonel vaguely. He would have liked to keep her longer, but with her strange premonition of him he felt powerless to detain her, or explain his reason for doing so. He instinctively knew she had told him all; his professional judgment told him that a more hopeless case had never come to his knowledge. Yet he was not daunted, only embarrassed. "No matter," he said. "Of course I shall have to consult with you again."

Her eyes again answered that she expected he would, and she added simply, "When?"

"In the course of a day or two," he replied quickly. "I will send you word."

She turned to go. In his eagerness to open the door for her, he upset his chair, and with some confusion, that was actually youthful, he almost impeded her movements in the hall, and knocked his broad-brimmed Panama hat from his bowing hand in a final gallant sweep. Yet as her small, trim, youthful figure, with its simple Leghorn straw hat confined by a blue bow under her round chin, passed away before him, she looked more like a child than ever.

The Colonel spent that afternoon in making diplomatic inquiries. He found his youthful client was the daughter of a widow who had a small ranch on the cross-roads, near the new Free-Will Baptist Church—the evident theater of this pastoral. They led a secluded life, the girl being little known in the town, and her beauty and fascination apparently not yet being a recognized fact. The Colonel felt a pleasurable relief at this, and a general satisfaction he could not account for. His few inquiries concerning Mr. Hotchkiss only confirmed his own impressions of the alleged lover—a serious-minded, practically abstracted man, abstentive of youthful society, and the last man apparently capable of levity of the affections or serious flirtation. The Colonel was mystified, but determined of purpose, whatever that purpose might have been.

The next day he was at his office at the same hour. He was alone—as usual—the Colonel's office being really his private lodgings, disposed in connecting rooms, a single apartment reserved for consultation. He had no clerk, his papers and briefs being taken by his faithful body-servant and ex-slave "Jim" to another firm who did his office work since the death of Major Stryker, the Colonel's only law partner, who fell in a duel some years previous. With a fine constancy the Colonel still retained his partner's name on his doorplate, and, it was alleged by the superstitious, kept a certain invincibility also through the *manes* of that lamented and somewhat feared man.

The Colonel consulted his watch, whose heavy gold case still showed the marks of a providential interference with a bullet destined for its owner, and replaced it with some difficulty and shortness of breath in his fob. At the same moment he heard a step in the passage, and the door opened to Adoniram K. Hotchkiss. The Colonel was impressed; he had a duelist's respect for punctuality.

The man entered with a nod and the expectant inquiring look of a busy man. As his feet crossed that sacred threshold the Colonel became all courtesy; he placed a chair for his visitor, and took his hat from his half-reluctant hand. He then opened a cupboard and brought out a bottle of whiskey and two glasses.

"A—er—slight refreshment, Mr. Hotchkiss," he suggested politely.

"I never drink," replied Hotchkiss, with the severe attitude of a total abstainer.

"Ah—er—not the finest Bourbon whiskey, selected by a Kentucky friend? No? Pardon me! A cigar, then—the mildest Havana."

"I do not use tobacco nor alcohol in any form," repeated Hotchkiss ascetically. "I have no foolish weaknesses."

The Colonel's moist, beady eyes swept silently over his client's sallow face. He leaned back comfortably in his chair, and half closing his eyes as in dreamy reminiscence, said slowly: "Your reply, Mr. Hotchkiss, reminds me of—er—sing'lar circumstance that—er—occurred, in point of fact—at the St. Charles Hotel, New Orleans. Pinkey Hornblower—personal friend—invited Senator Doolittle to join him in social glass. Received, sing'larly enough, reply similar to yours. 'Don't drink nor smoke?' said Pinkey. 'Gad, sir, you must be mighty sweet on the ladies.' Ha!" The Colonel paused long enough to allow the faint flush to pass from Hotchkiss's cheek, and went on, half closing his eyes: " 'I allow no man, sir, to discuss my personal habits,' declared Doolittle, over his shirt collar. 'Then I reckon shootin' must be one of those habits,' said Pinkey coolly. Both men drove out on the Shell Road back of cemetery next morning. Pinkey put bullet at twelve paces through Doolittle's temple. Poor Doo never spoke again. Left three wives and seven children, they say—two of 'em black."

"I got a note from you this morning," said Hotchkiss, with badly concealed impatience. "I suppose in reference to our case. You have taken judgment, I believe."

The Colonel, without replying, slowly filled a glass of whiskey and water. For a moment he held it dreamily before him, as if still engaged in gentle reminiscences called up by the act. Then tossing it off, he wiped his lips with a large white handkerchief, and leaning back comfortably in his chair, said, with a wave of his hand, "The interview I requested, Mr. Hotchkiss, concerns a subject—which I may say is—er—er—at present *not* of a public or business nature—although *later* it might become—er—er—both. It is an affair of some—er—delicacy."

The Colonel paused, and Mr. Hotchkiss regarded him with increased impatience. The Colonel, however, continued with unchanged deliberation: "It concerns—er—er—a young lady—a beautiful, high-souled creature, sir, who, apart from her personal loveliness—er—er—I may say is of one of the first families of Missouri, and—er—not remotely connected by marriage with one of—er—er—my boyhood's dearest friends." The latter, I grieve to say, was a pure invention of the Colonel's—an oratorical addition to the scanty information he had obtained the previous day. "The young lady," he continued blandly, "enjoys the further distinction of being the object of such attention from you as would make this interview—really—a confidential matter—er—er—among friends and—er—er—relations in present and future. I need not say that the lady I refer to is Miss Zaidee Juno Hooker, only daughter of Almira Ann Hooker, relict of Jefferson Brown Hooker, formerly of Boone County, Kentucky, and latterly of—er—Pike County, Missouri."

The sallow, ascetic hue of Mr. Hotchkiss's face had passed through a livid and then a greenish shade, and finally settled into a sullen red. "What's all this about?" he demanded roughly.

The least touch of belligerent fire came into Starbottle's eye, but his bland courtesy did not change. "I believe," he said politely, "I have made myself clear as between—er—gentlemen, though perhaps not as clear as I should to—er—er—jury."

Mr. Hotchkiss was apparently struck with some significance in the lawyer's reply. "I don't know," he said, in a lower and more cautious voice, "what you mean by what you call 'my attentions' to—any one —or how it concerns you. I have not exchanged half a dozen words with—the person you name—have never written her a line—nor even called at her house."

He rose with an assumption of ease, pulled down his waistcoat, buttoned his coat, and took up his hat. The Colonel did not move.

"I believe I have already indicated my meaning in what I have called 'your attentions,' " said the Colonel blandly, "and given you my 'concern' for speaking as—er—er—mutual friend. As to *your* statement of your relations with Miss Hooker, I may state that it is fully corroborated by the statement of the young lady herself in this very office yesterday."

"Then what does this impertinent nonsense mean? Why am I summoned here?" demanded Hotchkiss furiously.

"Because," said the Colonel deliberately, "that statement is infamously—yes, damnably to your discredit, sir!"

Mr. Hotchkiss was here seized by one of those impotent and inconsistent rages which occasionally betray the habitually cautious and timid man. He caught up the Colonel's stick, which was lying on the table. At the same moment the Colonel, without any apparent effort, grasped it by the handle. To Mr. Hotchkiss's astonishment, the stick separated in two pieces, leaving the handle and about two feet of narrow glittering steel in the Colonel's hand. The man recoiled, dropping the useless fragment. The Colonel picked it up, fitted the shining blade in it, clicked the spring, and then rising with a face of courtesy yet of unmistakably genuine pain, and with even a slight tremor in his voice, said gravely—

"Mr. Hotchkiss, I owe you a thousand apologies, sir, that—er—a weapon should be drawn by me—even through your own inadvertence—under the sacred protection of my roof, and upon an unarmed man. I beg your pardon, sir, and I even withdraw the expressions which provoked that inadvertence. Nor does this apology prevent you from holding me responsible—personally responsible—*elsewhere* for an indiscretion committed in behalf of a lady—my—er—client."

"Your client? Do you mean you have taken her case? You, the counsel for the Ditch Company?" asked Mr. Hotchkiss, in trembling indignation.

"Having won *your* case, sir," replied the Colonel coolly, "the—er—usages of advocacy do not prevent me from espousing the cause of the weak and unprotected."

"We shall see, sir," said Hotchkiss, grasping the handle of the door and backing into the passage. "There are other lawyers who"—

"Permit me to see you out," interrupted the Colonel, rising politely.

—"will be ready to resist the attacks of blackmail," continued Hotchkiss, retreating along the passage.

"And then you will be able to repeat your remarks to me *in the street,*" continued the Colonel, bowing, as he persisted in following his visitor to the door.

But here Mr. Hotchkiss quickly slammed it behind him, and hurried away. The Colonel returned to his office, and sitting down, took a sheet of letter-paper bearing the inscription "Starbottle and Stryker, Attorneys and Counselors," and wrote the following lines:—

HOOKER *versus* HOTCHKISS

DEAR MADAM,—Having had a visit from the defendant in above, we should be pleased to have an interview with you at two P.M. to-morrow.

Your obedient servants,

STARBOTTLE AND STRYKER

This he sealed and dispatched by his trusted servant Jim, and then devoted a few moments to reflection. It was the custom of the Colonel to act first, and justify the action by reason afterwards.

He knew that Hotchkiss would at once lay the matter before rival counsel. He knew that they would advise him that Miss Hooker had "no case"—that she would be nonsuited on her own evidence, and he ought not to compromise, but be ready to stand trial. He believed, however, that Hotchkiss feared such exposure, and although his own instincts had been at first against this remedy, he was now instinctively in favor of it. He remembered his own power with a jury; his vanity and his chivalry alike approved of this heroic method; he was bound by no prosaic facts—he had his own theory of the case, which no mere evidence could gainsay. In fact, Mrs. Hooker's admission that he was to "tell the story in his own way" actually appeared to him an inspiration and a prophecy.

Perhaps there was something else, due possibly to the lady's wonderful eyes, of which he had thought much. Yet it was not her simplicity that affected him solely; on the contrary, it was her apparent intelligent reading of the character of her recreant lover—and of his own! Of all the Colonel's previous "light" or "serious" loves, none had ever before flattered him in that way. And it was this, combined with the respect which he had held for their professional relations, that precluded his having a more familiar knowledge of his client, through serious questioning or playful gallantry. I am not sure it was not part of the charm to have a rustic *femme incomprise* as a client.

Nothing could exceed the respect with which he greeted her as she entered his office the next day. He even affected not to notice that she had put on her best clothes, and, he made no doubt, appeared as when she had first attracted the mature yet faithless attentions of Deacon Hotchkiss at church. A white virginal muslin was belted around her slim figure by a blue ribbon, and her Leghorn hat was drawn around her oval cheek by a bow of the same color. She had a Southern girl's narrow feet, encased in white stockings and kid slippers, which were crossed primly before her as she sat in a chair, supporting her arm by her faithful parasol planted firmly on the floor. A faint odor of southernwood exhaled from her, and, oddly enough, stirred the Colonel with a far-off recollection of a pine-shaded Sunday-school on a Georgia hillside, and of his first love, aged ten, in a short starched frock. Possibly it was the same recollection that revived something of the awkwardness he had felt then.

He, however, smiled vaguely, and sitting down, coughed slightly, and placed his finger-tips together. "I have had an—er—interview with Mr. Hotchkiss, but—I—er—regret to say there seems to be no prospect of—er—compromise."

He paused, and to his surprise her listless "company" face lit up with an adorable smile. "Of course!—ketch him!" she said. "Was he mad when you told him?" She put her knees comfortably together and leaned forward for a reply.

For all that, wild horses could not have torn from the Colonel a word about Hotchkiss's anger. "He expressed his intention of employing counsel—and defending a suit," returned the Colonel, affably basking in her smile.

She dragged her chair nearer his desk. "Then you'll fight him tooth and nail?" she asked eagerly; "you'll show him up? You'll tell the whole story your own way? You'll give him fits?—and you'll make him pay? Sure?" she went on breathlessly.

"I—er—will," said the Colonel almost as breathlessly.

She caught his fat white hand, which was lying on the table, between her own and lifted it to her lips. He felt her soft young fingers even through the lisle-thread gloves that encased them, and the warm moisture of her lips upon his skin. He felt himself flushing—but was unable to break the silence or change his position. The next moment she had scuttled back with her chair to her old position.

"I—er—certainly shall do my best," stammered the Colonel, in an attempt to recover his dignity and composure.

"That's enough! You'll *do* it," said she enthusiastically. "Lordy! Just you talk for *me* as ye did for *his* old Ditch Company, and you'll fetch it —every time! Why, when you made that jury sit up the other day— when you got that off about the Merrikan flag waving equally over the rights of honest citizens banded together in peaceful commercial pursuits, as well as over the fortress of official proflig—"

"Oligarchy," murmured the Colonel courteously.

—"oligarchy," repeated the girl quickly, "my breath was just took away. I said to maw, 'Ain't he too sweet for anything!' I did, honest Injin! And when you rolled it all off at the end—never missing a word (you didn't need to mark 'em in a lesson-book, but had 'em all ready on your tongue)—and walked out— Well! I didn't know you nor the Ditch Company from Adam, but I could have just run over and kissed you there before the whole court!"

She laughed, with her face glowing, although her strange eyes were cast down. Alack! the Colonel's face was equally flushed, and his own beady eyes were on his desk. To any other woman he would have voiced the banal gallantry that he should now, himself, look forward to that reward, but the words never reached his lips. He laughed, coughed slightly, and when he looked up again she had fallen into the same attitude as on her first visit, with her parasol point on the floor.

"I must ask you to—er—direct your memory to—er—another point: the breaking off of the—er—er—er—engagement. Did he—er—give any reason for it? Or show any cause?"

"No; he never said anything," returned the girl.

"Not in his usual way?—er—no reproaches out of the hymn-book? —or the sacred writings?"

"No; he just *quit*."

"Er—ceased his attentions," said the Colonel gravely. "And naturally you—er—were not conscious of any cause for his doing so."

The girl raised her wonderful eyes so suddenly and so penetratingly without replying in any other way that the Colonel could only hurriedly say: "I see! None, of course!"

At which she rose, the Colonel rising also. "We—shall begin proceedings at once. I must, however, caution you to answer no questions, nor say anything about this case to any one until you are in court."

She answered his request with another intelligent look and a nod. He accompanied her to the door. As he took her proffered hand, he raised the lisle-thread fingers to his lips with old-fashioned gallantry. As if that act had condoned for his first omissions and awkwardness, he became his old-fashioned self again, buttoned his coat, pulled out his shirt frill, and strutted back to his desk.

A day or two later it was known throughout the town that Zaidee Hooker had sued Adoniram Hotchkiss for breach of promise, and that the damages were laid at five thousand dollars. As in those bucolic days the Western press was under the secure censorship of a revolver, a cautious tone of criticism prevailed, and any gossip was confined to personal expression, and even then at the risk of the gossiper. Nevertheless, the situation provoked the intensest curiosity. The Colonel was approached—until his statement that he should consider any attempt to overcome his professional secrecy a personal reflection withheld further advances. The community were left to the more ostentatious information of the defendant's counsel, Messrs. Kitcham and Bilser, that the case was "ridiculous" and "rotten," that the plaintiff would be non-suited, and the fire-eating Starbottle would be taught a lesson that he could not "bully" the law, and there were some dark hints of a conspiracy. It was even hinted that the "case" was the revengeful and preposterous outcome of the refusal of Hotchkiss to pay Starbottle an extravagant fee for his late services to the Ditch Company. It is unnecessary to say that these words were not reported to the Colonel. It was, however, an unfortunate circumstance for the calmer, ethical consideration of the subject that the Church sided with Hotchkiss, as this provoked an equal adherence to the plaintiff and Starbottle on the part of the larger body of non-church-goers, who were delighted at a possible exposure of the weakness of religious rectitude. "I've allus had my suspicions o' them early candle-light meetings down at that gospel shop," said one critic, "and I reckon Deacon Hotchkiss didn't rope in the gals to attend jest the psalm-singing." "Then for him to get up and leave the board afore the game's finished and try to sneak out of it," said another— "I suppose that's what they call *religious*."

It was therefore not remarkable that the court-house three weeks later was crowded with an excited multitude of the curious and sympathizing. The fair plaintiff, with her mother, was early in attendance, and under the Colonel's advice appeared in the same modest garb in which she had first visited his office. This and her downcast, modest demeanor were perhaps at first disappointing to the crowd, who had evidently expected a paragon of loveliness in this Circe of that grim, ascetic defendant, who sat beside his counsel. But presently all eyes were fixed on the Colonel, who certainly made up in *his* appearance any deficiency of his fair client. His portly figure was clothed in a blue dress coat with brass buttons, a buff waistcoat which permitted his frilled shirt-front to become erectile above it, a black satin stock which confined a boyish turned-down collar around his full neck, and immaculate drill trousers, strapped over varnished boots. A murmur ran round the court. "Old 'Personally Responsible' has got his war-paint on"; "The Old War-Horse is smelling powder," were whispered comments. Yet for all that, the most irreverent among them recognized vaguely, in this bizarre figure, something of an honored past in their country's history, and possibly felt the spell of old deeds and old names that had once thrilled their boyish pulses. The new District Judge returned Colonel Starbottle's profoundly punctilious bow. The Colonel was followed by his Negro servant, carrying a parcel of hymn-books and Bibles, who, with a courtesy evidently imitated from his master, placed one before the opposite counsel. This, after a first curious glance, the lawyer somewhat superciliously tossed aside. But when Jim, proceeding to the jury-box, placed with equal politeness the remaining copies before the jury, the opposite counsel sprang to his feet.

"I want to direct the attention of the Court to this unprecedented tampering with the jury, by this gratuitous exhibition of matter impertinent and irrelevant to the issue."

The Judge cast an inquiring look at Colonel Starbottle.

"May it please the Court," returned Colonel Starbottle with dignity, ignoring the counsel, "the defendant's counsel will observe that he is already furnished with the matter—which I regret to say he has treated —in the presence of the Court—and of his client, a deacon of the church—with—er—great superciliousness. When I state to your Honor that the books in question are hymn-books and copies of the Holy Scriptures, and that they are for the instruction of the jury, to whom I shall have to refer them in the course of my opening, I believe I am within my rights."

"The act is certainly unprecedented," said the Judge dryly, "but unless the counsel for the plaintiff expects the jury to *sing* from these hymn-books, their introduction is not improper, and I cannot admit the objection. As defendant's counsel are furnished with copies also, they cannot plead 'surprise,' as in the introduction of new matter, and as plaintiff's counsel relies evidently upon the jury's attention to his opening, he would not be the first person to distract it." After a pause he added, addressing the Colonel, who remained standing, "The Court is with you, sir; proceed."

But the Colonel remained motionless and statuesque, with folded arms.

"I have overruled the objection," repeated the Judge; "you may go on."

"I am waiting, your Honor, for the—er—withdrawal by the defendant's counsel of the word 'tampering,' as refers to myself, and of 'impertinent,' as refers to the sacred volumes."

"The request is a proper one, and I have no doubt will be acceded to," returned the Judge quietly. The defendant's counsel rose and mumbled a few words of apology, and the incident closed. There was, however, a general feeling that the Colonel had in some way "scored," and if his object had been to excite the greatest curiosity about the books, he had made his point.

But impassive of his victory, he inflated his chest, with his right hand in the breast of his buttoned coat, and began. His usual high color had paled slightly, but the small pupils of his prominent eyes glittered like steel. The young girl leaned forward in her chair with an attention so breathless, a sympathy so quick, and an admiration so artless and unconscious that in an instant she divided with the speaker the attention of the whole assemblage. It was very hot; the court was crowded to suffocation; even the open windows revealed a crowd of faces outside the building, eagerly following the Colonel's words.

He would remind the jury that only a few weeks ago he stood there as the advocate of a powerful Company, then represented by the present defendant. He spoke then as the champion of strict justice against legal oppression; no less should he to-day champion the cause of the unprotected and the comparatively defenseless—save for that paramount power which surrounds beauty and innocence—even though the plaintiff of yesterday was the defendant of to-day. As he approached the court a moment ago he had raised his eyes and beheld the starry flag flying from its dome, and he knew that glorious banner was a symbol of the perfect equality, under the Constitution, of the rich and the poor, the strong and the weak—an equality which made the simple citizen taken from the plough in the field, the pick in the gulch, or from behind the counter in the mining town, who served on that jury, the equal arbiters of justice with that highest legal luminary whom they were proud to welcome on the bench to-day. The Colonel paused, with a stately bow to the impassive Judge. It was this, he continued, which lifted his heart as he approached the building. And yet—he had entered it with an uncertain—he might almost say—a timid step. And why? He knew, gentlemen, he was about to confront a profound —ay! a sacred responsibility! Those hymn-books and holy writings handed to the jury were *not,* as his Honor had surmised, for the purpose of enabling the jury to indulge in—er—preliminary choral exercise! He might, indeed, say, "Alas, not!" They were the damning, incontrovertible proofs of the perfidy of the defendant. And they would prove as terrible a warning to him as the fatal characters upon Belshazzar's wall. There was a strong sensation. Hotchkiss turned a sallow green. His lawyers assumed a careless smile.

It was his duty to tell them that this was not one of those ordinary "breach-of-promise" cases which were too often the occasion of ruthless mirth and indecent levity in the court-room. The jury would find nothing of that here. There were no love-letters with the epithets of endearment, nor those mystic crosses and ciphers which, he had been credibly informed, chastely hid the exchange of those mutual caresses known as "kisses." There was no cruel tearing of the veil from those sacred privacies of the human affection; there was no forensic shouting out of those fond confidences meant only for *one.* But there was, he was shocked to say, a new sacrilegious intrusion. The weak pipings of Cupid were mingled with the chorus of the saints—the sanctity of the temple known as the "meeting-house" was desecrated by proceedings more in keeping with the shrine of Venus; and the inspired writings themselves were used as the medium of amatory and wanton flirtation by the defendant in his sacred capacity as deacon.

The Colonel artistically paused after this thunderous denunciation. The jury turned eagerly to the leaves of the hymn-books, but the larger gaze of the audience remained fixed upon the speaker and the girl, who sat in rapt admiration of his periods. After the hush, the Colonel continued in a lower and sadder voice: "There are, perhaps, few of us here, gentlemen—with the exception of the defendant—who can arrogate to themselves the title of regular church-goers, or to whom these humbler functions of the prayer-meeting, the Sunday-school, and the Bible-class are habitually familiar. Yet"—more solemnly—"down in our hearts is the deep conviction of our shortcomings and failings, and a laudable desire that others, at least, should profit by the teachings we neglect. Perhaps," he continued, closing his eyes dreamily, "there is not a man here who does not recall the happy days of his boyhood, the rustic village spire, the lessons shared with some artless village maiden, with whom he later sauntered, hand in hand, through the woods, as the simple rhyme rose upon their lips—

'Always make it a point to have it a rule,
Never to be late at the Sabbath-school.'

He would recall the strawberry feasts, the welcome annual picnic, redolent with hunks of gingerbread and sarsaparilla. How would they feel to know that these sacred recollections were now forever profaned in their memory by the knowledge that the defendant was capable of using such occasions to make love to the larger girls and teachers, whilst his artless companions were innocently—the Court will pardon me for introducing what I am credibly informed is the local expression—'doing gooseberry'?" The tremulous flicker of a smile passed over the faces of the listening crowd, and the Colonel slightly winced. But he recovered himself instantly, and continued—

"My client, the only daughter of a widowed mother—who has for years stemmed the varying tides of adversity, in the western precincts of this town—stands before you to-day invested only in her own innocence. She wears no—er—rich gifts of her faithless admirer—is panoplied in no jewels, rings, nor mementos of affection such as lovers delight to hang upon the shrine of their affections; hers is not the glory with which Solomon decorated the Queen of Sheba, though the defendant, as I shall show later, clothed her in the less expensive flowers of the king's poetry. No, gentlemen! The defendant exhibited in this affair a certain frugality of—er—pecuniary investment, which I am willing to admit may be commendable in his class. His only gift was characteristic alike of his methods and his economy. There is, I understand, a certain not unimportant feature of religious exercise known as 'taking a collection.' The defendant, on this occasion, by the mute presentation of a tin plate covered with baize, solicited the pecuniary contributions of the faithful. On approaching the plaintiff, however, he himself slipped a love-token upon the plate and pushed it towards her. That love-token was a lozenge—a small disk, I have reason to believe, concocted of peppermint and sugar, bearing upon its reverse surface the simple words, 'I love you!' I have since ascertained that these disks may be bought for five cents a dozen—or at considerably less than one half cent for the single lozenge. Yes, gentlemen, the words 'I love you!'— the oldest legend of all; the refrain 'when the morning stars sang together'—were presented to the plaintiff by a medium so insignificant that there is, happily, no coin in the republic low enough to represent its value.

"I shall prove to you, gentlemen of the jury," said the Colonel solemnly, drawing a Bible from his coat-tail pocket, "that the defendant for the last twelve months conducted an amatory correspondence with the plaintiff by means of underlined words of Sacred Writ and church psalmody, such as 'beloved,' 'precious,' and 'dearest,' occasionally appropriating whole passages which seemed apposite to his tender passion. I shall call your attention to one of them. The defendant, while professing to be a total abstainer—a man who, in my own knowledge, has refused spirituous refreshment as an inordinate weakness of the flesh—with shameless hypocrisy underscores with his pencil the following passage, and presents it to the plaintiff. The gentlemen of the jury will find it in the Song of Solomon, page 548, chapter ii., verse 5." After a pause, in which the rapid rustling of leaves was heard in the jury-box, Colonel Starbottle declaimed in a pleading, stentorian voice, " 'Stay me with—er—*flagons,* comfort me with—er—apples—for I am—er—sick of love.' Yes, gentlemen!—yes, you may well turn from those accusing pages and look at the double-faced defendant. He desires—to—er—be—'stayed with flagons'! I am not aware at present what kind of liquor is habitually dispensed at these meetings, and for which the defendant so urgently clamored; but it will be my duty, before this trial is over, to discover it, if I have to summon every barkeeper in this district. For the moment I will simply call your attention to the *quantity.* It is not a single drink that the defendant asks for— not a glass of light and generous wine, to be shared with his inamorata, but a number of flagons or vessels, each possibly holding a pint measure—*for himself!'*

The smile of the audience had become a laugh. The Judge looked up warningly, when his eye caught the fact that the Colonel had again winced at this mirth. He regarded him seriously. Mr. Hotchkiss's counsel had joined in the laugh affectedly, but Hotchkiss himself sat ashy pale. There was also a commotion in the jury-box, a hurried turning over of leaves, and an excited discussion.

"The gentlemen of the jury," said the Judge, with official gravity, "will please keep order and attend only to the speeches of counsel. Any discussion *here* is irregular and premature, and must be reserved for the jury-room after they have retired."

The foreman of the jury struggled to his feet. He was a powerful man, with a good-humored face, and, in spite of his unfelicitous nickname of "The Bone-Breaker," had a kindly, simple, but somewhat emotional nature. Nevertheless, it appeared as if he were laboring under some powerful indignation.

"Can we ask a question, Judge?" he said respectfully, although his voice had the unmistakable Western American ring in it, as of one who was unconscious that he could be addressing any but his peers.

"Yes," said the Judge good-humoredly.

"We're finding in this yere piece, out o' which the Kernel hes just bin a-quotin', some language that me and my pardners allow hadn't orter be read out afore a young lady in court, and we want to know of you—ez a fa'r-minded and impartial man—ef this is the reg'lar kind o' book given to gals and babies down at the meetin'-house."

"The jury will please follow the counsel's speech without comment," said the Judge briefly, fully aware that the defendant's counsel would spring to his feet, as he did promptly.

"The Court will allow us to explain to the gentlemen that the language they seem to object to has been accepted by the best theologians for the last thousand years as being purely mystic. As I will explain later, those are merely symbols of the Church"—

"Of wot?" interrupted the foreman, in deep scorn.

"Of the Church!"

"We ain't askin' any questions o' *you,* and we ain't takin' any answers," said the foreman, sitting down abruptly.

"I must insist," said the Judge sternly, "that the plaintiff's counsel be allowed to continue his opening without interruption. You" (to defendant's counsel) "will have your opportunity to reply later."

The counsel sank down in his seat with the bitter conviction that the jury was manifestly against him, and the case as good as lost. But his face was scarcely as disturbed as his client's, who, in great agitation, had begun to argue with him wildly, and was apparently pressing some point against the lawyer's vehement opposal. The Colonel's murky eyes brightened as he still stood erect, with his hand thrust in his breast.

"It will be put to you, gentlemen, when the counsel on the other side refrains from mere interruption and confines himself to reply, that my unfortunate client has no action—no remedy at law—because there were no spoken words of endearment. But, gentlemen, it will depend upon *you* to say what are and what are not articulate expressions of love. We all know that among the lower animals, with whom you may possibly be called upon to classify the defendant, there are certain signals more or less harmonious, as the case may be. The ass brays, the horse neighs, the sheep bleats—the feathered denizens of the grove call to their mates in more musical roundelays. These are recognized facts, gentlemen, which you yourselves, as dwellers among nature in this beautiful land, are all cognizant of. They are facts that no one would deny—and we should have a poor opinion of the ass who, at —er—such a supreme moment, would attempt to suggest that his call was unthinking and without significance. But, gentlemen, I shall prove to you that such was the foolish, self-convicting custom of the defendant. With the greatest reluctance, and the—er—greatest pain, I succeeded in wresting from the maidenly modesty of my fair client the innocent confession that the defendant had induced her to correspond with him in these methods. Picture to yourself, gentlemen, the lonely moonlight road beside the widow's humble cottage. It is a beautiful night, sanctified to the affections, and the innocent girl is leaning from her casement. Presently there appears upon the road a slinking, stealthy figure, the defendant on his way to church. True to the instruction she has received from him, her lips part in the musical utterance" (the Colonel lowered his voice in a faint falsetto, presumably in fond imitation of his fair client), " 'Keeree!' Instantly the night becomes resonant with the impassioned reply" (the Colonel here lifted his voice in stentorian tones), " 'Keerow.' Again, as he passes, rises the soft 'Keeree'; again, as his form is lost in the distance, comes back the deep 'Keerow.' "

A burst of laughter, long, loud, and irrepressible, struck the whole court-room, and before the Judge could lift his half-composed face and take his handkerchief from his mouth, a faint "Keeree" from some unrecognized obscurity of the court-room was followed by a loud "Keerow" from some opposite locality. "The Sheriff will clear the court," said the Judge sternly; but, alas! as the embarrassed and choking officials rushed hither and thither, a soft "Keeree" from the spectators at the window, *outside* the court-house, was answered by a loud chorus of "Keerows" from the opposite windows, filled with onlookers. Again the laughter arose everywhere—even the fair plaintiff herself sat convulsed behind her handkerchief.

The figure of Colonel Starbottle alone remained erect—white and rigid. And then the Judge, looking up, saw—what no one else in the court had seen—that the Colonel was sincere and in earnest; that what he had conceived to be the pleader's most perfect acting and most elaborate irony were the deep, serious, mirthless *convictions* of a man without the least sense of humor. There was the respect of this conviction in the Judge's voice as he said to him gently, "You may proceed, Colonel Starbottle."

"I thank your Honor," said the Colonel slowly, "for recognizing and doing all in your power to prevent an interruption that, during my thirty years' experience at the bar, I have never been subjected to without the privilege of holding the instigators thereof responsible—*personally* responsible. It is possibly my fault that I have failed, oratorically, to convey to the gentlemen of the jury the full force and significance of the defendant's signals. I am aware that my voice is singularly deficient in producing either the dulcet tones of my fair client or the impassioned vehemence of the defendant's response. I will," continued the Colonel, with a fatigued but blind fatuity that ignored the hurriedly knit brows and warning eyes of the Judge, "try again. The note uttered by my client" (lowering his voice to the faintest of falsettos) "was 'Keeree'; the response was 'Keerow-ow.'" And the Colonel's voice fairly shook the dome above him.

Another uproar of laughter followed this apparently audacious repetition, but was interrupted by an unlooked-for incident. The defendant rose abruptly, and tearing himself away from the withholding hand and pleading protestations of his counsel, absolutely fled from the court-room, his appearance outside being recognized by a prolonged "Keerow" from the bystanders, which again and again followed him in the distance.

In the momentary silence which followed, the Colonel's voice was heard saying, "We rest here, your Honor," and he sat down. No less white, but more agitated, was the face of the defendant's counsel, who instantly rose.

"For some unexplained reason, your Honor, my client desires to suspend further proceedings, with a view to effect a peaceable compromise with the plaintiff. As he is a man of wealth and position, he is able and willing to pay liberally for that privilege. While I, as his counsel, am still convinced of his legal irresponsibility, as he has chosen publicly to abandon his rights here, I can only ask your Honor's permission to suspend further proceedings until I can confer with Colonel Starbottle."

"As far as I can follow the pleadings," said the Judge gravely, "the case seems to be hardly one for litigation, and I approve of the defendant's course, while I strongly urge the plaintiff to accept it."

Colonel Starbottle bent over his fair client. Presently he rose, unchanged in look or demeanor. "I yield, your Honor, to the wishes of my client, and—er—lady. We accept."

Before the court adjourned that day it was known throughout the town that Adoniram K. Hotchkiss had compromised the suit for four thousand dollars and costs.

Colonel Starbottle had so far recovered his equanimity as to strut jauntily towards his office, where he was to meet his fair client. He was surprised, however, to find her already there, and in company with a somewhat sheepish-looking young man—a stranger. If the Colonel had any disappointment in meeting a third party to the interview, his old-fashioned courtesy did not permit him to show it. He bowed graciously, and politely motioned them each to a seat.

"I reckoned I'd bring Hiram round with me," said the young lady, lifting her searching eyes, after a pause, to the Colonel's, "though he *was* awful shy, and allowed that you didn't know him from Adam, or even suspect his existence. But I said, 'That's just where you slip up, Hiram; a pow'ful man like the Colonel knows everything—and I've seen it in his eye.' Lordy!" she continued, with a laugh, leaning forward over her parasol, as her eyes again sought the Colonel's, "don't you remember when you asked me if I loved that old Hotchkiss, and I told you, 'That's tellin',' and you looked at me—Lordy! I knew *then* you suspected there was a Hiram *somewhere,* as good as if I'd told you. Now you jest get up, Hiram, and give the Colonel a good handshake. For if it wasn't for *him* and *his* searchin' ways, and *his* awful power of language, I wouldn't hev got that four thousand dollars out o' that flirty fool Hotchkiss—enough to buy a farm, so as you and me could get married! That's what you owe to *him*. Don't stand there like a stuck fool starin' at him. He won't eat you—though he's killed many a better man. Come, have *I* got to do *all* the kissin'?"

It is of record that the Colonel bowed so courteously and so profoundly that he managed not merely to evade the proffered hand of the shy Hiram, but to only lightly touch the franker and more impulsive finger-tips of the gentle Zaidee. "I—er—offer my sincerest congratulations—though I think you—er—overestimate—my—er—powers of penetration. Unfortunately, a pressing engagement, which may oblige me also to leave town to-night, forbids my saying more. I have—er—left the—er—business settlement of this—er—case in the hands of the lawyers who do my office work, and who will show you every attention. And now let me wish you a very good afternoon."

Nevertheless, the Colonel returned to his private room, and it was nearly twilight when the faithful Jim entered, to find him sitting meditatively before his desk. " 'Fo' God! Kernel, I hope dey ain't nuffin de matter, but you's lookin' mighty solemn! I ain't seen you look dat way, Kernel, since de day pooh Massa Stryker was fetched home shot froo de head."

"Hand me down the whiskey, Jim," said the Colonel, rising slowly.

The Negro flew to the closet joyfully, and brought out the bottle. The Colonel poured out a glass of the spirit and drank it with his old deliberation.

"You're quite right, Jim," he said, putting down his glass, "but I'm —er—getting old—and—somehow—I am missing poor Stryker damnably!"

Ben Hecht

:

CRIME WITHOUT PASSION

Mr. Lou Hendrix looked at the lady he had been pretending to love for the past six months and, being a lawyer, said nothing. Mr. Hendrix was a gentleman who could listen longer to female hysterics without unbending than was normal. This, he would have said, was due to his aloof and analytical mind. Then, also, the events which were taking place in this boudoir at the moment were of a familiar pattern. Some eight or nine times Mr. Hendrix had been the hero of just such climaxes as this, when new love had entered his life, and necessitated similar farewells.

The young lady who, this time, was doing the screaming was a nymph of the cabarets known as Brownie. Her full name was Carmen Browne. She danced, and very effectively, at the El Bravo Club where, devoid of plumage as an eel, she led the Birds of Paradise number. In this she was ravishing as a Dream of Fair Women.

Why so young and delicious a siren as Brownie should be so disturbed over the amorous defection of Mr. Hendrix would have confused anyone who knew this gentleman or merely took a one-minute look at him. He was not Romeo nor was he Adonis, nor was he even such a male as one associates with the general practice of seduction. He was a little man with that objectionable immaculateness which reminds one, instanter, of sheep's clothing. He was one of those popinjays of the flesh pots with the face of a tired and sarcastic boy. His sideburns were a wee too long, his smile unduly persistent (like a ballet dancer's), his voice far too gentle to have deceived anyone, ex-

580

cept perhaps a woman, as to his spiritual composition. But one can always depend on the ladies to misunderstand the combination of gentleness and sideburns.

Brownie, who among her own kind was considered not only quite a reader of books but a sort of practical authority on masculine characteristics, had misunderstood Lou Hendrix amazingly. Carry on as she would now, she was no match for this caballero of the law who, out of a clear sky, was engaged in giving her what she called "the go-by." As her monologue of screams, epithets and sobs progressed the lovely and muscular girl understood it all. She perceived, much too late for any use, that she had to do with as purring a hypocrite, rogue and underhanded soul as one might flush in a seven-day hunt on Broadway, which, according to the chroniclers Brownie most admired, is the world's leading water hole for human beasts of prey.

Looking around at the pretty apartment in which Mr. Hendrix had installed her and in which she had lorded it over her friends for the six months and from which she must now exit, love's dream being ended, Brownie spread herself on the couch and filled her Sybaritic diggings with a truly romantic din. From the more coherent utterances of this tear-stained beauty it seemed that she was innocent of all dallyings with a certain Eddie White, an ex-college hero, and that since leaving this same Mr. White, whose love interest she had been before the Birds of Paradise number was staged, she had never once permitted him to lay a finger on her. She was, wailed Brownie, being wrongly accused. Then, sitting up, her greenish eyes popping with rage until they looked like a pair of snake heads, Brownie laughed, as she would have said, scornfully, and declared that she could see through Mr. Hendrix and his so-called jealousy. He was getting rid of her because he didn't love her any more. He was tired of her and putting her on the escalator—that was all there was to it.

To this, Mr. Hendrix, thoroughly seen through, made no reply and Brownie, announcing that she was not going to be made a sucker of, fell back on the couch, beat some cushions with her fists and shook with grief. The telephone rang. Brownie straightened on the couch.

"It's probably for you," she said.

"More likely it's Mr. White," said Mr. Hendrix.

The taunt brought Brownie to her feet.

"If it's for me, by any mischance," said Mr. Hendrix, "say I'm not here."

Brownie spoke into the phone.

"Who?" she asked. "No, he's not here. No, I don't know when he'll be here. No, no, I don't expect him." Hanging up, she looked bitterly at Mr. Hendrix. "Your office," she said. "Always making me lie for you."

"You might have been a bit more polite," said Mr. Hendrix.

The heartlessness of this suggestion sent Brownie back to the couch and her grief. She resumed her sobs. Mr. Hendrix continued to regard her with creditable, if villainous, detachment. His heart was in the highlands with another lassie. But even discounting that factor Mr. Hendrix felt he was pursuing a wise course in ridding himself of so obstreperous an admirer as lay howling here. He had no use for over-emotional types. They were inclined to drive diversion, which was Mr. Hendrix' notion of Cupid, out of the window with their caterwauling.

Mr. Hendrix' soul, in fact, was a sort of china closet and he was firm in his aversion to flying hooves. He belonged to that tribe of Don Juans, rather numerous at the Broadway hole, who never hang themselves for love. Tears he regarded as bad sportsmanship and heartbreak was to him plain blackmail. Beauty—and by beauty Mr. Hendrix meant chiefly those delicious and agile Venuses of the cabaret floorshows— beauty had been put into Broadway (if not into the world) for man's delight; certainly not for his confusion and despair. And this little barrister lived elegantly, if rather villainously, by this conception.

A number of things, all obvious to the analytical Mr. Hendrix, were now operating in Brownie's mind and making her wail—Eddie's vengeful delight at her getting the go-by from his successor; the tittering of the little group of columnists, hoofers, waiters and good-time Charlies whom she called the World; the lessening of her status as a siren—she might even be demoted from leading the Birds of Paradise number, and through all these considerations—the Nerve of the Man, throwing her down as if she were some Nobody! As for the more passional side of the business, the pain in her heart at losing someone she had so stupidly loved and misunderstood and at losing the foolish Broadwayish dream of wedlock she had cherished for half a year, Brownie chose not to mention these in her ravings, being too proud.

Mr. Hendrix, still preserving his finest courtroom manner of Reason and Superiority, watched on in silence and fell to wondering what he had ever seen in this red-headed, almost illiterate creature with her muscular legs and childish face to have ever considered her charming or desirable. But he was given small time to meditate this problem of idealization. Brownie, with a yell that set the base of his spine to tingling, leaped from the couch, stared wildly around and then, emitting a series of shrill sounds, had at the furnishings of the Love Nest. She pulled a portière down, hurled two vases to the floor, swung a chair against the wall and smashed it, beat Mr. Hendrix' framed photograph to bits against the edge of the piano, seized a clock from the mantelpiece and bounced it on the floor and was making for Mr. Hendrix' derby, which he had placed on a chair near the door, when he, with an unexpected shout, headed her off.

The barrister, defending his derby, received a blow on the side of his face that sent him spinning. A thrown object caught him behind the ear. Brownie's pointed shoes belabored his shins. He retreated. But the hysteria to which he had been coolly and analytically listening seemed suddenly to have been injected, like a virus, into his bloodstream. It had started with the tingling in the base of his spine. Smarting from blows and full of some sort of electric current which gave off oaths in his head, the little lawyer began to outbellow his now ex-paramour. He came at the lady and in his hand he held, almost unaware of the fact, a large brass candlestick.

What it was that made this popinjay, so renowned for coolness, strategy and cynicism in his twin professions of amour and the law, so completely shed his character, God alone, who was not at Mr. Hendrix' elbow at the moment, could have told; and perhaps a psychiatrist or two might also have made a guess at. But here he was much too far gone for analysis, his own or anyone else's, charging at the lovely Carmen Browne like a bantam cave man, screaming and swinging the heavy piece of brass in the air.

There was no precedent in Mr. Hendrix's life for such a turn of events and no hint in any of his former love doings that passion could so blind his faculties and hate so fill his heart. Yet blind he was and full of a clamorous hate that demanded something of him. From the oaths which escaped Mr. Hendrix during this preliminary skirmish with the brass candlestick, it seemed that what he hated was women; loathed and hated them with a fury out of the Pit. Announcing this he swung the piece of brass and the second swing exhilarated him more. It had struck squarely against Brownie's head dropping her to the carpet. Mr. Hendrix, out of breath, stood cursing and grimacing over her like a murderer.

Slowly the little lawyer's rage melted. His heart swelled with terror and the nape of his neck grew warm. Brownie lay as she had fallen. He leaned over. Her skull was cracked. Blood was running. Her eyes were closed. Her legs, exposed in an incongruously graceful sprawl, were inert. He put his ear to her bosom. There was no heart beating. He stood for several minutes holding his breath and listening automatically for sounds outside the door. The choking sensation in his lungs subsided and the cool, analytical mind that was Mr. Hendrix returned like some errant accomplice tiptoeing back to the scene of the crime.

Carmen Browne lay dead on her hearthstone. No more would she lead the Birds of Paradise number at the El Bravo Club. But Mr. Hendrix wasted no time considering this sentimental phase of the matter. He had committed a murder, without intent, to be sure; even in self-defense, looked at factually. But no, self-defense wouldn't hold, Mr. Hendrix was thinking swiftly. There rushed through his mind all the angles, holes, difficulties, improbabilities and prejudices of his case and in less than a minute the little lawyer had put himself on trial on a plea of self-defense and found himself guilty.

Since a young man, Mr. Hendrix had always been close to crime. He had had that unmoral and intellectual understanding of it which helps make one type of excellent lawyer. In action, defending a criminal, Mr. Hendrix had always been like some imperturbable surgeon. Guilt was a disease that could be cured, not by any operation on the soul of its victim, but by a process of mental legerdemain which convinced a jury that no guilt existed. Mr. Hendrix might have said that he served a cause beyond good and evil, that of extricating the victims of fleeting misadventures from the unjustly permanent results of their deeds.

Thus, far beyond most men who might have found themselves confronted by the strange and ugly dilemma of having unexpectedly committed a murder, Mr. Hendrix was prepared for his new role of criminal. He knew all the ropes, he knew all the pitfalls of the defense of such a case as this. He knew the psychology of the prosecution. And with an expert, if still slightly fevered mind, he knew the perfect details by which his guilt might be cured, the ideal evidence, persuasive and circumstantial, by which a jury could be cajoled to the verdict of not guilty.

In less than a minute, Mr. Hendrix had a full grasp of his case, seeing far into its convolutions and difficulties. He set about straightening these out.

But like some dramatic critic who, after observing plays for years with subtle and intimate understanding of them, is summoned suddenly on the stage and with the strange footlights glaring in his eyes told to perform the part whose words he knows, whose ideal gesture and intonation he has always dreamed about, Mr. Hendrix felt the panic of debut. To know and to act were phenomena surprisingly separate. This was what delayed the cautious barrister for another minute, a minute during which Mr. Hendrix' client, with beating heart and white face, mumbled for speed, chattered even of flight.

But at the end of this second minute Mr. Hendrix had elbowed this ignominious client into a far corner of his mind, seated him, as it were, at the counsel's table with orders to keep his mouth shut—and taken charge of the case. He leaned over and looked at the clock on the floor. The dial glass was broken. The clock had stopped, its hands at two minutes of four. Mr. Hendrix' thoughts were rapid, almost as if he were not thinking at all but knowing. He could move the hands forward to five o'clock. He could leave the premises undetected, if possible, and attach himself for the next two hours to a group of prospective alibi witnesses, remain with them during the hours between four-ten and seven and this would be the proof he had not been in the apartment at the time of the murder. Mr. Hendrix examined the watch on Carmen Browne's wrist. It too had stopped. It registered one minute after four. The two timepieces, evidently synchronized by their owner, told a graphic and substantially correct tale. At 3:58 the struggle had begun. At 4:01 the woman had been killed. He would have to set the wrist watch forward a full hour to preserve this interesting discrepancy in the stopped clocks.

The telephone rang. Mr. Hendrix straightened, not having touched either of the hour hands. He had actually anticipated a telephone ringing, and in this anticipation known the ruse of the forwarded time hands was stupid. At 3:50 Carmen Browne had answered a phone call, a record of which was with the switchboard man in the lobby. Now at 4:03—he consulted his own watch—she failed to answer. Other phone calls might likewise come before five o'clock, all of which Carmen Browne would fail to answer, thus establishing an important series of witnesses against the fact that the murdered woman had been alive between four and five o'clock; thus rendering his alibi of his own whereabouts during that time practically futile. There was also the possibility that the neighbors had heard their quarrel and noted the time of the screaming. And more than all these the chance that someone, a maid or the building agent (Carmen Browne had been consulting him about sub-letting her place) might enter the room before five o'clock.

It was the hour preceding 4:01 for which Mr. Hendrix needed an alibi. He already knew its vital ground work. At 3:50 Carmen Browne, alive, had told someone on the phone—probably Tom Healey of his own law firm—that he was not in her apartment. Mr. Hendrix' eyes had remained on his own wrist watch as his thoughts slipped through these pros and cons. It was 4:04. He glanced at the sprawled figure on the floor, shivered, but stood his ground. Another phase of his case had overcome him. He smiled palely, shocked at what had al-most been an oversight. He must not only provide an alibi for him-self but fortify it with evidence tending to prove someone other than he had done the deed. He must invent a mythical murderer—leave a trail of evidence for the sharp eyes and wits of the prosecution lead-ing to Another—a never-to-be-found another, but yet one always present in the Case.

Carmen Browne's fingerprints were on the broken clock, the smashed chair, the battered photo frame. This was wrong. It would reveal that it was Carmen who had been in the rage, smashing things, demanding something that had resulted in her murder—and this sort of a situation, brought out by the prosecution, might easily point to Lou Hendrix, known to have been her lover. No, said Lawyer Hendrix swiftly, it must have been her assailant, demanding something of Carmen Browne, who had been in the rage and done the smashing and struck the fatal blow. Mr. Hendrix established this fact circumstantially by wiping Car-men Browne's fingerprints from the objects in question with a silk hand-kerchief. He wiped also and more carefully the brass candlestick. The absence of fingerprints pointed to a certain self-consciousness on the part of the assailant after the deed but that was both legitimate and normal. Men of the deepest passion, and there was precedence for this, remem-bered to obliterate evidnce.

At the door, Mr. Hendrix, in his hat, overcoat and gloves, paused. He repeated to himself carefully, Carmen Browne had been attacked by some suitor, jealous of her real sweetheart, Mr. Hendrix, as witness the destroyed photograph of the latter. But why hadn't she used the gun the police would find in the desk drawer two feet from the spot where her body lay? There were of course normal explanations to be put forward. But Mr. Hendrix did not admire them legally. For fifteen precious seconds Lawyer Hendrix balanced the issue. During this space

Mr. Hendrix listened rather than thought. He listened to the prosecution pointing out to the jury that the reason Carmen Browne had not reached for this available weapon with which to defend herself was because she had not expected an attack from the assailant, because the assailant was one familiar to her against whom she had no thought of arming herself; and even further, because the assailant, all too familiar with the premises, knew where this gun was as well as did Carmen Browne, and prevented her from reaching it. All these values pointed shadowly, Mr. Hendrix perceived, at his client. He removed the gun from the drawer and dropped in into his coat pocket. He must be careful in disposing of the weapon and Mr. Hendrix's mind dwelt stubbornly on a dozen cases in which an attempt at post crime evidence disposal had been the connecting link with guilt. But Mr. Hendrix assured his client firmly that he would be more cautious in this regard than any of his previous defendants had been.

With the gun in his coat pocket Mr. Hendrix stepped out of the apartment. Now he was, he knew, purely in the hands of luck. A door opening, a neighbor appearing, would ruin his case instantly. But no untoward event happened. He had three floors to descend. He listened at the ornamental elevator doors. Both cages were going up. Mr. Hendrix walked quickly down the three flights and coolly, now, like a gambler rather than a lawyer, rehearsed the possible permutations of Luck.

He had entered the apartment at three o'clock that morning with Carmen Browne. But because it was his habit to preserve a surface air of respectability toward the attendants of the place, though he fancied they knew well enough what was going on, he had walked up to the apartment with Brownie. The switchboard operator concealed in an alcove in the lobby had not seen them come in, nor had the elevator boy on duty, as both were out of sight at the moment. If now he could leave the building with the equal but vitally more important luck of not being seen, his case would be more than launched.

The lobby was empty, but Mr. Hendrix did not make the mistake of slipping out too quickly, and coddling the presumption that no eyes had observed him. He knew too well the possibility of the unexpected witness and he paused to study the premises. The switchboard attendant, half hidden in the alcove, had his back to the lobby and was reading a newspaper. Both elevator cages were out of sight. There was no one else. Mr. Hendrix stepped into the street.

Here again he stopped to look for that unexpected witness. How often, he remembered grimly, had the best of his cases been tumbled by the appearance on the stand of those aimless, incalculable human strays who had "Seen the Defendant." Mr. Hendrix saw two of just that type. Two women were walking, but with their backs to him and away from the apartment. A delivery truck was passing. Mr. Hendrix noticed that the driver was talking to a companion and that neither of these passers looked in his direction. There was no one else. Mr. Hendrix turned his attention to the windows across the street. Only the first three floors mattered. Identification was impossible, or at least could be sufficiently challenged, from any greater height. The windows were empty. As for the windows of the building directly over him, if he kept close to the wall none could see him from these.

Satisfied with this rapid but concentrated scrutiny, Mr. Hendrix started walking toward the corner. If the triumph of intellect over nerves, of reason over the impulses of the senses, may be called heroism, then this smiling, casually moving little popinjay in the black derby and snug overcoat might well be called a hero. Innocence, even aimlessness, was in his every movement; and in his refusal, despite a driving curiosity, to look at the time on his wrist—a tell-tale gesture were it recorded by anyone—there was something approaching the loftiness of purpose which distinguished the ancient Ascetics. As he turned the corner, Mr. Hendrix, still unruffled, still amiably rhythmic in his movements, looked back to make sure no taxicabs had entered the street. None had.

He was now on Sixth Avenue and he moved more briskly. He had four blocks to walk and habit sent his eyes looking for a taxicab. But, alert to every variety of witness, he shook his head and stayed afoot. He smiled, remembering that his own bed in his own apartment was unmade. He had just turned in the night before when Brownie had telephoned and asked to meet him. Thus his housekeeper, who never arrived before noon, would establish simply the fact that he had slept at home. This was unnecessary, to be sure, unless some passerby had seen Brownie and a man enter the former's apartment at three this morning.

Mr. Hendrix arrived now at a Sixth Avenue cinema palace. He looked carefully over the small crowd waiting for tickets and then joined the line. In a few minutes he was being ushered into the roped enclosure at the rear of the auditorium. He slipped away quickly, however, and walked in the dark to the other side of the theater. He approached one of the ushers and demanded to know where he could report the loss of a pair of gloves. After a brief colloquy he was led to the office of the Lost and Found department and here Mr. Hendrix, very voluble and affable, explained his mishap. He was not, he smiled, usually so careless with his belongings but the picture had been so engrossing that he had forgotten all about his haberdashery. Then Mr. Hendrix gave his name, address, a description of the missing gloves and watched with a glow of deep creative satisfaction the time being written down on the blank form used for cataloguing such matters. "Four-eighteen," the man wrote and Mr. Hendrix, consulting his watch, pretended to be startled. Was it that late? he demanded. Good Lord! he had had no idea of the time. It was quite a long picture. And the Lost and Found official, drawn into chumminess by Mr. Hendrix' affability, agreed that the film was a little longer than most, but well worth sitting through—to which Mr. Hendrix assented.

Emerging from the movie palace, Mr. Hendrix rehearsed his case to date. The main body of his alibi was achieved. He had spent the time between two-thirty and four watching a movie. His continued presence at four-eighteen in this theater was written down in black and white. He had also taken care that it should be a movie he had already seen so as to be able to recite its plot were he questioned in the next few hours. And he had also provided a motive for seeing this particular movie. The film had to do with the character and career of a mythical state's attorney, and a newspaper friend of Mr. Hendrix who conducted a gossip column had asked him to contribute a few paragraphs from a legal point of view carping at the improbabilities of the scenario.

Mr. Hendrix' next port of call was an elegant speakeasy. Here he had a drink, engaged in an exchange of views with the bartender, who knew him, asked the correct time so he might adjust his watch. At 4:50 he stepped into a phone booth in the place and called his office. He inquired whether anybody had been trying to reach him that afternoon. The law clerk on duty for the firm, Tom Healey, answered as Mr. Hendrix had expected. Mr. Healey said he had been trying to find him in relation to a disposition but had been unable to locate him. At this Mr. Hendrix feigned a light anger. Where had the incompetent youth called? He had, said Mr. Healey, tried everywhere, even Miss Carmen Browne's apartment.

At this bit of information Mr. Hendrix, in his mind's eye addressing one of his future star witnesses, changed his voice. He grew angry and very obviously so, for he knew the laziness of people's memories and their slipshod powers of observation. He inquired sourly if Mr. Healey had spoken to Miss Browne. On hearing that he had, Mr. Hendrix said:

"Do you mind telling me how she seemed when you asked if I was there?"

"Well, I don't know," Mr. Healey said.

"Try and think," said Mr. Hendrix. "I'd like to know."

"Well," said Mr. Healey, "come to think of it, she struck me as a little curt or upset about something."

"Ha!" said Mr. Hendrix and, to the surprise of his office underling, called the young lady a villainous name.

"I don't want you to call me up at her place any more," he raised his voice. The clerk, Mr. Healey, said he would never do it again, but Mr. Hendrix, as though too enraged to notice this promise, continued, "I'm all washed up at that telephone number. Understand what I mean? You can just forget about it. Any other calls?"

"No," said Mr. Healey.

"O.K.," said Mr. Hendrix and hung up the phone with an angry bang.

He walked from the speakeasy with a light step which to Mr. Hendrix' office colleagues always characterized a Not Guilty verdict in sight. Now that the tingling at the base of his spine as well as the annoying warmth on the nape of his neck, as if a Prosecuting Staff were actually breathing on him, had gone entirely, Mr. Hendrix was beginning to feel not only relaxed but even amused. He could hear the Prosecution falling into this little trap he had just laid.

Question: So Mr. Hendrix told you that you needn't try to reach him at Miss Browne's apartment any more?

Answer: Yes, sir.

And Lawyer Hendrix looked winningly at the jury that sat in his mind's eye. Gentlemen of the Jury, consider this. As if, having committed a crime, the defendant would be so gauche as to give himself away by some such oafish remark to a law clerk—a type of person trained to remember what he hears. Not a casual stranger, mind you, but a man with sharp and practiced wits.

Mr. Hendrix, skittering happily along the street, cleared his throat, beamed and felt a desire to laugh. He had never quite so enjoyed a case.

What subtle and yet vital psychological proof of his innocence was the fact that he had just said to Tom Healey what he had; what perfect proof of the fact that he had been the victim of an obvious coincidence in saying he was washed up with Carmen Browne when she lay dead in her apartment. No guilty man would ever have said that.

From a drug store he was passing, Mr. Hendrix made another telephone call. He called Carmen Browne. Inquiring for her of the apartment switchboard operator a sharp excitement stirred him. Before his eyes the image of her body, sprawled gracefully and awfully on the floor at his feet, swayed for a moment. He hoped the crime had been discovered, although there were still chances to improve his Case. But the switchboard man calmly plugged in for Carmen Browne's apartment.

"She doesn't answer," he said after a pause.

"This is Mr. Hendrix calling," said Mr. Hendrix. "Has she been in at all? I've been trying to get her all day."

"Hasn't come in while I've been here," said the man.

"How long is that?" said Mr. Hendrix.

"Oh, about three hours," said the man.

"Thank you," said Mr. Hendrix and hung up.

He had told Tom Healey he was washed up with Carmen Browne and now he was trying to reach her, and Mr. Hendrix considered this paradox, in behalf of his client, with a smile. It revealed, Gentlemen of the Jury, a distracted man; a lover full of confusion as a result of— what? Of the fact, gentlemen, Mr. Hendrix purred to himself, that my client was jealous of the attentions he had found out someone was paying to Carmen Browne; that he did not believe the poor girl's protestations of innocence and, driven from her side by suspicions, was yet lured back to her by his deep love. Jealous, Gentlemen of the Jury, of the attentions being paid to Carmen Browne by this creature who that very afternoon had entered her apartment and against whom Carmen Browne had defended herself until struck down and killed.

To augment this phase of the case, Mr. Hendrix returned now to the apartment building in which Carmen Browne lay murdered. He approached the switchboard operator, who greeted him by name. Here Mr. Hendrix controlled a curious impulse that whitened the skin around his mouth. He felt impelled to ask this man whether he had noticed Mr. Hendrix in the building before, whether he had seen him during the few moments he had walked from the lobby an hour ago. Astonished at this impulse, Mr. Hendrix held his tongue for a space, aware that the switchboard man was looking at him with curiosity.

Question: How did the defendant seem?

Answer: Confused.

Gentlemen of the Jury, and how would a man consumed with jealousy seem while inquiring, against all his pride, if the woman he thought was wronging him, was home?

"Has Miss Browne come in since I called?" asked Mr. Hendrix.

"I haven't seen her," said the man. "I'll try her apartment again." There was no answer.

"Give her this note when she comes back," said Mr. Hendrix.

He wrote on the lower part of a business letter from his pocket:

"Darling, if you are innocent, don't torture me any more. Give me a chance to believe you. I'm willing to forget what I heard or thought I heard over the phone. As ever, Lou."

He placed this in a used envelope, scribbled her name on it, and sealed it.

Gentlemen of the Jury, can you imagine any man who had killed a woman he loved or had loved, so lost to all human reaction, so fiendishly wanton as to have written that little plea when he knew she was lying dead at his hands?

That was merely a rhetorical overtone, the human rather than evidential side of the note, but Mr. Hendrix filed it away in his memory as a bit of decoration. His alibi, Lawyer Hendrix murmured to himself, was now complete. But the secondary phase of the case needed further effort. The beauty of a case lay always in the elaborateness of diverse but corroborating detail—as if the world were crying the defendant's innocence from every nook and cranny. And happily at work, Mr. Hendrix had lawyer-like so far forgotten the human existence of his client as to whistle cheerily the while he turned over and re-turned over the major psychological problem in his mind.

Defense—Carmen Browne had been murdered by a man to whom she refused, after perhaps leading him on, to surrender herself. Also it might be that the killing had been one of those passional accidents which the sex instinct, run amok, precipitates. It might be that Carmen Browne had led a double life and was discovered in this double life by her slayer.

Ergo—Lou Hendrix, sharp-witted, observant, a veritable connoisseur of women, must suspect the existence of this other man. And Defendant Hendrix must also be jealous of him.

Witness to this—his talk to Tom Healey; his note to Carmen Browne now in the hands of the switchboard operator.

And Lawyer Hendrix, with the thrill of a gambler rolling a third lucky seven, remembered at this point a third witness—a veritable star witness, beautifully, if unwittingly, prepared for her role a few days ago. This was Peggy Moore.

Miss Moore danced at the El Bravo Club as a member of the ensemble. She had been Brownie's confidant for a year. Mr. Hendrix smiled blissfully recalling his conversation with Miss Moore less than a week ago and recalling also her general character, one made to order for the part he was to assign her.

This young lady was a tall, dark-haired Irish lassie with slightly bulging eyes and an expression of adenoidal and not unpleasing vacuity about her face. She was, as Brownie had frequently confided to him, a veritable love slave, a dithering creature incapable of thinking or talking on any subject other than the emotions stirred in her bosom by love or jealousy.

Some days ago Mr. Hendrix had selected this almost congenital idiot as the opening pawn in his decision to rid himself of Brownie. He had confided to Miss Moore's ears, so perfectly attuned to all tales of amorous agony, that he suspected Brownie of being still in love with his predecessor Eddie White. Miss Moore's eyes had bulged, her mouth opened as if to disgorge a fish hook and simultaneously a shrewd, if transparent emotion, had overcome her. Miss Moore, the victim of so much perfidy, had been convinced instanter of her chum's guilt and had launched at once into a series of lies, all defending Brownie's integrity and offering idiotic details of her devotion to her lawyer lover. Mr. Hendrix, intent on laying some foolish groundwork for his subsequent defection, had persisted, however, and, for no other reason than that he delighted in playing the human fraud whenever he could, had feigned sorrow and talked of woe.

Now Mr. Hendrix summoned Miss Moore on the telephone to meet him at the speakeasy he had recently quitted. He spoke guardedly, hinting at a lovers' quarrel, and pretending he needed her to verify some evidences of Brownie's guilt, just unearthed. Miss Moore, full of a laudable and loyal ambition to lie her head off in Brownie's behalf, as Mr. Hendrix had foreseen, arrived in a rush. And the two sat down at a table in a corner, Miss Moore to invent innocent explanations and alibis for her chum, at which like all over-tearful addicts of passion she was amazingly expert; and Mr. Hendrix to weave her artfully into his case.

But first Mr. Hendrix, aware of the lady's sensitivity toward all matters pertaining to love, proceeded to get himself drunk. He must be the lover stricken with jealousy and seeking to drown his pains in liquor, a characterization which this simple child and student of amour would remember only too vividly on the witness stand. Three drinks were consumed and then, honestly befuddled from such an unaccustomed dose, Mr. Hendrix launched into cross examination. And despite his thickened tongue and touch of genuine physical paralysis, Lawyer Hendrix remained as cool and analytical as if he were in a courtroom. He was not one to betray a client by any human weaknesses.

He put himself at Miss Moore's mercy. He must know the truth and she alone could tell him. Otherwise with too much brooding and uncertainty he would be sure to go out of his mind. His law practice was already suffering. He would lose all his money. Miss Moore nodded tenderly and understandingly at this saga of love woes. In reply she could assure Mr. Hendrix that he was being very foolish to be jealous of Eddie White because Mr. White wasn't even in town and besides Mr. White was engaged to marry a society girl in Newport. Mr. Hendrix sighed appreciatively at this walloping lie.

"It's not Eddie," said Mr. Hendrix; "it's somebody else. You know that as well as I. You're in her confidence. Don't try to lie to me, dearie. I caught her red-handed, talking over the phone. She hung up when I came into the room. She was making a date—and not with Eddie White."

Miss Moore paled at the thought of this dreadful contretemps, but kept her wits. Her chum's guilt frightened her but at the same time she saw through Mr. Hendrix' effort to lead her astray. Of course it was Eddie White of whom he was jealous. Miss Moore was certain of this and Mr. Hendrix, listening to her somewhat hysterical defense of Brownie, sufficient to have convicted that young lady of a hundred infidelities had he been interested, realized exactly what was in his companion's mind. He considered for a moment the plan of involving Eddie White in his case. He had thought of it before—Brownie's previous lover, a known hot-headed young gentleman given to nocturnal fisticuffs in public places. But for the second time he dismissed this phase. Eddie would have an alibi and the establishing of Eddie's physical innocence, however psychologically promising his guilt might have looked, would embarrass his client's case.

For the next hour Mr. Hendrix drank and discussed his jealousy, pleading with Miss Moore to be kind to him and reveal what she knew; and hinting at gifts in return for such service. But Miss Moore only increased the scope of her lies.

"Have you seen Brownie today?" Miss Moore finally broke off, winded.

Mr. Hendrix weaved in his seat and looked at her with bleary drunken eyes.

"No," he said. "I don't trust myself to see her. God knows what I would do—feeling this way."

"You're just worked up about absolutely nothing," said Miss Moore and rose. She had to toddle off to the El Bravo where she performed during the dinner hour. Mr. Hendrix accompanied her to the door.

"Tell Brownie," he whispered, "I'll be over to the club tonight. And . . . and give her a last chance to prove her innocence."

"I'll give her the message," said Miss Moore and sighed.

Alone Mr. Hendrix returned to the phone booth. He sat down heavily and put in a call for Carmen Browne. His case was ready. He desired to hear the news of the finding of the body. An annoying tingle touched the base of his spine as he waited for the apartment switchboard to answer. He wondered how drunk he was. Drunk, to be sure, but sober enough to know exactly every phase and weigh every nuance. The moment he heard of the crime he would rush over, be detained by the police and with the aid of his intoxicated condition act thoroughly irrational and grief-stricken. He would hint at no alibis, reveal not a shred of his case until the coroner's inquest.

The switchboard operator finally answered. Mr. Hendrix inquired thickly for Miss Browne. He was told Miss Browne was not in. He hung up. Rising and swaying for a moment, Mr. Hendrix, thoroughly at peace with the world, except for this intermittent tingle, decided on the best course. He would go to the El Bravo Club, order his dinner and wait there till Brownie's absence was noticed and a search started.

*

The El Bravo orchestra was rendering a dance number. The dance floor was crowded. Mr. Hendrix looked dizzily at the circling figures. He had selected a table far to the side, one of those at which the performers and their friends grouped themselves during the evening. The stuffiness of the air made Mr. Hendrix feel drowsy. Looking up, he beheld a familiar figure approaching. It was Eddie White, whom he had pleased to style the ignorant drop-kicker. Mr. Hendrix smiled. He noticed tiredly that Mr. White seemed a little drunk.

The ex-college hero, still a sturdy tanned and muscular product of the Higher Education, greeted Mr. Hendrix calmly. He dropped into a chair at the table and inquired, with an eye roving over the place, how tricks were. Mr. Hendrix said they were fine.

There was a pause during which the music filled the café with glamorous and exciting sounds.

"Didn't know you were such a movie fan," said Mr. White apropos of nothing and Mr. Hendrix felt himself sobering up as if in a cold shower.

"Just what do you mean?" Mr. Hendrix managed to inquire and very casually.

His companion was busy looking them over on the dance floor and offering a roguish eye to a few of the tastier numbers. Mr. Hendrix stared at him in silence and felt the tingle return to his spine.

"Saw you going into the Roxy this afternoon," Mr. White resumed.

"You did," said Mr. Hendrix and then added, as if he were looping the loop, "What time was that?"

"What time?" Mr. White repeated, looking at the little lawyer with a dull, athlete's stare. "Oh, a little after four, I should say."

"You're crazy," said Mr. Hendrix, "if you think you saw me going into the Roxy after four. Why, I came out about twenty after four, after seeing the whole show."

"I don't care what you saw," said Mr. White. "I saw you going in at about a quarter after. I was gonna say hello but I thought the hell with it. How'd you like the picture? Ought to be in your line—all about one of those crooked legal sharks."

In the brief space during which Mr. Hendrix was now silent his thoughts were very rapid. Mr. White, God help Mr. Hendrix, was that most objectionable of all humans known to a legal case—the aimless stray that the Prosecution was wont to drag, rabbit fashion, out of its hat with which to confound the guilty. And Mr. Hendrix knew without thinking the full significance of this witness, Eddie White. If the defendant had been seen entering the movie theater after four, he had been seen entering after the murder had been committed. But that was the least damaging phase. The defendant had left the movie theater at 4:20, having lied to the attendants and told them he had spent an hour and a half in the place. With the fact of this lie established, the prosecution could take apart piece by piece the obvious mechanism of his alibi. There was no alibi. There was no case. In fact, to the contrary, Eddie White's simple statement of the time of day—after four—revealed all of the defendant's subsequent actions as those of a thoroughly guilty man, and Mr. Hendrix leaned across the table and put a hand on the athlete's arm.

"It must have been somebody else you saw," he purred.

"Listen, don't tell me," said Mr. White. "I saw you looking around, buying your ticket and ducking in."

Mr. Hendrix winced at the damning phraseology.

"I know it was about a quarter after four," pursued Mr. White, "because I had a date outside. And don't get so excited. It wasn't with Brownie."

The tingle at the base of the Hendrix spine was almost lifting him out of his seat.

"That's a lie," said Mr. Hendrix thickly.

"What's that?" Mr. White demanded.

"I said you're lying," Mr. Hendrix repeated slowly. "You didn't see me."

"Oh, that's what you said, is it?" Mr. White was unexpectedly grim. "Listen, I never liked you and I don't take talk off a guy I got no use for. Get that."

And for the second time that day an unprecedented mood overcame the little lawyer. He made an effort to stop the words which suddenly filled his head but he heard himself saying them and wondering confusedly who it was who was drunk—he who was listening or he who was speaking. He was telling Mr. White what a liar, numbskull and oaf he was and Mr. White stood up. Words continued, Mr. Hendrix aware that he and Mr. White were both talking at once. But the music made a blur in his ears and the El Bravo Club swayed in front of his eyes. Then Mr. Hendrix realized, and darkly, that the towering Mr. White's hand was on his collar and that he was being lifted out of his seat. The

El Bravo orchestra was rolling out a jazz finale and nobody seemed to have noticed as yet the fracas taking place at this side table. As Mr. Hendrix felt himself being hoisted to his feet, a sense of nausea and helplessness overcame him. He thrust his hand into his coat pocket.

"Calling me a liar, eh?" Mr. White was growling in the Hendrix ear. He added a number of epithets.

The little lawyer saw for an instant a fist pull back that never landed. Mr. Hendrix had removed a gun from his coat pocket, a gun of whose existence in his hand he was as unaware as he had been of the brass candlestick. The gun exploded and Mr. White with a look of suddenly sober astonishment fell back into a chair. The music at this moment finished with a nanny goat blare of trumpets. No heads turned. No waiters came rushing. Shaking as if his bones had turned into castanets, Mr. Hendrix stood looking at the crumpled athlete and watched his head sink over the table. The mouth was open. The athlete's fingers hanging near the floor were rigid.

Music started again and Mr. Hendrix turned his eyes automatically toward the dance floor. Blue and pink floodlights were shining on it and out from behind the orchestra shell came a line of almost naked girls. White legs kicked, smiles filled the air. Leading the chorus line Mr. Hendrix saw Carmen Browne. She was dancing.

The little lawyer grew sick. He shut his eyes. Then he opened them. They were full of pain and bewilderment. It was no hallucination. It was Brownie. Extending under her ear at the back of her head he saw strips of court plaster. She was alive and restored.

Mr. Hendrix knew exactly what had happened. The last time he had called her apartment, the switchboard man, failing to recognize his liquor-thickened voice, had withheld the information he might have offered Mr. Hendrix—that Carmen Browne was alive, that she had summoned a doctor, that she had left the apartment.

And even as he was thinking of this tiny detail, a hundred other details crowded into the Hendrix mind. He remembered his accusations to Brownie that she still loved Eddie White; his statement to Peggy Moore last week and this afternoon that he was too jealous to trust himself; his attack on Carmen Browne, his subsequent drunkenness, his idiotic antics in the movie theater—as if he were shadowing Eddie White—what else could his rushing in and rushing out mean? Everything Mr. Hendrix had accomplished since 4:02 this afternoon pointed only at one conclusion—that he hated Eddie White, that he had almost killed his sweetheart out of jealousy over White, that, still burning with this emotion, he had tracked White down and murdered him in cold blood.

Mr. Hendrix, during these brief moments staring at the crumpled athlete, wanted to scream, so macabre did all these events strike him, but his voice trailed off into a moan. What was this insane thing he had done for his client! Exonerated him! Mr. Hendrix, still shaking, slipped down into his chair. He, Louis Hendrix, the shining legal intelligence, had like some Nemesis convicted himself—and not of manslaughter, which might have been the verdict otherwise—but of premeditated murder in the first degree. There was no case. No defense was possible. There was nothing left to do but to flee like some thug.

Mr. Hendrix looked at his wrist. He had twenty minutes to make the ten o'clock train for Chicago. From Chicago he would travel to New Orleans and thence into Mexico. He had a wallet full of bills. The side exit of the El Bravo was ten feet away. But Mr. Hendrix, struggling to get to his feet, swayed and fell forward. The dozen drinks he had so shrewdly tossed down his gullet to help him act his part joined the hideous plot he had hatched against himself. He was too drunk, too dizzy to stand up and move quickly.

They found the little barrister hunched in his seat staring at the murdered athlete. The gun was still in his hand. Mr. Hendrix was mumbling passionlessly:

"Guilty. Guilty. Guilty."

Rabelais

:

ON JUDGE BRIDLEGOOSE AND
LORD JOHN THE LOONY

from *Gargantua and Pantagruel*

HOW PANTAGRUEL PERSUADED PANURGE
TO SEEK COUNSEL OF A FOOL

"Here is the story, Panurge: it happened in Paris at the cookshop by
the Petit Châtelet. A hungry porter was eating his bread in front of a
roasting goose; as the meat turned on the spit, he held up the bread to
be flavored and perfumed by the vapor emanating from the cooking.
The cook did not interfere with him. But when the porter had wolfed
down the last mouthful, the cook seized him by the throat, and demanded payment for the smoke of his roast meat. The other replied that
he had in no wise damaged his meats, deprived him of anything, or in-
curred any debt. The smoke in question evaporated and was lost, whether
the porter stood by or not. Nor had any one in Paris ever seen or heard
of the sale of smoke from roast meats in the city streets.

"The cook replied that he was not compelled to feed porters and like
riffraff with the aroma of his goose; he swore that if the porter did not
pay him, he would pull his teeth out. The porter drew his cudgel and
stood on the defensive. A great altercation ensued; idle Parisians
thronged from all sides to witness the debate. Appropriately enough,
Lord John the Loony, a citizen of Paris, happened to be there. Seeing
him, the cook said to the porter:

" 'Will you abide by our noble Lord John's decision in this matter?'

" 'Ay, by God's blood, so I will,' the porter agreed.

"Lord John listened to their pleas, then ordered the porter to produce a coin from his belt. The porter presented him with a *philip* or sou, a very old coin struck with the effigy of Philip V. Lord John took it and laid it on his own left shoulder as though weighing it. Next, he made it ring on the palm of his left hand as though testing the metal's alloy. Finally, he laid it against his right eye, as though to see if it were well struck. The whole operation was performed amid a deep silence: the loafers watched curiously; the cook confidently; the porter in despair.

"Then Lord John made the coin ring several times over the counter, and, with judicial majesty, holding his jester's wand as he might a scepter, adorning the marten cap on his head with paper ears ridged like organ-pipes, he cleared his throat deliberately, two or three times, and announced in a loud voice:

" 'The court decrees that the porter who ate his bread by the smoke of the roast has duly and civilly paid the cook with the jingle of his money. Further, the said court orders each to return to his eachery without cost or damages. Case dismissed.'

"This decision handed down by the Paris fool seemed eminently just and admirable to the learned authorities I quoted above. Indeed, they doubted whether a more logical and judicious settlement could have been made by the Parliament of Paris, the Rota of Rome, or the Areopagites in Athens.

"My advice, Panurge, is to consult a fool."

HOW PANTAGRUEL ATTENDED THE TRIAL
OF JUDGE BRIDLEGOOSE, WHO DECIDED
CASES ACCORDING TO THE TURN OF THE
DICE

Next day, at the appointed hour, Pantagruel reached Miralingua. The president, senators and counselors invited them to attend the hearing; Judge Bridlegoose was to defend and justify the sentence he had pronounced against Touchcircle, a tax-assessor. To the court of the hundred judges, this decision of Bridlegoose's had not seemed at all equitable. Pantagruel accepted their invitation, and, going in, found Bridlegoose seated in the middle of the enclosure.

As the case progressed, Bridlegoose, for all argument, replied only that he was getting old, and that his sight was failing; he cited, into the bargain, various other vexations and calamities brought on by senescence. As legal proof, Bridlegoose begged to quote: *not. per Archid.* D LXXXVI, *c. tanta.*

(Here he invoked the division of canon law, noted by the Archdeacon Guido Baisius of Reggio. His quotation hinged on the case of a bishop, who had worked in the fields before saying mass, and who was excused by the Pope on the score of old age.)

Unable to read the dice as clearly as in the past, Bridlegoose compared himself to Isaac, who, being old and dimsighted, mistook Jacob for Esau. Thus, having to decide the case in question, he had doubtless taken a four for a five; he begged to assure the learned judges that he had used a very small pair of dice. But, according to the applying of law, the imperfections of nature must not be considered criminal, as is supported by *ff. de re milit., l. qui cum uno; ff. de reg. jur., l. fere; ff. de edil. ed. per totum; ff. de term. mo.; l. Divus Adrianus; resolu. per Lud. Ro. in l.: si vero, ff. solu. matri.*

(Here, I may add, that *ff* stands for the *Digest,* a vast codification of Roman civil law made by Tribonian at the request of the Emperor Justinian in the sixth century; rediscovered in the twelfth, it served as foundation for the teaching of all jurisprudence. The principal part of the *Digest* was the *Pandects;* thus *ff* is perhaps a corruption of the Greek *rho* or *pi* . . . *l* stands for *lex,* or law . . . *c* for the *Code* of Justinian . . . *d* for the *Decrees* of Gratian.)

This learned argument made use of all manner of authorities: the divine Hadrian's punishment for removing milestones, to be administered with a regard to the delinquent's age . . . the law concerning men born with one testicle . . . the comment of Ludovicus Romanus (Pontanus of Spoleto), a fifteenth-century commentator.

Anyone, therefore, who failed to observe these legal rulings, would not be accusing the man, but rather Nature, as is evident in *l. maximum vitium C. de lib. praeter,* a law establishing a certain equality among male and female heirs.

"Now, my friend," said Trinquamelle, or Blusterer, the Lord High President of the Court, "what dice are you speaking of?"

"The dice of sentence and judgments, or, in Latin, *alea judiciorum,* the hazards of decisions," Bridlegoose explained. "Let me invoke *doct. 26. q. ij. c. Sors; l. nec emptio, ff. de contrah, empt; l. quod debetur, ff. de pecul., et ibi Bartol.*"

(Here Bridlegoose offered laws, together with the comment of Bartolo, professor at Pisa in the fifteenth century.)

"You, too, gentlemen, employ these dice in your sovereign court, as do all other judges when sitting upon a case. Henri Ferrandat of Nevers, in his comments on the *Decretals,* and also *no. gl. in c. fin. de sortil.,* and *l. sed cum ambo, ff. de judi., ubi doct.* state plainly that fate or hazard is a worthy, honest, useful and necessary element in the decision of differences and lawsuits. This is brought out even more clearly in *Bal., Bart.* and *Alex.,* in *C. communia, de l. Si duo."*

(Here Bridlegoose was quoting Baldus, Bartolo and Alexandro Tartagno, all Italian jurisconsults, and the law recommending the drawing of lots when several co-heirs could not agree.)

"And how do you judge, my friend?" Blusterer inquired.

"I shall answer you briefly," said Bridlegoose, "thus following the instructions of the law *Ampliorem, in refutatoriis, C. de appela* and the *Gl. l. j. ff. quod met, cau,* which enjoin brevity. Ay, gentlemen: *gaudent brevitate moderni,* we moderns rejoice in brevity. Well then, gentlemen, I judge just as you yourselves do, according to the custom of the judicatory office, which our law commands us always to observe. Here, I invoke, *ut, no. extra. de consuet., c. ex literis, et ibi Innoc.,* a body of rules made by Pope Gregory IX.

"First, I view and review, read and re-read, ponder, weigh, thumb and digest the bills of complaint, subpoenas, appearance by proxy, reports of hearings, investigations, instruments of deposition, petitions, articles of evidence, allegations, rejoinders, rebuttals, requests, inquests, surrejoinders, surrebuttals, confirmation of former testimony, acts, writs, bulls, exceptions taken, grievances, objections, counter-objections . . . confrontation of witnesses and accused; confrontation of the various co-accused . . . certificates, libels and apostoles requesting the judge to refer the case to another court . . . letters of attorney; royal letters; instruments of compulsion, forcing a clerk to produce a document . . . declinatories, questioning the court's competence . . . anticipatories, arguing the opponent's probable plea . . . references to other jurisdictions . . . returns of cases to the judges that had referred them . . . conclusions, accessory contestations, appointments, appeals, confessions, notifications or executions of sentence . . . and all other such spiceries and sweetmeats. . . ."

The last terms referred to the judge's bribes or overcharges, which made law so profitable a pursuit.

"Ay," said Bridlegoose, "I do this as any good judge should, in conformance with *no Spec. de ordinario,* III, *et tit. de offi. om. ju., fi., et de rescriptis praesenta.,* I, as Speculator, or Guillaume Durand, indicates in his repertory of canon law.

"On the end of the table in my chambers, I place all the bags containing the defendant's plea, and I allow him the first hazard of the dice, just as you gentlemen do, according to *et est not., l. Favorabiliores, ff. de reg. jur., et in c. cum sunt eod. tit. lib.* VI, which says: *Cum sunt partium jura obscura, reo favendum est potius quam actori,* when the law is obscure, the defendant is to be favored rather than the plaintiff. This famous maxim from the *Sixte,* added by Pope Boniface VIII to the five books of Gregory IX's *Decretals,* I interpret literally.

"This done—just like yourselves, gentlemen—I place the plaintiff's dossier at the other end of the table, *visum visu,* face to face, for *opposita, juxta se posita, magis elucescunt, ut not. in l. i. videamus, ff. de his qui sunt sui vel alie. juri. et in l. munerum j. mixta ff. de muner. et honor.* Then I throw the dice for the plaintiff, too."

"But, my friend," Blusterer asked, "how do you determine the obscurity of arguments offered by the litigants?"

"Exactly as you, gentlemen," Bridlegoose replied. "When there are many bags on either end of the table, I use my small dice, just as you do, gentlemen, in accordance with the law: *Semper in stipulationibus, ff. de reg. jur,* and the capital, poetical law called *q. eod. tit.* which begins with a hexameter: *Semper in obscuris quod minimum est sequimur,* and which tells us, when in doubt, to take the less consequential course. This rule, moreover, has been adopted by canon law, *in c., in obscuris, eod. tit. lib.* VI.

"Of course I have other large, handsome and most suitable dice, which I use—like you gentlemen—when the matter is more liquid, that is to say, when the bags bearing the pleas are lighter."

"But when you had done all this," Blusterer insisted, "how did you pass sentence, my friend?"

"Just like yourselves, gentlemen," said Bridlegoose. "I decided in favor of the party who won at the judiciary, tribonian and praetorial throw of dice. This is recommended by our laws, *ff. qui po. in pig., l. potior. leg. creditor., C. de consul., l.* I, *et de reg. jur., in* VI: *Qui prior est tempore potior est jure,* the first comer has the best legal case."

BRIDLEGOOSE'S EXPLANATION OF WHY
HE EXAMINED THE DOCUMENTS OF CASES
HE JUDGED BY DICING

"Very well, my friend," said Blusterer, "but, since you pass sentence by the throw and hazard of dice, why do you not settle the matter then and there, the very same day and hour the litigants appear before you? Of what use are the papers and writs in the litigants' bags?"

"I find these documents as useful as you, gentlemen, find like documents, in similar instances. They are helpful in three exquisite, requisite and authentic manners: first, for formality; secondly, as physical exercise; thirdly, from considerations of time."

Bridlegoose then went on to explain.

(1) To begin with, form must be observed. If not, whatever a judge decided was valueless, as proved by *Spec. tit. de instr. edi. et tit. de rescrip praesent.* Besides, the gentlemen of the court knew only too well that, in judicial proceedings, formalities destroyed the materiality and substance of the cases. Bridlegoose supported this statement by *forma mutata mutatur substantia, ff. ad exhib., l. Julianus ff. ad leg. falcid., l. Si is qui quadringenta, et extra., de deci., c. ad audientiam, et de celebra. miss., c. in quadam.* In other words: substance, a permanent element, changed in nature with a change of form.

(2) Next, all these documents served Bridlegoose, as they served his honorable judges, here assembled, in the way of honest and healthful exercise. Here he quoted the late Master Othoman Vadare, an excellent physician—as the court would say *C. de comit. et archi., lib.* XII, referring to the law, in the twelfth book of Justinian's *Code,* concerning the physicians and surgeons in the pay of the emperor or a municipality. Well, Othoman Vadare had frequently told Bridlegoose that lack of bodily exercise was the sole cause of the unhealthiness and short lives of all judges, including the worshipful court now hearing him, Bridlegoose.

Bartolo noted this admirably in *l.* I. *C. de senten. quae pro eo quod,* the very first law in the *Code.* Thus, both his colleagues now trying him, and himself, at the bar, were justified in taking such exercise. *Accessorium natura sequitur principalis, de reg. jur. lib.* VI *et l. cum principalis, et l. nihil dolo., ff. eod. titu.; ff. de fidejusso., l. fidejussor, et extra. de offi. de leg., c. j.* conceded certain honest and recreative sport. Moreover, *ff. de al. lus. et aleat., l. solent, et autent, ut omnes obediant, in princ., coll.* VII. *et ff. de praescript. verb., l. si gratuitam, et l. j. C de spect., lib.* XI, concurred in this statement. Again, St. Thomas Aquinas *in secunda secundae, quaest.* CLXVIII stated that there is much to be gained from games. And Dom Alberic de Rosata, the fourteenth-century canonist of Bergamo, *fuit magnus practicus,* and a solemn doctor, agreed, on the authority of Barbatia in *prin. consil. . . . .* The reason was exposed clearly in *per gl. in proemio ff.* § *ne autem tertii,* which ordered third-year students to keep a holiday celebrating the memory of Papinian.

Interpone tuis interdum guadia curis, was what Dionysius Cassius said, in his *Distichs,* a collection of aphorisms in Latin hexameters. Bridlegoose need not translate for his judges an axiom known by every student in Europe.

Once, indeed, in the year 1489, Bridlegoose had had a financial matter to settle in the High Court of Financial Jurisdiction. By particular, peculiar (and pecuniary!) permission of the usher, he gained access to the Lord High Treasurers. My Lords of Miralingua, Bridlegoose's present judges, knew well that *pecunias obediunt omnia,* money answereth all things, as *Ecclesiastes* puts it. On this score, see *Bald. in l. Singularia, ff. si certum pet., et Salic., in l. recepticia, C. de constit. pecun., et Card., in Cle.* I *de baptis.,* to cite the authority of Salycetus, and of Jean Lemoyne. On entering, Bridlegoose found these lofty judges playing the old game of fly, a schoolboy favorite, in which one person plays the part of the fly, and the others strike at him, as though to drive him off. This salubrious exercise was indulged in before or after dinner.

To be sure, it was altogether indifferent to Bridlegoose at which time they chose to play, *hic not.* (It must here be observed that this game is honest, healthy, time-hallowed and legal.) *A Musco inventore, de quo C., de petit. haered., l. si post motam.* And *Muscarii* (which some take to mean musk-vendors, but others to mean fly-layers from *musca,* the Latin for fly) were excusable by law in *l.* I. *C., de excus. artif., lib.* X.

Bridlegoose recalled that Master Tielman Picquet was "it"; he would never forget Picquet's laughter, as the gentlemen of the court ruined their caps, swatting him with them. Amid guffaws of mirth, he told them that this banging of their caps did not excuse them, when they returned home, from satisfying their wives, according to *c.* I. *extra., de praesump., et ibi gl.*

"Now, *resolutorie loquendo,*" said Bridlegoose, "I should say, as you gentlemen might, that there is no exercise more fragrant, in this jurisprudential universe, than the emptying of bags, the thumbing of briefs, the consultation of documents, the filling of baskets, and the examination of cases. I cite for confirmation *ex Bart. et Jo. de Pra., in l. falsa de condit. et demon. ff.,* invoking both Bartolo, as before, and Joannes de Prato, the Florentine jurist of the last century."

(3) Bridlegoose's last reason for studying the documents involved a question of time. Like the gentlemen now sitting in judgment upon him, he realized that time brought all things to maturity. Time made everything clear; time was the father of truth, as Aulus Gellius' old poet said: *Gl. in l. I. C. de servit., Autent., de restit. et ea quae pa., et Spec. tit. de requis. cons,* merely went to confirm this.

"Accordingly, like yourselves, gentlemen, I put off, delay and postpone my definitive sentence, so that the suit, having been thoroughly sifted, winnowed and thrashed out, may, in process of time, attain its full maturity. Thus, when the fatal throw of the dice takes place, the condemned party will bear its misfortune more cheerfully, according to *no. glo. ff. de excu. tut., l. Tria onera:*

> *Portatur leviter, quod portat quisque libenter.*
>
> *A load borne willing is light to bear.*"

On the contrary, sentence passed when the suit is crude, unripe, and in its earliest stages, would cause the same discomfort as, according to physicians, prematurely lancing an abscess, or purging the human body of a peccant humor before its digestion. Was it not written in *Autent., Haec constit. in inno, const., prin.,* and repeated in *gl. in c. Caeterum, extra., de jura. calum,* that:

> *Quod medicamenta morbis exhibent, hoc jura negotiis.*

Further, Nature admonished us to pluck fruits when they were ripe (see *Instit. de re. div. is ad quem, et ff. de act. empt. l. Julianus*) . . . to marry our daughters when they were ripe (see *ff. de donat inter vir. et uxor. l. cum hic status, si quia sponsa, et 27 q., I. c., sicut dict gl.*):

> *Jammatura thoris plenis adoleverat annis Virginitas.*
>
> *Virginity, now ripe in course of years, nuptial and full.* . . .

In conclusion, then, Nature warned us to do nothing save in full maturity, according to XXXIII. *q.* II. *ult. ex* XXXIII *d. c. ult.*

BRIDLEGOOSE TELLS THE STORY OF THE
MAN WHO SETTLED CASES

"In this connection," Bridlegoose continued, "I recall a man living at Smarve, near Ligugé, in the days I was a law student at Poitiers, under Professor Axiom, *Brocardium juris.* This man was called Perrin Dandin, or, as we should say, Tom Noddy. An honorable soul, who worked his land and sang in the church choir; a fellow of credit, about the age of most of yourselves, gentlemen. Well, Tom Noddy used to say that he had seen and known that great, worthy man, Council of Lateran: indeed, Tom Noddy remembered the large red hat Council of Lateran wore. He had also, he said, seen Council of Lateran's wife, the lady Pragmatic Sanction, with her broad blue satin ribbon and her huge jade beads.

"This worthy man used to settle more lawsuits than were ever tried in the court at Poitiers, in the auditory of Montmorillon, with its hundred parishes, and in the town hall at Parthenay-le-Vieux. Every dissension, difference or wrangle in Chauvigny, Nouaillé, Croutelles, Esgne, Ligugé, La Motte, Lusignan, Vivonne, Mezeaulx, Etables, and neighboring hamlets, was settled by Tom Noddy as by a supreme judge—though remember, he was no judge, but simply an honest man! May I draw your attention, on this head, gentlemen, to *Arg. in l. sed si unius, ff. de jureju., et de verb. oblig., l. continuus.*

"No hog killed in the region, but he had some part of the pork chops and sausage; no banquet, feast or wedding, no gossips' reunion or churching of woman, but he was present; no home or tavern but welcomed him. And why? To reconcile two parties at a variance. For Tom Noddy never settled a difference without first making the disputants drink together, as a token of reconciliation, amity and joy to come, *ut no. per doct., ff. de peri. et comm., rei vend. l. I,* which deals with the selling of wine.

"Tom Noddy had a son, Stephen or Steve. A lusty, roistering lad (so help me God!) who wanted to follow in his father's footsteps and reconcile litigants, for, as you know:

> *Saepe solet similis filius esse patri,*
> *Et sequitur leviter filia matris iter,*

> *The son is wont to be more like his father,*
> *The daughter following her mother, rather.*

"Gl., VI. *q.* I *c.: Si quis; g. de cons., d.* V. *c,* I. *fin.; et est no. per doct., C. de impu. et aliis subst., l. ult. et l. legitimae, ff. de stat. hom., gl. in l. quod si nolit, ff. de edil. ed., l. quis, C. ad le. Jul. majest. Excipio filios a moniali susceptos ex monacho, per gl. in c. Impudicas,* XXVII *q.* I., bears this out, but excepts the sons and daughters of monks and nuns.

"Indeed, Steve Noddy actually dared assume the title of settler-out-of-court.

"Now he was active and vigilant in this business, for *vigilantibus jura subveniunt, ex. l. pupillus, ff quae in fraud, cred., et idib. l. non enim, et instit. in procoemio,* to quote a law which justifies the watchful and penalizes the negligent. So much so, that he sniffed a difference, as in *ff. si quad. pau. fec., l. Agaso, gl, in verbo olfecit i. nasum ad culum posuit."*

(Here Bridlegoose referred to the law concerning a groom, whose horse sniffed at a mule, in an innyard. The mule kicked out, breaking the groom's leg. Could the groom sue the master of the mule? The law, defining *olfecit*—sniffed—as "placing nose against arse," ruled that he could.)

"Gentlemen," Bridlegoose went on, "Steve Noddy never got wind of a variance or dispute, but he intruded to accommodate the quarrellers. Now it is written in the *Second Epistle of St. Paul to the Thessalonians* that: *Qui non laborat non manducat,* if any would not work, neither should he eat. Further, *gl. ff. de dam. infect., l. quamvis, et currere* at a great pace:

Vetulam compellit egestas;

Necessity makes the old hag trot.

Consult, too, *gl. ff. de lib. agnos., l. Si quis pro qua facit; l. si plures, C. de cond. incer.* Yet in these undertakings, Steve Noddy was so unfortunate as to prove unable to settle even the most minor argument. Instead of reconciling the parties, he exasperated and antagonized them further. You know Dionysius Cato's distich, gentlemen:

Sermo datur cunctis, animi sapientia paucis,

and you know *gl. ff. de alie. ju. mu. caus. fa. l.* II.

"The innkeepers of Smarve vowed that, in one year of Steve Noddy's régime, they had not sold as much wine of reconciliation (so they called the Liguge tipple) as in a half-hour under his father's dispensation.

"Now some time later, Stephen happened to complain to his father, attributing the causes of his failure to the perversity of his contemporaries. The son roundly objected that, had the world formerly proved so wayward, refractory, quarrelsome and irreconcilable, Tom Noddy would not have won the honors and title of a perfect peacemaker. In this, Stephen was wrong, since the law forbids children to reproach their fathers: see *gl. et Bar., l,* III, § *Si quis ff. de condi. ob caus., et autene., de nup.,* § *Sed quod sancitum, coll.* IV.

"Tom Noddy then told his son Stephen that he should do otherwise. The old man quoted:

> *'Quand "oportet" vient en place,*
> *Il convient qu'ainsi se face,*

> *When Lord Necessity rules you,*
> *This is the course you should pursue'*

and I, Bridlegoose, draw your attention to *gl. C. de apell., l. eos etiam.* There lay the rub, gentlemen. Old Noddy reproached Stephen with never making peace. And why? Because Stephen attempted to handle these cases when they were green, raw, indigestible. Why had Tom Noddy always succeeded? Because he assumed responsibility when the variances were waning, coming to a head, pretty well digested. So says *gl.:*

> *Dulcior est fructus post multa pericula ductus,*

> *The sweetest fruit an orchard bears is one*
> *Which has known trials to bear and risks to run*

as you, gentlemen, know from *l. non moriturus, C. de contrah et comit. stip.*

"Did not Stephen know, Tom Noddy asked, the proverb which pronounced the physician happiest, when summoned at the decline of an illness? Such a malady would run its course, and solve its own problem, even were the medico not called in. Old Tom Noddy's cases would have found their own settlement in a last plea, since the litigants' purses were drained; plaintiff and defense would have given over, since there was no cash in hand to prosecute or defend:

> *Deficiente pecu, deficit omne, nia.*

> *Money lacking, all is lacking.*

"The only thing needed then was a paranymph, to act like the best man at a wedding, or like the sponsor of a candidate for a degree. Let such a man but broach the question of an agreement, and each party would be spared the pernicious shame of believing that the other would accuse it of yielding first, of apologizing because it was in the wrong, of coming to terms because it felt the shoe pinching.

"At such a juncture, old Tom Noddy arrived as seasonably as peas with bacon, or as parsley with fish; here lay his advantage and his luck. And he assured his splendid son that, by following the same system, he could establish peace, or at least make a truce, between the great king Louis XII and the Venetians, or between the Emperor and the Swiss, or between the English and the Scots, or between the Pope and the Duke of Ferrara. Need Tom Noddy go further? Ay, he could, with God's help, reconcile the Turkish sultan and the Persian shah, the Muscovite czar and the Tartar chieftains.

"Tom Noddy impressed this fact upon his son: he would approach these powers when both were weary of war; when their treasuries were empty; when their subjects' purses were drained; when their domains were sold; when their property was mortgaged; when their provisions and munitions were exhausted. Then, at this precise moment, by God or by His Mother! they would be forced to take a breathing spell, to curb the fury of their wicked ambition. Such was the doctrine of *gl.* XXXVII *d. c. S. quando:*

> *Odero si potero; si non, invitus amabo.*
>
> *If hate I can, I will; but otherwise*
> *Reluctant, I shall look with loving eyes."*

HOW LAWSUITS ARE SPAWNED AND HOW THEY ATTAIN FULL GROWTH

Bridlegoose's address continued as follows:

"That, gentlemen, is why, like yourselves, I temporize, awaiting a lawsuit's maturity and its full growth in all its limbs—that is, in its documents and the bags they are kept in. Here I base my stand upon *Arg. in l. si major., C. commu. divi. et de cons., d.* I. *c. Solennitates, et ibi gl.*

"A suit at its birth seems to me—and to you, also, gentlemen—formless and imperfect. A bear, newborn, has neither feet, nor hands, nor skin, nor hair, nor head; by dint of maternal licking, it attains perfection in all its limbs. See *no. doct., ff. ad leg. Aquil., l.* II, *in fi.* Similarly, like yourselves, gentlemen, I attend the birth of a lawsuit. To begin with, it is shapeless, and without distinct limbs. It consists of but one or two documents; it is, in this state, an ugly beast. But heap writ upon writ, pack and pile brief upon brief, and your lawsuit may be termed full-sinewed and well-boned, since *forma dat esse rei, l. Si is qui, ff. ad. leg. § Falci, in c. cum dilecta, extra., de rescrip.; Barbatia, consil. 12., lib. 2* and before him *Bald. in c. ulti. extra de consue., et l. Julianus, ff. ad exib.,* and *l. Quaesitum, ff. de lega.* III."

(Here Bridlegoose quoted Barbatia and Petrus Baldus, both Italian jurisconsults of the fifteenth and fourteenth century respectively.)

"The manner of this is set down in *gl. p. q.* I. *c. Paulus:*

> *Debile principium melior fortuna sequetur.*

"Just as you yourselves, gentlemen, the sergeants, ushers, summoners, pettifoggers, attorneys, commissioners, advocates, judges of the peace, tabellions or notaries, clerks, scribes and pedestrian judges (I mean the judges of minor courts compelled to walk to and from the tribunal) *de quibus tit, est lib.* III *Cod.,* draw vigorously and continuously upon the purses of the litigants, licking here and there, until they equip the suits with head, feet, claws, beak, teeth, hands, veins, arteries, nerves, muscles and humors. These are, in so many words, the bags containing their writs, as you may read in *gl. de cons. de* IV. *c. accepisti:*

> *Qualis vestis erit, talia corda gerit.*

"*Hic not,* gentlemen, note here that, in this respect, the litigants are happier than the officers of justice, since *beatius est dare quam accipere, ff. comm., l.* III. *et extra. de celebra, miss., c. cum Marthae, et 24 q. j. c. Odi gl.:*

> *Affectum dantis pensat censura tonantis.*

"In this way, then, lawsuits grow to be well rounded, full of charm and fairly fashioned, or, as the canonical gloss expresses it:

> *Accipe, sume, cape sunt verba placentia Papae,*
>
> *To take, accept, receive in goodly measure*
> *Are things that give a Pope the greatest pleasure,*

which Alberic de Rosata says more pointedly in *Verb. Roma:*

> *Roma manus rodit; quas rodere non valet, odit;*
> *Dantes custodit; non dantes spernit et odit.*

And why, gentlemen? Simply because:

"Ad praesens ova cras pullis sunt meliora, to-day's eggs are better than to-morrow's hens, and one bird in hand is worth two in the bush. This we know from *gl. in l. Cum hi, ff. de transac.* The inconvenience of the contrary is set down in *gl. c. de allu., l. F.:*

> *Cum labor in damno est, crescit mortalis egestas.*
>
> *When work is wasted, human need increases.*

"The true meaning of the word *lawsuit* is something that suits the lawyer; legal procedure means something ceded or yielded *pro,* to the benefit of, the judge. We have a glorious quip to celebrate it:

> *Litigando jura crescunt;*
> *Litigando jus acquiritur;*

and, indeed, the body of the law swells as cases are pleaded, just as the bodies of lawyer and judge swell, too. *Item gl. in c. illud, ext. de praesumpt., et C. de prob., l. instrumenta, l. Non nudis;*

> *Et, cum non prosunt singula, multa juvant,*
>
> *Singly, things fail; united they prevail."*

"Very good, very good," Blusterer interjected. "But, my friend, pray tell the court how you proceed in a criminal case when the guilty party was seized in *flagrante crimine?"*

"Exactly as you, gentlemen," Bridlegoose made answer. "I permit the plaintiff to leave the court; I urge him, as an introductory measure, to take a long sleep. Before reappearing in my presence, he is warned to submit a valid, duly certified statement of his sleep, following *gl. 32 q.* VII, *c. Si quis cum,*

> *Quandoque bonus dormitat Homerus*

or, as Horace says, even Homer nods now and again.

"This mere action brings on some further development, which, in turn, produces still another, just as, link by link, you fashion a coat-of-mail. Gradually, document by document, the suit grows, until, eventually, it is perfectly formed in all its members. I then return to my dice. Nor, indeed, do I intervene at this point without considerable reason or experience."

In confirmation, Bridlegoose told a story about a certain Gascon in camp at Stockholm. Gratianauld, the fellow was called; he hailed from

St. Sever. Having gambled away all his pay, he was furious, for, as Bridle-goose's judges knew, *pecunia est alter sanguis,* money is a man's very lifeblood, as is proved by *Anto. de Butrio in c. accedens.,* II, *extra., ut lit. non contest., et Bald. in l. si tuis., C. de op. li. per no., et l. advocati, C. de advo. div. jud.: Pecunia est vita hominis et optimus fidejussor in necessitatibus:* money is man's life, and his best counselor in an emergency.

The gambling ended, Gratianauld then said loudly in his Gascon dialect:

"*Pao cap de bious, hillotz, que maulx de pipe bous tresbyre; ares que pergudes sont les mies bingt et quouatte baguettes, ta pla donnerien picz, trucz et patactz. Sey degun de bous aulx qui boille truquar ambe iou à belz embiz?*"

This meant:

"God's head, my hearties, may the blindest drunkenness ever distilled in barrel knock you over! Now that I have lost my two dozen coppers, I might as well give you what for, with fist, cuff and kick! Is there one man among you, who will fight me, man to man? By God, I challenge the lot of you!"

Since no one answered him, he passed on to the camp of the hundred-pounders or German lansquenets, repeating the same words, and inviting them to combat. But they merely replied:

"*Der Guascongner thut schich usz mitt eim jedem ze schlagen, aber er ist geneigter zu staelen; darumb, lieben fravven, hend serg zu inuerm hausraut:* the Gascon makes as if to fight everybody, but he is more apt to steal from us; therefore, dear wives, keep an eye on our luggage."

So none of their race offered to take on our Gascon.

Next, he repaired to the camp of the French adventurers, speaking as before, and gaily challenging them, to the accompaniment of various Gasconado gambols. Here, too, no one replied.

At last, at the end of the camp, he lay down, close to the tent of fat Christian, Knight of Crissé. Here he fell fast asleep.

Suddenly, a French freelance, who had lost all his money too, determined to fight with the Gascon.

> *Ploratur lachrymis amissa pecunia veris.*
>
> *With genuine tears, he wept his vanished cash.*

Bridlegoose here cited *glos. de paenitent. dist. 3, c. Sunt plures.*

Having roamed the camp with drawn sword, the Frenchman at last came upon the sleeping Gascon.

"Ho, lad!" he cried, "get up, in the devil's name! I've lost all my money just as you have. Let us fight lustily and have at one another, clapperclaw. Take care my sword isn't longer than your rapier!"

The Gascon, in a daze, replied:

"*Cap de sainct Arnault, quau seys tu, qui me rebeillez? Que mau de taoverne te gyre. Ho, sainct Siobé, cap de Guascoigne, ta pla dormis iou, quand aquoest taquain me bingut estée.*"

Which, being interpreted, meant:

"By St. Arnold's noddle, who are you, waking me up like that? May a drunken rheumatism floor you! Ho, by St. Sever, patron of Gascony, I was sound asleep when the scoundrel woke me up!"

Again, the Frenchman invited him to fight, but the Gascon replied:

"My poor lad, I would make mincemeat of you, now that I have rested. Lie down there and take a nap, as I did. Afterwards, we can fight."

Having forgotten his losses, he had lost all his pugnacity. In conclusion, instead of fighting and probably killing each other, they went off and drank together, each pawning his sword to do so.

"It was sleep," Bridlegoose wound up, "which accomplished this miracle, and pacified the arrant fury of two contentious champions. Here I remind you, gentlemen, of the golden words of Jean André in *c. ult. de sent. et re judic., libro sexto: Sedendo et quiescendo fit anima prudens,* the spirit is made wise by rest and repose."

HOW PANTAGRUEL VINDICATED BRIDLEGOOSE'S JUDGMENT BY DICE

When Bridlegoose had stopped talking, Blusterer ordered him to withdraw from the court. This was done. Then Blusterer addressed Pantagruel:

"O most august prince, this parliament, sitting as the highest court of justice, and the marquisate of Miralingua, which it represents, are mightily beholden to you. We are beholden, not only for your generous benefactions, but also for the sound judgment and the admirable learning, with which Almighty God, dispenser of all good things, has endowed you. Reason therefore demands that we ask you for your decision in this extraordinary, paradoxical and unparalleled case. Bridlegoose, in your presence, sight and hearing, has confessed that he passed judgment, according to the turn of the dice. We humbly beseech you to pass whatever sentence you may deem just and equitable."

"Gentlemen," Pantagruel replied, "you know very well that, in my condition, I can scarcely profess to pass judgment in matters of controversy. However, since you are pleased to pay me such honor, instead of acting as judge, allow me to act as suppliant.

"I observe, in the person of Bridlegoose, certain virtues which, on their own account, would seem to merit pardon. In the first place, gentlemen, he is an old man. Secondly, consider his simplicity. Both age and simplicity are, I should say, qualities deserving of pardon and excuse by our own laws. In the third place, I find yet another legal reason that pleads in Bridlegoose's favor. Why not let this one and only error of his be washed out, effaced, and annihilated in the immense sea of the equitable decisions he has handed down in the past? Why not forget it, and remember the forty long years of a career, during which no single reprehensible act has ever been brought up against him? It is as though I were to throw one drop of salt water into the river Loire: no one would feel it, no one would recognize it as salty. I cannot help thinking that God's intervention was manifest, since the whole series of Bridlegoose's decrees, before this last one, was approved and ratified by your venerable and sovereign court. I might add that He often wishes His glory to appear in the dulling of the wise, in the fall of the mighty, in the exalting of the meek and humble.

"You mentioned obligations you owed my family; I do not recognize them. I prefer to invoke the time-hallowed affection you have known us to bear you, on either side of the Loire, in the maintenance of your dignity and office. On that score, and omitting the three legal considerations I established before, I would beg you, for once, to grant Bridlegoose your pardon. Conditionally, I hasten to add; and on the following conditions.

"First, he shall give or promise satisfaction to the party wronged by his sentence. (I will provide for this myself, and amply.) Secondly, I suggest you appoint a young, learned, wise, skillful and honorable attorney, to assist him in his judiciary office. Let this junior officer's deliberation and counsel decide finally, henceforth, all cases brought before the court.

"If, of course, you decide to remove Bridlegoose wholly from the bench, I beg you to make me a free present and gift of him. Within my realm and dominion, I can find room and place to employ him and utilize his services.

"In conclusion, gentlemen, I shall implore Almighty God, our beneficent creator, and the dispenser of all blessings, to maintain you forever in His mercy and grace."

Concluding, Pantagruel bowed to the court and withdrew from the hall. At the door, Panurge, Epistemon, Friar John and the rest were waiting for him; they mounted their horses and returned to Gargantua.

On the way, Pantagruel related the story of Bridlegoose's trial, point by point. Friar John said he had known Tom Noddy in the days when he lived at the Abbey of Fontenay-le-Comte, under the noble Abbot Ardillon. Gymnastes testified that Tom Noddy was in the tent of the fat Christian, Chevalier de Crissé, when the Gascon challenged the French adventurer. Panurge displayed incredulity at the success of Bridlegoose's aleatory justice over so long a period. Epistemon said:

"A similar story is told of a certain Provost of Montlhéry. But what extraordinary luck to continue successfully for so many years! I would not be amazed at one or two chance decisions, especially in ambiguous, equivocal, intricate, perplexing and obscure cases. But forty years . . . !"

PANTAGRUEL'S STRANGE TALE OF THE PERPLEXITIES OF HUMAN JUDGMENT

Pantagruel then told them the following story of a controversy debated before Caius Dolabella, proconsul in Asia.

A married woman gave birth to a child named Abeecee. Shortly after her husband's death, she married again, bearing his successor a son, named Eefgee. Now the affection that stepfathers and stepmothers bear children of earlier marriages is proverbial. In this case, it ran true to form. The stepfather and his own son trapped Abeecee in an ambush and killed him.

Having discovered their treachery and wickedness, the mother determined to punish them; accordingly, she slew both, thus avenging her firstborn. She was at once apprehended and brought before Caius Dolabella. There, unabashed, she faced the issue squarely, confessing her crime, and maintaining that she was logically and legally justified. Such, then, was the crux of the trial.

The proconsul found the problem so thorny that he was at a loss. The woman's crime was, to be sure, a most serious one, since she had killed her second husband and their son. Yet the cause of this double murder seemed to Dolabella to be quite natural, and grounded upon the rights of nations. Had they not premeditated the murder of Abeecee? And why? Not because he had insulted or injured them but solely to possess his inheritance.

In order to settle the case, Dolabella sent to the Areopagites at Athens, asking them their opinion. This court, for reply, suggested that, in a hundred years, the contestants be personally cited before them, to reply to certain questions which had been left out of the record. It amounted to saying that they were so perplexed at so inextricable a problem, that they were at a loss as to what to say or do.

"Whatever happened," said Pentagruel, "judgment by dice could not have proved wrong. If luck had gone against the wife after all, she deserved to be punished for taking into her hands a vengeance that belonged to the state. If luck had favored her, the decision would have seemed to be based upon the wrong done her, and her mad grief. The only thing that astonishes me is how Bridlegoose was able to remain lucky for so many years."

"I must own, I could not answer your question categorically," said Epistemon. "But, conjecturally, I would attribute Bridlegoose's luck in his decisions to a favorable aspect of the heavens, and to the intervention of spiritual forces. Bridlegoose was kindly and sincere; he mistrusted his knowledge and capacity; he knew the antinomies and contradictions of laws, decrees, statutes and ordinances. He was also aware of the trickery, by which the infernal calumniator transforms himself into an angel of light, through the person of his minions: dishonest lawyers, attorneys, counselors and other like tools. He knew Satan could turn black into white, make each of two parties believe itself right. Has the most shadowy case ever lacked a lawyer to carry it into court? How else would lawsuits flourish in this, our world? Were it not so, the equitable judge would commend himself humbly to God; he would invoke the help of heavenly grace; he would be governed by the sacrosanct spirit, by chance, by the perplexity of the definitive sentence. By this lot, he would seek counsel of his decree and of his own good pleasure, which we call an unbiased judgment of the court. Ay, and what I called spiritual forces—the motory intelligences—would make the dice fall the way of the upright party in a lawsuit; they would support justice, maintaining the righteous in his cause, as the rabbis have it. In this way, chance would harbor no harm; on the contrary, through dice, the divine spirit would work to dissipate the doubts and anxieties of men."

Epistemon realized that the officials of the Miralinguan parliament of Miralingua were obviously iniquitous and corrupt. Yet he refused to think, say or believe that they could, under any circumstance, consider judgment by hazard worse than such judgment as they themselves, with their bloody hands and perverse hearts, might possibly decree.

What made the abuse even more glaring was that their jurisdiction was ruled by Tribonian, an evil, perfidious barbarian; a man so corrupt, malign and iniquitous as to sell laws, edicts, bills, constitutions and ordinances at public auction, cash down, to the highest bidder. Piece by piece, scrap by scrap, Tribonian had drawn up their mincemeat code, suppressing and abolishing the whole law, the meat and body and spirit of right. For he feared that the latter might remain permanent, like the works of ancient jurisconsults, as immortalized in the Twelve Tables and the Praetorian edicts. This would have exposed to the entire world his dishonesty and baseness.

Therefore, it would often prove better—or less harmful, at any rate—for parties at variance at law, to walk upon caltrops (spikes set on the ground to maim cavalry horses) than to appeal to such courts for rightful redress.

Indeed, Cato, in his time, wished and advised that the law courts be paved with caltrops.

Joseph Sheridan Le Fanu

:

MR. JUSTICE HARBOTTLE

On this case, Doctor Hesselius has inscribed nothing more than the words, "Harman's Report," and a simple reference to his own extraordinary Essay on "the Interior Sense, and the Conditions of the opening thereof."

The reference is to Vol. I. Section 317, Note Z^a. The note to which reference is thus made, simply says: "There are two accounts of the remarkable case of the Honorable Mr. Justice Harbottle, one furnished to me by Mrs. Trimmer of Tunbridge Wells (June, 1805); the other at a much later date, by Anthony Harman, Esq. I much prefer the former; in the first place, because it is minute and detailed, and written, it seems to me, with more caution and knowledge; and in the next, because the letters from Doctor Hedstone, which are embodied in it, furnish matter of the highest value to a right apprehension of the nature of the case. It was one of the best declared cases of an opening of the interior sense, which I have met with. It was affected, too, by the phenomenon, which occurs so frequently as to indicate a law of these eccentric conditions; that is to say, it exhibited, what I may term, the contagious character of this sort of intrusion of the spirit-world upon the proper domain of matter. So soon as the spirit-action has established itself in the case of one patient, its developed energy begins to radiate, more or less effectually, upon others. The interior vision of

620

forlorn and deserted state, I can tell you in a general way what it was like. It was built of dark-red brick, and the door and windows were faced with stone that had turned yellow by time. It receded some feet from the line of the other houses in the street; and it had a florid and fanciful rail of iron about the broad steps that invited your ascent to the hall-door, in which were fixed, under a file of lamps, among scrolls and twisted leaves, two immense "extinguishers" like the conical caps of fairies, into which, in old times, the footmen used to thrust their flambeaux when their chairs or coaches had set down their great people, in the hall or at the steps, as the case might be. That hall is paneled up to the ceiling, and has a large fireplace. Two or three stately old rooms open from it at each side. The windows of these are tall, with many small panes. Passing through the arch at the back of the hall, you come upon the wide and heavy well-staircase. There is a back staircase also. The mansion is large, and has not as much light, by any means, in proportion to its extent, as modern houses enjoy. When I saw it, it had long been untenanted, and had the gloomy reputation beside of a haunted house. Cobwebs floated from the ceilings or spanned the corners of the cornices, and dust lay thick over everything. The windows were stained with the dust and rain of fifty years, and darkness had thus grown darker.

When I made it my first visit, it was in company with my father, when I was still a boy, in the year 1808. I was about twelve years old, and my imagination impressible, as it always is at that age. I looked about me with great awe. I was here in the very center and scene of those occurrences which I had heard recounted at the fireside at home, with so delightful a horror.

My father was an old bachelor of nearly sixty when he married. He had, when a child, seen Judge Harbottle on the bench in his robes and wig a dozen times at least before his death, which took place in 1748, and his appearance made a powerful and unpleasant impression, not only on his imagination, but upon his nerves.

The Judge was at that time a man of some sixty-seven years. He had a great mulberry-colored face, a big, carbuncled nose, fierce eyes, and a grim and brutal mouth. My father, who was young at the time, thought it the most formidable face he had ever seen; for there were evidences of intellectual power in the formation and lines of the forehead. His voice was loud and harsh, and gave effect to the sarcasm which was his habitual weapon on the bench.

the child was opened; as was, also, that of its mother, Mrs. Pyneweck; and both the interior vision and hearing of the scullery-maid, were opened on the same occasion. After-appearances are the result of the law explained in Vol. II. Section 17 to 49. The common center of association, simultaneously recalled, unites, or *re*-unites, as the case may be, for a period measured, as we see, in Section 37. The *maximum* will extend to days, the *minimum* is little more than a second. We see the operation of this principle perfectly displayed, in certain cases of lunacy, of epilepsy, of catalepsy, and of mania, of a peculiar and painful character, though unattended by incapacity of business."

The memorandum of the case of Judge Harbottle, which was written by Mrs. Trimmer of Tunbridge Wells, which Doctor Hesselius thought the better of the two, I have been unable to discover among his papers. I found in his escritoire a note to the effect that he had lent the Report of Judge Harbottle's case, written by Mrs. Trimmer to Doctor F. Heyne. To that learned and able gentleman accordingly I wrote, and received from him, in his reply, which was full of alarms and regrets on account of the uncertain safety of that "valuable MS.," a line written long since by Doctor Hesselius, which completely exonerated him, inasmuch as it acknowledged the safe return of the papers. The Narrative of Mr. Harman, is, therefore, the only one available for this collection. The late Dr. Hesselius, in another passage of the note that I have cited, says, "As to the facts (non-medical) of the case, the narrative of Mr. Harman exactly tallies with that furnished by Mrs. Trimmer." The strictly scientific view of the case would scarcely interest the popular reader; and, possibly, for the purposes of this selection, I should, even had I both papers to choose between, have preferred that of Mr. Harman, which is given, in full, in the following pages.

CHAPTER I

The Judge's House

Thirty years ago, an elderly man, to whom I paid quarterly a small annuity charged on some property of mine, came on the quarter-day to receive it. He was a dry, sad, quiet man, who had known better days, and had always maintained an unexceptionable character. No better authority could be imagined for a ghost story.

He told me one, though with a manifest reluctance; he was drawn into the narration by his choosing to explain what I should not have remarked, that he had called two days earlier than that week after the strict day of payment, which he had usually allowed to elapse. His reason was a sudden determination to change his lodgings, and the consequent necessity of paying his rent a little before it was due.

He lodged in a dark street in Westminster, in a spacious old house, very warm, being wainscoted from top to bottom, and furnished with no undue abundance of windows, and those fitted with thick sashes and small panes.

This house was, as the bills upon the windows testified, offered to be sold or let. But no one seemed to care to look at it.

A thin matron, in rusty black silk, very taciturn, with large, steady, alarmed eyes, that seemed to look in your face, to read what you might have seen in the dark rooms and passages through which you had passed, was in charge of it, with a solitary "maid-of-all-work" under her command. My poor friend had taken lodgings in this house, on account of their extraordinary cheapness. He had occupied them for nearly a year without the slightest disturbance, and was the only tenant, under rent, in the house. He had two rooms; a sitting-room, and a bedroom with a closet opening from it, in which he kept his books and papers locked up. He had gone to his bed, having also locked the outer door. Unable to sleep, he had lighted a candle, and after having read for a time, had laid the book beside him. He heard the old clock at the stair-head strike one; and very shortly after, to his alarm, he saw the closet-door, which he thought he had locked, open stealthily, and a slight dark man, particularly sinister, and somewhere about fifty, dressed in mourning of a very antique fashion, such a suit as we see in Hogarth, entered the room on tip-toe. He was followed by an elder man, stout, and blotched with scurvy, and whose features, fixed as a corpse's, were stamped with dreadful force with a character of sensuality and villainy.

This old man wore a flowered-silk dressing-gown and ruffles, and he remarked a gold ring on his finger, and on his head a cap of velvet, such as, in the days of perukes, gentlemen wore in undress.

This direful old man carried in his ringed and ruffled hand a coil of rope; and these two figures crossed the floor diagonally, passing the foot of his bed, from the closet-door at the farther end of the room, at the left, near the window, to the door opening upon the lobby, close to the bed's head, at his right.

He did not attempt to describe his sensations as these figures passed so near him. He merely said, that so far from sleeping in that room again, no consideration the world could offer would induce him so much as to enter it again alone, even in the daylight. He found both doors, that of the closet, and that of the room opening upon the lobby, in the morning fast locked, as he had left them before going to bed.

In answer to a question of mine, he said that neither appeared the least conscious of his presence. They did not seem to glide, but walked as living men do, but without any sound, and he felt a vibration on the floor as they crossed it. He so obviously suffered from speaking about the apparitions, that I asked him no more questions.

There were in his description, however, certain coincidences so very singular, as to induce me, by that very post, to write to a friend much my senior, then living in a remote part of England, for the information which I knew he could give me. He had himself more than once pointed out that old house to my attention, and told me, though very briefly, the strange story which I now asked him to give me in greater detail.

His answer satisfied me; and the following pages convey its su[b]stance.

Your letter (he wrote) tells me you desire some particulars a[bout] the closing years of the life of Mr. Justice Harbottle, one of the [ ] of the Court of Common Pleas. You refer, of course, to the [extraor]dinary occurrences that made that period of his life long [a] theme for "winter tales" and metaphysical speculation. I [ ] know perhaps more than any other man living of those [ ] particulars.

The old family mansion, when I revisited Londo[n] thirty years ago, I examined for the last time. During [ ] have passed since then, I hear that improvement, wi[th] demolitions, has been doing wonders for the quarter [in] which it stood. If I were quite certain that the ho[use was pulled] down, I should have no difficulty about naming [the street in which it] stood. As what I have to tell, however, is not li[ ] ting value, and as I should not care to get into [ ] lent on that particular point.

How old the house was, I can't tell. Peopl[e] [said] Harbottle, a Turkey merchant, in the reign [of] good opinion upon such questions; but h[e] the child was opened; as was, also, that of its mother, Mrs. Pyneweck; and both the interior vision and hearing of the scullery-maid, were opened on the same occasion. After-appearances are the result of the law explained in Vol. II. Section 17 to 49. The common center of association, simultaneously recalled, unites, or *re*-unites, as the case may be, for a period measured, as we see, in Section 37. The *maximum* will extend to days, the *minimum* is little more than a second. We see the operation of this principle perfectly displayed, in certain cases of lunacy, of epilepsy, of catalepsy, and of mania, of a peculiar and painful character, though unattended by incapacity of business."

The memorandum of the case of Judge Harbottle, which was written by Mrs. Trimmer of Tunbridge Wells, which Doctor Hesselius thought the better of the two, I have been unable to discover among his papers. I found in his escritoire a note to the effect that he had lent the Report of Judge Harbottle's case, written by Mrs. Trimmer to Doctor F. Heyne. To that learned and able gentleman accordingly I wrote, and received from him, in his reply, which was full of alarms and regrets on account of the uncertain safety of that "valuable MS.," a line written long since by Doctor Hesselius, which completely exonerated him, inasmuch as it acknowledged the safe return of the papers. The Narrative of Mr. Harman, is, therefore, the only one available for this collection. The late Dr. Hesselius, in another passage of the note that I have cited, says, "As to the facts (non-medical) of the case, the narrative of Mr. Harman exactly tallies with that furnished by Mrs. Trimmer." The strictly scientific view of the case would scarcely interest the popular reader; and, possibly, for the purposes of this selection, I should, even had I both papers to choose between, have preferred that of Mr. Harman, which is given, in full, in the following pages.

CHAPTER I

The Judge's House

Thirty years ago, an elderly man, to whom I paid quarterly a small annuity charged on some property of mine, came on the quarter-day to receive it. He was a dry, sad, quiet man, who had known better days, and had always maintained an unexceptionable character. No better authority could be imagined for a ghost story.

He told me one, though with a manifest reluctance; he was drawn into the narration by his choosing to explain what I should not have re-marked, that he had called two days earlier than that week after the strict day of payment, which he had usually allowed to elapse. His rea-son was a sudden determination to change his lodgings, and the con-sequent necessity of paying his rent a little before it was due.

He lodged in a dark street in Westminster, in a spacious old house, very warm, being wainscoted from top to bottom, and furnished with no undue abundance of windows, and those fitted with thick sashes and small panes.

This house was, as the bills upon the windows testified, offered to be sold or let. But no one seemed to care to look at it.

A thin matron, in rusty black silk, very taciturn, with large, steady, alarmed eyes, that seemed to look in your face, to read what you might have seen in the dark rooms and passages through which you had passed, was in charge of it, with a solitary "maid-of-all-work" under her command. My poor friend had taken lodgings in this house, on ac-count of their extraordinary cheapness. He had occupied them for nearly a year without the slightest disturbance, and was the only tenant, under rent, in the house. He had two rooms; a sitting-room, and a bed-room with a closet opening from it, in which he kept his books and papers locked up. He had gone to his bed, having also locked the outer door. Unable to sleep, he had lighted a candle, and after hav-ing read for a time, had laid the book beside him. He heard the old clock at the stair-head strike one; and very shortly after, to his alarm, he saw the closet-door, which he thought he had locked, open stealthily, and a slight dark man, particularly sinister, and somewhere about fifty, dressed in mourning of a very antique fashion, such a suit as we see in Hogarth, entered the room on tip-toe. He was followed by an elder man, stout, and blotched with scurvy, and whose features, fixed as a corpse's, were stamped with dreadful force with a character of sensuality and villainy.

This old man wore a flowered-silk dressing-gown and ruffles, and he remarked a gold ring on his finger, and on his head a cap of velvet, such as, in the days of perukes, gentlemen wore in undress.

This direful old man carried in his ringed and ruffled hand a coil of rope; and these two figures crossed the floor diagonally, passing the foot of his bed, from the closet-door at the farther end of the room, at the left, near the window, to the door opening upon the lobby, close to the bed's head, at his right.

He did not attempt to describe his sensations as these figures passed so near him. He merely said, that so far from sleeping in that room again, no consideration the world could offer would induce him so much as to enter it again alone, even in the daylight. He found both doors, that of the closet, and that of the room opening upon the lobby, in the morning fast locked, as he had left them before going to bed.

In answer to a question of mine, he said that neither appeared the least conscious of his presence. They did not seem to glide, but walked as living men do, but without any sound, and he felt a vibration on the floor as they crossed it. He so obviously suffered from speaking about the apparitions, that I asked him no more questions.

There were in his description, however, certain coincidences so very singular, as to induce me, by that very post, to write to a friend much my senior, then living in a remote part of England, for the information which I knew he could give me. He had himself more than once pointed out that old house to my attention, and told me, though very briefly, the strange story which I now asked him to give me in greater detail.

His answer satisfied me; and the following pages convey its substance.

Your letter (he wrote) tells me you desire some particulars about the closing years of the life of Mr. Justice Harbottle, one of the judges of the Court of Common Pleas. You refer, of course, to the extraordinary occurrences that made that period of his life long after a theme for "winter tales" and metaphysical speculation. I happen to know perhaps more than any other man living of those mysterious particulars.

The old family mansion, when I revisited London, more than thirty years ago, I examined for the last time. During the years that have passed since then, I hear that improvement, with its preliminary demolitions, has been doing wonders for the quarter of Westminister in which it stood. If I were quite certain that the house had been taken down, I should have no difficulty about naming the street in which it stood. As what I have to tell, however, is not likely to improve its letting value, and as I should not care to get into trouble, I prefer being silent on that particular point.

How old the house was, I can't tell. People said it was built by Roger Harbottle, a Turkey merchant, in the reign of King James I. I am not a good opinion upon such questions; but having been in it, though in its forlorn and deserted state, I can tell you in a general way what it was like. It was built of dark-red brick, and the door and windows were faced with stone that had turned yellow by time. It receded some feet from the line of the other houses in the street; and it had a florid and fanciful rail of iron about the broad steps that invited your ascent to the hall-door, in which were fixed, under a file of lamps, among scrolls and twisted leaves, two immense "extinguishers" like the conical caps of fairies, into which, in old times, the footmen used to thrust their flambeaux when their chairs or coaches had set down their great people, in the hall or at the steps, as the case might be. That hall is paneled up to the ceiling, and has a large fireplace. Two or three stately old rooms open from it at each side. The windows of these are tall, with many small panes. Passing through the arch at the back of the hall, you come upon the wide and heavy well-staircase. There is a back staircase also. The mansion is large, and has not as much light, by any means, in proportion to its extent, as modern houses enjoy. When I saw it, it had long been untenanted, and had the gloomy reputation beside of a haunted house. Cobwebs floated from the ceilings or spanned the corners of the cornices, and dust lay thick over everything. The windows were stained with the dust and rain of fifty years, and darkness had thus grown darker.

When I made it my first visit, it was in company with my father, when I was still a boy, in the year 1808. I was about twelve years old, and my imagination impressible, as it always is at that age. I looked about me with great awe. I was here in the very center and scene of those occurrences which I had heard recounted at the fireside at home, with so delightful a horror.

My father was an old bachelor of nearly sixty when he married. He had, when a child, seen Judge Harbottle on the bench in his robes and wig a dozen times at least before his death, which took place in 1748, and his appearance made a powerful and unpleasant impression, not only on his imagination, but upon his nerves.

The Judge was at that time a man of some sixty-seven years. He had a great mulberry-colored face, a big, carbuncled nose, fierce eyes, and a grim and brutal mouth. My father, who was young at the time, thought it the most formidable face he had ever seen; for there were evidences of intellectual power in the formation and lines of the forehead. His voice was loud and harsh, and gave effect to the sarcasm which was his habitual weapon on the bench.

This old gentleman had the reputation of being about the wickedest man in England. Even on the bench he now and then showed his scorn of opinion. He had carried cases his own way, it was said, in spite of counsel, authorities, and even of juries, by a sort of cajolery, violence, and bamboozling, that somehow confused and overpowered resistance. He had never actually committed himself; he was too cunning to do that. He had the character of being, however, a dangerous and unscrupulous judge; but his character did not trouble him. The associates he chose for his hours of relaxation cared as little as he did about it.

CHAPTER II

Mr. Peters

One night during the session of 1746 this old Judge went down in his chair to wait in one of the rooms of the House of Lords for the result of a division in which he and his order were interested.

This over, he was about to return to his house close by, in his chair; but the night had become so soft and fine that he changed his mind, sent it home empty, and with two footmen, each with a flambeau, set out on foot in preference. Gout had made him rather a slow pedestrian. It took him some time to get through the two or three streets he had to pass before reaching his house.

In one of those narrow streets of tall houses, perfectly silent at that hour, he overtook, slowly as he was walking, a very singular-looking old gentleman.

He had a bottle-green coat on, with a cape to it, and large stone buttons, a broad-leafed low-crowned hat, from under which a big powdered wig escaped; he stooped very much, and supported his bending knees with the aid of a crutch-handled cane, and so shuffled and tottered along painfully.

"I ask your pardon, sir," said this old man in a very quavering voice, as the burly Judge came up with him, and he extended his hand feebly towards his arm.

Mr. Justice Harbottle saw that the man was by no means poorly dressed, and his manner that of a gentleman.

The Judge stopped short, and said, in his harsh peremptory tones, "Well, sir, how can I serve you?"

"Can you direct me to Judge Harbottle's house? I have some intelligence of the very last importance to communicate to him."

"Can you tell it before witnesses?" asked the Judge.

"By no means; it must reach *his* ear only," quavered the old man earnestly.

"If that be so, sir, you have only to accompany me a few steps farther to reach my house, and obtain a private audience; for I am Judge Harbottle."

With this invitation the infirm gentleman in the white wig complied very readily; and in another minute the stranger stood in what was then termed the front parlor of the Judge's house, *tête-à-tête* with that shrewd and dangerous functionary.

He had to sit down, being very much exhausted, and unable for a little time to speak; and then he had a fit of coughing, and after that a fit of gasping; and thus two or three minutes passed, during which the Judge dropped his roquelaure on an arm-chair, and threw his cocked-hat over that.

The venerable pedestrian in the white wig quickly recovered his voice. With closed doors they remained together for some time.

There were guests waiting in the drawing-rooms, and the sound of men's voices laughing, and then of a female voice singing to a harpsichord, were heard distinctly in the hall over the stairs; for old Judge Harbottle had arranged one of his dubious jollifications, such as might well make the hair of godly men's heads stand upright, for that night.

This old gentleman in the powdered white wig, that rested on his stooped shoulders, must have had something to say that interested the Judge very much; for he would not have parted on easy terms with the ten minutes and upwards which that conference filched from the sort of revelry in which he most delighted, and in which he was the roaring king, and in some sort the tyrant also, of his company.

The footman who showed the aged gentleman out observed that the Judge's mulberry-colored face, pimples and all, were bleached to a dingy yellow, and there was the abstraction of agitated thought in his manner, as he bid the stranger good night. The servant saw that the conversation had been of serious import, and that the Judge was frightened.

Instead of stumping upstairs forthwith to his scandalous hilarities, his profane company, and his great china bowl of punch—the identical bowl from which a bygone Bishop of London, good easy man, had

baptized this Judge's grandfather, now clinking round the rim with silver ladles, and hung with scrolls of lemon peel—instead, I say, of
stumping and clambering up the great staircase to the cavern of his
Circean enchantment, he stood with his big nose flattened against the
window-pane, watching the progress of the feeble old man, who clung
stiffly to the iron rail as he got down, step by step, to the pavement.

The hall-door had hardly closed, when the old Judge was in the hall
bawling hasty orders, with such stimulating expletives as old colonels
under excitement sometimes indulge in nowadays, with a stamp or two
of his big foot, and a waving of his clenched fist in the air. He commanded the footman to overtake the old gentleman in the white wig,
to offer him his protection on his way home, and in no case to show his
face again without having ascertained where he lodged, and who
he was, and all about him.

"By—, sirrah! if you fail me in this, you doff my livery to-night!"

Forth bounced the stalwart footman, with his heavy cane under his
arm, and skipped down the steps, and looked up and down the street
after the singular figure, so easy to recognize.

What were his adventures I shall not tell you just now.

The old man, in the conference to which he had been admitted in
that stately panelled room, had just told the Judge a very strange story.
He might be himself a conspirator; he might possibly be crazed; or
possibly his whole story was straight and true.

The aged gentleman in the bottle-green coat, on finding himself
alone with Mr. Justice Harbottle, had become agitated. He said,

"There is, perhaps you are not aware, my lord, a prisoner in Shrewsbury jail, charged with having forged a bill of exchange for a hundred
and twenty pounds, and his name is Lewis Pyneweck, a grocer of that
town."

"Is there?" says the Judge, who knew well that there was.

"Yes, my lord," says the old man.

"Then you had better say nothing to affect this case. If you do, by
—I'll commit you; for I'm to try it," says the Judge, with his terrible
look and tone.

"I am not going to do anything of the kind, my lord; of him or his
case I know nothing, and care nothing. But a fact has come to my
knowledge which it behoves you well to consider."

"And what may that fact be?" inquired the Judge; "I'm in haste,
sir, and beg you will use dispatch."

"It has come to my knowledge, my lord, that a secret tribunal is in process of formation, the object of which is to take cognizance of the conduct of the judges; and first, of *your* conduct, my lord: it is a wicked conspiracy."

"Who are of it?" demands the Judge.

"I know not a single name as yet. I know but the fact, my lord; it is most certainly true."

"I'll have you before the Privy Council, sir," says the Judge.

"That is what I most desire; but not for a day or two, my lord."

"And why so?"

"I have not as yet a single name, as I told your lordship; but I expect to have a list of the most forward men in it, and some other papers connected with the plot, in two or three days."

"You said one or two just now."

"About that time, my lord."

"Is this a Jacobite plot?"

"In the main I think it is, my lord."

"Why, then, it is political. I have tried no State prisoners, nor am like to try any such. How, then, doth it concern me?"

"From what I can gather, my lord, there are those in it who desire private revenges upon certain judges."

"What do they call their cabal?"

"The High Court of Appeal, my lord."

"Who are you sir? What is your name?"

"Hugh Peters, my lord."

"That should be a Whig name?"

"It is, my lord."

"Where do you lodge, Mr. Peters?"

"In Thames Street, my lord, over against the sign of the Three Kings."

"Three Kings? Take care one be not too many for you, Mr. Peters! How come you, an honest Whig, as you say, to be privy to a Jacobite plot? Answer me that."

"My lord, a person in whom I take an interest has been seduced to take a part in it; and being frightened at the unexpected wickedness of their plans, he is resolved to become an informer for the Crown."

"He resolves like a wise man, sir. What does he say of the persons? Who are in the plot? Doth he know them?"

"Only two, my lord; but he will be introduced to the club in a few days, and he will then have a list, and more exact information of their plans, and above all of their oaths, and their hours and places of meeting, with which he wishes to be acquainted before they can have any suspicions of his intentions. And being so informed, to whom, think you, my lord, had he best go then?"

"To the king's attorney-general straight. But you say this concerns me, sir, in particular? How about this prisoner, Lewis Pyneweck? Is he one of them?"

"I can't tell, my lord; but for some reason, it is thought your lordship will be well advised if you try him not. For if you do, it is feared 'twill shorten your days."

"So far as I can learn, Mr. Peters, this business smells pretty strong of blood and treason. The king's attorney-general will know how to deal with it. When shall I see you again, sir?"

"If you give me leave, my lord, either before your lordship's court sits, or after it rises, to-morrow. I should like to come and tell your lordship what has passed."

"Do so, Mr. Peters, at nine o'clock to-morrow morning. And see you play me no trick, sir, in this matter; if you do, by ——, sir, I'll lay you by the heels!"

"You need fear no trick from me, my lord; had I not wished to serve you, and acquit my own conscience, I never would have come all this way to talk with your lordship."

"I'm willing to believe you, Mr. Peters; I'm willing to believe you, sir."

And upon this they parted.

"He has either painted his face, or he is consumedly sick," thought the old Judge.

The light had shone more effectually upon his features as he turned to leave the room with a low bow, and they looked, he fancied, unnaturally chalky.

"D— him!" said the Judge ungraciously, as he began to scale the stairs: "he has half-spoiled my supper."

But if he had, no one but the Judge himself perceived it, and the evidence was all, as anyone might perceive, the other way.

CHAPTER III

Lewis Pyneweck

In the meantime, the footman dispatched in pursuit of Mr. Peters speedily overtook that feeble gentleman. The old man stopped when he heard the sound of pursuing steps, but any alarms that may have crossed his mind seemed to disappear on his recognizing the livery. He very gratefully accepted the proffered assistance, and placed his tremulous arm within the servant's for support. They had not gone far, however, when the old man stopped suddenly, saying,

"Dear me! as I live, I have dropped it. You heard it fall. My eyes, I fear, won't serve me, and I'm unable to stoop low enough; but if *you* will look, you shall have half the find. It is a guinea; I carried in it my glove."

The street was silent and deserted. The footman had hardly descended to what he termed his "hunkers," and begun to search the pavement about the spot which the old man indicated, when Mr. Peters, who seemed very much exhausted, and breathed with difficulty, struck him a violent blow, from above, over the back of the head with a heavy instrument, and then another; and leaving him bleeding and senseless in the gutter, ran like a lamplighter down a lane to the right, and was gone.

When, an hour later, the watchmen brought the man in livery home, still stupid and covered with blood, Judge Harbottle cursed his servant roundly, swore he was drunk, threatened him with an indictment for taking bribes to betray his master, and cheered him with a perspective of the broad street leading from the Old Bailey to Tyburn, the cart's tail, and the hangman's lash.

Notwithstanding this demonstration, the Judge was pleased. It was a disguised "affidavit man," or footpad, no doubt, who had been employed to frighten him. The trick had fallen through.

A "court of appeal," such as the false Hugh Peters had indicated, with assassination for its sanction, would be an uncomfortable institution for a "hanging judge" like the Honorable Justice Harbottle. That sarcastic and ferocious administrator of the criminal code of England, at that time a rather pharisaical, bloody, and heinous system of justice, had reasons of his own for choosing to try that very Lewis Pyneweck, on whose behalf this audacious trick was devised. Try him he would. No man living should take that morsel out of his mouth.

Of Lewis Pyneweck of course, so far as the outer world could see, he knew nothing. He would try him after his fashion, without fear, favor, or affection.

But did he not remember a certain thin man, dressed in mourning, in whose house, in Shrewsbury, the Judge's lodgings used to be, until a scandal of his ill-treating his wife came suddenly to light? A grocer with a demure look, a soft step, and a lean face as dark as mahogany, with a nose sharp and long, standing ever so little awry, and a pair of dark steady brown eyes under thinly-traced black brows—a man whose thin lips wore always a faint unpleasant smile.

Had not that scoundrel an account to settle with the Judge? had he not been troublesome lately? and was not his name Lewis Pyneweck, some time grocer in Shrewsbury, and now prisoner in the jail of that town?

The reader may take it, if he pleases, as a sign that Judge Harbottle was a good Christian, that he suffered nothing ever from remorse. That was undoubtedly true. He had nevertheless done this grocer, forger, what you will, some five or six years before, a grievous wrong; but it was not that, but a possible scandal, and possible complications, that troubled the learned Judge now.

Did he not, as a lawyer, know, that to bring a man from his shop to the dock, the chances must be at least ninety-nine out of a hundred that he is guilty?

A weak man like his learned brother Withershins was not a judge to keep the high-roads safe, and make crime tremble. Old Judge Harbottle was the man to make the evil-disposed quiver, and to refresh the world with showers of wicked blood, and thus save the innocent, to the refrain of the ancient saw he loved to quote:

Foolish pity
Ruins a city.

In hanging that fellow he could not be wrong. The eye of a man accustomed to look upon the dock could not fail to read "villain" written sharp and clear in his plotting face. Of course he would try him, and no one else should.

A saucy-looking woman, still handsome, in a mob-cap gay with blue ribbons, in a saque of flowered silk, with lace and rings on, much too fine for the Judge's housekeeper, which nevertheless she was, peeped into his study next morning, and, seeing the Judge alone, stepped in.

"Here's another letter from him, come by the post this morning. Can't you do nothing for him?" she said wheedlingly, with her arm over his neck, and her delicate finger and thumb fiddling with the lobe of his purple ear.

"I'll try," said Judge Harbottle, not raising his eyes from the paper he was reading.

"I knew you'd do what I asked you," she said.

The Judge clapt his gouty claw over his heart, and made her an ironical bow.

"What," she asked, "will you do?"

"Hang him," said the Judge with a chuckle.

"You don't mean to; no, you don't, my little man," said she, surveying herself in a mirror on the wall.

"I'm d—d but I think you're falling in love with your husband at last!" said Judge Harbottle.

"I'm blest but I think you're growing jealous of him," replied the lady with a laugh. "But no; he was always a bad one to me; I've done with him long ago."

"And he with you, by George! When he took your fortune and your spoons and your ear-rings, he had all he wanted of you. He drove you from his house; and when he discovered you had made yourself comfortable, and found a good situation, he'd have taken your guineas and your silver and your ear-rings over again, and then allowed you half a dozen years more to make a new harvest for his mill. You don't wish him good; if you say you do, you lie."

She laughed a wicked saucy laugh, and gave the terrible Rhadamanthus a playful tap on the chops.

"He wants me to send him money to fee a counselor," she said, while her eyes wandered over the pictures on the wall, and back again to the looking-glass; and certainly she did not look as if his jeopardy troubled her very much.

"Confound his impudence, the *scoundrel!*" thundered the old Judge, throwing himself back in his chair, as he used to do *in furore* on the bench, and the lines of his mouth looked brutal, and his eyes ready too leap from their sockets. "If you answer his letter from my house to please yourself, you'll write your next from somebody else's to please me. You understand, my pretty witch, I'll not be pestered. Come, no pouting; whimpering won't do. You don't care a brass farthing for the villain, body or soul. You came here but to make a row. You are one of Mother Carey's chickens; and where you come, the storm is up. Get you gone, baggage! get you *gone!*" he repeated with a stamp; for a knock at the hall-door made her instantaneous disappearance indispensable.

I need hardly say that the venerable Hugh Peters did not appear again. The Judge never mentioned him. But oddly enough, considering how he laughed to scorn the weak invention which he had blown into dust at the very first puff, his white-wigged visitor and the conference in the dark front parlor was often in his memory.

His shrewd eye told him that allowing for change of tints and such disguises as the playhouse affords every night, the features of this false old man, who had turned out too hard for his tall footman, were identical with those of Lewis Pyneweck.

Judge Harbottle made his registrar call upon the crown solicitor, and tell him that there was a man in town who bore a wonderful resemblance to a prisoner in Shrewsbury jail named Lewis Pyneweck, and to make inquiry through the post forthwith whether anyone was personating Pyneweck in prison, and whether he had thus or otherwise made his escape.

The prisoner was safe, however, and no question as to his identity.

CHAPTER IV

Interruption in Court

In due time Judge Harbottle went circuit; and in due time the judges were in Shrewsbury. News traveled slowly in those days, and newspapers, like the wagons and stage-coaches, took matters easily. Mrs. Pyneweck, in the Judge's house, with a diminished household—the greater part of the Judge's servants having gone with him, for he had given up riding circuit, and traveled in his coach in state—kept house rather solitarily at home.

In spite of quarrels, in spite of mutual injuries—some of them, inflicted by herself, enormous—in spite of a married life of spited bickerings—a life in which there seemed no love or liking or forbearance, for years—now that Pyneweck stood in near danger of death, some-

thing like remorse came suddenly upon her. She knew that in Shrewsbury were transacting the scenes which were to determine his fate. She
knew she did not love him; but she could not have supposed, even a
fortnight before, that the hour of suspense could have affected her
so powerfully.

She knew the day on which the trial was expected to take place. She
could not get it out of her head for a minute; she felt faint as it drew towards evening.

Two or three days passed; and then she knew that the trial must be
over by this time. There were floods between London and Shrewsbury,
and news was long delayed. She wished the floods would last for ever.
It was dreadful waiting to hear; dreadful to know that the event was
over, and that she could not hear till self-willed rivers subsided; dreadful to know that they must subside and the news come at last.

She had some vague trust in the Judge's good nature, and much in
the resources of chance and accident. She had contrived to send the
money he wanted. He would not be without legal advice and energetic
and skilled support.

At last the news did come—a long arrear all in a gush: a letter
from a female friend in Shrewsbury; a return of the sentences, sent up
for the Judge; and most important, being most easily got at, being
told with great aplomb and brevity, the long-deferred intelligence of
the Shrewsbury Assizes in the *Morning Advertiser*. Like an impatient
reader of a novel, who reads the last page first, she read with dizzy
eyes the list of the executions.

Two were respited, seven were hanged; and in that capital catalogue
was this line:

"Lewis Pyneweck—forgery."

She had to read it half a dozen times over before she was sure she
understood it. Here was the paragraph:

"Sentence, Death—7.

"Executed accordingly on Friday the 13th instant, to wit:

"Thomas Primer, *alias* Duck—highway robbery.

"Flora Guy—stealing to the value of 11*s*. 6*d*.

"Arthur Pounden—burglary.

"Matilda Mummery—riot.

"Lewis Pyneweck—forgery, bill of exchange."

And when she reached this, she read it over and over, feeling very
cold and sick.

This buxom housekeeper was known in the house as Mrs. Carwell—Carwell being her maiden name, which she had resumed.

No one in the house except its master knew her history. Her introduction had been managed craftily. No one suspected that it had been concerted between her and the old reprobate in scarlet and ermine.

Flora Carwell ran up the stairs now, and snatched her little girl, hardly seven years of age, whom she met in the lobby, hurriedly up in her arms, and carried her into her bedroom, without well knowing what she was doing, and sat down, placing the child before her. She was not able to speak. She held the child before her, and looked in the little girl's wondering face, and burst into tears of horror.

She thought the Judge could have saved him. I daresay he could. For a time she was furious with him; and hugged and kissed her bewildered little girl, who returned her gaze with large round eyes.

That little girl had lost her father, and knew nothing of the matter. She had been always told that her father was dead long ago.

A woman, coarse, uneducated, vain, and violent, does not reason, or even feel, very distinctly; but in these tears of consternation were mingling a self-upbraiding. She felt afraid of that little child.

But Mrs. Carwell was a person who lived not upon sentiment, but upon beef and pudding; she consoled herself with punch; she did not trouble herself long even with resentments; she was a gross and material person, and could not mourn over the irrevocable for more than a limited number of hours, even if she would.

Judge Harbottle was soon in London again. Except the gout, this savage old epicurean never knew a day's sickness. He laughed and coaxed and bullied away the young woman's faint upbraidings, and in a little time Lewis Pyneweck troubled her no more; and the Judge secretly chuckled over the perfectly fair removal of a bore, who might have grown little by little into something very like a tyrant.

It was the lot of the Judge whose adventures I am now recounting to try criminal cases at the Old Bailey shortly after his return. He had commenced his charge to the jury in a case of forgery, and was, after his wont, thundering dead against the prisoner, with many a hard aggravation and cynical gibe, when suddenly all died away in silence, and, instead of looking at the jury, the eloquent Judge was gaping at some person in the body of the court.

Among the persons of small importance who stand and listen at the sides was one tall enough to show with a little prominence; a slight mean figure, dressed in seedy black, lean and dark of visage. He had just handed a letter to the crier, before he caught the Judge's eye.

That Judge descried, to his amazement, the features of Lewis Pyneweck. He had the usual faint thin-lipped smile; and with his blue chin raised in air, and as it seemed quite unconscious of the distinguished notice he had attracted, he was stretching his low cravat with his crooked fingers, while he slowly turned his head from side to side—a process which enabled the Judge to see distinctly a stripe of swollen blue round his neck, which indicated, he thought, the grip of the rope.

This man, with a few others, had got a footing on a step, from which he could better see the court. He now stepped down, and the Judge lost sight of him.

His lordship signed energetically with his hand in the direction in which this man had vanished. He turned to the tipstaff. His first effort to speak ended in a gasp. He cleared his throat, and told the astounded official to arrest that man who had interrupted the court.

"He's but this moment gone down *there*. Bring him in custody before me, within ten minutes' time, or I'll strip your gown from your shoulders and fine the sheriff!" he thundered, while his eyes flashed round the court in search of the functionary.

Attorneys, counselors, idle spectators, gazed in the direction in which Mr. Justice Harbottle had shaken his gnarled old hand. They compared notes. Not one had seen anyone making a disturbance. They asked one another if the Judge was losing his head.

Nothing came of the search. His lordship concluded his charge a great deal more tamely; and when the jury retired, he stared round the court with a wandering mind, and looked as if he would not have given sixpence to see the prisoner hanged.

CHAPTER V

Caleb Searcher

The Judge had received the letter; had he known from whom it came, he would no doubt have read it instantaneously. As it was he simply read the direction:

To the Honorable
  The Lord Justice

Elijah Harbottle,
One of his Majesty's Justices of
the Honorable Court of Common Pleas.

It remained forgotten in his pocket till he reached home.

When he pulled out that and others from the capacious pocket of his coat, it had its turn, as he sat in his library in his thick silk dressing-gown; and then he found its contents to be a closely-written letter, in a clerk's hand, and an enclosure in "secretary hand," as I believe the angular scrivinary of law-writings in those days was termed, engrossed on a bit of parchment about the size of this page. The letter said:

"Mr. Justice Harbottle,——My Lord,

"I am ordered by the High Court of Appeal to acquaint your lordship, in order to your better preparing yourself for your trial, that a true bill hath been sent down, and the indictment lieth against your lordship for the murder of one Lewis Pyneweck of Shrewsbury, citizen, wrongfully executed for the forgery of a bill of exchange, on the ——th day of —— last, by reason of the wilful perversion of the evidence, and the undue pressure put upon the jury, together with the illegal admission of evidence by your lordship, well knowing the same to be illegal, by all which the promoter of the prosecution of the said indictment, before the High Court of Appeal, hath lost his life.

"And the trial of the said indictment, I am further ordered to acquaint your lordship is fixed for the 10th day of —— next ensuing, by the right honorable the Lord Chief-Justice Twofold, of the court aforesaid, to wit, the High Court of Appeal, on which day it will most certainly take place. And I am further to acquaint your lordship, to prevent any surprise or miscarriage, that your case stands first for the said day, and that the said High Court of Appeal sits day and night, and never rises; and herewith, by order of the said court, I furnish your lordship with a copy (extract) of the record in this case, except of the indictment, whereof, notwithstanding, the substance and effect is supplied to your lordship in this Notice. And further I am to inform you, that in case the jury then to try your lordship should find you guilty, the right honorable the Lord Chief-Justice will, in passing sentence of death upon you, fix the day of execution for the 10th day of ——, being one calendar month from the day of your trial."

It was signed by

"CALEB SEARCHER,
"Officer of the Crown Solicitor in the
Kingdom of Life and Death."

The Judge glanced through the parchment.

" 'Sblood! Do they think a man like me is to be bamboozled by their buffoonery?"

The Judge's coarse features were wrung into one of his sneers; but he was pale. Possibly, after all, there was a conspiracy on foot. It was queer. Did they mean to pistol him in his carriage? or did they only aim at frightening him?

Judge Harbottle had more than enough of animal courage. He was not afraid of highwaymen, and he had fought more than his share of duels, being a foul-mouthed advocate while he held briefs at the bar. No one questioned his fighting qualities. But with respect to this particular case of Pyneweck, he lived in a house of glass. Was there not his pretty, dark-eyed, over-dressed housekeeper, Mrs. Flora Carwell? Very easy for people who knew Shrewsbury to identify Mrs. Pyneweck, if once put upon the scent; and had he not stormed and worked hard in that case? Had he not made it hard sailing for the prisoner? Did he not know very well what the bar thought of it? It would be the worst scandal that ever blasted a judge.

So much there was intimidating in the matter, but nothing more. The Judge was a little bit gloomy for a day or two after, and more testy with every one than usual.

He locked up the papers; and about a week after he asked his housekeeper, one day, in the library:

"Had your husband never a brother?"

Mrs. Carwell squalled on this sudden introduction of the funereal topic, and cried exemplary "piggins full," as the Judge used pleasantly to say. But he was in no mood for trifling now, and he said sternly:

"Come, madam! this wearies me. Do it another time; and give me an answer to my question." So she did.

Pyneweck had no brother living. He once had one; but he died in Jamaica.

"How do you know he is dead?" asked the Judge.

"Because he told me so."

"Not the dead man?"

"Pyneweck told me so."

"Is that all?" sneered the Judge.

He pondered this matter; and time went on. The Judge was growing a little morose, and less enjoying. The subject struck nearer to his thoughts than he fancied it could have done. But so it is with most undivulged vexations, and there was no one to whom he could tell this one.

It was now the ninth; and Mr. Justice Harbottle was glad. He knew nothing would come of it. Still it bothered him; and to-morrow would see it well over.

[What of the paper, I have cited? No one saw it during his life; no one, after his death. He spoke of it to Dr. Hedstone; and what purported to be "a copy," in the old Judge's handwriting, was found. The original was nowhere. Was it a copy of an illusion, incident to brain disease? Such is my belief.]

CHAPTER VI

Arrested

Judge Harbottle went this night to the play at Drury Lane. He was one of those old fellows who care nothing for late hours, and occasionally knocking about in pursuit of pleasure. He had appointed with two cronies of Lincoln's Inn to come home in his coach with him to sup after the play.

They were not in his box, but were to meet him near the entrance, and to get into his carriage there; and Mr. Justice Harbottle, who hated waiting, was looking a little impatiently from the window.

The Judge yawned.

He told the footman to watch for Counselor Thavies and Counselor Beller, who were coming; and, with another yawn, he laid his cocked-hat on his knees, closed his eyes, leaned back in his corner, wrapped his mantle closer about him, and began to think of pretty Mrs. Abington.

And being a man who could sleep like a sailor, at a moment's notice, he was thinking of taking a nap. Those fellows had no business to keep a judge waiting.

He heard their voices now. Those rake-hell counselors were laughing, and bantering, and sparring after their wont. The carriage swayed and jerked, as one got in, and then again as the other followed. The door clapped, and the coach was now jogging and rumbling over the pavement. The Judge was a little bit sulky. He did not care to sit up and open his eyes. Let them suppose he was asleep. He heard them laugh with more malice than good-humor, he thought, as they observed it. He would give them a d—d hard knock or two when they got to his door, and till then he would counterfeit his nap.

The clocks were chiming twelve. Beller and Thavies were silent as tombstones. They were generally loquacious and merry rascals.

The Judge suddenly felt himself roughly seized and thrust from his corner into the middle of the seat, and opening his eyes, instantly he found himself between his two companions.

Before he could blurt out the oath that was at his lips, he saw that they were two strangers—evil-looking fellows, each with a pistol in his hand, and dressed like Bow Street officers.

The Judge clutched at the check-string. The coach pulled up. He stared about him. They were not among houses; but through the windows, under a broad moonlight, he saw a black moor stretching lifelessly from right to left, with rotting trees, pointing fantastic branches in the air, standing here and there in groups, as if they held up their arms and twigs like fingers, in horrible glee at the Judge's coming.

A footman came to the window. He knew his long face and sunken eyes. He knew it was Dingly Chuff, fifteen years ago a footman in his service, whom he had turned off at a moment's notice, in a burst of jealousy, and indicted for a missing spoon. The man had died in prison of the jail-fever.

The Judge drew back in utter amazement. His armed companions signed mutely; and they were again gliding over this unknown moor.

The bloated and gouty old man, in his horror, considered the question of resistance. But his athletic days were long over. This moor was a desert. There was no help to be had. He was in the hands of strange servants, even if his recognition turned out to be a delusion, and they were under the command of his captors. There was nothing for it but submission, for the present.

Suddenly the coach was brought nearly to a standstill, so that the prisoner saw an ominous sight from the window.

It was a gigantic gallows beside the road; it stood three-sided, and from each of its three broad beams at top depended in chains some eight or ten bodies, from several of which the cere-clothes had dropped away, leaving the skeletons swinging lightly by their chains. A tall ladder reached to the summit of the structure, and on the peat beneath lay bones.

On top of the dark transverse beam facing the road, from which, as from the other two completing the triangle of death, dangled a row of these unfortunates in chains, a hangman, with a pipe in his mouth, much as we see him in the famous print of the "Idle Apprentice," though here his perch was ever so much higher, was reclining at his ease and listlessly shying bones, from a little heap at his elbow, at the skeletons that hung round, bringing down now a rib or two, now a hand, now half a leg. A long-sighted man could have discerned that he was a dark fellow, lean; and from continually looking down on the earth from the elevation over which, in another sense, he always hung, his nose, his lips, his chin were pendulous and loose, and drawn down into a monstrous grotesque.

This fellow took his pipe from his mouth on seeing the coach, stood up, and cut some solemn capers high on his beam, and shook a new rope in the air, crying with a voice high and distant as the caw of a raven hovering over a gibbet, "A rope for Judge Harbottle!"

The coach was now driving on at its old swift pace.

So high a gallows as that, the Judge had never, even in his most hilarious moments, dreamed of. He thought he must be raving. And the dead footman! He shook his ears and strained his eyelids; but if he was dreaming, he was unable to awake himself.

There was no good in threatening these scoundrels. A *brutum fulmen* might bring a real one on his head.

Any submission to get out of their hands; and then heaven and earth he would move to unearth and hunt them down.

Suddenly they drove round a corner of a vast white building, and under a *porte-cochère*.

CHAPTER VII

Chief-Justice Twofold

The Judge found himself in a corridor lighted with dingy oil-lamps, the walls of bare stone; it looked like a passage in a prison. His guards placed him in the hands of other people. Here and there he saw bony and gigantic soldiers passing to and fro, with muskets over their shoulders. They looked straight before them, grinding their teeth, in bleak fury, with no noise but the clank of their shoes. He saw these by glimpses, round corners, and at the ends of passages, but he did not actually pass them by.

And now, passing under a narrow doorway, he found himself in the dock, confronting a judge in his scarlet robes, in a large courthouse. There was nothing to elevate this temple of Themis above its vulgar kind elsewhere. Dingy enough it looked, in spite of candles lighted in decent abundance. A case had just closed, and the last juror's back was seen escaping through the door in the wall of the jury-box. There were some dozen barristers, some fiddling with pen and ink, others buried in briefs, some beckoning, with the plumes of their pens, to their attorneys of whom there were no lack; there were clerks to-ing and fro-ing, and the officers of the court, and the registrar, who was handing up a paper to the judge; and the tipstaff, who was presenting a note at the end of his wand to a king's counsel over the heads of the crowd between. If this was the High Court of Appeal, which never rose day or night, it might account for the pale and jaded aspect of everybody in it. An air of indescribable gloom hung upon the pallid features of all the people here; no one ever smiled; all looked more or less secretly suffering.

"The King against Elijah Harbottle!" shouted the officer.

"Is the appellant Lewis Pyneweck in court?" asked Chief-Justice Twofold, in a voice of thunder, that shook the woodwork of the Court, and boomed down the corridors.

Up stood Pyneweck from his place at the table.

"Arraign the prisoner!" roared the Chief; and Judge Harbottle felt the panels of the dock round him, and the floor, and the rails quiver in the vibrations of that tremendous voice.

The prisoner, *in limine,* objected to this pretended court, as being sham, and non-existent in point of law; and then, that, even if it were a court constituted by law (the Judge was growing dazed), it had not and could not have any jurisdiction to try him for his conduct on the bench.

Whereupon the chief-justice laughed suddenly, and every one in court, turning round upon the prisoner, laughed also, till the laugh grew and roared all round like a deafening acclamation; he saw nothing but glittering eyes and teeth, a universal stare and grin; but though all the voices laughed, not a single face of all those that concentrated their gaze upon him looked like a laughing face. The mirth subsided as suddenly as it began.

The indictment was read. Judge Harbottle actually pleaded! He pleaded "Not guilty." A jury was sworn. The trial proceeded. Judge Harbottle was bewildered. This could not be real. He must be either mad, or *going* mad, he thought.

One thing could not fail to strike even him. This Chief-Justice Two-fold, who was knocking him about at every turn with sneer and gibe, and roaring him down with his tremendous voice, was a dilated effigy of himself; an image of Mr. Justice Harbottle, at least double his size, and with all his fierce coloring, and his ferocity of eye and visage, enhanced awfully.

Nothing the prisoner could argue, cite, or state was permitted to retard for a moment the march of the case towards its catastrophe.

The chief-justice seemed to feel his power over the jury, and to exult and riot in the display of it. He glared at them, he nodded to them; he seemed to have established an understanding with them. The lights were faint in that part of the court. The jurors were mere shadows, sitting in rows; the prisoner could see a dozen pairs of white eyes shining, coldly, out of the darkness; and whenever the judge in his charge, which was contemptuously brief, nodded and grinned and gibed, the prisoner could see, in the obscurity, by the dip of all these rows of eyes together, that the jury nodded in acquiescence.

And now the charge was over, the huge chief-justice leaned back panting and gloating on the prisoner. Every one in the court turned about, and gazed with steadfast hatred on the man in the dock. From the jury-box where the twelve sworn brethren were whispering together, a sound in the general stillness like a prolonged "hiss-s-s!" was heard; and then, in answer to the challenge of the officer, "How say you, gentlemen of the jury, guilty or not guilty?" came in a melancholy voice the finding, "Guilty."

The place seemed to the eyes of the prisoner to grow gradually darker and darker, till he could discern nothing distinctly but the lumen of the eyes that were turned upon him from every bench and side and corner and gallery of the building. The prisoner doubtless thought that he had quite enough to say, and conclusive, why sentence of death should not be pronounced upon him; but the lord chief-justice puffed it contemptuously away, like so much smoke, and proceeded to pass sentence of death upon the prisoner, having named the 10th of the ensuing month for his execution.

Before he had recovered the stun of this ominous farce, in obedience to the mandate, "Remove the prisoner," he was led from the dock. The lamps seemed all to have gone out, and there were stoves and charcoal-fires here and there, that threw a faint crimson light on the walls of the corridors through which he passed. The stones that composed them looked now enormous, cracked and unhewn.

He came into a vaulted smithy, where two men, naked to the waist, with heads like bulls, round shoulders, and the arms of giants, were welding red-hot chains together with hammers that pelted like thunderbolts.

They looked on the prisoner with fierce red eyes, and rested on their hammers for a minute; and said the elder to his companion, "Take out Elijah Harbottle's gyves"; and with a pincers he plucked the end which lay dazzling in the fire from the furnace.

"One end locks," said he, taking the cool end of the iron in one hand while with the grip of a vise he seized the leg of the Judge, and locked the ring round his ankle. "The other," he said with a grin, "is welded."

The iron band that was to form the ring for the other leg lay still red-hot upon the stone floor, with brilliant sparks sporting up and down its surface.

His companion in his gigantic hands seized the old Judge's other leg, and pressed his foot immovably to the stone floor; while his senior in a twinkling, with a masterly application of pincers and hammer, sped the glowing bar round his ankle so tight that the skin and sinews smoked and bubbled again, and old Judge Harbottle uttered a yell that seemed to chill the very stones, and make the iron chains quiver on the wall.

Chains, vaults, smiths, and smithy all vanished in a moment; but the pain continued. Mr. Justice Harbottle was suffering torture all round the ankle on which the infernal smiths had just been operating.

His friends Thavies and Beller were startled by the Judge's roar in the midst of their elegant trifling about a marriage *à la mode* case which was going on. The Judge was in panic as well as pain. The street-lamps and the light of his own hall-door restored him.

"I'm very bad," growled he between his set teeth; "my foot's blazing. Who was he that hurt my foot? 'Tis the gout—'tis the gout!" he said, awaking completely. "How many hours have we been coming from the playhouse? 'Sblood, what has happened on the way? I've slept half the night?"

There had been no hitch or delay, and they had driven home at a good pace.

The Judge, however, was in gout; he was feverish too; and the attack, though very short, was sharp; and when, in about a fortnight, it subsided, his ferocious joviality did not return. He could not get this dream, as he chose to call it, out of his head.

CHAPTER VIII

Somebody Has Got into the House

People remarked that the Judge was in the vapors. His doctor said he should go for a fortnight to Buxton.

Whenever the Judge fell into a brown study, he was always conning over the terms of the sentence pronounced upon him in his vision— "in one calendar month from the date of this day"; and then the usual form, "and you shall be hanged by the neck till you are dead," &c. "That will be the 10th—I'm not much in the way of being hanged. I know what stuff dreams are, and I laugh at them; but this is continually in my thoughts, as if it forecast misfortune of some sort. I wish the day my dream gave me were passed and over. I wish I were well purged of my gout. I wish I were as I used to be. 'Tis nothing but vapors, nothing but a maggot." The copy of the parchment and letter which had announced his trial with many a snort and sneer he would read over and over again, and the scenery and people of his dream would rise about him in places the most unlikely, and steal him in a moment from all that surrounded him into a world of shadows.

The Judge had lost his iron energy and banter. He was growing taciturn and morose. The Bar remarked the change, as well they might. His friends thought him ill. The doctor said he was troubled with hypochondria, and that his gout was still lurking in his system, and ordered him to that ancient haunt of crutches and chalk-stones, Buxton.

The Judge's spirits were very low; he was frightened about himself; and he described to his housekeeper, having sent for her to his study to drink a dish of tea, his strange dream in his drive home from Drury Lane playhouse. He was sinking into the state of nervous dejection in which men lose their faith in orthodox advice, and in despair consult quacks, astrologers, and nursery story-tellers. Could such a dream mean that he was to have a fit, and so die on the 10th? She did not think so. On the contrary, it was certain some good luck must happen on that day.

The Judge kindled; and for the first time for many days, he looked for a minute or two like himself, and he tapped her on the cheek with the hand that was not in flannel.

"Odsbud! odsheart! you dear rogue! I had forgot. There is young Tom—yellow Tom, my nephew, you know, lies sick at Harrogate; why shouldn't he go that day as well as another, and if he does, I get an estate by it? Why, lookee, I asked Doctor Hedstone yesterday if I was like to take a fit any time, and he laughed, and swore I was the last man in town to go off that way."

The Judge sent most of his servants down to Buxton to make his lodgings and all things comfortable for him. He was to follow in a day or two.

It was now the 9th; and the next day well over, he might laugh at his visions and auguries.

On the evening of the 9th, Doctor Hedstone's footman knocked at the Judge's door. The doctor ran up the dusky stairs to the drawing-room. It was a March evening, near the hour of sunset, with an east wind whistling sharply through the chimney-stacks. A wood fire blazed cheerily on the hearth. And Judge Harbottle, in what was then called a brigadier-wig, with his red roquelaure on, helped the glowing effect of the darkened chamber, which looked red all over like a room on fire.

The Judge had his feet on a stool, and his huge grim purple face confronted the fire, and seemed to pant and swell, as the blaze alternately spread upward and collapsed. He had fallen again among his blue devils, and was thinking of retiring from the Bench, and of fifty other gloomy things.

But the doctor, who was an energetic son of Aesculapius, would listen to no croaking, told the Judge he was full of gout, and in his present condition no judge even of his own case, but promised him leave to pronounce on all those melancholy questions, a fortnight later.

In the meantime the Judge must be very careful. He was overcharged with gout, and he must not provoke an attack, till the waters of Buxton should do that office for him, in their own salutary way.

The doctor did not think him perhaps quite so well as he pretended, for he told him he wanted rest, and would be better if he went forthwith to his bed.

Mr. Gerningham, his valet, assisted him, and gave him his drops; and the Judge told him to wait in his bedroom till he should go to sleep.

Three persons that night had specially odd stories to tell.

The housekeeper had got rid of the trouble of amusing her little girl at this anxious time by giving her leave to run about the sitting-rooms and look at the pictures and china, on the usual condition of touching nothing. It was not until the last gleam of sunset had for some time faded, and the twilight had so deepened that she could no longer discern the colors on the china figures on the chimneypiece or in the cabinets, that the child returned to the housekeeper's room to find her mother.

To her she related, after some prattle about the china, and the pictures, and the Judge's two grand wigs in the dressing-room off the library, an adventure of an extraordinary kind.

In the hall was placed, as was customary in those times, the sedan-chair which the master of the house occasionally used, covered with stamped leather, and studded with gilt nails, and with its red silk blinds down. In this case, the doors of this old-fashioned conveyance were locked, the windows up, and, as I said, the blinds down, but not so closely that the curious child could not peep underneath one of them, and see into the interior.

A parting beam from the setting sun, admitted through the window of a back room, shot obliquely through the open door, and lighting on the chair, shone with a dull transparency through the crimson blind.

To her surprise, the child saw in the shadow a thin man dressed in black seated in it; he had sharp dark features; his nose, she fancied, a little awry, and his brown eyes were looking straight before him; his hand was on his thigh, and he stirred no more than the waxen figure she had seen at Southwark fair.

A child is so often lectured for asking questions and on the propriety of silence, and the superior wisdom of its elders, that it accepts most things at last in good faith; and the little girl acquiesced respectfully in the occupation of the chair by this mahogany-faced person as being all right and proper.

It was not until she asked her mother who this man was, and observed her scared face as she questioned her more minutely upon the appearance of the stranger, that she began to understand that she had seen something unaccountable.

Mrs. Carwell took the key of the chair from its nail over the footman's shelf, and led the child by the hand up to the hall, having a lighted candle in her other hand. She stopped at a distance from the chair, and placed the candlestick in the child's hand.

"Peep in, Margery, again, and try if there's anything there," she whispered; "hold the candle near the blind so as to throw its light through the curtain."

The child peeped, this time with a very solemn face, and intimated at once that he was gone.

"Look again, and be sure," urged her mother.

The little girl was quite certain; and Mrs. Carwell, with her mob-cap of lace and cherry-colored ribbons, and her dark brown hair, not yet powdered, over a very pale face, unlocked the door, looked in, and beheld emptiness.

"All a mistake, child, you see."

"*There*, ma'am! see there! He's gone round the corner," said the child.

"Where?" said Mrs. Carwell, stepping backward a step.

"Into that room."

"Tut, child! 'twas the shadow," cried Mrs. Carwell angrily, because she was frightened. "I moved the candle." But she clutched one of the poles of the chair, which leant against the wall in the corner, and pounded the floor furiously with one end of it, being afraid to pass the open door the child had pointed to.

The cook and two kitchen-maids came running upstairs, not knowing what to make of this unwonted alarm.

They all searched the room; but it was still and empty, and no sign of anyone's having been there.

Some people may suppose that the direction given to her thoughts by this odd little incident will account for a very strange illusion which Mrs. Carwell herself experienced about two hours later.

CHAPTER IX

The Judge Leaves His House

Mrs. Flora Carwell was going up the great staircase with a posset for the Judge in a china bowl, on a little silver tray.

Across the top of the well-staircase there runs a massive oak rail; and, raising her eyes accidentally, she saw an extremely odd-looking stranger, slim and long, leaning carelessly over with a pipe between his finger and thumb. Nose, lips, and chin seemed all to droop downward into extraordinary length, as he leant his odd peering face over the banister. In his other hand he held a coil of rope, one end of which escaped from under his elbow and hung over the rail.

Mrs. Carwell, who had no suspicion at the moment, that he was not a real person, and fancied that he was someone employed in cording the Judge's luggage, called to know what he was doing there.

Instead of answering, he turned about, and walked across the lobby, at about the same leisurely pace at which she was ascending, and entered a room, into which she followed him. It was an uncarpeted and unfurnished chamber. An open trunk lay upon the floor empty, and beside it the coil of rope; but except herself there was no one in the room.

Mrs. Carwell was very much frightened, and now concluded that the child must have seen the same ghost that had just appeared to her. Perhaps, when she was able to think it over, it was a relief to believe so; for the face, figure and dress described by the child were awfully like Pyneweck; and this certainly was not he.

Very much scared and very hysterical, Mrs. Carwell ran down to her room, afraid to look over her shoulder, and got some companions about her, and wept, and talked, and drank more than one cordial, and talked and wept again, and so on, until, in those early days, it was ten o'clock, and time to go to bed.

A scullery-maid remained up finishing some of her scouring and "scalding" for some time after the other servants—who, as I said, were few in number—that night had got to their beds. This was a low-browed, broad-faced, intrepid wench with black hair, who did not "vally a ghost not a button," and treated the housekeeper's hysterics with measureless scorn.

The old house was quiet, now. It was near twelve o'clock, no sounds were audible except the muffled wailing of the wintry winds, piping high among the roofs and chimneys, or rumbling at intervals, in under gusts, through the narrow channels of the street.

The spacious solitudes of the kitchen level were awfully dark, and this skeptical kitchen-wench was the only person now up and about, in the house. She hummed tunes to herself, for a time; and then stopped and listened; and then resumed her work again. At last, she was destined to be more terrified than even was the housekeeper.

There was a back-kitchen in this house, and from this she heard, as if coming from below its foundations, a sound like heavy strokes that seemed to shake the earth beneath her feet. Sometimes a dozen in sequence, at regular intervals; sometimes fewer. She walked out softly into the passage, and was surprised to see a dusky glow issuing from this room, as if from a charcoal fire.

The room seemed thick with smoke.

Looking in, she very dimly beheld a monstrous figure, over a furnace, beating with a mighty hammer the rings and rivets of a chain.

The strokes, swift and heavy as they looked, sounded hollow and distant. The man stopped, and pointed to something on the floor, that, through the smoky haze, looked, she thought, like a dead body. She remarked no more; but the servants in the room close by, startled from their sleep by a hideous scream, found her in a swoon on the flags, close to the door, where she had just witnessed this ghastly vision.

Startled by the girl's incoherent asseverations that she had seen the Judge's corpse on the floor, two servants having first searched the lower part of the house, went rather frightened upstairs to inquire whether their master was well. They found him, not in his bed, but in his room. He had a table with candles burning at his bedside, and was getting on his clothes again; and he swore and cursed at them roundly in his old style, telling them that he had business, and that he would discharge on the spot any scoundrel who should dare to disturb him again.

So the invalid was left to his quietude.

In the morning it was rumored here and there in the street that the Judge was dead. A servant was sent from the house three doors away, by Counselor Traverse, to inquire at Judge Harbottle's hall-door.

The servant who opened it was pale and reserved, and would only say that the Judge was ill. He had had a dangerous accident; Doctor Hedstone had been with him at seven o'clock in the morning.

There were averted looks, short answers, pale and frowning faces, and all the usual signs that there was a secret that sat heavily upon their minds, and the time for disclosing which had not yet come. That time would arrive when the coroner had arrived, and the mortal scandal that had befallen the house could be no longer hidden. For that morning Mr. Justice Harbottle had been found hanging by the neck from the banister at the top of the great staircase, and quite dead.

There was not the smallest sign of any struggle or resistance. There had not been heard a cry or any other noise in the slightest degree indicative of violence. There was medical evidence to show that, in his atrabilious state, it was quite on the cards that he might have made away with himself. The jury found accordingly that it was a case of suicide. But to those who were acquainted with the strange story which Judge Harbottle had related to at least two persons, the fact that the catastrophe occurred on the morning to the 10th March seemed a startling coincidence.

A few days after, the pomp of a great funeral attended him to the grave; and so, in the language of scripture, "the rich man died, and was buried."

Robert Benchley

:

"TAKE THE WITNESS!"

Newspaper accounts of trial cross-examinations always bring out the cleverest in me. They induce daydreams in which I am the witness on the stand, and if you don't know some of my imaginary comebacks to an imaginary cross-examiner (Doe vs. Benchley: 482-U.S.-367-398), you have missed some of the most stimulating reading in the history of American jurisprudence.

These little reveries usually take place shortly after I have read the transcript of a trial, while I am on a long taxi ride or seated at a desk with plenty of other work to do. I like them best when I have work to do, as they deplete me mentally so that I am forced to go and lie down after a particularly sharp verbal rally. The knowledge that I have completely floored my adversary, and the imaginary congratulations of my friends (also imaginary), seem more worth while than any amount of fiddling work done.

During these cross-questionings I am always very calm. Calm in a nice way, that is—never cocky. However frantic my inquisitor may wax (and you should see his face at times—it's purple), I just sit there, burning him up with each answer, winning the admiration of the courtroom, and, at times, even a smile from the judge himself. At the end of my examination, the judge is crazy about me.

Just what the trial is about, I never get quite clear in my mind. Sometimes the subject changes in the middle of the questioning, to allow for the insertion of an especially good crack on my part. I don't think that

652

I am ever actually the defendant, although I don't know why I should feel that I am immune from trial by a jury of my peers—if such exist.

I am usually testifying in behalf of a friend, or perhaps as just an impersonal witness for someone whom I do not know, who, naturally, later becomes my friend for life. It is Justice that I am after—Justice and a few well-spotted laughs.

Let us whip right into the middle of my cross-examination, as I naturally wouldn't want to pull my stuff until I had been insulted by the lawyer, and you can't really get insulted simply by having your name and address asked. I am absolutely fair about these things. If the lawyer will treat me right, I'll treat him right. He has got to start it. For a decent cross-examiner, there is no more tractable witness in the world than I am.

Advancing toward me, with a sneer on his face, he points a finger at me. (I have sometimes thought of pointing my finger back at him, but have discarded that as being too fresh. I don't have to resort to clowning.)

Q: You think you're pretty funny, don't you? (*I have evidently just made some mildly humorous comeback, nothing smart-alecky, but good enough to make him look silly.*)

A: I have never given the matter much thought.

Q: Oh, you haven't given the matter much thought, eh? Well, you seem to be treating this examination as if it were a minstrel show.

A (*Very quietly and nicely*): I have merely been taking my cue from your questions. (*You will notice that all this presupposes quite a barrage of silly questions on his part, and pat answers on mine, omitted here because I haven't thought them up. At any rate, it is evident that I have already got him on the run before this reverie begins.*)

Q: Perhaps you would rather that I conducted this inquiry in baby talk?

A: If it will make it any easier for you. (*Pandemonium, which the Court feels that it has to quell, although enjoying it obviously as much as the spectators.*)

Q (*Furious*): I see. Well, here is a question that I think will be simple enough to elicit an honest answer: Just how did you happen to know that it was eleven-fifteen when you saw the defendant?

A: Because I looked at my watch.

Q: And just why did you look at your watch at this particular time?

A: To see what time it was.

Q: Are you accustomed to looking at your watch often?

A: That is one of the uses to which I often put my watch.

Q: I see. Now, it couldn't, by any chance, have been ten-fifteen instead of eleven-fifteen when you looked at your watch this time, could it?

A: Yes, sir. It could.

Q: Oh, it *could* have been ten-fifteen?

A: Yes, sir—if I had been in Chicago. (*Not very good really. I'll work up something better. I move to have that answer stricken from the record.*)

When I feel myself lowering my standards by answering like that. I usually give myself a rest, and, unless something else awfully good pops into my head, I adjourn the court until next day. I can always convene it again when I hit my stride.

If possible, however, I like to drag it out until I have really given my antagonist a big final wallop which practically curls him up on the floor (I may think of one before this goes to press), and, wiping his forehead, he mutters, "Take the witness!"

As I step down from the stand, fresh as a daisy, there is a round of applause which the Court makes no attempt to silence. In fact, I have known certain judges to wink pleasantly at me as I take my seat. Judges are only human, after all.

My only fear is that, if I ever really am called upon to testify in Court, I won't be asked the right questions. That *would* be a pretty kettle of fish!